1994

Yearbook
of Science
and the
Future

1994

Yearbook
of Science
and the
Future

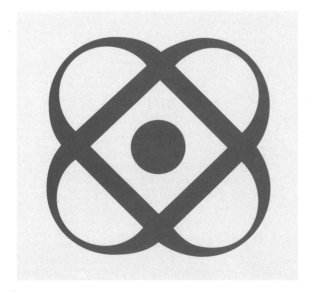

Encyclopædia

Britannica, Inc.

Chicago
Auckland
London
Madrid
Manila
Paris
Rome
Seoul
Sydney
Tokyo
Toronto

1994

Yearbook of Science and the Future

Library of Congress Catalog Card Number: 69-12349
International Standard Book Number: 0-85229-588-X
International Standard Serial Number: 0096-3291

Encyclopædia Britannica, Inc.

Chairman of the Board
Robert P. Gwinn

President
Peter B. Norton

Encyclopædia Britannica Publishing Group

President
Joseph J. Esposito

Executive Vice President, Associate Publisher
Karen M. Barch

Editor
David Calhoun

Associate Editor
Charles Cegielski

Editorial Staff
Daphne Daume, Karen Sparks,
Arthur Latham, Melinda Shepherd

Creative Director, Art
Cynthia Peterson

Operations Manager, Art
Marsha Mackenzie

Senior Picture Editor
Kathy Nakamura

Picture Editors
Roberta Homan Gardner,
Julie Kunkler Stevens, Amy Zweig

Layout Artists and Illustrators
Kathryn Diffley, John L. Draves,
Steven N. Kapusta, James I. Montes

Art Production Supervisor
Stephanie Motz

Art Staff
Patricia A. Henle, Diana M. Pitstick

Manager, Cartography
Barbra A. Vogel

Cartography Staff
Laurie Anderson, Kathryn Piffl

Manager, Copy Department
Sylvia Wallace

Copy Supervisors
Julian Ronning, Barbara Whitney

Copy Staff
Elizabeth A. Blowers, Lynette Bertsche,
Philip Colvin, Anthony L. Green,
John Mathews, Deirdre McAllister,
Letricia Riley

Manager, Production Control
Mary C. Srodon

Production Control Staff
Marilyn L. Barton, Stephanie A. Green

Contents

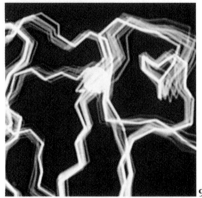

156 The Animal That Walks by Itself
by Juliet Clutton-Brock

Long stereotyped as having the same independent, aloof personality as its wild ancestor, the domestic cat is now known to show amazingly diverse social activity and to be capable of adapting its behavior to its circumstances.

178 Intelligent Vehicle-Highway Systems
by Michael J. Cassidy

Engineers are turning to computers and various high-tech devices to reduce traffic congestion. They envision cars that will drive themselves and compute new routes to bypass traffic jams as they are developing.

190 Climate in the Ice
by Michael C. Morrison

Scientists from the U.S. and Europe are coring the Greenland ice cap to retrieve an unprecedented 200,000-year record of the Earth's climate. Their findings will shed light on past and future climate changes.
SIDEBAR: GRIP—Partner Project of GISP2
by Bernhard Stauffer

208 Baikal—The Greatest Great Lake
by Charles R. Goldman

Siberia's Lake Baikal is the oldest and deepest large freshwater ecosystem. Russian and foreign scientists have mounted a joint effort to study the lake and the threats to it from human enterprises.

226 Chaos, Quarks, and Quantum Leaps: What's in a Scientific Name?
by Stephen S. Hall

Scientists who bestow colorful, metaphorical names on their discoveries may be making their work more meaningful to the public. But they do so at the considerable risk of attracting criticism and ridicule from their colleagues.

Encyclopædia Britannica Science Update

The Science Year in Review

A Science Classic

Institutions of Science
by Anne R. Gibbons

In the 1950s a handful of biologists began studying the effects of a new U.S. nuclear weapons plant on the local environment. Their work laid the foundations for what is today a world-class laboratory for ecological research.

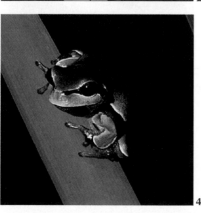

Kathryn Diffley

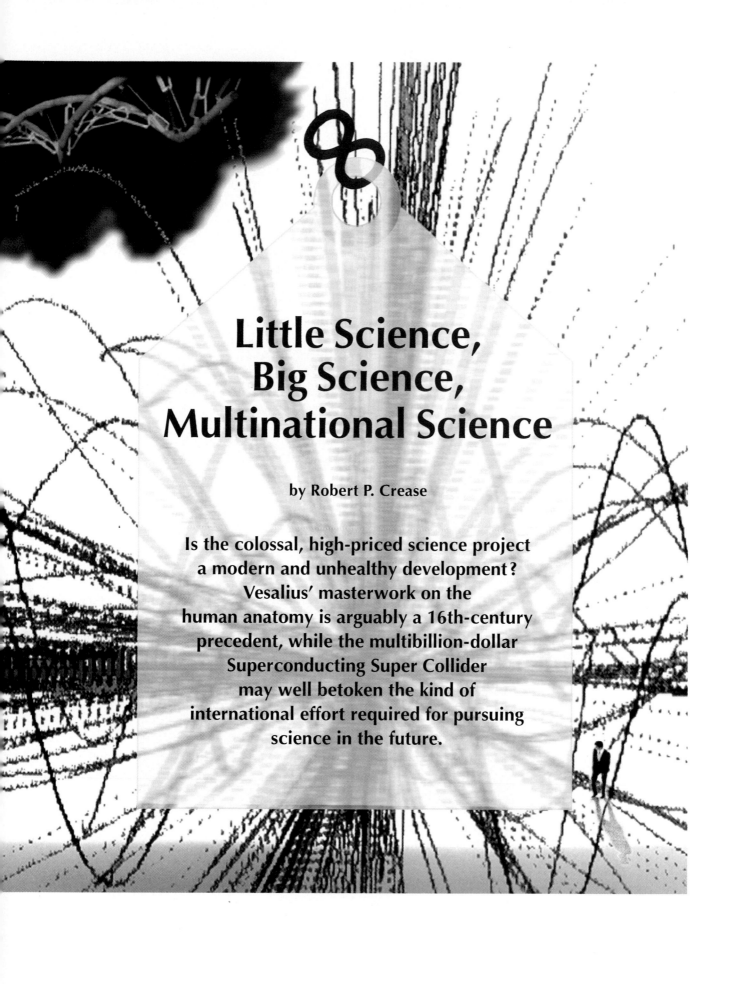

Little Science, Big Science, Multinational Science

by Robert P. Crease

Is the colossal, high-priced science project
a modern and unhealthy development?
Vesalius' masterwork on the
human anatomy is arguably a 16th-century
precedent, while the multibillion-dollar
Superconducting Super Collider
may well betoken the kind of
international effort required for pursuing
science in the future.

ROBERT P. CREASE is Assistant Professor of Philosophy at the State University of New York at Stony Brook and Historian at Brookhaven National Laboratory, Upton, New York.

(Overleaf) Illustration by Kathryn Diffley

This is an era of sprawling scientific megaprojects. Topping the list is space station *Freedom*, which in 1984 was estimated to cost $8 billion and to have a vehicle in orbit by 1992. Still firmly on the ground in 1993, it is now projected to cost $40 billion to build and $100 billion to operate over a 30-year life span. The Superconducting Super Collider, a particle accelerator under construction outside Waxahachie, Texas, will cost an estimated $8 billion or more by its completion around 1999. The Human Genome Project, launched in 1988 to map and sequence all the genes in the human organism, is a 15-year, $3 billion effort to which over half a dozen foreign countries have pledged substantial contributions. The Hubble Space Telescope, launched in April 1990, took a dozen years to build and put into orbit and cost $1.5 billion. Each space shuttle flight costs about $1 billion. Numerous other scientific fields have multiyear, multidisciplinary, multinational projects whose price tags approach the $1 billion mark.

Over three decades ago the trend toward large and expensive scientific projects was baptized Big Science, in a rough analogy with big business. Heated arguments have erupted ever since over the virtues and vices of this development. Does Big Science represent a dramatic new phase in the practice of science, fraught with dangers we barely recognize and possibly heralding a decline in the quality of science? Or does it represent simply the next stage in a natural evolution, a stage whose scale is simply a function of the questions we are now able to ask and whose arrival is neither unexpected nor unwanted and even offers unprecedented opportunities?

Both positions were advanced at the very beginning of the debate—the first by the scientist who coined the phrase, the second by the science historian who popularized it.

Dangers and opportunities

The author of the phrase was Alvin Weinberg, an articulate if sometimes iconoclastic physicist who at the time was director of Oak Ridge (Tennessee) National Laboratory. On May 4, 1961, Weinberg used it in an address on the potential dangers to science and society of large-scale scientific ventures such as giant particle accelerators and the manned space program. The speech was delivered to a meeting of the American Rocket Society, which fell, as it happened, the day before Alan Shepard's suborbital ride in *Freedom 7* to become the first American to blast into space. "I wasn't very popular," Weinberg recalled about the reaction of his audience. Still, when the address, "Impact of Large-Scale Science on the United States," was reprinted in the journal *Science* two months later, few disputed the justice of Weinberg's comments, and the article was enormously influential.

At the time, neither of the two principal examples of Big Science that Weinberg discussed had really matured. Forefront particle accelerators could still be built at universities, and Project Mercury was still in its infancy. Nevertheless, in hindsight Weinberg managed to diagnose several dangers that lay ahead for these and projects of a similar scale, including

10

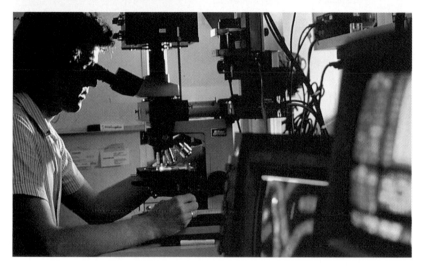

Superconducting magnets 15 meters (50 feet) in length and weighing 15 tons each (top left) are among the major components of the Superconducting Super Collider, a particle accelerator that will cost an estimated $8 billion or more by its completion at the end of the 1990s. A researcher relates cloned DNA fragments to a specific human chromosome (left) as part of the 15-year, $3 billion Human Genome Project to map and sequence all the genes in the human organism. The Hubble Space Telescope (above), carried into orbit aboard a U.S. space shuttle in April 1990, took a dozen years to build and deploy, at a cost of $1.5 billion. All three projects are examples of today's Big Science, and they continue the trend to which physicist Alvin Weinberg called attention more than three decades ago.

"moneyitis" (spending too much money rather than thought), "journalitis" (deciding the merits of scientific projects in public rather than scientific forums), and "administratitis" (too much attention to administering rather than doing science). Weinberg worried that the outcome would be a decline in the quality of science projects. In an age of Big Science, he wrote, "issues of scientific or technical merit tend to get argued in the popular, not the scientific, press, or in the congressional committee room rather than in the technical-society lecture hall; the spectacular rather than the perceptive becomes the scientific standard." Finally, he worried about the impact on social institutions such as universities: "I do believe that Big Science can ruin our universities, by diverting the universities from their primary purpose and by converting university professors into administrators, housekeepers, and publicists."

Weinberg invited comparison between Big Science projects and the pyramids, the Roman Colosseum, and the palace at Versailles. While the civilization that built each of these projects considered it a symbol of pride, magnificence, and ambition, Weinberg said that in some cases the

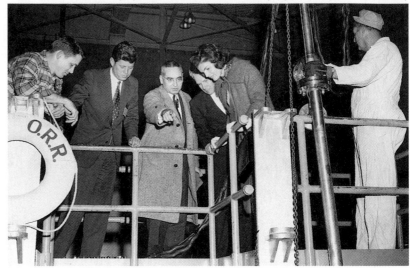

Alvin Weinberg (above right, pointing), director of Oak Ridge (Tennessee) National Laboratory, conducts U.S. Pres. John F. Kennedy and his wife, Jacqueline, on a visit to the laboratory in the early 1960s. Many of Weinberg's concerns about the aberrance of Big Science and its potential danger to science and society were questioned by Yale University historian Derek de Solla Price (above), who saw the recent exponential increase in scale of large scientific projects as merely a continuation of a trend going back two or three centuries. Because any normal growth process cannot continue accelerating forever, Price argued that Big Science may represent the point of departure from an exponential growth curve to one of logistic growth (below). A logistic curve is limited by a ceiling toward which growth moves, but at an ever slackening pace.

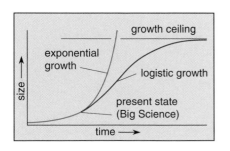

project also helped lead to that civilization's decline. "Our real purpose," he concluded, "is the enriching and broadening of human life."

A year later, however, a more enthusiastic attitude toward Big Science was promulgated by science historian Derek de Solla Price of Yale University, who presented a series of lectures at Brookhaven National Laboratory, Upton, New York, June 19–29, 1962, published the following year as *Little Science, Big Science*. Price agreed with Weinberg about the recent exponential increase in the scale of large scientific projects, and he noted that it presaged certain cultural shifts in the way science was practiced; for instance, it tended to suppress certain positive traits in scientists such as "mavericity." But with a historian's instincts and methods, he also questioned whether it was correct to dramatize the change from Little Science to Big Science as abrupt and aberrant. "Did it all happen very quickly," he asked, "with historical roots no deeper in time than the Manhattan Project, Cape Canaveral rocketry, the discovery of penicillin, and the invention of radar and electronic computers?"

The answer he gave was a flat "no." He marshaled statistics and other evidence, such as data on the number of scientific journals and on the growth of scientific manpower, to argue that the current exponential growth of science was only a continuation of a very old trend. "One has little trouble," he wrote, "in showing that general exponential growth has been maintained for two or three centuries." Moreover, it was illusory to think that the impact of science on modern life was a recent phenomenon. "Science has always been modern; it has always been exploding into the population, always on the brink of its expansive revolution."

Still, Price concurred with Weinberg that important changes lay ahead for science. Exponential growth in any natural process, he pointed out, never continues onward to infinity but eventually reaches a point of saturation and slackens off, following a "logistic curve." Big Science may represent the moment when exponential gives way to logistic growth. But where Weinberg emphasized danger, Price emphasized opportunity.

12

Big Science, he said, is the beginning of a time when scientists must of necessity become increasingly socially active and responsible. Their involvement in extrascientific questions, he wrote, was required "for the internal reconstruction of the entire social fabric of science and for the external problems of science in the service of man."

In recent years the cases for and against Big Science have been argued again and again, and the arguments originally advanced by Weinberg and Price have been adapted, improved, and fine-tuned. Indeed, the discussion of the effect of scale on the practice of science has an even greater urgency than it did three decades ago, for science is on the threshold of yet another era, which one can call Multinational Science, in a rough analogy with multinational corporations. Even to begin to evaluate the validity of the arguments, however, requires delving into the history of large-scale scientific projects and the nature of experimentation.

Sixteenth-century precedents

As Price hinted, every recent era has witnessed "big" science undertakings, which to contemporaries seemed grandiose in ambition and extravagant in cost and objective. Consider the work of the 16th-century physician Andreas Vesalius, who was born in Flanders, studied in Paris, and held professorships and carried out investigations in Padua, Bologna, and Pisa. His dissection of cadavers convinced him of the need for a new textbook of human anatomy to replace the theories and methods of the Greek physician Galen, and about 1540 he initiated a far-ranging study of the human body, which took him to enormous lengths in pursuit of firsthand research for the project. He traveled to Venice to hire the finest draftsmen (probably from the painter Titian's studio) to execute extremely detailed illustrations under his supervision. He also sought out the best woodcutters to cut the printing blocks—blocks made of specially

Two "maps" spanning 450 years—one the delineation of the vena cava by Jan Stevensz van Calcar for Andreas Vesalius' De humani corporis fabrica libri septem of 1543 (below) and the other the result of modern research into human genetic diseases (below left)—represent the state of the art in knowledge of the human body in their respective eras. In its scale the comprehensive, exhaustively detailed Fabrica, which transformed anatomy into a scientific discipline, can be considered a 16th-century precedent for today's scientific megaprojects. The opus has even been cited as a precursor of the Human Genome Project, a reasonable analogy given the scope, ambition, and international character of the two undertakings.

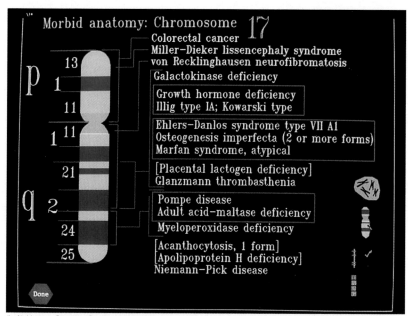

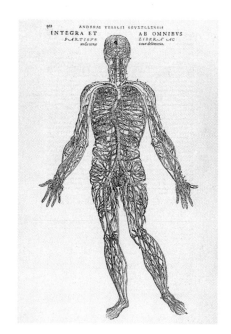

(Left) Human Genome Center, Lawrence Berkeley Laboratory; (right) Philadelphia Museum of Art: Purchased: SmithKline Beecham Corporation Fund (accession # '49-97-41e)

treated pear wood and fastidiously worked with Venetian techniques to enhance quality. To publish the work Vesalius chose a preeminent printer from Basel, and in August 1542 he carefully wrapped the precious blocks for the several-week-long journey over the Alps. His 700-page magnum opus, *De humani corporis fabrica libri septem* ("The Seven Books on the Structure of the Human Body"), the first comprehensive textbook on anatomy, was published in 1543.

The *Fabrica,* as the work came to be known, revealed no earth-shattering discoveries, announced no dramatic new cures, and produced no spectacular conclusions. Yet its comprehensiveness, systematic character, and exhaustive detail brought about a revolution in anatomic understanding, techniques, and pedagogy. It is unclear exactly how much the project cost Vesalius and where all the funds came from. Nevertheless, some idea of the scale can be gleaned from the fact that, early in the 20th century when an eminent Dutch publishing house undertook merely to reprint Vesalius' book, it abandoned the scheme upon discovering the extraordinary expense involved—about $40,000 in 1924 dollars, a "Big Publishing" project ahead of its time. A former head of the Human Genome Organization once cited the *Fabrica* as a precursor of the Human Genome Project. Certainly there is ideological mileage to be had in claiming Vesalius as an intellectual ancestor. Nevertheless, given the comprehensiveness, international character, ambition, and probably even expense of the two undertakings, the analogy is not unreasonable.

Or consider another 16th-century project, the building of Uraniborg, the observatory of the Danish astronomer Tycho Brahe, on the island of Hven (present-day Ven) in The Sound. Because of the isolated location, an entire infrastructure had to be built to support the observatory, including workshops, a windmill, a paper mill, printing houses, a chemical laboratory, and guardhouses. In addition to these structures, giant quadrants, armillary spheres, and other pretelescopic instruments, machinery, furnaces, books, and other supplies were also needed. The work force came from all over Europe and included Dutch architects, Danish, Italian, and Dutch artists, and Danish laborers. For about two decades Brahe used the facilities of the observatory to collect the most accurate astronomical observations to date, which superseded those of Ptolemy's *Almagest* and which would provide the foundation for articulating the Copernican theory (which, however, Brahe himself balked at embracing). The data did not come cheap; the sum Brahe received each year for the project, about 2,400 dalers, amounted to roughly 1% of the total revenues of the Danish king, Frederick II. In comparison, the annual U.S. allocation for all of its civilian basic research programs is a little less than 1% of the gross national product, with the annual allocation to the Superconducting Super Collider project currently 5% of that.

Electricity, radium, the Bomb, and beyond

In the 18th century electrical phenomena inspired numerous large and expensive studies. Scientists from Great Britain's Royal Society constructed a wire more than 3,660 meters (12,000 feet) long in an attempt

Nationalhistoriske Museum Frederiksborg, Denmark; photo, Artothek

The Granger Collection, New York

Like the Fabrica *of Vesalius, Tycho Brahe's late 16th-century observatory Uraniborg, depicted in an 1862 painting (left) by Henrik Hanson, may be regarded as a predecessor of the modern Big Science project. The facility's isolated location on the island of Hven required a large supporting infrastructure, and for its construction and outfitting, artistic and technical talent was drawn from all over Europe. Brahe and his assistants (above, shown in an early 17th-century colored engraving) used the observatory for about two decades to collect astronomical observations, for which the annual support, from the Danish monarchy, was considerable.*

to determine the velocity of what was then called the "electric fluid" and on one occasion passed current through a basin at the Tuileries Palace gardens in Paris. In the era before modern batteries and generators, huge, imposing devices were needed to create and store large quantities of electrical force for such experiments, pictures of which adorn encyclopedias and treatises of the day. These machines, observed Price, "in their time seemed to stretch man's scientific engineering to its ultimate capability and to give him the power to manufacture the most extreme physical forces of the universe, rivaling the very lightning and perhaps providing keys to the nature of matter and of life itself. In a way, our dreams for modern accelerators pale by comparison."

At the beginning of the 20th century, research into radioactivity taxed financial resources of investigators far beyond their ordinary means. Pierre and Marie Curie spent two years refining boxcar loads of the mineral pitchblende by time-consuming, painstaking means to extract tiny amounts of radium: one part radium to 200 million parts ore. Radium's medical uses predictably caused the price of pitchblende to skyrocket, and radium was soon 100 times more expensive by weight than diamonds. By 1920 Marie Curie could not afford enough radium for studies at her Radium Institute in Paris, which was dedicated to pure research and only distantly related to the French university system. To address the problem a nationwide campaign among U.S. women was organized by the editor in chief of an American women's magazine to raise $100,000, enough to

The Institution of Electrical Engineers, London

Eighteenth-century experimentation with electricity called for massive equipment— like the "gigantic friction machine" (above) illustrated in a 1787 treatise by Martin van Marum—to create and store electrical force. According to Derek de Solla Price, with such machines humans aspired no less than "to manufacture the most extreme physical forces of the universe . . . perhaps providing the keys to the nature of matter and of life itself. In a way, our dreams for modern accelerators pale by comparison."

buy a gram of radium. The radium was presented to Curie in 1921 by U.S. Pres. Warren G. Harding.

And while radioactivity research involved extraordinary leaps in expense, other projects of the '20s and '30s involved collaborations of unprecedented size between scientists and industry as well; for example, the development of microwave technology and of projects to provide hydroelectric power in California. During World War II costs and collaborations grew still further with the Manhattan Project to build the atomic bomb and the push to develop microwave radar.

In the aftermath of World War II, the development of the national laboratory system in the U.S. involved not only a further jump in the

Marie Curie (third from left) stands with U.S. Pres. Warren G. Harding after having been presented with a gram of precious radium that had been purchased through the efforts of a $100,000 fund-raising campaign among U.S. women. The time-consuming, painstaking process of extracting minute amounts of the element from many tons of the mineral pitchblende, combined with its demand for medical uses, caused the price of radium to skyrocket far beyond the financial resources of Curie and other investigators.

UPI/Bettmann

scale of laboratories but also new dimensions of interaction among science, technology, and industry. Large-scale collaborations involving all three enterprises went from being exceptional to practically normative. Ordinary investigations in nuclear and particle physics, even ones in which the data were taken on comparatively small pieces of equipment, now generally involved hooking this equipment up to some large utility apparatus, such as an accelerator or a reactor, whose construction was federally funded and had large industrial participation and whose very operation and maintenance required a large support staff.

This was the era that, in 1961, Weinberg baptized Big Science. And in the ensuing three decades even Little Science became expensive. For instance, to do science now with high-quality semiconductors (which is ordinarily considered Little Science), one needs such items as molecular beam epitaxy machines, enclosures of exceptionally high cleanliness called clean rooms, lasers that work on short time scales, X-ray systems, electron microscopes with atomic resolution, and materials of extremely high purity. And to do such science effectively, one generally needs data that have been acquired by other scientists working with the large research reactors in national laboratories—meaning that even today's Little Science depends on Big Science. Scientists today deal with a tightly connected fabric of information gained from a variety of sources, and it would be artificial, misleading, and pointless to try to parse the contributions of Little and Big Science in order to compare their significance.

Big Science on the threshold

Big Science takes different forms in different fields. In astronomy and high-energy physics it tends to involve large and expensive pieces of hardware with which a comparatively small number of experiments can

Brookhaven National Laboratory

Sprawled across 2,132 hectares (5,265 acres) are the accelerators, storage rings, and more than 250 buildings and other structures that make up Brookhaven National Laboratory, Upton, New York. The development of Brookhaven and other institutions of the U.S. national laboratory system after World War II involved new dimensions of interaction between science, technology, and industry wherein collaborations between the three types of enterprises went from being the exception to being nearly the norm.

Technicians in anticontamination suits work in a clean room where wafers of semiconductor chips are baked in a furnace at high temperature. Science with semiconductor materials, ordinarily considered Little Science, now demands expensive and sophisticated equipment, materials, and techniques and draws on information and technology spun off from Big Science. Since Weinberg's era of the 1960s, science both big and little has become so intertwined that it is difficult and perhaps pointless to try to discriminate the relative significance of each.

be performed at any one time, such as the Hubble Space Telescope, various ground-based radio and optical telescopes, and the Superconducting Super Collider. By contrast, the large projects of materials science tend to take the form of utilities that supply many users simultaneously, such as the Advanced Photon Source at Argonne (Illinois) National Laboratory (with 68 beam lines) and the projected Advanced Neutron Source at Oak Ridge National Laboratory (with about 50 instrument stations). In the life sciences the big projects take the form of research projects that coordinate the efforts of a rank and file of single investigators who work in small laboratories on relatively small grants. Nevertheless, the cumulative cost of such a project may be huge. From the perspective of total expense, for one to exclude from Big Science, say, the programs for AIDS and cancer research, which are multibillion-dollar, multiyear, federally funded efforts, seems prejudicial. The annual cost of U.S. AIDS research alone is about $800 million.

Today science is on another threshold, one having to do with the growing international character of its involvements. While the projects of Little Science were sometimes national and those of Big Science were routinely national and sometimes international, those of the newcomer, Multinational Science, are routinely international, as no single nation has the resources to construct and support them. Multinational Science, with its multinational collaborations, entails the introduction of its own new set of problems—among them fluctuating currency rates, foreign travel restrictions, tariff and trade restrictions, customs regulations, patents, and international politics—into the day-to-day practice of science.

True, Big Science projects have been international from time to time. One thinks of the dramatic 1975 Apollo-Soyuz rendezvous and docking of spacecraft from the U.S. and the U.S.S.R. or of CERN, the high-energy physics laboratory whose headquarters are in Geneva, which was formed in the early 1950s with the participation of a dozen European nations. But the respective space programs of the U.S. and the U.S.S.R. were quite capable of functioning independently. And even though Eu-

18

ropean nations had to collaborate to create and maintain a world-class accelerator laboratory, the United States was able to create and maintain several such laboratories on its own. Today, as the experience of the Superconducting Super Collider (SSC) reveals, such single-country independence is on the brink of being no longer feasible.

The SSC, in fact, is an emblematic instance of Multinational Science. From the time it was conceived and approved, it was planned that countries other than the United States would contribute a significant portion of the expense. Of its total $8,250,000,000 projected cost, $1.7 billion is to be raised from other countries, either in cash or in kind. Japan was expected to be the principal foreign partner, donating between several hundred million and a billion dollars, and other nations— including Russia, India, China, Taiwan, and South Korea—are expected to contribute smaller amounts in kind as well to make up the difference. Even the two major experimental detectors under construction at the SSC were conceived and approved with the expectation of substantial foreign contributions. The $8,250,000,000 SSC figure includes about $250 million for each detector, but an equal amount must be sought in cash or in kind from the other countries whose scientists are participating in the experiments. International participation is thus a necessity for the SSC, rather than the political gesture that it was for Apollo-Soyuz or the regional strategy that it was for CERN.

Science as intellectual inquiry and science as social practice

Multinational Science highlights another kind of problem concerning outside influences on the practice of science. Scientists tend to assume that the genuine practice of science retains an objectivity over, and an

Although Big Science projects have been international from time to time in the past, they have differed in character from the kind of science project that is multinational of necessity. The dramatic 1975 U.S.-Soviet Apollo-Soyuz space linkup (below left, artist's conception) was a cooperative effort by two space programs that were quite capable of functioning independently. And in 1955, when the first director of CERN, Felix Bloch, laid the laboratory's foundation stone with the collaboration of 12 European nations (below), accelerator facilities of the same class could still be built and supported several times over by the U.S. on its own.

(Left) NASA; (right) CERN

A construction crew at work on the Superconducting Super Collider (SSC) near Waxahachie, Texas, completes an access shaft and "stub" tunnels (above) that will receive the boring machine for carving out the accelerator's 87-kilometer (54-mile) circular main tunnel. Meanwhile, progress on the SSC's superconducting magnets continues in the 9,300-square meter (100,000-square foot) magnet development laboratory (above right) outside Waxahachie. Given the critical nature of foreign contribution to the SSC and its two major experimental detectors, the project is an emblematic instance of true Multinational Science.

independence from, whatever social influences either make it possible or result from it. What will be uncovered by research into the existence of elementary particles, the atomic nucleus, chromosomal structure, the human immune system, or the origin of the universe is ultimately independent of the motives a society has for supporting the research. Although social concerns may determine whether scientists receive the support needed to have the opportunity to make discoveries, the discoveries themselves are not determined by such influences but by nature.

On the other hand, historians, sociologists, and social critics have long recognized the effects of social influences on science, and studies of these effects have become much more sophisticated in the 20th century with the work of such individuals as Boris Hessen, Robert Merton, and Thomas Kuhn. How to reconcile the undeniable influence of social factors on science with science's equally undeniable objectivity (that is, its measure of independence from any specific context) is one of the thorniest issues in contemporary philosophy of science. The projects of Multinational Science make this issue more pointed, because they are much more subject to social influences than previous undertakings. Decisions involving the planning, execution, and operation of multinational projects from their overall conception down to their tiniest details are now more likely to be negotiated in political rather than scientific circles. Such factors as the political ambitions and responsibilities of world leaders, national labor practices, national sensitivities to handling and disposal of radioactive materials and other environmentally threatening substances, and the stability of national economies will affect the decisions of those involved in multinational scientific projects. A project of Multinational Science will be as much of a social as a scientific project. Does this increasing presence of political, economic, and even cultural factors in the practice of science pose a threat to its objectivity?

For temperamental and professional reasons scientists tend to shun posing this kind of question. But the issue, which in its broadest sense concerns how science as a social practice is related to science as an intellectual inquiry, will inevitably surface more and more in discussions of Multinational Science. One way toward clarifying the issue is to consider that a scientific experiment can be evaluated by two different sorts of measures. First, it can be seen as the execution of an act that is part of a purely intellectual inquiry into nature that is valuable for its own sake. Second, it can be seen as a purely social event—that is, as distributing so much money, creating so many jobs, forging certain alliances, creating various relationships between institutions, generating technological spin-offs, and so forth—that might have value regardless of the success or failure of the intellectual program motivating it.

The experiment as a production

In this respect one might compare a scientific experiment to a theatrical event, which can be evaluated artistically with respect to its performance or socially with respect to its production—how much money it costs, how much money it brings in, how many actors it employs—even though the artistic and social values may have little to do with one another. Similarly, a scientific project possesses two different kinds of values, one related to its value as an act performed in the service of an intellectual inquiry, the other related to its social value as a production. The controversy concerning Big versus Little Science is not about the inherent intellectual value of most of the questions being posed. There are few doubts about the desirability of knowing such things as the nature of elementary particles or the atomic nucleus, the human genome, or the origin of the universe. If projects to do such things could be accomplished at a Little Science scale, no hesitation would be expressed about doing them. Instead, the controversy is generated by the awareness that the escalation in scale of the productions that are needed to answer such questions entails, first, increased competition for funds among productions (scientific or otherwise) and, second, a concomitant growth in the social involvement of these productions.

The concern about competition among scientific productions arises from the fact that, assuming a finite level of funding, the bigger one of them is, the fewer are the others that can be supported. Critics of the space station, for instance, have noted that in supporting it NASA has had to cancel many worthy projects involving planetary probes and other spacecraft. Furthermore, competition may not be limited to projects within one field, such as space research, but may occur between scientific disciplines—physics and geology, say, or biology and oceanography. Some materials scientists have complained that the immense cost of building and running the SSC ultimately threatens projects in their own field. And the huge international projects of Multinational Science inevitably become involved in competition with nonscientific ones in education, housing, or defense.

The concern about the growing social involvement of scientific productions stems from the idea that the bigger this involvement is, the more likely the project is to be evaluated and supervised according to its social rather than intellectual values. Thus, the larger the scale of a production, the more of an investment society makes in it, and the more likely social values are to influence the project. Consider the increased public and political attention paid to accelerators as they have grown ever larger. In the early 1930s particle accelerators were tabletop devices that few except interested scientists knew about. Only a few years later, however, they were already big enough that their installation attracted local attention. When, for instance, New York City's Columbia University installed a circular cyclotron with a magnet yoke 3.7 meters (12 feet) across in the basement of its physics building in the late 1930s—a machine able to accelerate particles to an energy of about 8 MeV (million electron volts)—a special concrete base had to be poured in the basement floor and the machine's 65-ton electromagnet installed with the help of the U.S. Navy. Local newspapers wrote admiringly of "Big Bertha," Columbia's new piece of "atomic artillery."

In the 1950s a string of much bigger accelerators were built, including the Cosmotron, a 3-GeV (billion electron volt) accelerator at Brookhaven National Laboratory in 1952; the Bevatron, a 6.2-GeV machine at the University of California at Berkeley in 1954; and the Alternating Gradient Synchrotron in 1960, a 33-GeV device also at Brookhaven. These were too large for universities alone to build, and their construction required a large collaboration with industry subject to extensive governmental regulations concerning contracting practices and other matters. Nevertheless, the decision to build them and where to locate them remained outside the scope of public debate, and they generally made the news only upon their completion. This situation changed not long after, in the mid-1960s, when the Atomic Energy Commission began to look into sites for a new 200-GeV accelerator. Commission representatives encountered regional politicians, local media, and even an occasional marching band on their tours of prospective sites, and the opinions of community organizations such as the local branch of the National Association for the Advancement

Over a few short years in the 1930s, particle accelerators grew from tabletop machines almost exclusively of scientific interest to devices big enough to attract public attention. When in 1935 Columbia University installed its cyclotron (right) in the basement of the Pupin Physics Laboratories on upper Broadway in New York City, a special concrete base had to be poured. Sections of the machine's 65-ton electromagnet were delivered by the U.S. Navy in a 13-truck caravan and taken into the building down a special sloping trench. When the cyclotron went into operation three years later, local media covered the story, dubbing the machine a "leviathan" and the "Big Bertha of atomic artillery."

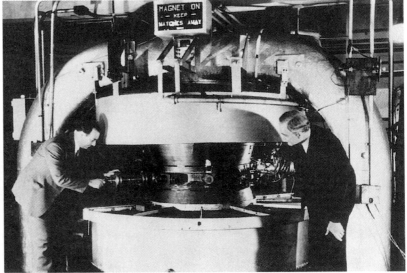

UPI/Bettmann

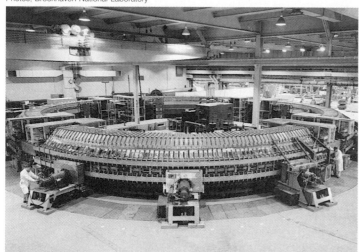

of Colored People were sought. Ever since, the process of building a new world-class particle accelerator has been a highly political event.

The SSC, again, is emblematic of the scientific-social relationship today. It would create over 7,000 direct-employment jobs in Texas alone (excluding indirect, or "ripple" jobs) once its magnet factory was up to full strength, and it has more than 22,000 contracts in 45 states. Texas, as it happened, was a key state in former president George Bush's 1992 reelection strategy. Small wonder that the project became ensnared in election-year maneuvering between Congress and the administration, with Bush dropping his objection to a nuclear test ban in return for renewed congressional support of the accelerator. Small wonder, too, that Pres. Bill Clinton has backed the project as part of his economic recovery program.

Does NASA operate in a vacuum?

Five times more expensive than the SSC to build and operate, space station *Freedom* is an even bigger public-works project. According to NASA, the project will provide about 75,000 jobs and has contracts in 37 states, the District of Columbia, and several foreign countries. This foreign commitment led to unintentional comedy at one point in congressional debate when Rep. Alan Mollohan (Dem., W.V.) rebuked congressional critics of the space station, saying that dropping the project would mean backing out of contracts with foreign nations that were already signed. "It strikes me," Mollohan said, "that many of our colleagues voice their opposition to the space station as if NASA operates in a vacuum. It does not." Wry scientists wondered whether Mollohan's remark might not encourage Congress to target the station's life-support systems in the next round of belt-tightening.

Mollohan's remark demonstrates that jobs and local economies are not the only values that can accrue to large-scale scientific productions; international politics and national reputations can also be involved. Indeed, while the space station has been scolded regularly by scientific panels for

In the 1950s machines like the Columbia University cyclotron were overshadowed by a string of bigger accelerators, including Brookhaven's Cosmotron (above left), which started operation in 1952, and its Alternating Gradient Synchrotron (above), which started operation in 1960. Although the size of those machines required collaboration with industry for building them and thus made them subject to extensive government regulation, the decisions about whether and where to build them remained outside the scope of public debate. In the mid-1960s that situation began to change, however, as the construction of new major accelerators became ever more a political and social process.

23

having low scientific value, it has been defended just as regularly by the administration and in Congress as invaluable in bolstering national prestige. And supporters of such projects regularly cite spin-offs—in computer technology, materials science, precision manufacturing, and the like—as another kind of value that needs no link to a project's scientific outcome. Quantitative studies of the value to local industries of such spin-offs, in terms of increased markets and lower manufacturing costs, have been conducted at CERN and in the U.S., although the methodology of such studies has been questioned. These studies purport to prove that certain kinds of scientific productions are good social investments regardless of the value of the science involved.

The challenge posed by Multinational Science is how to negotiate between the intellectual value of a project and its social values as a production when the latter become more numerous and complex. For a scientist to claim that a megaproject today is justified by its scientific merit alone would be just as unreasonable as for a politician to say that it should be evaluated merely as a public-works project.

Getting more from less

Eventually the intellectual questions that scientists wish to pose may run up against hurdles that are beyond the resources even of Multinational Science to overcome. In his address as retiring president of the American Physical Society in January 1954, Enrico Fermi illustrated this in a

The social aspects of space station Freedom, *which involves commitments between the U.S. and several foreign countries, extend far beyond local jobs and economies to encompass international politics and national reputations. Multinational Science productions like* Freedom *are challenging scientists, governments, and the public to find ways to negotiate successfully between the scientific value of the projects and their social values when the latter become more numerous and complex.*

NASA

humorous vein by showing a graph of particle accelerator growth, which projected that the machines would soon be so large as to orbit the planet. Confronted with physical restrictions on such projects, scientists may have to devise ways of addressing the same questions through ingenious lower-scale productions.

Particle physicists, for instance, do this in at least two ways—through specialized accelerators called "factories" and through underground laboratories. The SSC is designed to collide counterrevolving beams of particles at 20 TeV (trillion electron volts) each and to hunt for resulting phenomena across a wide energy spectrum. But here and there in the energy spectrum already opened up by previous accelerators are pockets of unexplored territory, areas containing phenomena that are known to be interesting and probably to conceal surprises but that have not been adequately studied in the push to higher and higher energies. Accelerators can be built whose entire purpose is to examine such an energy pocket—typically, by creating a specific particle in collisions and watching how it decays. Such accelerators are called factories because they mass-produce phenomena whose study may yield answers to questions otherwise obtainable only by much larger accelerators. Factories marry opportunity and ingenuity; to make them effective, accelerator physicists must devise machines whose luminosity, or particle-collision rate, is at least 100 times that of ordinary accelerators.

Several factories are in the planning stages. One is the phi (φ) factory, called Daphne (or Daφne), planned for operation at Frascati in Italy. The φ particle is created at a total particle collision energy of 1.02 GeV and thus calls for an accelerator to collide two beams of particles of more than 500 MeV each. The φ particle is a peculiar quantum mechanical state, and its decay allows scientists to pose key questions about the nature of quantum mechanics and a phenomenon known as CP violation, a tiny but possibly very significant asymmetry in behavior between matter and antimatter. Construction of Daphne started in early 1993 and is expected to be completed in about two years. The reason for its speedy construction is that the Frascati scientists have made a production shortcut by building Daphne in the same building that housed a now obsolete machine.

A second type of factory can be built to explore the energy pocket around 3.5–4 GeV. Such an accelerator can mass-produce two different kinds of interesting particles, tau leptons (heavy relatives of the electron) and charmed mesons (mesons containing fundamental particles called charmed quarks), whose rare decays create a window on high-energy phenomena. A tau-charm factory is currently under consideration for Seville, Spain. A third type of factory mass-produces B mesons (mesons containing bottom, or beauty, quarks) at an energy of about 10 GeV and examines their rare decays. One such B factory is in the planning stages in Japan, and another is under discussion for the U.S. In the 1980s scientists at the Stanford Linear Accelerator Center struggled to turn their largest accelerator into a Z factory (the Z^0 particle is created at about 91 GeV), but problems with the machine meant that it was

25

quickly superseded in this function by CERN's largest accelerator, the Large Electron-Positron Collider (LEP).

While factories represent ingenuity in selecting interesting phenomena to study, underground laboratories take a shortcut in the production of experiments to address megaproject-class questions. These laboratories use the Earth as a shield to screen out cosmic rays. Under such conditions experiments can be performed that may be able to detect phenomena whose existence otherwise would be revealed only through prohibitively large accelerators. Such phenomena include the predicted, but yet to be observed, decay of the proton; the magnetic monopole, a hypothetical particle that possesses only one (either a north or a south) magnetic pole; and neutrino oscillation, a suspected phenomenon in which neutrinos—fundamental particles that exist in three distinct types—transform in flight from one type to another. The largest of these underground laboratories is under Italy's Gran Sasso mountains, where several experiments involving scientists from more than a dozen countries are under way.

Toward multinational interdependence

As Multinational Science continues to grow, and scientific inquiries require ever larger and more complex productions to carry out, the

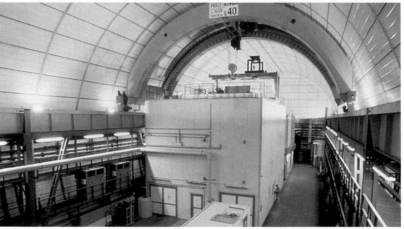

One way to address megaproject-class questions without the restrictions imposed by the projects themselves is through ingenious lower-scale productions. At Gran Sasso National Laboratory (top) in northern Italy, experiments involving scientists from more than a dozen countries are under way in a tunnel below the Gran Sasso mountains. There, in underground halls, shielding from the Earth itself permits searching for phenomena that could otherwise be created only in prohibitively large accelerators. In one of the halls (bottom) a tank containing 30 tons of gallium in aqueous solution is used to detect neutrinos from the Sun to help answer questions about solar nuclear processes and settle the vexing issue of whether neutrinos, previously thought to be massless, have a small mass and can transform from one kind into another.

Photos, Laboratori Nazionale del Gran Sasso, Instituto Nazionale di Fisica Nucleare

Working as a "megacollaboration," more than 300 experimenters spread over 33 institutions and 4 countries routinely collect, analyze, and publish data from a single particle detector experiment located at the Fermi National Accelerator Laboratory in Illinois. In the future, projects of even this magnitude may seem small as scientists, methods, and instruments throughout the world move toward greater interdependence in order to maximize the means for exploring nature.

incentive to find such shortcuts will also increase. The result will be greater collaboration between the world's scientists and greater interdependence of instruments and methods in order to maximize means for exploring nature.

The huge underground caverns of the Gran Sasso laboratory, for instance, are oriented toward the laboratory at CERN, hundreds of kilometers away. The orientation is not apparent inside the cavern, nor does it show up on any ordinary map drawn to scale. Gran Sasso's planners realized that, at some future time, the laboratory might be used in a joint experiment with CERN, wherein some future accelerator at CERN creates neutrinos that, after traveling through the Earth, are detected at Gran Sasso as part of an experiment to study neutrino oscillation. Such an experiment is not yet planned, and so far the orientation remains a curiosity. Nevertheless, this tiny detail, which may well turn out to be crucial decades hence, is an invisible sign of the growing interdependence of scientific projects as well as the growing interdependence of the science of different nations.

FOR ADDITIONAL READING

Robert P. Crease, *The Play of Nature: Experimentation as Performance* (Indiana University Press, 1993).

Peter Galison and Bruce Hevly (eds.), *Big Science: The Growth of Large-Scale Research* (Stanford University Press, 1992).

Frank A.J.L. James (ed.), *The Development of the Laboratory: Essays on the Place of Experiment in Industrial Civilization* (American Institute of Physics, 1989).

Derek John de Solla Price, *Little Science, Big Science* (Columbia University Press, 1963).

Alvin Martin Weinberg, *Reflections on Big Science* (MIT Press, 1967).

A Matter of Antimatter

by Robert L. Forward

**Although anathema to the ordinary world, particles of antimatter
recently have been kept in existence for long periods
in special traps of electric and magnetic fields.
Scientists soon expect to make the first
antiatoms and look forward to
harnessing antimatter for
human benefit.**

Antimatter as a material for research and practical use is no longer
science fiction. Formerly found only in such visionary settings as the
warp engines of the starship *Enterprise,* antimatter is now being made
and stored daily at laboratories around the world. Despite its proclivity
to annihilate with anything made of "normal" matter that it contacts,
antimatter has been slowed down, captured, and kept for months at a
time in "bottles" made of electric and magnetic fields. Such containers,
filled with antiparticles or antiatoms, may soon be transported across
continents to be used by physicists for basic studies into the fundamental
mysteries of nature, by doctors for finding and treating cancer, and by
engineers for various practical uses, including isotopic imaging, nuclear
transmutation, and—one of these days—space propulsion.

What is antimatter?

Human beings, and virtually all forms of matter known of in the universe, are made of atoms. Each of those atoms comprises a heavy central
nucleus surrounded by one or more orbiting lightweight elementary
particles called electrons. The nucleus in turn is made up of heavy
elementary particles called protons and neutrons. The electron has a
negative electric charge, and since it is spinning, it also has a magnetic
field, which is oriented in a specific way to its spin direction (*see* Figure
1, page 31). The proton is positively charged, so the orientation of its
magnetic field with respect to its spin is reversed compared with that for
the electron. The neutron has no net electric charge, but it does have a
magnetic field generated by the motion of the positively and negatively
charged quarks that make up the neutron. The simplest atom that can
be formed is hydrogen, which contains one negatively charged electron
orbiting one positively charged proton.

By the 1920s the proton and the electron had been recognized as
the elementary charged constituents of atoms, but a comparison of their

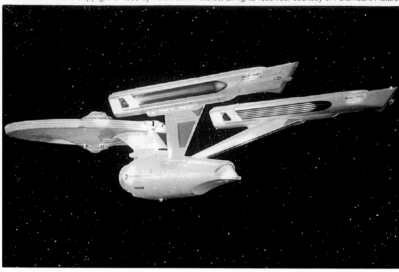

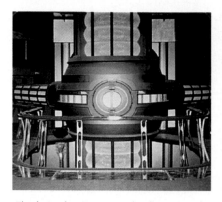

The lore of antimatter technology pervades popular science fiction. Star Trek fans know, for example, that the starship Enterprise (right) achieves faster-than-light travel by virtue of its two pod-mounted warp engines, which are powered by controlled matter-antimatter annihilations in the ship's dilithium-crystal reaction chamber (above). In the past decade science has caught up with fiction, and real technology now exists for making and controlling antimatter for research and practical applications.

ROBERT L. FORWARD *is an aerospace consultant and writer. He formerly served as Senior Scientist at the Hughes Aircraft Company Corporate Research Laboratories, Malibu, California.*

(Overleaf) Illustration by Jane Meredith

properties created a puzzle. Why did the elementary particle that carried the positive electric charge, the proton, weigh more than 1,800 times as much as the elementary particle that carried the negative electric charge, the electron? Experiments had shown that the charges, though opposite, were exactly equal in magnitude. Why should the masses not be the same as well?

The mystery remained until 1929, when the British physicist Paul Dirac combined the theories of quantum mechanics, electromagnetism, and relativity to obtain a new theory that explained many experimental observations that until then had had no explanation. In addition, the new theory predicted that there should be mirror-image twins—identical in mass but opposite in charge—of the proton and electron, which Dirac named the antiproton and antielectron. The prediction relieved the uncomfortable situation caused by the mass difference between the electron and the proton, for the proton and electron were not the oppositely charged twins of each other after all. Dirac's theory also predicted that if a particle and its antiparticle came together, they would annihilate each other; their electric charges would cancel, and their masses would be converted completely into energy.

As is shown in Figure 2, the properties that Dirac predicted for antimatter resemble those of normal matter reflected in a "magic" charge-reversing mirror. The antielectron, which is now known as the positron, should have the same mass as the electron but an opposite charge and an orientation of magnetic field direction to spin that is opposite that of the electron. In the same way, the antiproton is the mirror twin of the proton; the magnetic field orientation remains the same, but the charge and spin are reversed. In the case of the antineutron, because the neutron is uncharged, only the spin is reversed, while the magnetic field orientation remains the same.

Once the existence of antiparticles was postulated, it did not take long for either scientists or science-fiction writers to imagine the existence

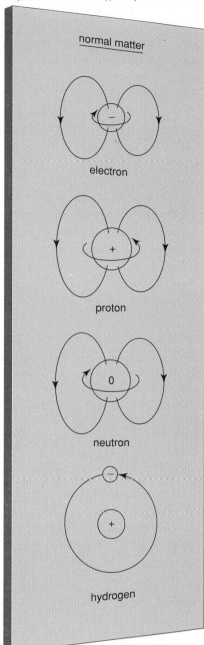

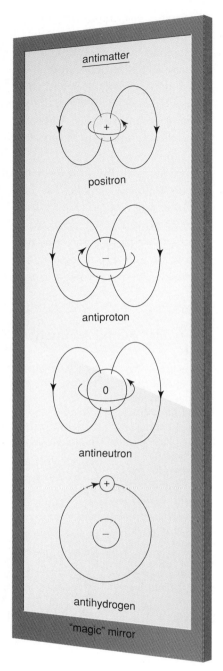

Figure 1: Properties of some basic components of matter are compared. The electron has a negative charge, a spin, and a magnetic field oriented in a specific way to the spin direction. For the positively charged proton, the magnetic field orientation with respect to spin is the reverse of the electron's. The neutron has no electric charge but does have a magnetic field. The hydrogen atom comprises an electron orbiting a proton.

Figure 2: An imaginary charge-reversing "magic" mirror shows up differences between normal matter and antimatter. Both the electric charge and the orientation of magnetic field to spin direction are reversed for positrons (antielectrons) and antiprotons, while only the latter property is reversed for antineutrons. An antihydrogen antiatom would be made up of a positron orbiting an antiproton.

of antiatoms, antibeings, antiplanets, antistars, and antigalaxies. Dirac himself, who shared the 1933 Nobel Prize for Physics for his work in quantum mechanics, discussed the possibilities of antimatter worlds and stars in his Nobel lecture. Many astronomers now believe that there are no large bodies of antimatter of any sort anywhere in the universe (*see* Sidebar 1), although the possibility cannot be ruled out. There are, however, antiparticles. And soon, likely within a few years, scientists will combine antiprotons with positrons, and the first antiatoms will be made.

Discovery of the first known antimatter particle

The antimatter predictions of Dirac's equations created quite a stir. Those who thought about testing Dirac's idea by trying to make antimatter, however, had a problem. In order to conserve charge, matter and antimatter particles must be made in pairs. To make even one electron-positron pair would require the concentration of enough energy in one place to create the mass of two electrons out of nothing. The amount

1—Where Has All the Antimatter Gone?

According to the known laws of physics, particles and antiparticles must invariably be created in pairs. If matter and antimatter are always made in equal amounts, then half the universe should be antimatter. There should be antimatter galaxies containing antimatter stars illuminating antimatter planets that are perhaps populated with antimatter beings.

If antimatter galaxies exist, they should have large, tenuous clouds of antihydrogen gas surrounding them, just as the Milky Way Galaxy sits inside its own cloud of hydrogen gas. In regions where normal-matter galaxies and antimatter galaxies border each other, hydrogen from their clouds would overlap. In this region positrons from antihydrogen would annihilate with electrons from hydrogen, releasing gamma-ray photons having a characteristic energy of 511 thousand electron volts (keV).

Astronomers using gamma-ray detectors flown on orbiting astronomical satellites have looked carefully for 511-keV radiation indicative of such matter-antimatter annihilation. Occasionally some is detected, but each instance can be explained in terms of a normal-matter neutron star, supernova, or other object that produces positrons from its activity. No source has been found that indicates the existence of large amounts of antimatter anywhere in the universe.

This mystery of the missing antimatter is one of the major unsolved problems of physics. It may be that in the first instants of the big bang that gave birth to the universe, some subtle interaction among particles gave rise to an asymmetry of matter and antimatter—more normal-matter particles than antiparticles. Scientists hope that once the properties of particles and atoms of antimatter can be compared in detail with those of normal matter, such speculations can be confirmed or disproved.

Opposing jets—thought to be streams of electrons and positrons—emerge from the best known natural antimatter source in the universe. The object, located almost at the heart of the Galaxy, has been dubbed the Great Annihilator because of its intense emission of telltale 511-keV gamma radiation.

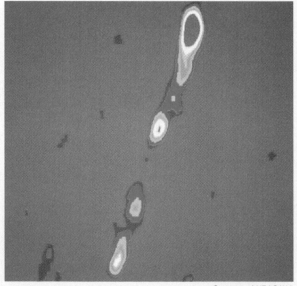

Courtesy of NRAO/AUI

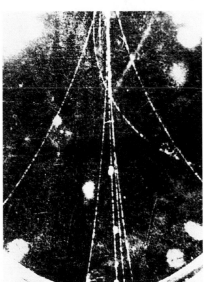

of energy needed was determined by that most famous of Einstein's equations: $E = mc^2$.

If m is taken to be the mass of two electrons, and c the speed of light, then the minimum amount of energy needed would be 1.022 billion electron volts (GeV; *see* Sidebar 2, page 34). There was no machine known that could accelerate particles to that energy. Particles having such energies did exist, however, in the cosmic rays that came from the sky.

In 1932, Carl Anderson of the California Institute of Technology built and operated a cosmic-ray detector using a cloud chamber that had a magnetic field passing through it. When a cosmic ray came from space, it usually hit a molecule of gas in the atmosphere. The energy released created a shower of particles, some of which would leave cloud tracks in the cloud chamber. The tracks could be photographed. If the particle had a positive charge, the track in the photograph would curve one way in the magnetic field. If it had a negative charge, the track would curve the other way. The thickness and curvature of the track gave Anderson a clue as to the charge and mass of the particle.

Anderson noticed that some of the tracks were exactly like those made by electrons but were curved oppositely. He called them positrons, not yet aware of Dirac's predicted antielectrons. Occasionally, when the shower of particles initiated at the top of his detector, he could see a pair of particles, one an electron and one a positron. In 1936 Anderson won the Nobel Prize for Physics for his discovery of the first antimatter particle. Now that the antielectron had been proved to exist, it was obvious that antiprotons and antineutrons also ought to exist. The discovery of these more massive antiparticles would have to wait another two decades.

Carl Anderson (top left) works with the cloud chamber that he used in 1932 to detect the positron, an antimatter particle whose existence Paul Dirac (top right) had predicted three years earlier. In an early photograph by Anderson of a cosmic-ray-induced particle shower (above), cloud tracks made by electrons curve one way in a strong magnetic field, while tracks made by positrons curve the same amount but in the opposite way.

Creation of heavier antiparticles

By the mid-1950s, driven by the pressures of World War II and the Manhattan Project to build an atomic bomb, physicists had finally developed particle accelerators powerful enough to make antiprotons, antineutrons, and even heavier antiparticles. They used a machine called a synchrotron, which consisted of a ring of vacuum pipe with a magnetic field passing through it. A charged particle like a proton, moving down the evacuated pipe, would be deflected by the magnetic field. By proper adjustment of the magnetic field strength, the trajectory of the proton could be kept inside the ring without hitting the walls. At one position along the ring were placed radio-frequency oscillators. These devices produced a traveling wave of electromagnetic energy that accelerated the proton like a surfer gaining speed on an ocean wave. With proper matching of the radio-frequency pushes and the magnetic field strength, the proton could be accelerated to higher and higher speeds, gaining energy with each revolution of the ring until the desired energy was obtained.

In 1955 the first antiprotons were detected at the University of California at Berkeley by bombardment of a piece of copper foil with accelerated protons. The next year the antineutron was produced at Berkeley by the passing of a beam of antiprotons through matter.

A decade later, in 1965, scientists at Brookhaven National Laboratory, Upton, New York, produced the antideuteron, the antimatter counterpart of the nucleus of deuterium, the hydrogen-2 isotope. Whereas the deuterium nucleus, or deuteron, consists of a proton bound to a neutron, the antideuteron consists of an antiproton bound to an antineutron. Even heavier antinuclei have been generated and detected. In 1978 physicists at the CERN laboratory near Geneva used their then-new Super Proton Synchrotron to produce large numbers of antideuterons, 99 antitritium nuclei, and 94 antihelium-3 nuclei. (The nucleus of antitritium comprises one antiproton and two antineutrons, while that of antihelium-3 comprises two antiprotons and one antineutron.) These heavier antiparticles were sensed by being sent into a detector, where they immediately annihilated. It would be another decade before methods were developed that

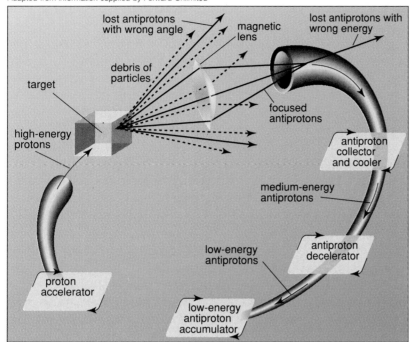

Figure 3: Schematic diagram outlines the current method for making and capturing antiprotons.

would preserve at least one type of precious antiparticle, the antiproton, after it had been made.

Making and capturing antiprotons

The basic method of making antiprotons is shown in Figure 3. Ordinary protons are accelerated to high energies in a proton accelerator. Scientists at CERN accelerate protons in the facility's older Proton Synchrotron until each particle has a kinetic energy of 26 GeV. At the Fermi National Accelerator Laboratory (Fermilab) near Chicago, the proton accelerator known as the main ring is operated at 120 GeV for antiproton production. Consequently, a high-speed proton at Fermilab has enough kinetic energy contained within it potentially to make 120 copies of itself, or 60 pairs of protons and antiprotons. In reality, however, almost all of that energy turns into electromagnetic radiation or particles other than the desired antiprotons.

The high-energy protons are then slammed into a target made of a thick wire of tungsten, copper, or other metal. In the wire the protons collide head on into one of the metal nuclei. The kinetic energy of the proton is released at a single point in space as a tiny fireball of energy. The released energy turns into a spray of photons (X-rays and gamma rays) and pairs of particles and antiparticles of many different kinds. Only a small fraction are proton-antiproton pairs. In CERN's 26-GeV machine, 0.4% of the accelerated protons manage to produce a proton-antiproton pair. At Fermilab the production efficiency is 4.7%.

Making antiprotons is only the first step. The researchers must next accomplish the difficult task of capturing them. The antiprotons emerge from the collision in a broad spray at a wide range of angles and ener-

35

gies. Furthermore, this spray must be separated from the other pairs of particles and antiparticles.

It is the antiproton's unique combination of mass and electric charge that allows it to be identified and separated from the rest of the collision debris. To collect the antiprotons coming out at different angles, researchers use a "magnetic lens," an arrangement of magnetic fields that curves the path of the moving antiprotons. Magnetic lenses are not particularly efficient; usually they capture and focus only 10–30% of the antiprotons created in the target.

The focused antiprotons must then be put into a collector that can hold them. The kind of collector currently used at antiproton-generating facilities is actually a long evacuated ring of pipe. The entrance to the collecting ring is placed at the focal point for the antiprotons. Magnets surrounding the ring bend the paths of the antiprotons moving through the vacuum pipe. If the speed and direction of the antiproton, the strength of the magnetic field, and the radius of the bend of the pipe are just right, the path of the particles will be bent just the right amount to travel down the center of the pipe without hitting the wall. A typical vacuum pipe is about ten centimeters (four inches) in diameter and hundreds of meters long. Threading the beam of particles through it is quite difficult. The best capture efficiency in the early 1990s was only 1%; of every 100 antiprotons made, at least 99 are lost.

Once the antiprotons are in the collecting ring, most of the hard work is over. The vacuum level in the ring is so low—i.e., molecules of ordinary gaseous matter are so few—that antiprotons can be stored in the rings for days at a time. Scientists can then add more high-energy antiprotons to increase the number being stored. A typical antiproton collector ring holds as many as a trillion antiprotons at any one time. This many antiprotons have a mass of about 1.7 trillionths of a gram. Although the number may sound small, if that amount of antimatter were annihilated with an equal amount of matter, the total energy released would be about 300 joules, enough to light a 100-watt bulb for three seconds—enough energy to see.

The antiproton collector ring also contains methods that—in a certain sense—"cool" the captured particles. When antiprotons are first made, they have a wide spread of energies and velocities, some moving faster and some slower than the average velocity. Particle physicists use various techniques to get all the antiprotons to travel at the same speed in the collector ring. Because of their high average speed, the antiprotons still have a high kinetic energy, but their "temperature" is lower because the energy variations are smaller than before and they thus have less relative motion between them.

At Fermilab, where the antiprotons are used for high-energy proton-antiproton collision experiments, means do not exist for further lowering the energy of the particles. But CERN scientists wanted both high- and low-energy antiprotons for various experiments and so installed additional equipment for deceleration and storage. At CERN, after the antiprotons are collected and cooled, they are sent to an antiproton

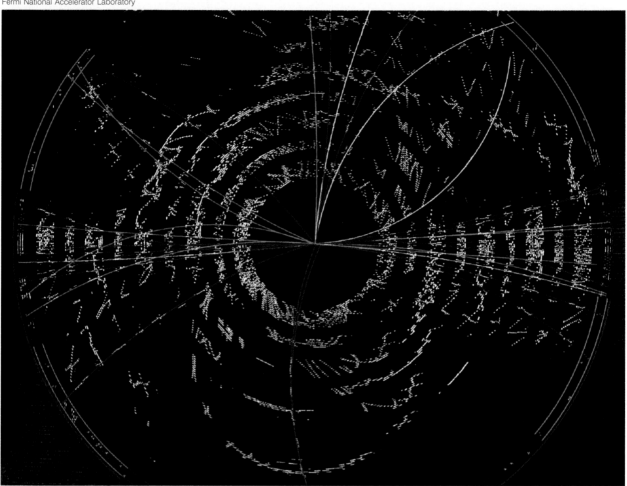

decelerator, which is really the Proton Synchrotron run backward. The slowed antiprotons are then transferred to a ring machine called a low-energy antiproton accumulator. When all the components are tuned correctly, the efficiency of cooling, transferring, decelerating, and storing the antiprotons at low energy is more than 90%. In view of the losses experienced while the antiprotons are made and captured, however, overall efficiency is low.

Collection efficiency at Fermilab is presently about 0.04%; one antiproton is collected for every 2,500 antiprotons made. If one accounts for the 5% production efficiency of the target, then only one antiproton is collected for every 50,000 high-energy protons sent into the target. In terms of energy, the efficiency is even worse. One antiproton, when annihilated with a proton, will produce 2 GeV of energy. But getting that one antiproton requires 50,000 protons, each with 120 GeV of energy—for a particle energy efficiency of one part in three million. Since the accelerator that supplies protons is only 5% efficient at converting common electric power into proton energy, the overall energy efficiency is only one part in 60 million. As a result, antimatter is presently a very expensive synthetic fuel—about $10 billion per microgram (a millionth

A spray of particles emerging from a high-energy proton-antiproton collision event at the Fermi National Accelerator Laboratory is reconstructed by computer from measurements made in a modern electronic particle detector. Such experiments, which aim to improve scientific understanding of the structure of matter, are one application for antimatter.

of a gram)—or two cents per million antiprotons. Nevertheless, there are ways to improve the efficiency. In any case, there are things that only antiprotons can do, making them worth even this exorbitant cost.

Trapping and storing antiprotons

A perennial problem for antimatter researchers is how to hold on to "stuff" that disappears in a burst of energy the instant it touches normal matter. As described above, CERN and Fermilab scientists have demonstrated one solution in the form of a large ring of pipe that uses magnetic fields to keep their antiprotons from hitting the normal-matter walls of the pipe. Nevertheless, even this kind of bottle is many meters in circumference and hardly portable. What scientists desire is a "tabletop" device that can cool, trap, and store antiprotons for a long time in a very small space.

Two of the three men who shared the 1989 Nobel Prize for Physics had developed two kinds of electromagnetic trap for charged particles. Although the traps were originally designed for holding single electrons and clouds of charged, ionized atoms, they can also be used as containers for charged antiparticles. Hans G. Dehmelt of the University of Washington invented a trap, called the Penning trap, that uses a combination of magnetic and electric fields. Wolfgang Paul of the University of Bonn, Germany, invented a similar trap that uses alternating radio-frequency fields to create the particle-trapping region.

The Low-Energy Antiproton Ring (LEAR) at CERN is used to slow down antiprotons to the lowest possible energy at which they can be stored in the ring. LEAR represents the final stage in the process at CERN in which antiprotons are created, captured, decelerated, and accumulated for the study of antimatter at low energies. It is the first machine ever built specifically for the deceleration and collection of antiprotons.

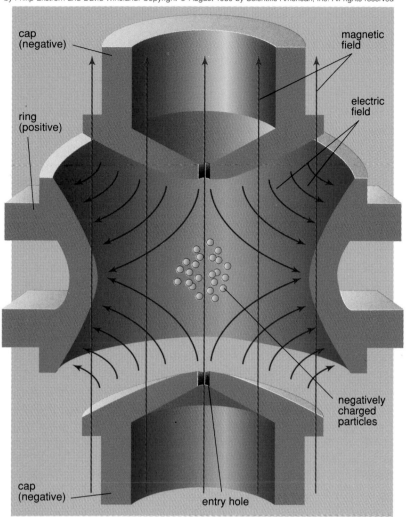

cap
(negative)

magnetic
field

ring
(positive)

electric
field

negatively
charged
particles

cap
(negative)

entry hole

Figure 4: Illustration depicts a Penning trap for holding negatively charged particles by means of steady electric and magnetic fields.

One version of the Penning trap, which was originally designed for electrons (*see* Figure 4), has a side wall made of a machined solid-metal ring about five centimeters in diameter. The inside surface of the ring has a hyperbolic shape. Above and below the hole in the ring are two domed, metal end caps, also with hyperbolic shapes. This assembly is placed in a vacuum chamber inside the bore of a superconducting electromagnet, which in turn sits in a large insulated jug containing liquid helium. The magnetic field from the superconducting magnet runs along the axis of the trap from one end cap to the other. A small hole in either end cap allows particles into the trap.

To capture an electron or other negatively charged particle once it enters the trap, the end caps are given a negative charge and the ring a positive charge. The negatively charged caps repel the negatively charged particle, turning it away from the two ends of the trap. As the particle attempts to move radially outward toward the positively charged ring, the magnetic field bends its path into a circle. If the magnetic field is strong enough and the trap is cold enough, the particle will never reach

39

the inside surface of the ring but will be permanently confined in a tiny circular orbit.

Since 1986, Gerald Gabrielse of Harvard University and co-workers have experimented with Penning traps at CERN to capture antiprotons. To improve the antiproton capture efficiency, they have modified the design of the traps by using a multiplicity of elongated cylindrical electrodes (*see* Figure 5) and flat, aluminum end "windows" instead of the compact, hyperbolically shaped electrodes of the Dehmelt design. The multiple electrodes allow them to make a trap inside a trap. The inner trap is designed to hold a cloud of electrons, while the outer trap is designed to hold antiprotons, which have the same negative electric charge as the electrons but are 1,836 times more massive. CERN's low-energy antiproton accumulator ring provides the antiprotons, sending them in short intense bunches through an evacuated pipe to the trap, which is positioned at the end of the pipe. The antiproton bunches are only 0.2 microseconds (millionths of a second) long and contain 100 million antiprotons each.

When the bunched antiprotons first hit the aluminum entrance window of the trap, their speed is so high that they pass right by the protons in the aluminum nuclei without annihilating. But as they penetrate the window and continue to encounter atoms, their negative charge repels electrons from those atoms out of their orbits. For each electron that an antiproton removes from an atom, the antiproton loses a little energy and slows down. The total speed lost by the antiproton in traversing the window depends on the window's thickness, which thus is critical to the success of the trap. If the window is too thick, all of the antiprotons will be stopped in the window and annihilate. On the other hand, if the window is too thin, the antiprotons will enter the trap with too much energy and escape. If the entrance window's thickness is chosen correctly, about 10,000 of the 100 million antiprotons that entered the window will pass through it with a velocity that is low enough for them to be turned around by the negative 3,000-volt potential of the exit window at the other end of the trap. The antiprotons then head back down the 12-centimeter-long trap toward the entrance window. When the antiprotons first entered the trap, the entrance window had a small positive voltage on it that allowed the antiprotons in at low energy. Just before the 0.2-microsecond-long pulse of antiprotons returns from the other end of the trap some 0.33 microseconds later, the trap is "slammed shut" by applying a negative 3,000 volts to the entrance window in less than 0.02 microseconds. The antiprotons are now trapped.

As a technique to slow the trapped antiprotons further, a cloud of electrons is confined in the trap before antiprotons are allowed in. Once the antiprotons are in the trap, they oscillate back and forth through the electron cloud, losing kinetic energy through repeated collisions with the electrons. Later the electrons are removed, leaving only the antiparticles.

In one experiment Gabrielse's team succeeded in trapping about 100,000 antiprotons and keeping them for two months without losses. One of their traps could easily hold as many as a trillion antiprotons.

40

The trap itself is very small in size. Once the circulating current has been established in the superconducting coils around the trap, it can be maintained by nine-volt batteries, allowing the trapped antiprotons to be transported from site to site, even across continents and oceans. (Their large thermoslike containers of liquid helium make the traps closer to pickup-truck portable than hand portable.)

Using trapped antiprotons

Trapped antiprotons have already been exploited in fundamental scientific research. By observing and comparing the motions of antiprotons and protons in their orbits in Penning traps, researchers have determined that the charge-to-mass ratios of the two particles are the same to within four parts in 100 million. Such comparisons are necessary to test current theories of particle physics, which predict that the magnitudes of the masses and charges of the proton and its antiparticle are identical.

Some of the more exciting, near-term applications for antiprotons are expected to be in medicine. Ted Kalogeropoulos, a physicist at Syracuse (New York) University, and his colleague Levi Gray determined that antiprotons in small amounts can be used to create images that reveal variations in density in the interior of an object, such as the human body. From simulated experiments by computer, they concluded that this new form of imaging will have several significant advantages over current medical imaging methods like X-ray–based computed tomography (CT). Antiproton imaging should give better pictures than CT scans, with a hundredth the radiation dose to the patient.

As discussed above, a moving antiproton is slowed down and eventually halted by its passage through matter. The place where it stops is highly predictable if the density distribution of the object that it penetrates is known. If one knows the average density of the human body, one can adjust the injection energy of the antiproton so that it penetrates a selected distance with an error of only a few millimeters. Thus, given careful aim and proper adjustment of the injection energy, antiprotons can be targeted anywhere within the body.

Once a negatively charged antiproton comes to a halt inside the body, it is promptly attracted to a positively charged nucleus. There it annihilates with a proton, producing a spray of gamma rays and short-lived charged particles called pions. These products have enough energy to emerge from the body (*see* Figure 6, page 42) and trigger suitable detectors, allowing their directions of travel to be determined and their paths retraced to the point within the body where the annihilation occurred. That point then can be compared with the predicted point for the antiproton injection energy used. If the actual stopping distance is shorter than the predicted distance, then an abnormality, *e.g.*, a dense cancer tumor, exists in the path of the injected antiproton. By injection of a number of antiprotons from different directions and with different injection energies, a density map of the human body can be created in three dimensions. If dense tumors are there, they will appear in the image. The same beam that images the tumor can also be used to destroy

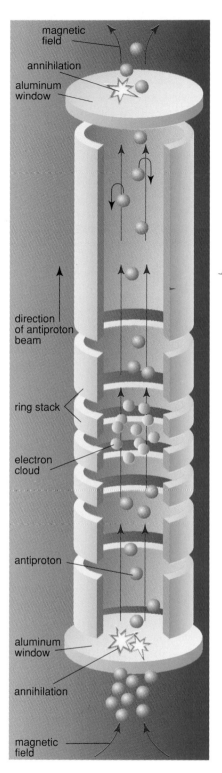

magnetic field
annihilation
aluminum window
direction of antiproton beam
ring stack
electron cloud
antiproton
aluminum window
annihilation
magnetic field

41

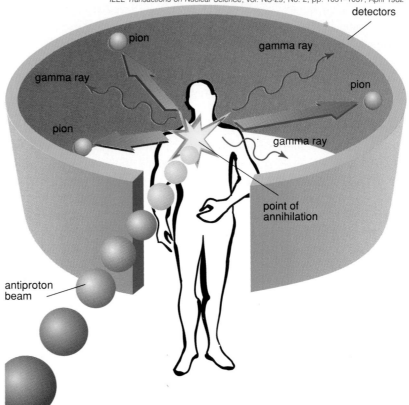

Figure 6: An antiproton having a given energy will travel a specific distance into the human body or other target before it annihilates with a proton of an atom inside the target. The products of the annihilation include charged pions and gamma rays, whose subsequent emergence from the body can be detected with suitable equipment and whose paths can then be traced backward to pinpoint the site of annihilation. By injection of beams of antiprotons from different directions and with different energies, the technique theoretically could be used to build up a picture of the body's interior. In addition, the energy deposited by the annihilation process could be used to destroy cancerous cells at the target point.

Adapted from L. Gray and T.E. Kalogeropoulos, IEEE Transactions on Nuclear Science, vol. NS-29, No. 2, pp. 1051–1057, April 1982

it. By increasing the number of antiprotons injected into a given location, doctors can deposit enough energy into the tumor to destroy it.

The number of antiprotons needed is not large. A million will produce a high-quality image of a plane through the body, and a billion will produce a high-quality three-dimensional image of a large volume like the head or chest area. More antiprotons would be needed to kill the tumors, depending on size. A trap containing one day's antiproton production from CERN or Fermilab would be sufficient to image a thousand patients or treat dozens of cancerous tumors.

Making and storing antihydrogen

The next step in developing an antimatter technology is to make and store antimatter in the form of antihydrogen atoms and molecules. Conceptually the task is easy. One merely combines antiprotons and positrons. Being of opposite charge, they will automatically attract each other. Unfortunately, like a comet being attracted to the Sun, the positron gains so much speed during its infall toward the antiproton that most of the time it just swings by and moves out again, avoiding capture. What is needed is a third type of particle nearby to drain some of the kinetic energy of the incoming positron so that it can be captured.

Although antihydrogen has yet to be made, two Antihydrogen Workshops have already been held as of 1992. The second, convened in July 1992 in Munich, Germany, was attended by more than 100 scientists.

There they described their ongoing work to be the first to make anti-hydrogen. Many of the approaches involve trapping a large number of positrons, which are fairly easy to make, and then putting an antiproton in the same trap. (A major challenge is to build a trap that will hold heavy and light particles with opposite charges at the same time.) Once in the trap, the antiproton will capture one positron, while the other positrons act as third particles to take away the excess energy.

Others at the conference described their techniques for holding the antihydrogen atoms once they are made. Since an antihydrogen atom has no net charge, it cannot be stored in the traps used to hold positrons and antiprotons. One proposal uses a trap made of ultraviolet laser beams. Another takes advantage of the fact that antihydrogen is diamagnetic—*i.e.,* strong magnetic fields tend to push the antihydrogen atom away. By means of strong persistent currents in two properly spaced rings of superconducting wire (*see* Figure 7), it is possible to create a three-dimensional magnetic bottle with a minimum field strength at its center that would act as a trap for antihydrogen atoms and even large "snowballs" of frozen antihydrogen. That the technique has already been demonstrated on normal hydrogen is especially encouraging.

Other scientists at the workshop described their planned experiments to use antihydrogen to test the fundamental laws of nature. Primarily, the experiments involve comparing atoms of antihydrogen and normal hydrogen with an eye for differences other than their opposite charges and

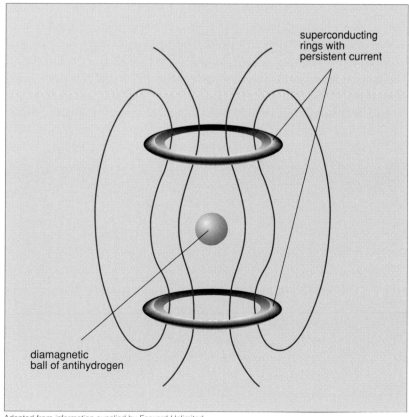

superconducting
rings with
persistent current

diamagnetic
ball of antihydrogen

Adapted from information supplied by Forward Unlimited

Figure 7: A three-dimensional "bottle" of steady magnetic fields can hold a quantity of antihydrogen atoms or even a ball of frozen antihydrogen. The magnetic fields keep the antihydrogen levitated and centered in the middle of the bottle, where the field strength is at a minimum.

mirror-reversed properties. There is good reason to suspect a difference—the known universe is made almost entirely of normal matter, and there must be some reason for that fact. In one experiment an international team (which appropriately includes scientists from the University of Pisa, Italy) plans to "drop" antihydrogen atoms in the gravity field of the Earth and see if they fall faster or slower than ordinary hydrogen atoms. No one really expects antiatoms to fall up instead of down, but nothing will be proved until the experiment has been done. Others are planning to measure the inertial mass, the magnetic moment, or the frequency of the light emitted by excited antihydrogen atoms. Even a negative experimental result will be scientifically important but, of course, the intriguing aspect is that a difference may be found.

Antimatter propulsion

One exciting future use for antimatter is in space propulsion—not for powering the faster-than-light drive of a futuristic starship but for more pragmatic engines called antimatter rockets. The simplest antimatter rocket engine is shown in Figure 8. The particular example illustrated consists of a nearly solid cylinder of tungsten about 28 centimeters (almost a foot) in both length and diameter and about 330 kilograms (about 730 pounds) in weight. Antiprotons are injected into a cavity in the center of the cylinder, where they annihilate with protons in hydrogen gas that is maintained there. Most of the gamma rays and charged pions that emerge from the annihilation process are stopped in the tungsten block, depositing their energy in the metal and heating it up. From one face of the metal cylinder to the other run long holes, through which is fed ordinary molecular hydrogen. The hydrogen enters the tungsten block cold and emerges at high temperatures (3,000° C, or 5,430° F), in the process keeping the tungsten from melting. The hot hydrogen gas is then expelled from a nozzle to create thrust. The speed of the emerging hydrogen is two to three times that obtainable from chemical rocket

Figure 8: A schematic illustrates the major details of a first-generation antimatter rocket.

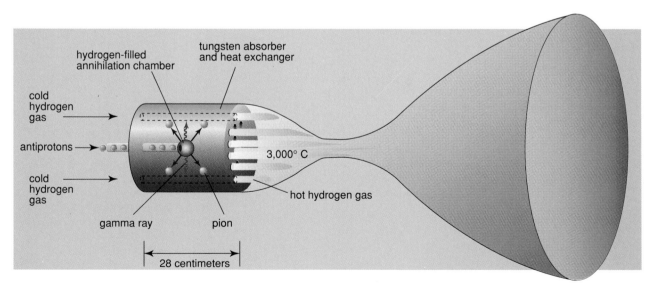

Adapted from information supplied by Forward Unlimited

fuels. The performance of this design is limited by the 3,410° C (6,170° F) melting point of tungsten. Reaction chambers made of magnetic fields rather than solid material are now being studied that would allow even higher exhaust velocities for the expelled hydrogen.

Studies of the optimal design for antimatter rocket systems have come up with some unexpected results. First, for missions near Earth and throughout the solar system, it is not efficient to use equal parts of matter and antimatter. The best arrangement is to use a few milligrams of antimatter to heat tons of expellant material—hydrogen, methane, or water—that is spewed from the exhaust nozzle. Second, only one size of antimatter rocket is needed, no matter what the mission is. With normal chemical rockets, the more difficult the mission, the more fuel the rocket must carry, and the larger the rocket becomes. But with optimized antimatter rockets, going up to low-Earth orbit, orbiting the Moon, making a round-trip journey to the surface of Mars, or traveling to the stars can all be done with the same size of vehicle.

The optimum antimatter vehicle carries a fuel tank that holds an amount of expellant having only four times the "dry" mass of the vehicle. (Most chemical rockets carry 20–60 times their dry mass in fuel.) If the mission is easy, the vehicle will take only a few milligrams of antimatter and use it to heat the expellant material to a hot gas and use that to propel the vehicle. If the mission is difficult, the vehicle will take along more antimatter, but the same amount of expellant, and use the antimatter to heat the expellant material to a blazing-hot plasma that has a much higher exhaust velocity. Even for a mission to the stars, the amount of antimatter needed is measured in kilograms, not tons.

The future

In the past, antimatter could be trapped and held only in the imagination. It is now an everyday reality. Before the century is out, antihydrogen and perhaps other antiatoms will be made and stored. As the 21st century progresses, antimatter will find new uses, and its price will come down as production increases. Antimatter may prove to be a practical source of power for vehicles and artificial human habitats in remote locations like the ocean bottom or the surface of the Moon or Mars. Minute streams of antiparticles guided by electromagnetic fields may become specialized tools for pinpoint welding tasks or for carving out intricate microscopic shapes in various materials. And one day, riding on a thrust of matter-antimatter annihilation, humans may set off for the stars.

FOR ADDITIONAL READING

B.W. Augenstein *et al.*, *Antiproton Science and Technology* (World Scientific, 1988).

David B. Cline, *Low Energy Antimatter* (World Scientific, 1986).

Robert L. Forward and Joel Davis, *Mirror Matter: Pioneering Antimatter Physics* (John Wiley & Sons, 1988).

Gerald Gabrielse, "Extremely Cold Antiprotons," *Scientific American* (December 1992, pp. 74–85).

The Revolution in Cosmology

by Edmund Bertschinger

Using powerful new instruments, scientists are looking far deeper into the universe than ever before. Their discoveries have created revolutionary changes in the science of cosmology.

EDMUND BERTSCHINGER is an Associate *Professor of Physics at the Massachusetts Institute of Technology, Cambridge.*

(Overleaf) Illustration by Don Davis

The greatest distance that astronomers have been able to see in the universe is about 15 billion light-years, the distance light travels in 15 billion years. (One light-year equals 9.5 trillion kilometers [5.9 trillion miles].) Although the universe could be much larger—it is unknown whether it is finite or infinite—it is believed that we can see no farther because the universe is only about 15 billion years old. Light emitted from greater distances, traveling 299,793 kilometers (186,300 miles) per second, has not had time yet to reach the Earth.

The potential existence of a finite age and ambiguities about the extent of the observed universe raise intriguing questions. How big are the largest objects in the universe? How did they form? How did the universe begin? What happened before that? The last question is difficult to address scientifically because of our inability to witness the events or to perform relevant experiments. However, the other questions represent major themes in cosmology, the study of the structure and evolution of the universe.

Twenty years ago it was widely believed that the universe is smooth on scales larger than about 50 million light-years. During the last decade, however, it has become clear that there are structures with sizes ranging up to about one billion light-years. Some of the recent discoveries support the basic cosmological models, but others have left behind casualties, including one of the favorite theories of the 1980s, the cold dark matter model.

The expanding universe

By the 1920s it was understood that the Milky Way Galaxy is a system of several billion stars in a disk thousands of light-years across. Millions of other galaxies could be seen as diffuse patches of starlight on photographic plates. Measurements of the starlight and other radiation emitted by these galaxies showed that the radiation is nearly always shifted toward longer wavelengths—the red end of the spectrum—relative to the radiation emitted by the Milky Way. These redshifts are due to the Doppler effect—a familiar example of this being the change in pitch of

NASA

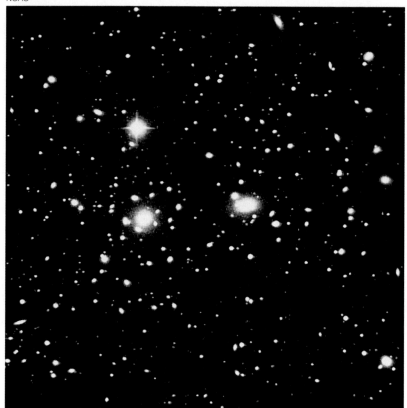

Free of the dust that obscures its disk and central bulge in visible light, the Milky Way Galaxy (opposite page) is viewed edge-on by the diffuse infrared background experiment aboard the Cosmic Background Explorer (COBE) satellite. The solar system lies within the disk, about 30,000 light-years from the center. The Coma cluster of galaxies (left) lies about 300 million light-years from the Earth. Measurements of the radiation emitted by these galaxies reveal that most of them are moving away from the Earth at speeds of more than 6,000 kilometers (4,000 miles) per second.

the siren of a passing ambulance—and they indicate that most galaxies move away from the Earth with speeds of more than 6,000 kilometers (4,000 miles) per second.

In 1924 Edwin Hubble of the Mount Wilson Observatory near Pasadena, California, measured the relative distances of nearby galaxies by measuring the apparent brightnesses and periods of Cepheid variable stars. Nearly 20 years earlier Henrietta Leavitt of the Harvard College Observatory had shown that the intrinsic luminosity (total amount of radiation emitted over a specified range of wavelengths) of a Cepheid variable is correlated with its period of variation (the average time required for completing a cycle of variations). Using this relation, Hubble discovered that the more distant galaxies recede more rapidly than the nearby ones, with a recession speed that is approximately proportional to the distance from the Earth. This relation is now known as the Hubble law, and the constant of proportionality is called the Hubble constant.

The systematic recession of external galaxies away from us does not violate the Copernican principle stating that the Earth occupies no special location in the universe. Like raisins in a rising loaf of bread, all galaxies recede from all others. Any galaxy could be taken as the center of expansion. If the expansion rate is everywhere the same, the same recession law would be measured by an observer on any galaxy. Thus, Hubble's discovery of a uniform expansion implies that the universe is expanding in the sense that the galaxies are moving steadily apart.

49

Redshifts are related to distance, according to Edwin Hubble's concept of an expanding universe. The velocity of recession from the Earth of a galaxy causes a shift toward the red end of the spectrum in the light received from that galaxy. Thus, the galaxies that are farthest away reveal the largest redshifts and are receding the fastest. The vertical arrow indicates the position of the element calcium in the fuzzy spectrum of the Virgo galaxy. The horizontal arrows show the calcium redshift, which becomes greater as the galaxies are more distant.

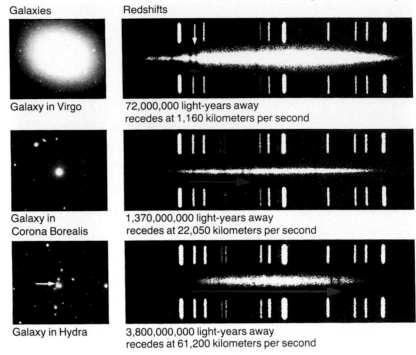

Galaxies | **Redshifts**

Galaxy in Virgo

72,000,000 light-years away
recedes at 1,160 kilometers per second

Galaxy in Corona Borealis

1,370,000,000 light-years away
recedes at 22,050 kilometers per second

Galaxy in Hydra

3,800,000,000 light-years away
recedes at 61,200 kilometers per second

If galaxies are moving apart today, then they were closer together in the past. Extrapolating the Hubble expansion back in time leads to the conclusion that all the galaxies were piled together about 15 billion years ago. The exact time depends on the value of the Hubble constant and other cosmological parameters whose values are not well known. The expansion age is uncertain by about five billion years, but it is in rough agreement with the ages of the oldest stars. At this initial moment of tremendous density and pressure, called the big bang, the matter in the universe began expanding rapidly.

The afterglow of the big bang

The expansion of a gas causes it to cool. The universe therefore must have been extremely hot during the early moments after the big bang. At temperatures greater than about 10,000 kelvins (K), the predominantly hydrogen gas ionized into free protons and electrons (0 K = −273° C or −460° F). Emission from this glowing hot gas filled the universe with thermal radiation. Collisions of photons (particles of light) with electrons kept the matter and radiation coupled in thermodynamic equilibrium at a common temperature that decreased as the universe expanded.

When the temperature dropped below about 3,500 K, protons and electrons could combine to form neutral atoms, and the universe became transparent to (penetrable by) the thermal radiation. This event is called recombination and is thought to have occurred about 300,000 years after the big bang. Since recombination, the radiation has traveled to the Earth unimpeded over a distance of nearly 15 billion light-years. The Hubble law implies that the gas at this distance is receding from the Earth at nearly the speed of light; consequently, the radiation is redshifted by a large factor (a little more than 1,000 times) in wavelength. According to the big-bang theory, the universe should therefore be seen glowing in microwaves with wavelengths about 1,000 times longer than red light.

Arno Penzias and Robert Wilson of the Bell Telephone Laboratories in New Jersey discovered this cosmic microwave background radiation in 1965. They found that the radiation was approximately isotropic (having the same intensity in all directions) and that the brightness corresponded to emission from a blackbody of temperature about 3 K ($-270°$ C, $-454°$ F). (A blackbody is a surface that completely absorbs all radiant energy falling upon it with no reflection.) Their serendipitous discovery, soon confirmed by other groups, effectively ruled out a rival to the big-bang theory, the steady-state theory, which posited that matter was continuously created so that a constant mean density was maintained forever despite the Hubble expansion.

The cosmic microwave background radiation is an important fossil remnant of the big bang. Accurate measurements of this radiation can provide clues to the physical conditions prevailing at the time the radiation was emitted and at later times if the radiation was subsequently scattered or absorbed. However, emission from the Earth's atmosphere and other terrestrial sources makes it difficult to perform accurate experiments from the ground. Thus, in November 1989 the Cosmic Background Explorer (COBE) satellite was launched by the U.S. National Aeronautics and Space Administration (NASA) to make detailed measurements of the cosmic microwave background radiation. Early in 1990 the first results from COBE were announced by John Mather and his colleagues at NASA's Goddard Space Flight Center, Greenbelt, Maryland. Using the Far Infrared Absolute Spectrophotometer (FIRAS), they measured the radiation spectrum (intensity of the radiation as a function of its frequency) and found that it fit the predicted blackbody spectrum to an accuracy within 1% of the peak intensity. The temperature of the radiation is 2.73 K with an uncertainty of only 0.01 of a degree. The COBE results were confirmed in 1990 with a rocket-borne instrument built by Herbert Gush, Mark Halpern, and Edward Wishnow of the University of British Columbia.

With more data from FIRAS, the COBE scientists reported that there is no deviation from a blackbody spectrum greater than 0.03% of the peak intensity. The perfection of the blackbody spectrum in all directions was strong evidence in support of the big-bang theory. These results also ruled out models in which the intergalactic gas was reheated to high temperatures by energetic processes occurring after recombination.

The incomplete big-bang theory

Like Darwin's theory of the evolution of species and Alfred Wegener's theory of continental drift, the big-bang theory is only a starting point for more detailed models of the universe. It is a framework that requires additional ideas for a complete and consistent physical theory of the evolution of the universe to be provided.

COBE (right) was launched in November 1989 by NASA to measure the cosmic microwave background radiation. Measurements by the satellite's Far Infrared Absolute Spectrophotometer were plotted together with a curve for a blackbody with a temperature of 2.74 K (opposite page, top). Their close fit provided strong evidence in support of the big-bang theory.

For example, the big bang does not specify the fate of the expanding universe. According to general relativity, Einstein's theory of gravitation, the universal expansion rate should be decreasing owing to the gravitational pull of the mass on itself. That is, the Hubble constant should be decreasing with time—albeit very slowly, perhaps being halved during the last 7.5 billion years. The expansion rate could eventually decrease to zero and then reverse itself, leading to a cosmic collapse. Alternatively, the universe might continue to expand forever.

The future of the cosmic expansion depends on the mean mass density of the universe. If it exceeds a tiny critical value—about four milligrams per Earth volume—then the gravitational tug will be enough to halt and reverse the expansion. The ratio, called Omega, of the mean mass density to this critical density is poorly known from observations and is unspecified by the big-bang theory. Most measurements suggest that Omega is about one-fifth (the mean density is only one-fifth of the critical density), implying that the universe will expand forever, but a few suggest that it may equal or exceed one.

E.S. Cheng, NASA Goddard Space Flight Center

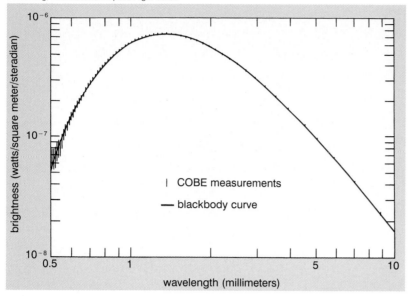

What is the universe made of?

The big-bang theory also does not fully specify the composition of the universe. According to the theory, nuclear fusion occurring during the first three minutes of the universe would produce a certain amount of helium, depending on the total amount of matter. Fusion calculations made during the last 25 years by Robert Wagoner of Stanford University, James Peebles of Princeton University, David Schramm of the University of Chicago, and others have shown that the observed abundance of helium could be explained if the amount of ordinary matter—that made of protons, neutrons, and electrons—corresponds to an Omega of only a few hundredths. This value is somewhat larger than the total amount of hydrogen, helium, and other elements observed in the universe, yet it is appreciably less than the amount estimated by weighing galaxies and clusters of galaxies.

To resolve this discrepancy, astronomers have obtained strong evidence that there exists some form of matter that is unseen but which exerts gravitational forces. The form of this "dark matter" is unknown. It might consist of some as-yet-undiscovered elementary particles; it could be made of small black holes left over from the big bang; or it could represent a deeper gap in our understanding of the laws of physics. Even the existence of dark matter is questioned by some astrophysicists. The nature, amount, and distribution of dark matter are among the most important unknowns today in cosmology.

Fluctuations in the microwave background radiation

After many years of unsuccessful searches, in 1992 fluctuations were detected in the cosmic microwave background radiation. This important discovery was made by George Smoot of the Lawrence Berkeley Laboratory, Berkeley, California, and his colleagues with the use of the differential microwave radiometers (DMRs) on the COBE satellite. The

From COBE Satellite reference George Smoot, *et al.*, *The Astrophysical Journal*, 396: L1-5, September 1, 1992

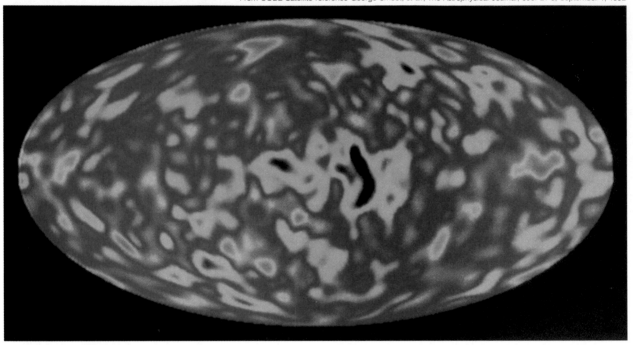

Extremely small temperature fluctuations in the cosmic microwave background radiation lurk among the pink and blue signal noises in a computer-enhanced map of the sky generated from data collected by COBE. The COBE researchers believe that the fluctuations provide the first evidence that accounts for the condensation of galaxies and clusters of galaxies from an otherwise structureless universe.

DMR compares the temperature of the blackbody radiation in different directions on the sky. After subtraction of a dipole pattern arising from the motion of the spacecraft relative to distant galaxies, residual fluctuations remained with a standard deviation of 30 microkelvins (μK; millionths of a kelvin) in areas of the sky 10° across. These fluctuations have an amplitude of just one part in 100,000 of the mean microwave background temperature. Achieving this level of sensitivity required careful data analysis and modeling of foreground emission from the Milky Way by Charles Bennett of the Goddard Space Flight Center and his colleagues.

Because the microwave background radiation comes to the Earth from a distance of 15 billion light-years, fluctuations subtending an angle of 10° correspond to a large physical size—about 5 billion light-years, larger than any previously known cosmic structure. COBE/DMR could not detect structures of smaller size because of its limited angular resolution of about 7°.

Relating the smaller-scale fluctuations that made galaxies and clusters of galaxies (with sizes smaller than 100 million light-years) to the fluctuations seen by COBE/DMR requires a specific theory that predicts the relative amplitudes of fluctuations with different sizes produced in the early universe. A broad class of such theories is based on the cosmic inflation paradigm proposed in 1981 by Alan Guth at the Stanford Linear Accelerator Center. Inflation-based theories posit that the big bang started with a tremendously rapid phase of expansion that stretched subatomic-length scales to sizes of millions and billions of light-years. As a result, microscopic fluctuations arising from the Heisenberg uncertainty principle of quantum mechanics would be stretched to cosmic sizes. These fluctuations could provide both the seeds around which galaxies

54

formed from the expanding debris of the big bang and the fluctuations that were detected by COBE/DMR. Inflation theory also predicts that Omega should almost exactly equal one.

As shown by Edward Wright of the University of California at Los Angeles and his colleagues, the fluctuations detected by COBE/DMR have approximately the correct amplitude to account for galaxies and larger structures in the universe if the inflation paradigm is correct. However, alternative theories have been proposed that might also be consistent with the COBE results. For example, Alexander Vilenkin of Tufts University, Medford, Massachusets, Albert Stebbins of the Fermi National Accelerator Laboratory, Batavia, Illinois, and others proposed that oscillating loops of cosmic string—exotic objects that may have been created in the early universe—would create fluctuations similar to those predicted by inflationary theories.

More direct tests of cosmological theories would come from measurements of microwave fluctuations of angular size between one-half and a few degrees. While these fluctuations have not yet been unambiguously discovered, during the past year interesting upper limits were set by several groups. On an angular scale of 5°, Robert Watson of the Victoria University of Manchester, England, and his colleagues placed an upper limit of about 50 µK by using a microwave receiver at an observatory in the Canary Islands. Similar results were obtained on slightly larger angular scales by Stephen Meyer of the Massachusetts Institute of Technology (MIT) and his colleagues by means of a receiver flown on a balloon to place it above much of the interfering atmosphere. On a scale between 1° and 2°, an upper limit of 40 µK was obtained by Todd Gaier and his colleagues at the University of California at Santa Barbara on the basis of measurements made at the South Pole, a favorable site because of its high elevation above sea level and the small amount of water vapor. These recent upper limits have not yet been carefully compared with the predictions of theories, but they should provide useful constraints on inflation-based and other theories.

Mapping the universe

The distribution of galaxies in space provides another measure of structure in the universe. The mean separation between galaxies more luminous than the Milky Way is about 30 million light-years; fainter galaxies are more numerous. However, galaxies are not uniformly scattered throughout the universe. Instead, they are strongly clustered, existing typically in groups only a few million light-years across.

Before the 1980s it was widely believed that the galaxy distribution was relatively uniform on scales larger than about 60 million light-years. Few galaxy distances had been measured, and redshifts were known for only about 5,000 galaxies. Galaxy maps were mainly confined to projections on the sky, making three-dimensional structures difficult to discern. A revolution in extragalactic astronomy occurred during the 1980s with the replacement of photographic plates by sensitive electronic detectors as the recording medium for the light collected by telescopes. The newer

Edward Wright, University of California, Los Angeles

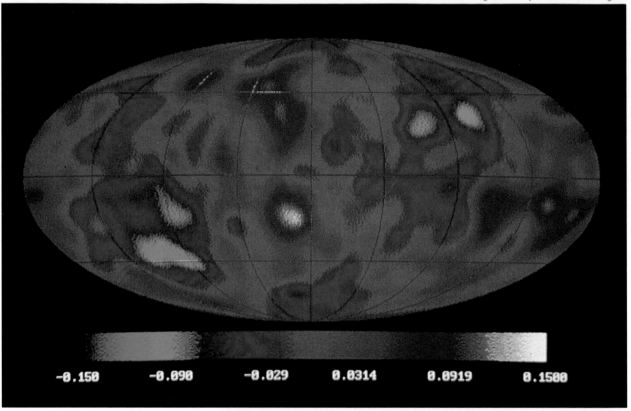

-0.150   -0.090   -0.029   0.0314   0.0919   0.1500

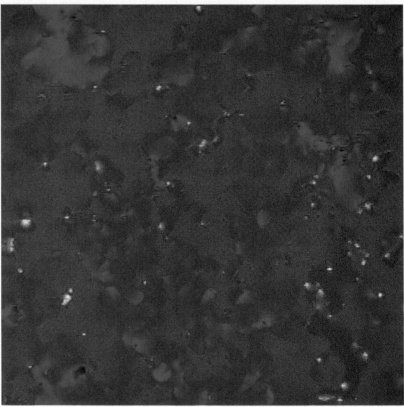

Random pattern of nonuniformity in the universe (above) is predicted by inflation theory, which posits that the big bang started with an exceedingly rapid phase of expansion that stretched microscopic fluctuations to sizes of millions and billions of light-years. They would be the seeds around which galaxies would form. The smaller-scale pattern of nonuniformity at the right might have arisen from oscillating loops of cosmic string—exotic objects that may have been created in the early universe.

François Bouchet, Institut d'Astrophysique, Paris; Dave Bennet, Lawrence Livermore National Laboratory; Albert Stebbins, Fermi National Accelerator Laboratory

technology reduced the time needed to measure a redshift by almost a factor of 100. Consequently, during the past decade more than 30,-000 galaxy redshifts have been measured. Because redshifts are much easier to measure than galaxy distances, astronomers often estimate the distances by using the Hubble law. Catalogs of galaxy redshifts and directions in the sky are called redshift surveys.

Technological developments have continued to increase the rate at which redshift surveys are conducted. Increasingly, large telescopes are being fitted with devices allowing dozens of galaxy redshifts to be measured simultaneously. Using fiber optics to gather the light from many different galaxy images at the focal plane of a 2.5-meter (8.2-foot)-diameter telescope, Stephen Shectman of the Observatories of the Carnegie Institution of Washington in Pasadena, California, and his colleagues routinely measure 1,000 galaxy redshifts per week of observing.

Voids, filaments, and pancakes

Galaxy redshift surveys have revealed a great deal of three-dimensional structure in the universe. The first major surprise came in 1981 with the announcement by Robert Kirshner of the University of Michigan and his colleagues that a volume more than 300 million light-years across, at a distance of one billion light-years in the constellation Boötes, contained no more than one-fourth the number of galaxies it should if galaxies were uniformly distributed. Many similar (though smaller) low-density regions, called voids, have been found during the last decade.

The distribution of two million galaxies covering 10% of the sky is shown as a map consisting of many tiny dots. Each dot represents a small area of sky that was photographed by a telescope in Australia. The star and galaxy positions on each of the 185 photographs were measured by a computer-controlled scanning machine. It shone a laser beam through each photograph and took measurements at more than one billion points to determine the position, brightness, and shape of every image. The dots are black where there are no galaxies, white where there are more than 20, and gray for numbers between 1 and 19. Individual galaxy clusters are represented by the small bright patches, while the elongated bright areas are superclusters and filaments.

S.J. Maddox, W.J. Sutherland, G.P. Efstathious, and J. Loveday, Oxford Astrophysics

Optical fibers attached to the 2.5-meter (8.2-foot)-diameter telescope at Las Campanas Observatory in Chile (right) gather the light from many different galaxy images at the focal plane of the telescope and carry it to a spectrograph, where a photon counter records the light's spectra. In this way dozens of galaxy redshifts can be measured simultaneously. The redshifts supply information that is crucial for determining the three-dimensional distribution of galaxies in the universe. A map of such a distribution (below) shows 3,962 galaxies, the farthest of which is 500 milllion light-years away. The nearly horizontal line of galaxies stretching across the diagram has been called the "Great Wall" and is the largest coherent structure of galaxies yet observed.

If large volumes are relatively deficient in galaxies, then the galaxies must cluster elsewhere. In 1986 Martha Haynes of Cornell University, Ithaca, New York, and Riccardo Giovanelli of Arecibo (Puerto Rico) Observatory showed that galaxies toward the constellations of Perseus and Pisces are concentrated into a linear filament about 10 times as long as it is wide. In front of this filament is a void, suggesting that the galaxies may have moved from the void into the filament.

The widespread existence of both voids and coherent chains of galaxies hundreds of millions of light-years in extent was confirmed by a redshift

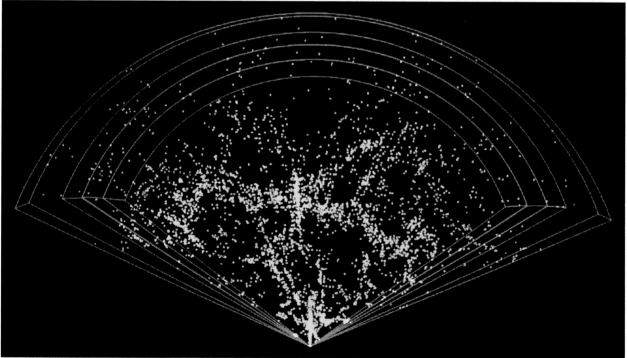

M.J. Geller and J.P. Huchra, Smithsonian Astrophysical Observatory

From "The density field of the local Universe,"
W. Saunders, *et al.*, reprinted by the permission of *Nature*, vol. 349, no. 6304, pp. 32–38, January 3, 1991, © Macmillan Magazines Ltd.

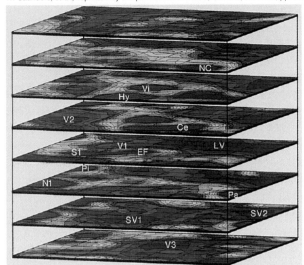

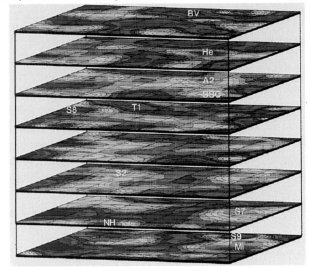

survey reported in 1986 by Valérie de Lapparent, Margaret Geller, and John Huchra of the Harvard-Smithsonian Center for Astrophysics. This study provided convincing evidence that galaxy groups themselves cluster on much larger scales. Coherent structures containing more than about 1,000 galaxies with a space density greater than twice the cosmic average are called superclusters.

Superclusters and voids came as a surprise to most cosmologists. However, Yakov Zel'dovich of the Institute of Applied Mathematics in Moscow had developed a theory of gravitational instability during the 1970s that predicted that galaxies should evacuate low-density regions, forming voids, while piling up in two-dimensional sheets that he called "pancakes." Further collapse in the pancakes would create filaments like the Perseus-Pisces chain.

In 1989 Geller and Huchra published new results from their redshift survey confirming the existence of large thin sheets of galaxies surrounding low-density voids. One such structure, nicknamed the "Great Wall" of galaxies, has an extent of nearly one billion light-years. Additional large-scale structure in the galaxy distribution was reported in 1991 by a team of astronomers from the U.K. and Canada studying galaxies detected by the Infrared Astronomical Satellite. They determined that the amount of structure was inconsistent with the predictions of a theoretical model called cold dark matter (*see* below). Even more surprising was the discovery reported in 1990 by a team of British and U.S. astronomers, led by Thomas Broadhurst of the University of Durham, England, that superclusters in two directions on the sky are spaced in a regular, quasi-periodic pattern approximately 800 million light-years apart.

The redshift surveys mentioned above often revealed structures comparable in size with the surveys themselves, suggesting that still larger structures might exist. Their existence might then be difficult to reconcile with the smoothness of the microwave background radiation on a scale of one billion light-years. However, Shectman and his colleagues

The first three-dimensional maps of the universe that show the density of galaxies were derived from measurements of redshifts of 2,400 galaxies that had been detected by the Infrared Astronomical Satellite. The Milky Way Galaxy is in the center of each. Superclusters and voids are indicated: NC (North Centaurus), Vi (Virgo), Hy (Hydra), V2 (new void), Ce (Centaurus), LV (Local Void), EF (Eridanus-Fornax), V1 (new void), S1 (new supercluster), N1 (N1600), Pi (Pisces), Pa (Pavo), SV1 (SSRS void 1), Sv2 (SSRS new void), V2 (new void), BV (Boötes void), He (Hercules), A2 (A2197/2199), SSC (Shapley's supercluster), B9 (new supercluster), T1 (Tully void 1), S2 (140–33), NH (Near Horologium), S7 (new supercluster), Mi (Microscopium), S9 (new supercluster). The map on the left shows a cube 220 million light-years across, with red indicating areas of high galaxy density (galaxy clusters) and blue revealing regions with few galaxies. The map on the right shows the density of galaxies in a cube 880 million light-years across. It reveals a universe that is lumpier on the large scale than was predicted by the current version of the cold dark matter theory.

determined from their new large redshift survey that the galaxies are distributed uniformly throughout the universe when viewed on a scale of more than one billion light-years.

The cosmic stream

If galaxies formed superclusters by moving out of voids, there should be detectable motion relative to the universal expansion. The Hubble law would not be exact. In fact, the Hubble law is known to break down when galaxies orbit around each other in clusters held together by gravity. Because gravity is long ranged, mass concentrations such as galaxy superclusters should cause departures from the Hubble law on scales larger than 60 million light-years, particularly if galaxies have large amounts of dark matter around them.

In 1986 a group of seven astronomers, including David Burstein of Arizona State University, Alan Dressler of the Observatories of the Carnegie Institution of Washington, and Sandra Faber of the University of California at Santa Cruz, reported that our Galaxy and those within a distance of about 350 million light-years are streaming toward the con-stellations of Hydra and Centaurus at a speed of about 600 kilometers (370 miles) per second in excess of the Hubble expansion. In 1988 these

Galaxies are mapped in a wedge of the sky extending to a distance of nearly four billion light-years. Although galaxy concentrations and underdense regions appear having a Hubble velocity of up to about 10,000 kilometers (6,200 miles) per second (corresponding to a size of about 600 million light-years), on the largest scales the distribution is nearly uniform.

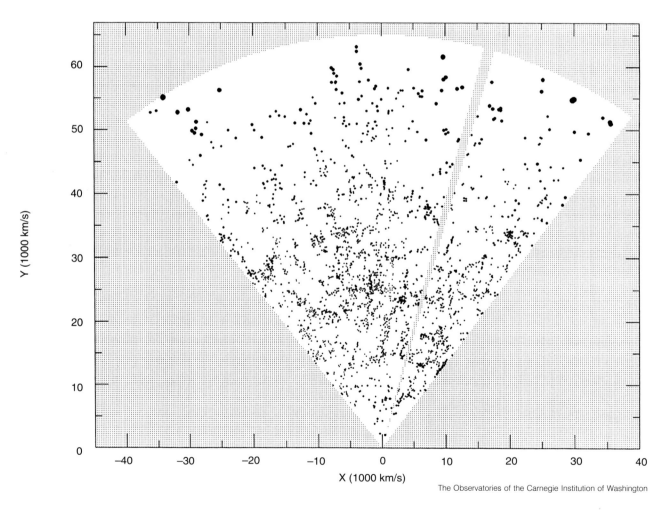

The Observatories of the Carnegie Institution of Washington

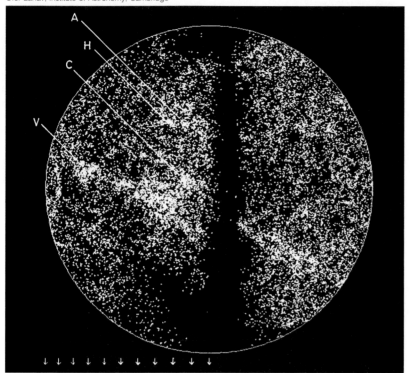

Computer-generated map shows a hemisphere of the sky containing galaxies in three galaxy catalogues. The Virgo (V), Centaurus (C), Hydra (H), and Antlia (A) galaxy clusters are indicated, and the dark band where no galaxies are recorded is the result of the absorption of light by our Milky Way Galaxy. Just below the Centaurus cluster is a large, dense concentration of galaxies, which has been named the Great Attractor. During the last several years astronomers have determined that galaxies more than 600 million light-years from the Great Attractor are streaming toward it at speeds of about 600 kilometers (370 miles) per second in excess of the Hubble expansion.

astronomers proposed that a huge concentration of mass, which they named the "Great Attractor," was responsible for the motion. A galaxy supercluster resides in the same direction, although it, too, might be tugged by a still more massive concentration.

The existence of the Great Attractor has been controversial because of the difficulty in measuring galaxy distances with sufficient accuracy to also measure departures from the Hubble law. More recent studies based on other methods yielded broad agreement with the results of Burstein and his colleagues, with some discrepancies, particularly at large distances. A group led by Marc Aaronson of the University of Arizona found that many galaxy clusters were streaming in the general direction of the Great Attractor. In 1990 Jeffrey Willick of the University of California at Berkeley reported that galaxies in the Perseus-Pisces supercluster were streaming toward the Great Attractor, implying that the gravitational effect of the Attractor extends over a distance of more than 600 million light-years. This conclusion was supported in 1992 with the results from a large new galaxy sample obtained by Donald Matthewson and his colleagues at the Mount Stromlo and Siding Spring observatories near Canberra, Australia.

If gravity is responsible for the cosmic streaming motions, then it should be possible to work backward from the motions to infer the location and masses of the objects creating the gravity field. In 1989 Edmund Bertschinger of MIT and Avishai Dekel of the Hebrew University of Jerusalem developed a method for reconstructing the cosmic mass distribution from measurements of galaxy redshifts and distances. Their

61

method was similar to one employed by geophysicists to find concentrations of dense minerals and light oil-bearing rock by measuring the strength of gravity on the Earth.

The Bertschinger-Dekel mass density reconstruction can be compared with galaxy maps made on the same scale to see whether the gravitational mass is associated with galaxies. The comparison was made with a galaxy redshift survey performed by Marc Davis at the University of California at Berkeley, Amos Yahil at the State University of New York at Stony Brook, Michael Strauss at the Institute for Advanced Study, Princeton, New Jersey, and others. The comparison reveals broad though imperfect agreement between the two maps. By measuring the average amount of mass per galaxy implied by the maps, Dekel and his colleagues estimated that the mean cosmic density is close to the critical value required for Omega = one. If this result is verified, it would provide strong support for theories of cosmic inflation. Even if Omega differs from one, the results provide evidence that gravity is responsible for creating the large-scale structure.

Theories of cosmic structure formation

On the basis of the evidence discussed above, most cosmologists believe that the big bang is an essential component of any complete theory of the universe. In addition, they agree that gravity is the dominant force acting on large-scale structures in the universe. The standard paradigm of cosmic structure formation supposes that the universe was almost perfectly smooth after the big bang. Small irregularities subsequently were amplified by gravity, according to the ideas developed by Zel'dovich and Peebles. However, even today there is little agreement beyond this basic scenario.

The key observational and theoretical advances occurring during the 1980s—the realization that most of the matter in the universe is dark, the mapping of large-scale structures, and the influx of ideas such as inflation from fundamental physics—provided the foundation for detailed theories of large-scale structure. An illustrative example is provided by the most popular theory during the late 1980s, that of cold dark matter. This theory, first suggested by Peebles, is based on inflation, and it therefore requires sufficient dark matter to make Omega equal one. Ordinary matter accounts for only 5% of the total, with new elementary particles making up the remainder. These particles are supposed to be much colder than the ordinary matter after the big bang; consequently, gravity causes them to coalesce into galaxies and large-scale structure without evaporating. A virtue of the cold dark matter theory is that it has almost no uncertain parameters. Thus, the theory is capable of making predictions that can be compared with astronomical observations. Like any scientific theory, it is capable of being disproved.

Computer calculations are needed to follow the complicated motions of gravitationally interacting dark matter particles. These calculations were pioneered in the 1980s by George Efstathiou of the University of Oxford, Simon White of the University of Arizona, Marc Davis, and Car-

James M. Gelb

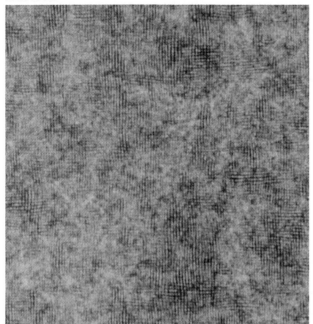

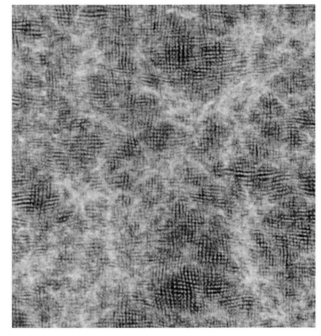

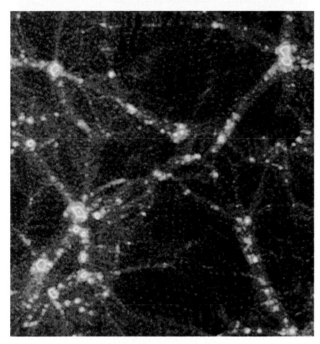

Computer simulations based on the cold dark matter theory reveal how galaxies are formed. At the upper left is a nearly uniform distribution of matter, showing only the tiny fluctuations that are predicted by the inflationary theory of extremely rapid expansion in the first moments after the big bang. Above, gravity causes the fluctuations to evolve into early traces of galaxies, and at the left these have grown into galaxies and clusters of galaxies.

los Frenk of the University of Durham. Their initial studies of the cold dark matter theory—using nearly 33,000 point masses to represent the clumps of dark matter in a volume about 400 million light-years across— gave encouraging agreement with the data available at that time.

The evidence for large-scale structure accumulating during the last five years has, however, been increasingly difficult to reconcile with the predictions of the cold dark matter theory. The most serious blow came from the COBE/DMR measurements of microwave background fluctuations. These measurements greatly reduced the uncertainty in the most significant unknown theoretical parameter, the amplitude of the initial fluctuations. Recent supercomputer calculations made by Bertschinger and James Gelb of MIT using up to 16 million particles show that, with the COBE/DMR amplitude, the galaxies that form in a cold dark matter universe are too massive compared with the real ones. Thus, although the COBE/DMR results are consistent with inflation and support the general paradigm of gravitational instability, it is now widely agreed that the cold dark matter theory must be modified or abandoned.

This rejection of a popular theory shows that the study of large-scale structure has become scientifically mature. However, theorists are now uncertain as to what theory will replace cold dark matter. Perhaps the solution is to add some hot dark matter, exemplified by massive neutrinos. Neutrinos are elementary particles that, unlike cold dark matter particles, are known to exist, but their mass is unknown. Alternatively, there may be a nonzero cosmological constant (a new physical constant corresponding to a nonzero density in otherwise empty space) that modifies the expansion rate of the universe. Albert Einstein proposed this idea in 1917 before Hubble's celebrated discovery. Einstein later retracted the concept, calling it his greatest blunder. Though misbegotten, the cosmological constant is once again being considered seriously by cosmologists.

Based on the recently determined amplitude of the initial fluctuations in the microwave background radiation, a computer simulation found that the galaxies that would form in a cold dark matter universe would be much more massive than those that actually exist. At the right is the density distribution of such a simulated galaxy.

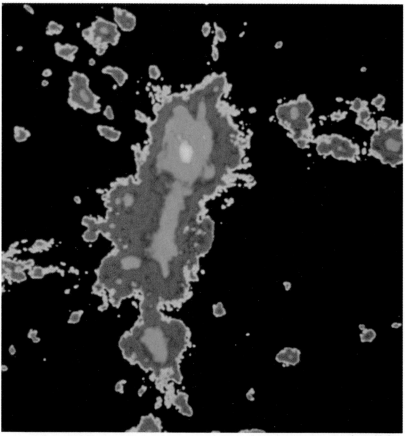

James M. Gelb

Cosmology has undergone several revolutions during the last three decades. Although astronomers still lack a satisfactory understanding of how the large-scale structures formed, it is encouraging that the theoretical foundations appear to be in place. Future discoveries may come from particle accelerators or laboratory experiments searching for dark matter particles, from astronomical galaxy redshift surveys of millions of galaxies, from computer calculations of galaxy formation, or from unforeseen breakthroughs in theoretical physics.

FOR ADDITIONAL READING

Alan Dressler, "The Great Attractor: Do Galaxies Trace the Large-Scale Mass Distribution?" *Nature* (April 4, 1991, pp. 391–397).

Alan Dressler, "The Large-Scale Streaming of Galaxies," *Scientific American* (September 1987, pp. 46–54).

Margaret J. Geller and John P. Huchra, "Mapping the Universe," *Science* (Nov. 17, 1989, pp. 897–903).

Samuel Gulkis, P.M. Lubin, S.S. Meyer, and R.F. Silverberg, "The Cosmic Background Explorer," *Scientific American* (January 1990, pp. 132–139).

Alan H. Guth and Paul J. Steinhardt, "The Inflationary Universe," *Scientific American* (May 1984, pp. 116–128).

Lawrence M. Krauss, *The Fifth Essence: The Search for Dark Matter in the Universe* (Basic Books, 1989).

Alan P. Lightman, *Ancient Light: Our Changing View of the Universe* (Harvard University Press, 1991).

Dennis Overbye, *Lonely Hearts of the Cosmos: The Story of the Scientific Quest for the Secret of the Universe* (HarperCollins, 1991).

Barry Parker, *Invisible Matter and the Fate of the Universe* (Plenum Press, 1989).

Michael Riordan and David Schramm, *The Shadows of Creation: Dark Matter and the Structure of the Universe* (W.H. Freeman & Co., 1991).

Joseph Silk, *The Big Bang* (W.H. Freeman & Co., 1989).

Joseph Silk, A.S. Szalay, and Yakov B. Zel'dovich, "The Large-Scale Structure of the Universe," *Scientific American* (October 1983, pp. 72–80).

Steven Weinberg, *The First Three Minutes: A Modern View of the Origin of the Universe* (Basic Books, 1988).

IMAGINING ALIENS

by Jack Cohen

Aliens in science fiction range from near human to creatures that are exotic and bizarre. Nevertheless, just any kind of alien is not possible. There are some rules of thumb that life-forms anywhere in the universe would have to follow.

Motion pictures and television have portrayed aliens in a wide range of shapes and sizes. On the opposite page, clockwise from the top left, a Martian from War of the Worlds (1953); Lieutenant Worf, a Klingon from the "Star Trek: The Next Generation" television series; E.T. from E.T. The Extra-Terrestrial (1982); Daleks, inside the metal containers, from Dr. Who and the Daleks (1966); and a beachball-type alien from Dark Star (1975).

JACK COHEN is a reproductive biologist, a laboratory consultant, and an adviser to several of the best-known science-fiction writers.

(Overleaf) Illustration by Ron Villani

Aliens have become part of our language and culture, successful imports from the literature of the fantastic. Their images on film, as in *E.T.* and the *Alien* series of films, have been popular. H.G. Wells's Martians from *War of the Worlds* became famous both from the notorious radio play and from the George Pal film. They were as frightening as later aliens, if less explicitly gory. Some aliens, notably the Klingons and Vulcans of television's "Star Trek," were made human-but-odd-looking as a way of labeling them as "travellers from a far countrie." Equally familiar are the variously spherical film aliens like the ever expanding mass in *The Blob* and the beach ball in *Dark Star*.

Aliens have usurped goblins, witches, and elves as the characters in contemporary myths with whom interactions are always uneasy. Vampires and werewolves were, perhaps, transitional forms, as are the various golems (like Frankenstein's) and even, perhaps, robots. There is a real difference, however. Very nearly everybody believes that these other creations—the goblins and werewolves—do not exist, that they are merely fantasies in the minds of the storytellers. However, a survey of modern orthodox biologists would find that a majority of them believe that there actually are other life-forms out there—real aliens. Those who have given this matter serious attention would argue (*see* below) that there may well be a million planets with life in our own home galaxy, the Milky Way. This is a conservative estimate, however, inasmuch as it would suggest that only one in a hundred million stars has such a planet.

There is no way to compare imaginary werewolves or elves in stories with real ones because there are not any real ones. However, the aliens created by the disciplined imaginations of science-fiction novelists can be compared with those allowed by the creative imaginations of scientists. Both are inspired and constrained by our understanding of evolutionary systems, and this exercise gives us a way to test such understanding.

First, however, we should look at the ambience of the stories in which such aliens appear. All of the most successful authors, from antiquity to the present day, have invented a context for the reader's imagination. Some of these contexts are closely related to the real world, like that of the Greek heroic myth, the western, or the gritty detective story. Others, like *The Thousand and One Nights* and J.R.R. Tolkein's *The Lord of the Rings*, instruct the reader to adopt a much more fanciful universe as the backdrop to the action. Many authors, from Lewis Carroll to Franz Kafka, invent a deliberately irrational milieu so that the story line can be freed from the common contexual assumptions of writer and reader.

The science-fiction genre has made this change of milieu its specialty, and it is the major difference from other genres of fiction. Both the western and the detective story have an agreed-upon common context between reader and author, and it is modifiable only by agreed-upon rules. The near perfection of the white-hat's aim with his gun, the ability of the "hero" to recover instantly from blows that would have felled any real man for a week, and the ubiquity of murders at English country houses are all very familiar. Often the humor of the western, or of the detective story, works by questioning those very assumptions.

By contrast, each science-fiction story has its own milieu; the reader is required to establish a working universe, different from any previously encountered in historical detail but consonant with our agreed-upon scientific world picture.

Some authors take scientific authenticity to the point of explicitly denying that certain aspects of our present, agreed-upon view of the world are "true." They invent new ones, with their own sets of constraints: the Sun's fusion energy has run down and the Sun is collapsing; human souls have physical existence; time travel can occur. There is a whole set of such agreed-upon "tropes" available to readers and writers because they have been used in so many previous stories that they form part of science fiction's "common unconscious." These include faster-than-light travel, perfect computer translators, teleportation devices, and other highly unlikely inventions. An author may use any of these tropes but must take care to import a set of constraints along with them. Faster-than-light flight might be enormously costly or uncomfortable, for example.

Four aliens from the cantina scene in the movie Star Wars *(1977) were among those in the bar that interacted with the humans in a way that most viewers considered believable.*

How lifelike are aliens?

The important element of the writer-reader transaction is that the portrayal of the aliens must be convincing, as far as is necessary for the story. The elements of this "convincingness" must be analyzed if one is to work out how alien portrayals are more or less believable. For example, the bar scene in *Star Wars* is convincing to most viewers. It is portrayed as the most "ordinary" view of any old spaceport bar, with the standard kinds of aliens picking up their different refreshments and kicks. None of the humans is shown to be surprised by the aliens (although a couple of the aliens are obviously surprised at seeing humans—a nice touch). This kind of authentication is very sophisticated and contrasts with the "Gosh-Wow!" of the "one inimical alien" confrontation. But moviegoers have become accustomed to such aspects of the filmmaker's art—to being carried into the worlds of Mickey Mouse, Tom and Jerry, and, especially, the Muppets.

The bases on which lifelike portrayals are accomplished can be very different: E.T., and the later design for Mickey Mouse, have outlines that caricature three-year-old human children; Ewoks (from the third *Star Wars* film) are simply a form of teddy bear and serve to revive nursery relationships; Tom the cat, Jerry the mouse, and Tweetie-Pie the bird have abstract movements and body language and are related so closely to our bullying/insecurity fears that they live for us; and the various Muppet characters are convincing by their exaggeration of human foibles. The *Alien* films have a series of toothy, ultimately dragonlike predators/ parasites that attach to our concepts of terror, our real biological built-in phobias. Such film images can carry viewers along without much need for knowledge about real living things. For example, the alien egg in the movie appears to lie dormant until a crew of humans just happens to stumble upon it. As in horror-film life-after-death stories, the viewer is prepared to go along with something unbelievable if it is embedded in an exciting story.

70

Humans are visual creatures, with visual imaginations. They are also verbal, however, and word pictures can be at least as powerful as film images. Words can evoke nursery-animal emotional links (fox = cunning, mouse = timid, hen = stupid, pig = child, etc.), so that an owllike alien seems wise even with no further description. For many—perhaps it once was for most—of us the word picture is more evocative because it leaves the imagination freer to create a potent image. There is a classic story of a 14-year-old science-fiction fan who was asked whether he preferred the television or the radio version of *Hitchhiker's Guide to the Galaxy*. He gave as his reason for preferring the radio version that the scenery was so much better!

Many of these tricks—visual, verbal, and nursery—are used in the above-mentioned *Star Wars* bar scene. There are ratlike faces, aggressive

Aliens are often based on animals that inhabit the Earth or on familiar storybook creatures. The Ewoks in the 1983 film Return of the Jedi *(top left) recall teddy bears, while the queen alien in the 1986 movie* Aliens *(top right) is a dragonlike monster. The Muppets (left) become lifelike with their exaggerated portrayals of human foibles and frailties.*

and foxy body language, and eyes positioned to give "wise" or "criminal" messages. Our human responses—some built in, some entirely cultural, most a combination—are tweaked most agreeably by those moving pictures. Similar responses are evoked by the ecology of the worlds shown in the *Star Wars* trilogy and other films. They have backgrounds, but especially organisms, that conform to our emotional prejudices regarding what planets should be like. These prejudices have been derived from our tiny sample of only one planet and include a built-in—nearly always unexamined—set of emotive judgments about animals, including alien animals.

We do not have many of these emotive associations with nonbiological parts of the science-fiction background. Other, less emotional, clues are used to make a science-fiction ambience believable. We do not care whether the spaceship is black or silver, if the terrain is sedimentary or igneous, if the vehicles are electric or steam-driven, even if the plants are reddish or bluish. We have learned enough of the space-physics background that judicious use of words like *orbit* and *solar flare* can help establish that part of the scene. Rocket-fuel chemistry is sufficiently common background that "specific impulse," and "liquid oxygen" can be introduced without explanation and add credibility. However, this willing suspension of disbelief can not be sustained if the author contradicts our general knowledge of what reality is. If the heroine has breakfast in London and then hops on her bicycle and arrives in New York City in time for lunch, it has to be a pretty spectacular bicycle or we will not permit the author to get away with geography we know is not real. Equally, if a spaceman runs up a spaceship ladder with a cubic foot of gold under his arm, we will not let the author get away with such light gold! We also expect authors to make the chemistries of atmospheres and seas approximately workable within the context of our own experience. There are still some stories and films that have planets with oxygen atmospheres but no life, but most authors now devise atmospheric compositions that are reasonable—or Earthlike—which is at least possible as an alternative if there is an Earthlike ecology. Thus, we require authentic physics, chemistry, and geography in our stories. How lifelike must the biology be?

Earthlike and "alien" ecologies

How likely is an Earthlike ecology? That is a question with many dimensions. It could mean "Given a lot of planets, how many will develop Earthlike ecologies?" but could also mean "How many unlikely things were necessary in the history of our planet to get where we are now?" The latter is an example of the anthropic problem. It is obvious that intelligent beings, able to ask the question, must have been produced on a planet whose physical and chemical characteristics allowed life to survive (at least during the evolution of those life forms). We did evolve on this planet, but we could be the only planet in the universe to have achieved intelligence. Discussed below are ways of judging the likelihood of the different steps in our evolution (and of the Earth's ecology in general), but they require a biological context and some argument.

First, however, we must decide what we mean by an Earthlike ecology. Would we, for example, accept seas full of bacterial-grade organisms (some of which are excreting oxygen, which is about 5% of the atmosphere), no life on land, and no higher organisms? This is the ecology that was typical of the Earth during three-quarters of its history. We must realize that the Earth's present ecology is not at all the most likely to have happened, given the Earth's history. The human species, too, has made enormous changes to the "natural" Earth ecology. Much of the Earth's land surface today is not at all natural. For example, much desert land is the result of nonsustainable exploitation for agriculture. That argument makes it seem as though our "present" terrestrial ecology is an odd one for an Earthlike planet. However, I believe that something rather like it will arise, sooner or later, as part of the likely changes on any planet where water is liquid (*see* below). Then again—to continue this argument—if intelligence-driven technology is usually achieved, there is a further stage at which most such exploited planets might suffer. There are some pessimists who see the ultimate destiny of the Earth to be a radioactive, chemically poisoned wasteland with no biological future. Life, in their view, is just a temporary (4×10^8 years . . .) phenomenon.

Even such pessimists, though, are basically romantics. They, like most of the rest of us, have a romantic view of an Earthlike ecology as having such features as the Amazon Rain Forest, a rocky shore with anemones in the rock pools, and coral reefs. This, I believe, is muddily optimistic thinking, but let's stay with it. Let us leave out the (most likely) Precambrian world and the (most feared) postholocaust world and focus on the Tertiary (Age of Mammals) or Quaternary (Age of Man) periods. "Earthlike ecology" in this context will mean like the Earth as it is now.

How likely is our kind of life?

What evidence can we use to support the likelihood of our kind of life, our kind of Tertiary ecology, and, particularly, each of the steps that resulted in *Homo sapiens* and the Quaternary Period? Some biologists, of whom the geneticist Conrad Waddington was among the best known, believed that the highest form of life anywhere would resemble Waddington. All those million planets would have Klingons, Vulcans, and so on, and all would be very like Waddington. Waddington would not have liked the *Star Wars* cantina scene. From his point of view, it is as unlikely as a scene of dogs and cats buying goods in a supermarket.

In contrast to that view, of evolution converging on the human form, Stephen Jay Gould in his book *Wonderful Life* argued that all of the larger evolutionary successes and failures in the terrestrial evolutionary story were, fundamentally, accidental. He was sure that if the meteorite at the end of the Cretaceous Period had missed the Earth, dinosaurs would still be around and there would be no Steve Gould.

I have a third way of looking at the likelihoods of alien life, a view rooted in a deep distinction between unique and multiple innovations during our evolutionary story here on Earth. Its arguments result in an "anthropo-fugal" view: no aliens are like human beings.

It seems to me that the history of life on Earth, the only real case study that is available, reveals many events that are unique. Feathers were invented only by the ancestors of birds, bone by the ancestors of vertebrates, and flowers by the ancestors of angiosperms. It is not possible to determine how likely these innovations were because they cannot be set in the context of other things that have happened instead. There is the story of a student who asked a rabbi, "Why was the thornbush chosen by God to be the vehicle to appear to Moses? Why not the myrtle or the olive tree?" The rabbi answered, "And if it had been the myrtle,

How many planets in the universe have ecologies similar to those on the Earth is a question that arises when people consider the possibility of aliens and the forms they might take. Any planet where the water is liquid might have such features as tree ferns and bromeliads in a rain forest (top left), sponge and fish at a coral reef (top right), and contoured farmland (right) that reveals human (alien?)-generated changes to the "natural" ecology.

(Top left) © Paul Franklin—Oxford Scientific Films; (top right) © David B. Fleetham—Oxford Scientific Films; (bottom) Larry Lefever—Grant Heilman

you would now be asking, 'Why not the thornbush?' If one is chosen, the alternatives are not!" Thus, "Why feathers?" is not a sensible question; we do not know what else might have fulfilled the function.

There are many other evolutionary events, however, that are to be found in different classes of plants and animals. For example, photosynthesis, flight, fur, and mating were all invented by many different evolutionary lines. These are what can be called universal solutions. Because they have appeared so often, and so variously, in the Earth's evolutionary story, it seems very likely that something of the same kind would happen in all similar planetary histories. This cannot be said of unique innovations, like feathers; all we know of them is that they happened, here on this planet, once. We know that they are possible, but I call them parochial (found only in this parish).

Enough is known about the detailed history of life on Earth for productive questions to be asked about each of its major innovations. Then universal/parochial distinctions can be used to estimate its probability on, for example, the other hundred million interesting—liquid-water— planets estimated to be in our Milky Way Galaxy.

The origin of life provides an interesting starting point. There are two very different intellectual stances that must be distinguished. The optimist says: "We have 32 different scenarios, each of which could— chemically—have produced life on Earth. But we don't know which did in fact, or if, perhaps, it was the 33rd or a 108th that we have not thought of." The pessimist asks: "How did chemical systems become life on Earth? How did it actually happen?" The first stance takes the position that if the 3rd scenario, for example, did not work on a particular planet, then the 10th, 11th, or 14th may have done so. The second stance assumes uniqueness and requires that any planet with life must have initiated it in the same way as occurred on Earth.

Graham Cairns-Smith, a member of the optimist group, has emphasized the interdependence of all the different chemical systems used by animals and plants. For example, our genetic material, DNA, needs special proteins to replicate itself, but it also needs other special proteins to produce the machinery that makes protein. It needs RNA, another nucleic acid with a complementary sequence to parts of the DNA, to transfer the code for the different proteins to the cell workshops that make them, and it needs a special protein to copy that RNA sequence from the DNA. There is a web of interdependence much like this in every cell; before it can do anything, it has to do something else first, and it needs the products of the second step to do the first step. This is not a problem for already-living things: because each bacterium, or each cell, is made from a preceding one, it receives all the machinery to make the new machinery, and the system continues. But, Cairns-Smith asks, how can such an interconnected system start? His answer is an analogy with a stone arch, in which each stone needs all the others for its stability; one can make such an arch by constructing a low-technology mound of stones to support the arch as it is built and then taking the mound away when the arch is self-supporting.

From T. Baird, A.G. Cairns–Smith, D.W. Mackenzie, and D.S. Snell, *Clay Minerals*, vol. 9, pp. 250–252, 1971

100 nm

Photomicrograph reveals a synthetic hectorite, a clay mineral. Graham Cairns-Smith based his theory of the origin of life on the replication of clay structures. Amino acids and other small organic molecules that are important to living organisms are adsorbed onto some of these clays, which then can assist them into polymerizing into complex proteins and other polymers, including the nucleic acids essential for life. Thus, primitive life combined clay with organic replication.

Cairns-Smith's "low-technology life" is the replication of clay structures. These can be seen to replicate all kinds of chemical and physical differences faithfully, in a variety of linear crystal systems. Amino acids and other small organic molecules that are important to living systems are adsorbed onto some of these clays, which can then assist their polymerization into complex proteins and other polymers—including nucleic acids. He believes that primitive life combined clay with organic replication. The low-technology clay was then "discarded" as soon as the organic system could service its own replication and synthesis.

This scenario is typical of the many reasonable suggestions for origins of life. In nearly all of them the complex organic living systems have been generated by simpler chemical systems. Carbon compounds readily make complicated chemistry in aqueous media. Thus, one can conclude that most of the planets that have liquid water start such systems; of the 5×10^9 Main Sequence suns in the Milky Way, say one in 50 has aqueous planets. But because there is no way of knowing how, or whether, such proto-living systems normally continue to develop, I assume only one in 100 would do so. Thus, there would be one million planets with life in our Galaxy.

Universals and parochials

The table lists some of the evolutionary innovations during the Earth's history. If they have occurred many times, they have been designated universal, and I have assumed that members of the same class will be found on most, if not all, planets with life. If they have occurred only once in the history of life on Earth, then they must be regarded as parochial. In this case few if any aliens will have comparable characteristics. Unfortunately, as is described below, those alien characters most often invented for the movie screen and also for innumerable science-fiction novels are all parochial and very unlikely to be found on real other worlds. Only a very few works have used the universals to good purpose.

In the table only a tiny fraction of the Earth's important evolutionary innovations have been listed. The decision as to which to include was guided by assumptions that are common in alien stories. Authors—and readers—assume that life has become multicellular, invaded the land, and invented photosynthesis, and most biologists would agree that these developments are likely to have happened in other worlds. However, authors have additionally assumed that the parochial knees, elbows, and fingers (not the universal jointed limbs) and the crossed airway and foodway will also be common. They show the creature to be alien by giving it a totally mammalian arm but coloring it blue and saying that it has copper-based blood, and that biology does not ring true at all.

There are other assumptions that are more thought-provoking. Our reproductive and excretory structures are mixed up, as are those of all the descendants of the fish-that-came-out-of-the-water: amphibians, reptiles, birds, and mammals. Several different terrestrial lineages have mixed excretory and reproductive functions, usually at the rear end of the animal, and so it seems likely that some of the animals on an alien

Evolutionary Innovations During the Earth's History

Innovation	How many times (when)	What organisms	Parochial/ Universal	How many planets?
origins of amino acids	one, extended (4.5 billion years, as seas appeared)	none, yet	Universal	10^8
origins of nucleotides	probably several, but evidence only of one (4.5 billion years)	not quite, yet	Universal	10^8
clay mineral replications	many and various (see Cairns-Smith)	low-technology "clay life"?	Universal	10^8
origin of DNA (or RNA?)	probably several, but evidence only of one (4 billion years?)	associated with clays, lipids, coacervates?	Universal	10^7
origin of prokaryotes ("cells")	probably several, but evidence only of one (4–2.8 billion years)	archaeobacterial and eukaryote progenitors	Universal	10^6
photosynthesis	at least three (3–1.5 billion years)	cyanobacteria, plants, violet bacteria	Universal	10^6
"evolutionary symbiosis" of prokaryotes	at least three (1.5 billion years–present)	eukaryotes, actinomycetes, some protists such as *Chaos* and *Giardia*	Universal	10^6
bone	once (450 million years?)	gnathostomes	Parochial	1
life on land	more than 20 (400–200 million years)	land plants, mollusks, insects, vertebrates	Universal	10^6
conflation of excretory and reproductive systems	four plus? (260 million years, 100 million years?, 400 million years?, 150 million years?)	land vertebrates, some crustaceans and arachnids, land gastropods	Parochial? (unique... each time!)	?
pentadactyl limb structure	once (260 million years?)	land vertebrates	Parochial	1
crossing of food/airway	once (260 million years?)	land vertebrates	Parochial	1
flight	ten plus (250 million years–present)	four fishes (+?) pterodactyls, birds, bats	Universal	10^6
increase of intelligence	three plus (300 million years?, 35 million years–present)	cephalopods, such as octopus; *Carnivora*, such as dogs; *Cetacea*, such as dolphins; primates, such as humans	Universal	10^6

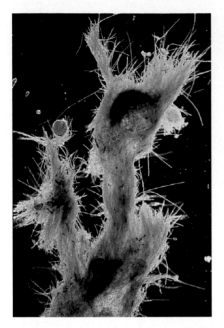

Evolutionary innovations that occurred many times during the Earth's history are designated as universal, while those that took place only once are parochial. Most biologists agree that universals are likely to have happened in other worlds. Above is a universal innovation, photosynthesis occurring in blue-green algae; the hair on the bear (above right) is a parochial, and flight (right) is considered a universal.

planet would also have this feature. This is an example of a universal solution that applies only sometimes. Fish and most invertebrate animals do not have this characteristic. Further, conducting tissue in plants and blood vessels in animals have not been listed because the two—or perhaps three or four—times they have evolved on Earth do not place them firmly in either the universal or parochial categories. As an example, large terrestrial oxygen-breathing aliens must have internal pumps and fluids, however they actually function. Thus, some universals inform us about deeper biological rules than we had thought were involved.

The giraffe and the elephant provide a useful example of such "deep" universals. Rudyard Kipling's *Just So Stories* provides a model for the evolutionary parables told to students: the giraffe's success comes because it can reach so much higher to browse and, because the elephant's weight does not permit it to use its feet for grasping, it uses its nose. These are two parochial solutions, obviously, and the elephant story is particularly unlikely. It is much more unlikely than most science-fiction aliens. Would you believe an animal that uprooted trees with its nose and also used it as a hose to wash itself down?

There is another way, however, of looking at the giraffe's neck and comparing it with the elephant's trunk that makes them the same universal solution. Perhaps the giraffe is not primarily tall but fast; like the okapi, which is a protogiraffe but without such a long neck, it has a strange gait. It "paces"; that is to say, the two legs on the same side move forward together. It does not use its back and rump muscles, as many mammals do, but its long front legs swing through a great arc; the longer its front legs, the faster it can run. There is, however, a problem with having very long front legs; while they do raise the head so the animal can eat foliage that other browsers cannot reach, they make having a drink afterward difficult. Water is always at ground level or below. Kneeling is definitely not recommended, since there are lions about, but straddling and dropping a long neck down to the water is not so dangerous. Thus, a long neck may permit such a fast animal to drink safely. The elephant's trunk is also primarily a tube to get water (though some have suggested that it was originally a snorkel). The elephant puts the tube on the front of its face, and the giraffe puts it behind its face, but it solves the same universal problem. Alien animals will also have strange tubes to get water without jeopardy, a common universal evolutionary solution.

What aliens will and will not have

Aliens will have universals, but they will not have our parochials. They will, of course, have their own parochials, just as the organisms on Earth do. The question that arises is how to judge the reasonableness—the biological credibility—of these alien parochials. To answer it I have used

An early science-fiction attempt to design an alien produced a creature (above) that was too much like a human to be a reasonable possibility. The elephant's trunk in the drawing by Rudyard Kipling for his Just So Stories *(below left) represents a universal solution to the need to obtain water without jeopardy. An alien designed for life under conditions of high gravity (below right) has a trunk for drinking and sturdy legs to support a heavy body.*

a simple rule of thumb: if there is a creature on Earth that does that class of trick, aliens can also do it. For example, I invented the Yilane, an intelligent reptile found in Harry Harrison's *West of Eden* on the alternate Earth missed by the meteorite that destroyed the dinosaurs. This beast had an interesting sex life, as the males had a double penis in a vascular penis-pouch (like lizards and snakes). The novel idea was that the females laid eggs into this pouch, and the torpid males incubated them while being guarded by the females. My justification for this odd parochial tactic is the sea horse, whose female lays her eggs into the male's pouch. None of our real reptiles do it, but I would not be surprised if one could. There is, after all, a frog whose male broods the eggs in his stomach.

This rule works quite well. It requires that the alien have some previous evolutionary "reason" for developing the characteristics that the

The Yilane, an intelligent reptile in Harry Harrison's West of Eden, *was designed with parochials found in at least one animal on the Earth. For example, the male Yilane has a pouch into which a female lays eggs, as does the sea horse.*

Illustration by Bill Sanderson

"Wonderful! Just wonderful! . . . So much for instilling them with a sense of awe."

author needs for the story line. Like the detective-story writer who is able to leave a cryptic clue because it is part of the everyday experience of the reader, the science-fiction author can, without being explicit, give the alien a property, or a faculty, that the reader could suppose such a creature to have. Good science-fiction aliens can latch onto our knowledge of the real world, and the story line should rely on just that.

The creatures in the movie *Aliens* are good gothic horror, but they do not work in the real world. They hang in cocoons, waiting years for a victim. In real life the creature whose behavior most closely resembles this is the parasitic cat-flea, which in its pupal cocoon awaits movement near it—sometimes for years—and then hatches and jumps onto a cat. There are also bedbugs that sit in the cracks in a cave wall waiting, perhaps tens of years, sharing their blood meals by sucking from each other until a mammal comes into the cave to sleep. Thus, the idea of the alien cocoon waiting perhaps has some legitimacy. What is unreasonable about the alien in the movie is the supposition that there can be a parasite so well adapted to its previously unknown new host that it can grow inside without exciting the host's immune responses. Also, this alien's size gets bigger very quickly, which makes conservation of mass a bit shaky.

However, the creatures in *Aliens* are not nearly as unlikely as all those characters that so closely resemble human beings that actors can take their parts. Examples include the Klingons and the Vulcans. It is simply

81

impossible that another planet would have had exactly the same mutations, exactly the same kind of fish—with bone—coming out of the water, the descendants of the fish becoming primates, the same accidental advantages to one (semiaquatic) primate in response to the same predators, the same climatic events. Australian marsupial mammals did much the same as their cousins in Europe and America; they made a good mole, a good wolf, and quite a good cat, but their attempt at an antelope was a kangaroo—and they started with cousins on the same planet!

You may have been asking yourself, "Why should we pay this man a salary as a professional biologist if he gives credence to these silly impossible aliens?" There are three brief answers. First, these exercises are useful tests, or "thought experiments," that flex and illuminate our ideas about real, terrestrial evolution. Second, by inventing a "life as we do not know it," we give ourselves a series of models against which to compare life as we do know it; we can tell how unlikely an elephant's trunk is. Third, and most important, it keeps us from being small-minded. In the laboratory, scientists investigate "foreground" problems that are set within the accepted orthodoxy of the day. By being prepared to have a different background, we can view today's science in a much larger context and anticipate—or even produce—tomorrow's science.

Some Exercises in Alien Biologies

In the best stories the plot development depends on the crucial biological trick that the alien uses—and that readers regard as "fair" because it is well known to them in another context. (If it is not a very well-known bit of biology, the author puts in an informative discussion earlier in the story, just as a detective-story writer would.) One of the earliest "biologically reasonable" alien ecologies was invented not by a biologist but by a physicist. Harry Stubbs, writing as Hal Clement, wrote *Mission of Gravity* in the early 1950s. In his story Mesklin was a very massive planet that had a rapid rotation; this had resulted in a shape like a discus, with gravitational forces of more than 650 g at the poles but only 4 g at the high-altitude equator. The polar inhabitants were shaped like centipedes, derived from marine jet-propelled forms. The story is set up so that a group of North Polar sailors on a kind of hinged raft journey "up" to the equator, where they meet a human enduring 4 g in a wheelchair and, much more surprisingly, encounter canoes and bows and arrows. Then they proceed to the South Pole, where they are supposed to repair a United Planets experiment concerning gravity. The climax of the story is physics but with enormous biological potency: the last problem on their journey is a cliff, hundreds of meters high—at 500 g! Throughout the story it has been emphasized that Up is dangerous; in order to be effective at the equator, the sailors must unlearn the habits of their polar homeland. Then they use a hot-air balloon to lift their equipment up the cliff! Thus, the author uses the concept of Idea as Hero—a biologically potent physics/psychology concept.

Clifford Simak produced a lovely variety of aliens. His rural settings provided the background to some truly amazing feats of imagination. His aliens are often godlike but prepared to engage with humans, with human-scale issues. *Aliens for Neighbours*, the title of one of his collections, gives the flavor exactly. Some of his other stories have—in various persuasive but impossible ways—people's minds ranging the galaxy in search of alien technologies. The aliens are described "from the inside" better than anybody else has done. There are, for example, those that could not perceive light and whose picture of their world was composed of sound reflections and those living deep underwater that did not know gravity or astronomy.

Larry Niven's *Known Space* series of novels concentrates on the human characters, but there are a beautiful series of alien landscapes and a few great characters. *Ringworld* is probably the best known, but all the others are enjoyable. Most of the aliens are backdrop, like the Outsiders, whose "spaceships"

are open to space and who follow starseeds (we are never told what they are) into and out of the galaxy on a 20,000-year cycle; they barter high technology with the other races. In the stories Bandersnatchi, which are great galleon-like predators; reflector sunflowers, which focus the Sun's light communally on any disturbance—and vaporize it; Pierson's puppeteers with their tripedal stance and pair of eyes/hands—and their remarkable cowardice—are all biologically reasonable, and there are many other good alien inventions. I do not like the idea that people can be forced into their "mature" Protector stage by Tree-of-Life root, but it does make for good stories, and it puts humans among the other races, not just visitors.

Niven also coauthored novels (especially with Jerry Pournelle) whose centerpiece is an alien-human interaction: *The Mote in God's Eye* and *Footfall* are biologically well-constructed, persuasive stories. Moties, with whom humans are at war, have many different forms, all asymmetrical. I do not like their anthropomorphisms, such as axillary hair, but some correspondence with the reader's anatomy is necessary for the reader to identify with alien motives. Other Motie properties are truly alien; for example, the "watchmaker" types succeed in invading human ships but then help the humans because their talent is to repair/improve anything mechanical. The little elephantine aliens in *Footfall* are also too mammalian, but their politics/psychology is the main point of the story, and that works well.

The most alien, and almost the most convincing, fictional life-forms are the cheela of *Dragon's Egg*, by Robert Forward, a physicist-engineer of the widest imagination. Cheela live on a neutron star and develop about a million times faster than humans. During the passage of their star toward the Earth, they evolve from pastoralists and hunter-gatherers to developers of a technology that surpasses ours in apparently miraculous ways. (This exemplifies Arthur C. Clarke's dictum that any sufficiently advanced science-technology looks like magic to those who do not understand it.) Forward can be criticized for his explanations of the cheela's motives as they explore,

Elephantine aliens in Footfall *by Larry Niven and Jerry Pournelle are too mammalian, but their politics/psychology works well in the story.*

© 1984 Michael Whelan

Among the most alien and most convincing fictional creatures are the cheela of Dragon's Egg *by Robert Forward. They live on a neutron star and develop about a million times faster than humans.*

Ralph McQuarrie © 1983 Image Generation, Inc.

discover, and wonder; they are much too much like ours. There is also a "small-universe" approach to discovery and to the viewpoint characters, both cheela and human: Too many things happen to too few folks too readily; everyone is at the right place at the right time; and there are not enough simple mistakes to make it ring true as science.

There is a whole genre of alien stories in which the alien elements serve to point up the romantic elements rather than to be underpinnings of that fictional "reality." Of these, the dragons of Anne McCaffrey's world of Pern are among the best known. These dragons have been designed and built by humans, using a local life-form—the "fire-lizard"— as raw material along with advanced terrestrial and other alien biotechnology. The other aliens, the "Menace from Outer Space" called Thread, can be viewed as ectopic Oort cloud inhabitants dragged in to the inner system by the cometary Red Star. The ecology of Pern is sketchy, limited to a few fire-lizard relatives (including tunnel-snakes) and some plants; nearly all the life is imported from Earth. The strength of these stories is not in their alien elements but in their humans in alien circumstances.

Two very different authors, David Brin and Gene Wolfe, have written many stories that depend critically upon the interactions of humans with rational-but-puzzlingly-different aliens. Brin's altered dolphins and chimpanzees ("chims") are almost human in their thinking and their politics, but in *The Uplift War* series he invented many alien species whose politics are radically—but rationally—different from ours. The tactic of juxtaposing different-but-terrestrial creatures with true aliens gives the reader a path into the much more different politics of the galactic community. Wolfe's aliens, like some of his humans, are set up as impossible to understand. This view, that the perceptions of humans are restricted by their sense organs and language to parochial— terrestrial—concerns, is a cop-out for some authors. In Wolfe's stories it lends credibility rather than mystery; Wolfe's aliens expose our inability to understand some of our fellow humans, just as Brin's do.

The aliens of "Star Trek," as of "Dr. Who" and other television series, are rarely other than humanlike because of the easy availability of actors for such parts. There are guest appearances of a few concocted alien species, but they are usually there only to be endowed with monstrous—and totally unscientific—metaphysical powers and to impress the viewer with the special effects. Tribbles were a notable, and popular, exception invented by David Gerrold. They are small furry hemispheres that squeak and purr but have no visible head or other extensions. They eat "anything organic" and breed amazingly fast, creating ever enlarging groups of live young littering their environs. I have invented a history of this organism, using its characters to illustrate the universal/parochial distinction. Its universal-symbiont characteristics, for living in a burrow with other organisms, are absence of a head, nonobvious feeding mechanism, hemispherical shape, fur, and rapid breeding in the right circumstances. Its parochial rapid-breeding trick could have been that demonstrated on Earth by *Gyrodactylus*, a tiny fluke parasite on the skin of fishes. This creature is usually born as a grandmother, with an embryo already in its uterus and, more often than not, another one inside that. This is a clever genetic trick, because all the embryos are (probably) inseminated at one copulation, so a fluke invading a new fish has a great genetic variety in it. Similarly, a proto-tribble invading a new burrow might exploit such variety.

The dragons of Pern, in the stories by Anne McCaffrey, were designed and built by humans, who used a life-form on Pern—the "fire-lizard"—as raw material and then added advanced terrestrial and other alien biotechnology.

My favorite alien scenario is another book by Larry Niven, with Pournelle and Steve Barnes. The *Legacy of Heorot* is a very cryptically titled novel whose nasty aliens do not appear onstage until halfway through the book. Called "grendels" by the colonists of an island on a fairly Earthlike planet, these carnivores look like squat crocodiles and have a supercharger mechanism. On "speed" a grendel is like a motorbike and overcomes the terrestrial technology entirely believably. Samlon, fishlike creatures living in local streams, provide food for colonists and, it turns out, also for grendels; but they are also the larvae of grendels.

This parochial breeding strategy is used sometimes by several frog species, including *Xenopus*, an aquatic toad from South Africa that was used for pregnancy testing. The colonists destroy the grendels without understanding their life cycle (though the reader has been given many hints) and, of course, the samlon now live to produce a plague of small, but still very dangerous, grendels. The universals of this system are very believable, and several parochials (such as female competition) flesh out the story's background with conviction. The exciting human story is resolved by its progressive understanding of the alien ecology.

In an episode from the original "Star Trek" television series, Capt. James Kirk (William Shatner) holds tribbles, small furry hemispheres that squeak and purr. They were notable exceptions to the usual aliens in the series, who were generally quite humanlike.

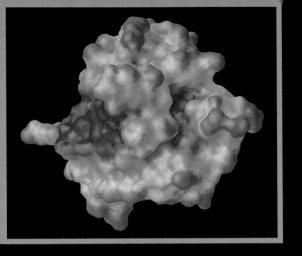
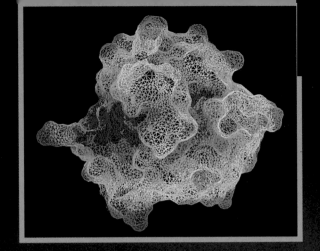

COMPUTER-AIDED MOLECULAR DESIGN

by Victoria A. Roberts

Computers have become essential in the determination
and analysis of the three-dimensional structures of
biological molecules, especially proteins. The
ultimate goal is the design of customized
proteins that can be used for medical
purposes and as molecular tools.

VICTORIA A. ROBERTS is an Assistant Member at The Scripps Research Institute, La Jolla, California. Her research focuses on the use of computational and computer graphics techniques for understanding and analyzing protein structure.

(Overleaf) Computers and computer graphics are being used to describe the intricate surface of biological molecules in many ways, thereby enhancing the understanding of how molecules interact with one another. Calculation of the fractal dimension over a protein surface provides a mathematical description of molecular shape, with purple and blue indicating the most concave regions and red those that are most convex (far left). The complex three-dimensional surface of the protein, shown by about 64,000 triangles (left), represents what a water or drug molecule would see as it approaches. The triangles were used to build a solid plastic model of the protein (right) by the process of stereolithography. In this process a precisely aimed, computer-driven laser solidifies liquid plastic in layers one-hundredth of an inch thick.

Stereolithography was done at the University of Utah in a collaboration with the University of North Carolina and The Scripps Research Institute. Calculations and computer graphics: M. E. Pique, The Scripps Research Institute. Photography: Mark Dastrup.

Although models of small molecules, consisting of a few dozen atoms, can be built by hand with molecular modeling tool kits and simple rules of chemical bonding, most molecules of biological interest have thousands of atoms, and their three-dimensional structure cannot be predicted from atomic connectivity alone. Determination of the three-dimensional structures of biological molecules, especially those of proteins, is essential for analyzing and designing new molecules. The techniques of X-ray crystallography and, more recently, nuclear magnetic resonance (NMR) spectroscopy are used to solve the atomic structures of large biological molecules. Both of these techniques rely on computers and computer programs to convert the basic experimental data into a three-dimensional atomic structure. These structures have greatly enhanced the understanding of biological molecules, particularly proteins, and form the basis of computer-aided molecular design.

The development of computational tools and computer graphics not only has allowed interpretation of the experimental data but has also been essential for visualizing the structures and analyzing and comparing protein shape. Predictions from computer-aided molecular design can be tested with the new protein-engineering techniques that involve manipulation of DNA. Results from these experiments are used to improve the computational analyses, which, in turn, will provide new hypotheses to be tested.

Role of proteins

Proteins are the most versatile biological molecules because they have a wide range of functions. They play two distinct roles. Fibrous proteins are the structural materials forming skin, hair, and parts of tendons and muscles that do not dissolve in water. The fibrous nature and the insolubility of these proteins make crystallization, which is essential for X-ray crystallography, almost impossible; consequently, little is known about their three-dimensional structure.

The second role is played by the globular proteins, which operate as machines on the molecular level and fold into complex three-dimensional structures. Most drugs in clinical use rely on interactions with globular proteins for their effectiveness. Enzymes are globular proteins that catalyze reactions. A catalyst takes a molecule, called a substrate, and alters the molecule's structure without changing its own structure. Enzymes lower the energy required for intermediate steps during chemical reactions so that the reaction can proceed at body temperature. Each enzyme performs a specific reaction, providing specific products. Examples include digestive enzymes that convert food to simple compounds, enzymes that build complex molecules such as other proteins and DNA, and muscle enzymes that produce mechanical work from chemical reactions.

Globular proteins also can function to transport molecules. For example, the proteins hemoglobin and myoglobin distribute oxygen. Hemoglobin, which resides in the red blood cells, binds oxygen at the lungs and delivers it to myoglobin in the muscles. Myoglobin stores the

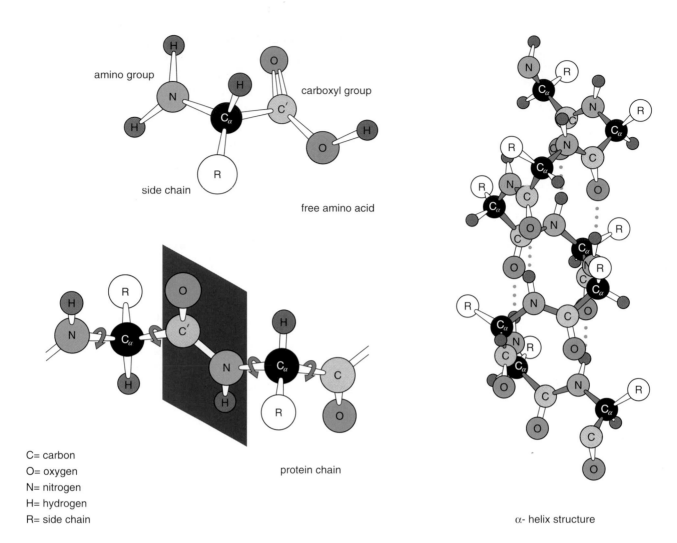

amino group

carboxyl group

side chain

free amino acid

C= carbon
O= oxygen
N= nitrogen
H= hydrogen
R= side chain

protein chain

α- helix structure

oxygen until it is required. Antibodies are globular proteins that protect an organism by binding to and thereby neutralizing foreign substances such as bacteria and viruses.

Proteins are chains of amino acids linked together by peptide bonds. There are 20 amino acids commonly found in proteins. Each has an identical backbone consisting of a central carbon atom attached to an amino group and a carboxyl group. The central carbon atom is also attached to a side chain, which distinguishes one type of amino acid from another. The carboxyl group of one amino acid is attached to the amino group of the next amino acid; this strong attachment is the peptide bond.

Each protein is made up of a unique chain of amino acids held together by peptide bonds, and this amino acid sequence determines the overall three-dimensional fold of the protein. When the nature of the peptide bond became understood, it was hoped that the structure of a protein could be predicted simply from knowledge of the sequence of amino acids making up the protein chain. Unfortunately, however, it is still not possible to predict the three-dimensional structure of a protein from its sequence of amino acids alone.

Proteins consist of chains of amino acids. An amino acid has a central carbon atom (Cα) attached to an amino group (NH$_2$), a carboxyl group (C'OOH), and a side chain (R). Amino acids are linked by strong peptide bonds that connect the carbon atom of the carboxyl group of one amino acid to the nitrogen atom of the amino group of the next amino acid, forming one water molecule. The backbone of the protein is the linear chain of N-Cα-C' atoms from each amino acid. The peptide bond (O-C-N-H) is a rigid unit that lies in a plane, but the backbone can rotate about the two bonds attached to the Cα (see arrows). The hydrogen atom on the amino group can interact with the oxygen of the carboxyl group, forming a hydrogen bond, which is important for forming specific structures of the peptide chain, such as the α helix.

89

There now exist powerful techniques for manipulating DNA to build a protein of any desired sequence. But even though, theoretically, any protein sequence can be made, experiments performed to understand the role of a particular amino acid side chain must be guided by biochemical and structural information. If an amino acid were randomly selected to be mutated, it is unlikely that the resulting mutant protein would provide useful information. On the other hand, the role of each amino acid side chain could be studied systematically through mutation, one at a time, of each amino acid of the protein to the other 19 amino acids. For a small protein made up of a chain of 100 amino acids, this exhaustive method would require making 19^{100} mutant proteins, which is an impossible task given that constructing each mutant protein requires several weeks or months. Therefore, it is essential to have three-dimensional information upon which to base predictions about the role of specific amino acids in protein structure and function.

Determination of the three-dimensional structure of proteins

Two techniques have been developed for determining the three-dimensional shape of proteins, X-ray crystallography and NMR spectroscopy. In X-ray crystallography a crystal of a protein is bombarded with X-rays, causing electrons of the atoms in the crystal to emit X-rays. The positions of these emitted X-rays are recorded on photographic film, creating a pattern of spots—a diffraction pattern—on the film. The information on the position and intensity of these spots can be converted mathematically to provide a representation of the distribution of electrons in the crystal (the electron density). For the large number of atoms in a typical protein (thousands), this step requires a huge number of computations. The atoms of the amino acids making up the protein chain are fit into the electron density, providing a three-dimensional atomic structure.

The first structure of a protein, myoglobin, was solved in the early 1960s by John Kendrew. It required calculations involving 40,000 spots making up the diffraction patterns obtained from crystals of the protein. After the diffraction pattern was obtained, the positions and intensities of the spots were laboriously punched onto computer tape, which was then fed into a computer. The computation of the electron density was verified by repetition of the calculations on a second computer because the calculations were too complex to be checked by hand. Once the electron density was calculated, the next problem arose. How could the sequence of amino acids of the protein be built into the electron density? To solve this problem, Kendrew built a three-dimensional model by making a forest of 1.2-meter (4-foot) steel rods spaced 2.5 centimeters (one inch) apart that were attached to a 1.8-meter (6-foot)-square piece of plywood, creating a three-dimensional grid. The electron density was mapped onto this grid with colored clips, and then the sequence of amino acid atoms was built into the electron density. This task was completed in 1960. Soon afterward, the structure of a second oxygen transport protein, hemoglobin, was solved in the laboratory of Max Perutz. Kendrew and Perutz received the Nobel Prize for Chemistry in 1962 for this work.

90

Nobel Prize winners Max Perutz (left) and John Kendrew (right) in their laboratory at the University of Cambridge demonstrate three-dimensional models of the first protein structures determined by X-ray crystallography.

These first two structures made it clear that protein structure is not a simple, repeating, easily predicted pattern. Instead, the precise sequence of the amino acids in each protein determines how it will fold into a three-dimensional structure. Because no one yet understands the rules for folding, the analysis of protein structure relies on determining large numbers of such structures. While solving the structure of myoglobin required a computer to convert the X-ray diffraction pattern into electron density, determining the atomic model was done without a computer. With this method there was no way to evaluate mathematically the fit of the atomic model to the electron density.

Researchers now collect the data on an electronic detector connected to a computer. When sufficient data are collected, the electron density is calculated directly from the data without requiring an intermediate step of entering the positions of the spots from the diffraction pattern into the computer. The development of computers, computer programs, and computer graphics now allows easy display and manipulation of the electron density, which is mapped onto a three-dimensional grid. A display can be rotated by a turn of a dial so that it can be viewed as a three-dimensional object even though it is a two-dimensional pattern on the computer screen. Using computer programs that have been developed for this task, a crystallographer fits the atoms of the amino acid sequence

91

C.-F. Kuo and J.A. Tainer, The Scripps Research Institute

Crystallographic studies of the DNA repair enzyme endonuclease III reveal a diffraction pattern that is an example of the basic experimental data of an X-ray crystallographic analysis. The X-ray photograph shows a regular array of spots with different intensities and is a two-dimensional section through a three-dimensional array of spots. The intensities are converted by a mathematical relationship called a Fourier series to provide the three-dimensional distribution of electron density in the crystal.

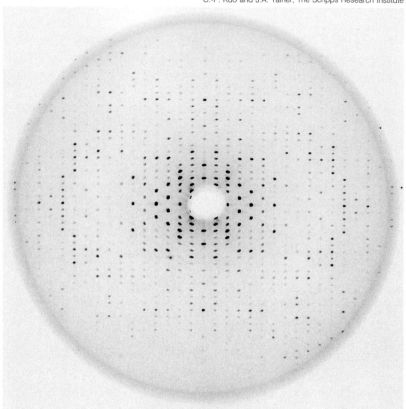

into the electron density map by rotating knobs or dials to move the atoms into regions having high electron density.

Unlike a physical model, computer graphics allows crystallographers to go inside proteins to study the data from any viewpoint and to expand the regions that are being investigated. The ability to move, color, and recontour objects by turning dials or moving a mouse is called interactive computer graphics. The speed and ability to manipulate objects represented by a large number of points is directly related to the speed of the computer and the efficiency of the computer graphics programs. Once an initial set of atomic coordinates has been built, the electron density for those coordinates can be calculated and compared with the experimental electron density. The atomic structure is refined with computer programs that adjust the coordinates to improve their fit to the experimental data while maintaining chemical bonding rules. Crystallographers use computer graphics to evaluate the refined coordinates and adjust the structure to give new atomic coordinates for the computer refinement program. Several cycles of interactive computer graphics and computer refinement are needed to provide the final three-dimensional structure.

The increase in computer power during the last 30 years has greatly decreased the time required for solving a structure once the necessary X-ray diffraction patterns have been obtained. Not only is the time needed for structure analysis greatly decreased, but also the quality of the resulting structure has improved. The increase in computer power has

92

resulted in the determination of hundreds of protein structures, which are deposited into a data base that most scientists can access. The next challenge is analyzing these structures in order to ascertain how proteins interact with one another and with other molecules, how proteins perform their functions and if researchers can affect those functions, and what properties are important for protein folding.

The technique of NMR spectroscopy has recently been applied to the determination of protein structure. NMR spectroscopy provides information about distances between hydrogen atoms in the protein that are spatially close to each other but not necessarily close to each other in the linear sequence of the amino acid chain making up the protein. Most atoms that make up the protein have hydrogen atoms attached. As in X-ray crystallography, powerful computers are essential for collecting the NMR data and converting the data so that they can be interpreted. With a list of distances and other information from the NMR data, researchers build possible structures by using computer programs that require considerable computing power. Distances from the derived atomic coordinates can then be compared with the experimental distances to determine how well the three-dimensional structure fits the NMR data. Unlike X-ray crystallography, this analysis usually provides a family of structures for a protein, with some regions of the protein having the same shape in all structures and some regions having variable shapes. The structurally variable regions may indicate areas of protein flexibility, which may have an important role in protein function.

General techniques for analyzing protein structure

Even with the large number of three-dimensional protein structures now determined, the basic principles of how proteins fold and function are

"Wall-eyed" (left and center panels) and "cross-eyed" (center and right panels) stereo views show a section of the protein chain of endonuclease III that has been fit into the electron density (blue mesh) obtained by X-ray crystallography. Modern computer graphics allows the crystallographer to interpret the electron density by placing the atoms of the amino acid sequence into the electron density. Atoms of the protein chain are colored yellow for carbon, light blue for nitrogen, and red for oxygen. The amino acids are numbered by their position in the sequence of the protein. The wall-eyed stereo can be viewed best with stereo glasses, but they are not needed for the cross-eyed stereo.

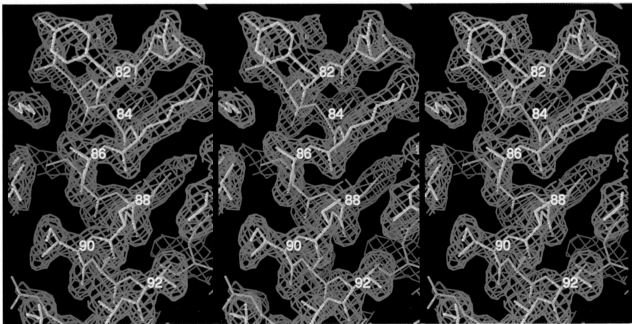

Computer graphics and photography: C.-F. Kuo, D.E. McRee, and J.A. Tainer, The Scripps Research Institute

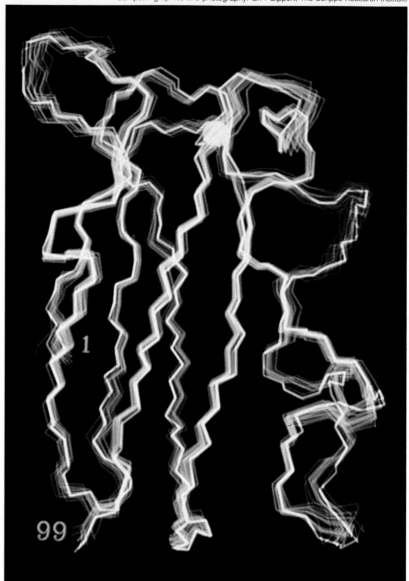

Computer graphics and photography: G.P. Gippert, The Scripps Research Institute

The structure of the globular protein plastocyanin, which transports electrons in plants, is revealed by nuclear magnetic resonance (NMR) spectroscopy. The backbone of the protein structure, determined by X-ray crystallography, is shown in blue and is superimposed on the multiple solutions provided by the NMR data, which are shown in orange. Where the structures are most similar, the lines overlap and appear white. In other regions the structures vary among one another as well as with the crystallographic structure, indicating regions that may have flexibility in water.

not understood. However, the rapid increase in computer power and visualization capabilities is allowing scientists to develop hypotheses useful for protein design. Questions to be investigated include what geometry of chemical groups is required for making a catalytic site, how electrons and small molecules such as oxygen travel through proteins, how proteins interact with one another and with other biologically important molecules, and what causes a protein to fold in a particular way. Answers to those questions will have diverse uses, such as drug design, diagnosis and treatment of diseases, and improved ways of capturing solar power.

Similarities among different proteins are being analyzed with computer graphics. Regions of proteins that are believed to have a specific function are being built into other proteins with computational techniques to test the knowledge of the requirements for those functions. Protein flexibility

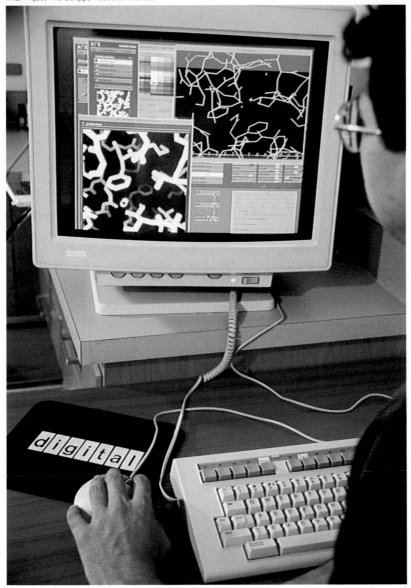

Interactive computer graphics allows a user to select options from the menus displayed on the screen by means of either a mouse on a pad (lower left) or a keyboard (lower center). Other menus are also hidden under the displayed menus, and the user can reveal them by burying those that are being displayed, similar to shuffling through a pile of papers on a desktop. A user can manipulate objects, such as molecules, on the screen in a number of ways, including rotating them, hiding them, and changing their size, color, and type of display. Multiple light sources in any color can be manipulated to highlight and shade objects, intensifying the perception of three-dimensionality. Any objects represented as a three-dimensional group of points or polygons can be entered into the graphics program for display and manipulation.

at the atomic level is being examined with two techniques; molecular dynamics and Monte Carlo methods. In molecular dynamics the forces on each atom caused by interactions with surrounding atoms are calculated, and then each atom is allowed to move for a brief period of time as determined by those forces. Then the forces are recalculated for each atom, and the process is repeated. In Monte Carlo methods each atom is moved a small amount. If the structure resulting from this move is more stable than the starting structure, the move is accepted. If the structure is less stable, acceptance or rejection of the move is determined randomly. Because of the large number of atoms in proteins, simulations of about 10^{-9} seconds are the longest that can be achieved. This is long enough to observe movements of amino acid side chains but insufficient to see large movements between two regions of a protein.

Testing the predictions from computational analyses can be done by use of protein engineering to construct the DNA of the desired protein followed by insertion of this DNA into an organism that will manufacture sufficient amounts of the protein for biochemical analysis or structure determination. Comparison of the actual properties of the engineered protein with the predicted properties suggested by computer-aided design will refine design techniques and enhance understanding of protein function.

Designing a more efficient protein

Examination of protein structure can reveal those amino acid side chains that might be most important for protein function and suggest possible improvements in that function. The enzyme superoxide dismutase (SOD) is important for protecting organisms from the toxic superoxide molecule, which is formed during metabolism and has been implicated in aging and degenerative diseases. SOD takes superoxide, a negatively charged molecule, and converts it to oxygen and hydrogen peroxide, which is processed further by other enzymes. SOD folds so that the side chains of amino acids on the surface of the enzyme create an electrostatic field. Most of the SOD protein presents a negative electrostatic surface to its environment, but the region surrounding the cavity that binds the superoxide molecule creates a positive electrostatic field, attracting the superoxide molecule (the substrate) into the cavity. As a result, SOD is incredibly efficient and is able to convert up to two billion superoxide molecules to oxygen and hydrogen peroxide per second.

Can this enzyme be improved? Near the superoxide binding cavity there is an amino acid with a negatively charged side chain. Would changing this amino acid to one with an uncharged side chain increase the positive charge near the cavity, improving attraction of the superoxide molecule and causing an increased rate of reaction? To test this hypothesis computationally, researchers performed the mutation with computer graphics by replacing the atoms of the negatively charged amino acid side chain with the atoms of a related but uncharged amino acid to make a mutant SOD protein. Calculation of the magnitude and direction of the electrostatic field for both the SOD and the mutant SOD proteins suggested that the mutant SOD should attract superoxide even more efficiently. The paths of superoxide molecules were calculated on the basis of the effects of the electrostatic field created by the SOD molecule and by Brownian motion (random motion caused by interactions with other molecules present, such as water molecules). More than 300,000 trajectories of superoxide about the SOD and the mutant SOD proteins were necessary to determine the rate at which the enzyme would successfully attract superoxide. The calculations predicted that the mutant SOD protein should attract the superoxide molecule more efficiently than the normal SOD protein.

Researchers tested these calculations by constructing the mutant SOD protein with protein-engineering techniques and measuring the rates of reaction for both the SOD and the mutant SOD proteins. The mutant

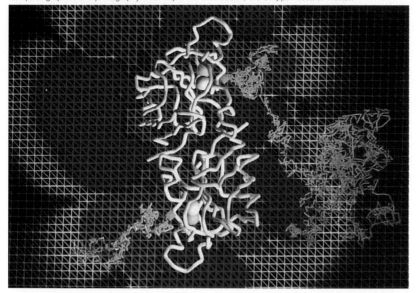

Movements of the superoxide molecule around the enzyme superoxide dismutase (SOD), calculated by C.L. Fisher at The Scripps Research Institute, are revealed in a computer-generated display. The electrostatic field surrounding the SOD molecule was mapped onto a three-dimensional grid, one plane of which is shown in this figure. In this plane positively charged regions of the electrostatic field are shown in red, and negatively charged regions are shown in blue, with the strongest parts of the field the most intensely colored. The backbone of the enzyme is shown as a white tube. This SOD molecule also contains copper atoms (yellow spheres), where the reaction with superoxide takes place, and zinc atoms (blue spheres). Two of the thousands of calculated superoxide trajectories, as determined by the electrostatic field about SOD and Brownian motion, are shown in purple. If, for a given trajectory, the superoxide molecule comes within a specified distance of either copper atom, the trajectory is counted as having led to a successful reaction.

SOD protein showed a threefold increase in rate, with the ability to convert about seven billion superoxide molecules per second. Therefore, computer-aided molecular design successfully predicted an improvement to an enzyme that already had a very fast rate of reaction.

Inhibiting the action of an enzyme

An important goal of drug design is to find molecules that inhibit or prevent the action of a particular enzyme. Inhibition is often caused when a molecule fits very tightly to a protein in the region where the substrate binds, thereby preventing substrate binding and stopping the action of the enzyme. It is important that drugs be selective so that inhibition of the desired enzyme of an invading organism, such as a bacterium, does not adversely affect essential biological activities of the person or animal being treated. Most clinically used drugs are chemically modified versions of previously known drugs. One of the most difficult tasks in drug design is to find a substance, termed a lead compound, that inhibits an enzyme but is structurally different from any known substrates or inhibitors for that particular enzyme. Traditionally, lead compounds are found by random screening. Sources for possible compounds come from plants or from molecules that are routinely used in chemical synthesis.

A new approach involving computational screening was used to find lead compounds that would inhibit an enzyme of the human immunodefiency virus (HIV), which is believed to cause AIDS. The HIV enzyme, termed a protease, cuts proteins by cleaving peptide bonds of specific amino acid sequences and is essential for viral replication. The three-dimensional structure of the protease was determined by X-ray crystallography. The computer program DOCK, developed by I.D. Kuntz and colleagues at the University of California at San Francisco, was used to create a negative image of the binding cavity from the protein structure and then compare this image with the atomic structures of 10,000 small

97

I.D. Kuntz, School of Pharmacy, University of California at San Francisco

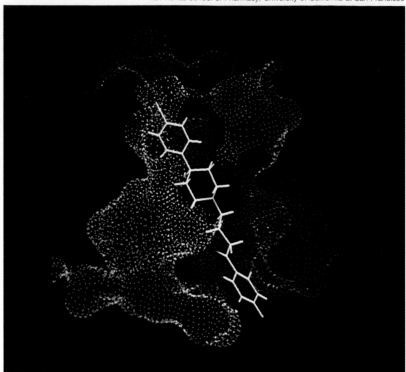

The molecular structure of an enzyme of the human immunodeficiency virus (HIV) was determined by X-ray crystallography. The enzyme, termed a protease, is crucial to the development of the virus, which causes AIDS (acquired immune deficiency syndrome). A computer program, DOCK, developed by I.D. Kuntz and colleagues at the University of California at San Francisco, was used to find a compound that inhibits the action of the protease and, therefore, could be useful in AIDS therapy.

molecules. Compounds were evaluated by molecular shape and chemical complementarity. Those that fit best were docked to the protein structure with computer graphics. One candidate was selected because it was commercially available and appeared to have complementary interactions with the protease. This compound was found to inhibit the action of the protein and may be a potential lead compound for inhibitor development and AIDS therapy. These experiments suggest that computational search using three-dimensional protein structure may become an important tool for discovering lead compounds and thereby furthering drug development.

Building a new function into a protein

With the increased understanding of protein structure, the question arises as to whether proteins can be created that will do a specified chemical transformation for which no enzyme exists. One approach to this problem is through the use of antibody molecules. Antibodies are a class of molecules created by the immune system, which protects against invading organisms. When an organism such as a bacterium or a virus attacks, the immune system creates a huge number of antibodies, some of which have the ability to bind to the invader. Those that bind well are created in large numbers and bind to the invading organism, starting a cascade of events that leads to the removal of the invader. The immune system can create molecules that recognize and bind to invading substances, or antigens, in just a few days, even though the immune system has never before seen the invading substance.

98

Antibodies rarely have catalytic properties; they function primarily to recognize and bind antigens. Scientists, however, have used the immune system to create catalytic antibodies by immunizing an animal, often a mouse, with a molecule that mimics the three-dimensional shape of a high-energy intermediate in a chemical reaction. The large number of antibodies produced by this immunization are screened for catalytic activity, which requires making large amounts of a particular antibody and then testing it. Currently this is a difficult task because, while many antibodies will bind the immunizing molecule, only a very few of them will have catalytic activity.

A second approach for designing a catalytic antibody would be to build a catalytic site into an antibody that binds to a molecule similar to the substrate for the desired reaction. This requires understanding the structure of the antibody, the geometry of amino acids necessary for creating a catalytic site, and the proper alignment of the catalytic site with the substrate. Fortunately, because of the large number of three-dimensional structures now available for antibodies and enzymes, there is sufficient information upon which to base this design strategy.

To test this strategy, a simple new function was built into an antibody. Metal ions are commonly used by enzymes as part of their catalytic mechanism. For example, the enzyme carbonic anhydrase, which converts carbon dioxide to bicarbonate (baking soda), has a zinc ion that

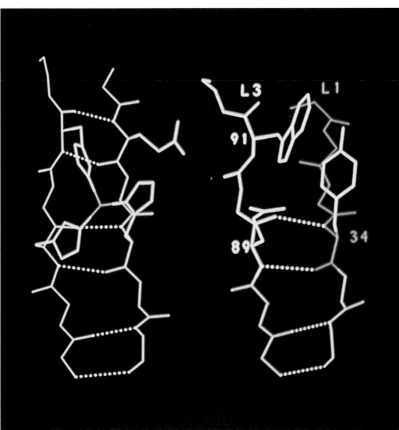

Computer graphics and photography: V.A. Roberts and J.A. Tainer, The Scripps Research Institute

Computer-generated graphics compare the zinc-binding site of carbonic anhydrase (left), an enzyme that uses a zinc atom to assist the hydrolysis of carbon dioxide to carbonate, and a region of an antibody (right). The three amino acids of carbonic anhydrase, shown in light blue, are histidine amino acids, which have nitrogen atoms in their five-membered ring side chains. One nitrogen from each five-membered ring forms a bond with the zinc atom, shown in orange, providing three total bonds between the zinc atom and the enzyme. The underlying backbone structure (light purple) of this region of carbonic anhydrase is held together by hydrogen bonds (shown as dashed lines), which are favorable interactions between the hydrogen atom of an amino group and the oxygen atom of a carboxyl group. On the right is shown a region of an antibody with a backbone structure similar to the zinc-binding region of carbonic anhydrase, including many of the hydrogen bonds. The side chains of amino acids 34, 89, and 91 (shown in yellow) extend from the antibody backbone in a manner similar to the three histidine amino acids of carbonic anhydrase. The similarity of the two structures suggests that a zinc-binding site could be built into antibodies by replacement of the side chains of amino acids 34, 89, and 91 with histidine side chains.

Computer graphics and photography: M. Pique, V.A. Roberts, and J.A. Tainer, The Scripps Research Institute

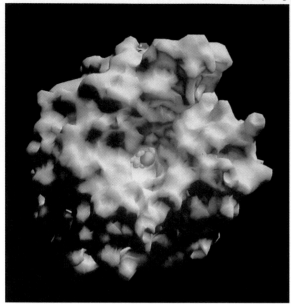 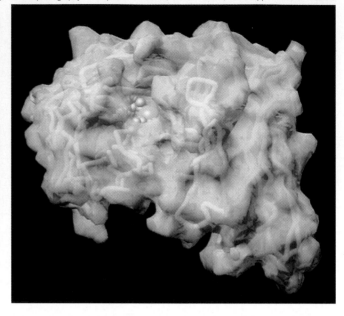

Molecular surface of carbonic anhydrase (above), as revealed by computer graphics, shows that the zinc atom (large silver sphere) lies at the bottom of a pit that is designed by nature to fit the substrate and to exclude most other molecules. Atoms of the attached histidine amino acids are shown as smaller spheres surrounding the zinc atom. For the zinc atom to be an effective catalyst, it must contact the substrate and, once the substrate is bound, must be sequestered from solvent. The pit of carbonic anhydrase is just large enough to allow substrate to enter and bind. A model of an antibody with a built-in zinc site (above right) shows the zinc atom (large blue sphere) positioned at the bottom of a pocket. The molecular surface of the antibody is partially transparent so that the underlying backbone structure of the antibody (colored tubes) can be seen. Three of the original antibody amino acids have been replaced by histidine amino acids. The atoms of the five-membered rings of the histidine amino acids, shown as smaller silver spheres surrounding the zinc atom, create a zinc-binding site in the antibody.

is essential for catalytic activity. This ion is bound to the protein with the side chains of three amino acids, called histidines. The backbone structure of the region of carbonic anhydrase that binds the zinc ion is similar to the region of antibodies that binds antigens. Therefore, a computer-generated design based on three-dimensional structure suggested that the replacement of specific antibody amino acids with the amino acid histidine would create a zinc binding site in the antibody. Researchers tested this hypothesis by constructing the mutated antibody with a protein-engineering technique called site-directed mutagenesis. The mutant antibody was found to bind zinc ions, whereas the original antibody did not. Thus, computer-aided design and analysis gave an accurate prediction for constructing a new function, that of metal ion binding, into a protein.

Future directions

Exciting future directions are opening up with the rapid increases in computer power and computer graphics capabilities. The three methods discussed above used the three-dimensional coordinates of proteins for improving catalysis, inhibiting activity, and adding new functions to proteins. Similar analyses to understand and manipulate structure and function will become more widely used in the immediate future. A major goal is to incorporate protein flexibility into these analyses. Protein flexibility has been shown to be essential for the biological activity of many proteins, including movement of molecules inside proteins, interactions between proteins, protein folding, and the catalytic mechanism of enzymes.

The oxygen-carrying protein hemoglobin is a good example of the importance of protein flexibility. Unlike the pocket for superoxide binding in SOD, there is no obvious channel in hemoglobin going from the surface of the protein to the oxygen-binding site. Instead, the oxygen must diffuse through the atoms of the protein, with adjustments of protein structure to allow oxygen movement. Hemoglobin consists of four chains of amino acids, each having similar structure and each binding a single oxygen molecule. Small local changes in protein structure that occur when the oxygen molecule binds are transferred through the protein structure, resulting in changes in the interactions among the four chains of hemoglobin that facilitate additional oxygen binding. The ability to simulate the details of structural changes like these would lead to enhanced understanding of these processes, and this knowledge could be used in protein design.

When proteins interact with one another, they change their shape to enhance the protein-protein interactions that have replaced the protein-water interactions. An example is the change that occurs in antibody structure upon binding an antigen. The flexibility in the loops of the antibody structure involved in binding may be essential for providing tight antigen binding. The crystallographic structure of an antibody alone

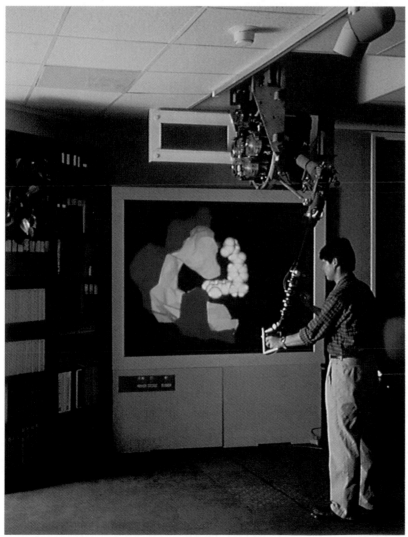

Bo Strain

A display combining visual, tactile, and kinesthetic aspects of a computer model of a molecular structure, developed at the University of North Carolina, helps scientists understand the molecule's behavior and function. A force-displaying remote manipulator docks a drug molecule in the receptor site of an enzyme. Both the visual display and the force and torque vectors are updated in real time, enabling a user to test for favorable binding.

may not have the same shape as the antibody when bound to the antigen. Because of the change in antibody shape, attempting to dock an antigen to the unbound antibody structure may give an incorrect answer if flexibility is not included.

The ultimate question in protein flexibility is how a globular protein folds into its three-dimensional structure. Because it is much easier to determine the sequence of amino acids of a protein than the three-dimensional protein structure, it would be very useful to be able to build models of proteins from their amino acid sequence alone. Currently, models of proteins of unknown structure are constructed from solved structures of related proteins. For a protein having no closely related known structure, there are methods to predict regions of local structure but not the overall fold, much less positions of specific amino acid side chains.

With current computational technology, these problems of flexibility cannot be approached by simulation of the complex molecular movement of individual atoms. The time it takes for a substrate to bind to its enzyme, for an antigen to bind to its antibody, for large changes to occur in protein structure, or for a small protein to fold may be on the order of seconds. The time step used to simulate the movement of atoms with molecular dynamics or Monte Carlo techniques is on the femtosecond (one-quadrillionth of a second) time scale. For a small globular protein of about 1,000 atoms, the calculation of one femtosecond of movement with a supercomputer requires about one second. Therefore, it would take 10^{15} seconds, or about 32 million years, to attempt to fold a protein by looking at the movements of individual atoms if that protein folded within one second! The task is complicated by proper simulation of water molecules around the protein, which are believed to be important for the pathway of folding as well as for stability of the final structure.

To simulate flexibility over long time periods, each amino acid needs to be represented by a simplified model. Several methods of simplification are being explored to see which techniques might provide useful information for manipulating protein structure. These methods have been applied to studying protein interactions and protein folding.

Ten to 15 years ago there were few methods for analyzing protein structure, and it was not considered a likely tool for drug design. Most work on protein structure was done in laboratories of research institutions. Now, not only do most large pharmaceutical firms have groups that use computational techniques for the visualization of molecules, but small companies have been formed that use three-dimensional protein structures as the basis for drug and protein design. The continuing rapid development in computer power, computer graphics, and computer programs combined with declining costs suggests that computer-aided molecular design will become commonplace. Molecular models can now be viewed even on inexpensive personal computers. The ability to analyze protein structure in many ways and the development of techniques to simulate protein flexibility may lead to knowledge of the basic rules underlying protein function and action and result in the development

102

Computer graphics and photography: M.E. Pique, The Scripps Research Institute

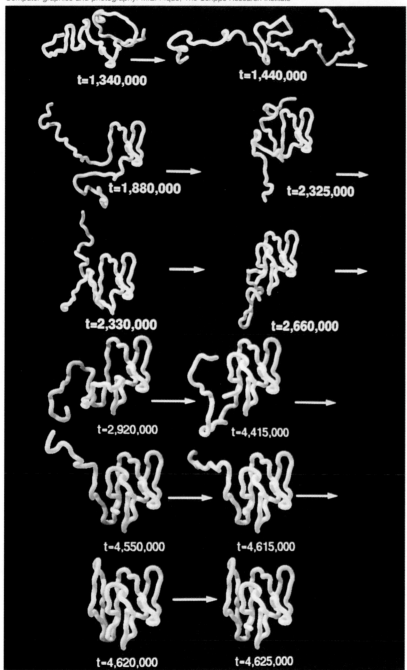

t=1,340,000   t=1,440,000

t=1,880,000   t=2,325,000

t=2,330,000   t=2,660,000

t=2,920,000   t=4,415,000

t=4,550,000   t=4,615,000

t=4,620,000   t=4,625,000

FOR ADDITIONAL READING

C. Branden and J. Tooze, *Introduction to Protein Structure* (Garland Publishing, Inc., 1991).

E.D. Getzoff, D.E. Cabelli, C.L. Fisher, H.E. Parge, M.S. Viezzoli, L. Banci, and R.A. Hallewell, "Faster Superoxide Dismutase Mutants Designed by Enhancing Electrostatic Guidance," *Nature* (July 23, 1992, pp. 347–351).

M. Karplus and J.A. McCammon, "The Dynamics of Proteins," *Scientific American* (April 1986, pp. 42-51).

J.M. Moore, C.A. Lepre, G.P. Gippert, W.J. Chazin, D.A. Case, and P.E. Wright, "High-Resolution Solution Structure of Reduced French Bean Plastocyanin and Comparison with the Crystal Structure of Poplar Plastocyanin," *Journal of Molecular Biology* (1991, pp. 533–555).

A.J. Olson and D.S. Goodsell, "Visualizing Biological Molecules," *Scientific American* (November 1992, pp. 76–81).

Elizabeth Pennisi, "Water, Water Everywhere," *Science News* (Feb. 20, 1993, pp. 121–123).

J. Skolnick and A. Kolinski, "Simulations of the Folding of a Globular Protein," *Science* (Nov. 23, 1990, pp. 1121–1125).

M.D. Uehling, "Birth of a Molecule," *Popular Science* (February 1992, pp. 74ff.).

of customized proteins that will function as molecular tools. These molecules may be used for tasks for which there are no naturally occurring enzymes, such as performing industrial reactions, cleaving specific sequences of DNA to facilitate protein engineering, and treating diseases.

THROUGH A PROBE BRIGHTLY:
THE NEW MICROSCOPY

by Jean-Paul Revel

Revolutionary advances in the design of microscopes have produced instruments capable of resolving the atomic structure of materials and of moving individual atoms.

The unaided human eye can resolve objects only if they are more than about 50 micrometers (1/500 inch) apart, a limit imposed by the spacing of the visual elements in the eye's retina. Microscopes and hand lenses extend the limits of human vision to much smaller things. In the best microscopes built along classical principles, objects separated by as little as 0.2 micrometer (1/125,000 inch) can theoretically be distinguished. The detail that can be observed in practice depends both on the quality of the lenses that are used in the construction of the microscope and on the wavelength of the radiation (visible light in the case of the standard microscope) used to visualize the object. It is important to appreciate that resolution is not the only factor in seeing. There must also be good enough contrast to allow objects to stand out against the background. In fact, objects much below the limit of resolution can nevertheless be detected if there is sufficient contrast.

During the last few years there has been a remarkably rapid development in microscopic techniques, with major improvements in the ability to achieve both good contrast and high resolution. This was made possible by the realization that lenses could be used for imaging in ways that circumvented the limitations inherent in the approaches to microscopy used for the last hundred years, when microscopes employing visible light essentially reached the limits of their capabilities. In a separate development microscopes were invented that do not use lenses at all and so are not limited by the latter's shortcomings.

Both of these lines of progress have revolutionized the field of microscopy. To place these advances in perspective, it is appropriate to start with a brief review of the development of microscopic techniques, followed by a consideration of contrast and modern ways to achieve it. Finally, microscopy without lenses will be described. Throughout this article the emphasis will be on the visualization of biological samples, but similar and sometimes even more spectacular gains have been made in visualizing other types of materials.

Photos, Ann Ronan at Image Select International, London

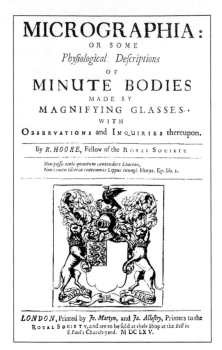

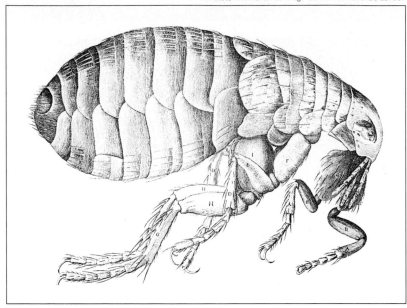

The beginnings of microscopy

The first microscopes apparently were built at the end of the 16th or early in the 17th century by Hans and Zacharias Janssen of Middelburg, The Netherlands. Although the exact origin of microscopes is somewhat murky, it is well documented that by 1610 Galileo was using a microscope alternately described as making a fly look "as big as a hen" or "as big as a lamb." A little more that 50 years elapsed before Robert Hooke published his book *Micrographia,* which summarized his discoveries with the microscope. In it there is a picture of a flea, the carrier for the plague that was raging at the time, though neither he nor anyone else knew that. Other early contributions were due to Marcello Malpighi, who made extensive observations on capillaries in the lung and many other biological tissues. Most of these pioneers already used instruments that, like modern ones, were compound microscopes; that is, they had an optical train consisting of two lenses in succession. One exception was the great microscopist Antonie van Leeuwenhoek, who used high-power single lenses (hand lenses) instead.

Through a series of gradual refinements, microscope lenses and, as a result, microscopes were slowly improved. Both spherical aberration (which arises because rays passing through the rim of the lens are more strongly refracted than rays passing through its middle) and chromatic aberration (which causes light of different wavelengths to be brought to a different focus) had been overcome by the 19th century. Ernst Abbe, a physicist at the University of Jena, Germany, changed the then-prevalent empirical approach to the design of microscopes. In collaboration with Carl Zeiss, who had a small instrument workshop in Jena, he launched a systematic investigation on how to build the best microscope. Through his research Abbe came to realize that the best lenses were made of glass with a high refractive index (n). The refractive index is a measure of the interaction of light with the medium it traverses; it is expressed as the ratio of the velocity of light in the medium of interest to that in a vacuum. To give good resolution a lens also needs to allow entrance of the largest bundle of rays possible. This is given by the angle α, measured between the outermost ray that can enter the lens and the optical axis. These two quantities, n and α, are combined in a number called the Numerical Aperture, defined as NA $= n \sin \alpha$. The best lenses have a high NA. To take advantage of such a lens, light entering it has to illuminate it fully (or else α is not as large as possible); that is, the illuminating system (in a microscope, the condenser) has to be of matching quality (have a similar NA).

Abbe's ideas, published in 1873, led to the construction of light microscopes as good as standard instruments of today. His work was quickly recognized as a major step forward. This is well illustrated in a verse declaimed by the British microscopist J.W. Stephenson: "Objectives and their laws were hidden by the night/ God said: Let Abbe be and all was light."

The resolving power (r) of a lens can be expressed by the relation $r = 0.5 \lambda / n \sin \alpha$, where λ is the wavelength of the light and n the refractive index of the glass and of the medium around the sample and in the space between it and the lens. The expression $n \sin \alpha$ is, as has been described, the numerical aperture (NA) of the lens. Since the trigonometric function "$\sin \alpha$" has a maximum value of 1, and the refractive index, n, for air is 1, the NA of a lens system in air cannot be greater than 1. The resolution of a lens in air thus becomes $0.5 \lambda / 1$, meaning that in air the resolution is roughly equal to 0.5 times the wavelength of the radiation used for imaging. This is often written as $\lambda / 2$. With the best glasses, and by immersing the lenses in oil (a medium of refractive index higher than air), a numerical aperture as high as, say, 1.5, to take a round number, can be achieved. Until recently higher NAs could not be reached, and this limitation led to the belief that the only way to improve resolution significantly was to make λ smaller by using radiation of shorter wavelength than light in the visible range.

Use of short wavelengths

In 1904 August Köhler used ultraviolet (UV) light to try to improve resolution, but because the change in λ when going from visible to UV light is not very great, the improvement in resolution was not spectacular. Additional problems were that human eyes do not see in the UV range and that the optics of the microscope had to be made of materials transparent to UV radiation.

A much more dramatic advance took place in the 1920s when the French physicist Louis-Victor de Broglie realized that electrons had wave properties, which led to the idea that they, like photons, could be used for imaging. Because electrons are of much shorter wavelength than photons of visible or UV light, microscopes using electrons for imaging are capable of much higher resolutions. Many people throughout the world contributed to the development of electron microscopes, but Max

Photos, Ann Ronan
at Image Select International, London

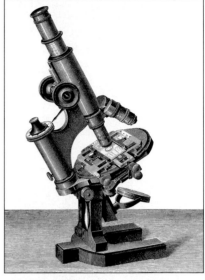

Carl Zeiss (above), a German manufacturer of optical instruments, collaborated with the German physicist Ernst Abbe in the late 1800s to produce light microscopes (top) as good as the standard instruments of today.

107

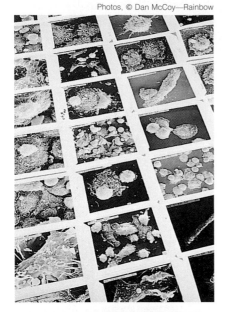

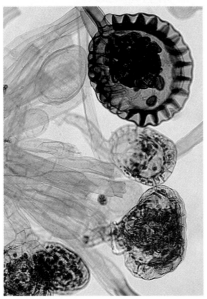

Electron microscopy, in which electrons are used for imaging, can visualize structures as small as individual atoms. At the top are scanning electron micrographs of cells attacking foreign invaders. In the photomicrograph above, spore sacs, which are naturally almost transparent, have been stained with dye to make them more visible.

Knoll and Ernst Ruska at the Technical University in Berlin are recognized as major protagonists of the new technology. In 1986, just a few years before his death, Ruska received a rather belated Nobel Prize for his contributions.

Electron microscopy has facilitated many remarkable discoveries, including the visualization of structures as fine as individual atoms. However, electron microscopes cannot be used to image thick specimens. The beam of most common instruments, operating with electrons accelerated to 100,000 volts, can penetrate effectively only through samples less than 0.1 micrometer thick. Special million-volt microscopes are needed to visualize thicker samples or samples of metals, which are "electron dense." Electron microscopes must by and large operate in a vacuum, since even a thin column of air can disrupt the path of electrons or even stop them. Thus, only specially preserved biological materials can be studied.

Electron microscopy will not be discussed in detail because it represents the path of classical evolution, which takes advantage of short wavelengths to increase resolution, and not the revolutionary paths under consideration here. For the same reason, X-ray microscopy will not be discussed in spite of many novel and exciting developments that have taken place with such instruments.

How one sees images: contrast

With Abbe's work in 1873, light-microscope technology reached the point where further improvement in the resolution of such instruments would not be an easy task and would be likely to produce incremental rather than dramatic gains. As indicated above, however, resolution is not everything. In microscopy and for visual detection in general, an essential property of objects is that they not be transparent, another way of saying that there must be contrast. For example, glass is difficult to see unless it is tinted or placed so that it reflects light from its surface. Either method produces the contrast that allows objects to stand out from the background. Unfortunately, most biological objects are almost completely transparent. The classical way to obtain enough contrast to see cellular detail is to stain, using dyes that bind to the structures of interest and thus make them stand out. An important first step toward today's optical revolution was the slow realization that contrast could be achieved by a number of other means besides staining. Although some dyes can be used in living cells (supravital dyes), most staining techniques require that the cells be made permeable and/or placed under conditions otherwise incompatible with life.

Until the 1970s there were a limited number of ways to obtain contrast. In the mid-1930s Frits Zernike from Groningen, The Netherlands, developed phase contrast, which utilizes the difference in the index of refraction between the specimen and the surrounding medium to allow visualization of even colorless transparent objects. Zernike received a Nobel Prize for Physics for this achievement even though early skeptics had grumbled that "if this was of any value, it would have been invented long ago." The next advance was interference contrast, which can be used not just for contrast but also to measure the mass of microscopic objects (*i.e.,* weigh them). Here, two in-phase beams of light are used. One is allowed to pass through the sample and another through the medium next to the sample. The beam that was allowed to pass through the sample has to go through more material (experiences a longer optical path) and thus emerges out of phase with the beam that only had to go through the medium around the sample. When the two beams are brought back together, they interact and produce interference colors, proportional to the amount of material in the sample itself. More recently, differential interference contrast, or DIC, was first implemented by Georges Nomarski in Paris. This approach produces striking images whose three-dimensional appearance depends on the concentration of materials and not the actual shape of the object.

A generally useful, and now widely applied, technique to obtain contrast has been fluorescence. In this method the sample is illuminated by light of relatively short (blue or lower) wavelength. Molecules that can absorb energy at those wavelengths become raised to a higher energy state (excited). As the excited molecules return to a lower energy state, they release a photon of somewhat longer wavelength than the one that raised them to the excited level. The emission of this light by the sample is called fluorescence. In a fluorescence microscope only the emitted light participates in the formation of the image because "barrier" filters prevent the exciting radiation of shorter wavelengths from reaching the imaging part of the microscope. Since the image is formed only by light emitted from the regions of the sample containing fluorescent molecules, the background is dark and the sample bright, a high-contrast situation. Even a little light on a dark background can be detected easily. This is a much more favorable situation than the one existing in standard

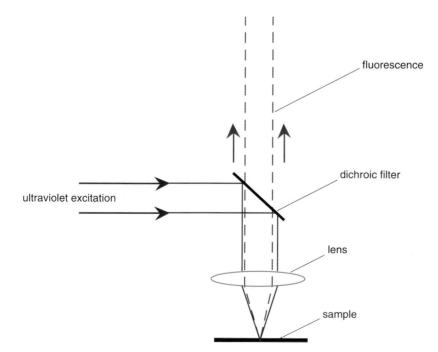

Epifluorescence, a widely used configuration for fluorescence microscopy, is shown in this simplified diagram. A short-wave ultraviolet excitation beam is relected by a dichroic filter (which reflects some wavelengths and not others) and is focused by a lens on the sample, where it excites fluorescence. The same lens then uses the emitted fluorescence to form an image of the sample. Because the fluorescence is of longer wavelength than the excitation beam, it passes through the dichroic filter.

microscopy, where detection depends on the absorption of a small percentage of the incoming light so that the object is only a little less bright than the area surrounding it. Biologists have put the relatively high contrast available by fluorescence to good advantage by coupling fluorescent dyes to antibodies that can bind very specifically to proteins and to other molecules inside cells.

In fluorescence and other high-contrast approaches, it is possible to detect small signals because the background is kept relatively dark. An important aspect of the revolution in microscopy is the application of novel methods to improve the signal-to-background ratio.

The beginning of the revolution: video enhancement

The clear realization that finding ways to enhance the contrast permits the detection of objects even below the resolution of the microscope was a major contribution to modern microscopy. In 1981 Shinya Inoue of the University of Pennsylvania and Bob Allen of Dartmouth College, Hanover, New Hampshire, and their collaborators took advantage of the video recording of images to enhance visualization of objects thought beyond the realm of standard microscopy. The signal detected by the eye or film is the difference between the brightness of the background and that of the object. The contrast is usually expressed as

$$\frac{\text{Background - object}}{\text{Background}}$$

With the human eye or film there is relatively little that can be done to change this ratio. With a video camera, however, it is possible to adjust the background intensity independently and so change the relative level of the signal. By reducing the background illumination, the absorption caused by the signal becomes an increasingly large percentage of the total. Thus video microscopy permits one to see small structures that cannot be detected by conventional microscopy.

One of the earliest achievements permitted by the technique was the visualization of single microtubules, intracellular structures that are only 25 nanometers wide, 10 times below the resolution of the light microscope. Because microtubules are so minute, their structure was first discovered by electron microscopy. The electron microscope, however, cannot be used to observe live cells, and thus only static snapshots of microtubules preserved in fixed cells are attainable. The microtubules form the structures responsible for the distribution of chromosomes during cell division and are involved in the motion of many other cellular components. Using video-enhanced microscopy, it became possible not just to detect their presence but also to follow the behavior of individual microtubules in living cells. This has led to a much clearer understanding of their multiple roles.

Video enhancement has even permitted the visualization of structures that are smaller than microtubules, such as individual DNA molecules stained with fluorescent dyes. The dynamic behavior of single DNA molecules can be studied even though DNA is only two nanometers across, 100 times below the nominal resolution of the light microscope. It

110

is important to note, however, that although all of these very small objects are made visible by enhancing contrast, they are not resolved; thus, two DNA molecules lying closely side by side would not be distinguishable from each other.

The second revolution: analog versus digital

Good control over contrast has also been achieved by modification of the way in which the image is acquired. All the microscopes described so far are analog. This means that the objective lens of the microscope processes the information concerning all points of the object at the same time, and the resulting images consist of graded, continuous shades. The alternate way to acquire the image is digital, which turns out to have many advantages (and a few drawbacks as well).

The digital medium is ideally suited to computer-controlled acquisition and manipulation and, as a result, many microscopes are now interfaced with digital microprocessors. In a digital instrument the information about the object that is being examined is recorded one point at a time, serially. The digital image consists of small areas, called pixels, of a given intensity and shade of gray or color. Paintings such as those of the pointillist Georges Seurat can be called digital. From up close the painting is seen to be formed by small rectangular areas of pure color, each one a single brush stroke. From far away these strokes merge and cannot be distinguished.

"Portrait of His Sister" by Georges Lemmen is painted in the pointillist style, in which small strokes or dots of pure color are applied to a surface in such a way that they merge and form a coherent image from a distance. Digital microscopy operates on the same principle. A digital instrument records the information about an object one point at a time, serially. The digital image consists of pixels, small areas of a given intensity and shade of gray or color. Each pixel is then represented by a number denoting its brightness and other properties and is placed sequentially in a computer file. Computer software can then perform arithmetic operations on such files to enhance contrast and accentuate detail.

(Below and detail) Georges Lemmen, Belgian, 1865–1916, "Portrait of His Sister," oil on canvas, 1891, 62 x 51 cm, A.A. McKay Fund, 1961.42; © 1990 The Art Institute of Chicago, all rights reserved

Each pixel of a digital image is represented by a number denoting its brightness and other properties and placed sequentially in a file. The position of these numbers in the file represents the position of the pixel in the image. Such data files can be bulky and may consume large amounts of computer memory, but they are easy to manipulate. Computer software can perform arithmetic operations on such files in order to enhance contrast, detect and sharpen edges, and accentuate detail by assigning different colors to represent less easily distinguishable shades of gray—all much faster and more conveniently than is possible with film or video, the typical analog recording media. These manipulations can easily be carried out after the image has been acquired. In fact, digital images are so advantageous that it is common practice to digitize images originally acquired in the analog mode. Digital recording of images promises to cause a revolution of its own. For many purposes film will be superseded by media such as magnetic or optical disks, which are well suited to digital recording.

In a microscope where the image is acquired in digital fashion, the lens is used mainly to illuminate the sample one point at a time. The illuminating beam, commonly an intense beam of laser light, is scanned over the sample in a raster (the pattern produced by scanning from side to side in lines from top to bottom). The light that is reflected, emitted, or transmitted by the sample is then collected and projected onto a detector, often a photomultiplier. Manipulating the operating characteristics of the photomultiplier readily allows for adjustment of contrast and brightness.

The introduction of reasonably priced, good-resolution, charge-coupled device (CCD) cameras can also provide digital control of images. With such devices it is possible to visualize samples without resorting to phase contrast or DIC. These approaches can be used for any type of microscopy. Thus, both digital acquisition and manipulation of the image allow significant gains in the ability to visualize very small objects.

A modern microscope: the confocal approach

Some of the benefits to be gained by contrast enhancement and digital approaches can be seen in such instruments as the confocal microscope. In a standard microscope the observer sees a sharp image of what is in the focal plane superimposed on the out-of-focus image of objects above and below it. This in fact prevents the observer from profiting fully from the sharp in-focus image, especially in thick specimens—those more than a micrometer or so. Not only does the out-of-focus part of the image cause blurring, it also forms most of the background illumination, and contrast is thus decreased by those parts of the image that are out of focus. In a confocal microscope the illuminating beam is scanned across the object, and the light emanating from the region that is scanned is seen by a detector, one element at a time. An aperture is placed in front of the detector in such a way that light coming from objects in the focal plane passes through it, but light from the out-of-focus planes is spread over a wide area and as a result mostly misses the aperture. This gives very high-contrast images of the objects in the focal plane. The result is

112

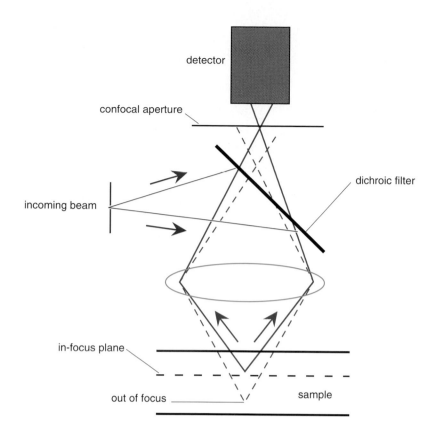

detector

confocal aperture

dichroic filter

incoming beam

in-focus plane

out of focus

sample

better detection of objects too small to be resolved by the microscope. In fact, with the imaging setup used there is also an improvement in the resolution from 0.2 to 0.14 micrometer. That is because the shape of the Airy disk (the bright, diffuse central spot of light formed by an optical system imaging a point source of light) changes in confocal microscopy, allowing the images of two objects to be closer to each other than usual before becoming indistinguishable.

Even more interesting is the ability of the confocal microscope to carry out optical sectioning of even very thick objects. The computer used to acquire the images stores successive in-focus optical slices in memory. These files can then be used to reconstruct such objects in space. This has been most useful in studies of the complex shapes and interrelationships of neurons and many other objects.

Laser scanning microscopy, often combined with confocal approaches, has permitted the measurement of many interesting events within the live cell. For example, calcium ions released from intracellular stores interact with many molecules involved in cell motility or other changes. Introducing dyes that fluoresce in the presence of such ions makes it possible to follow the changes in concentration of this ion during, for example, muscular contraction or after fertilization of an egg by sperm. It also has led to a better understanding of the mechanisms that prevent more than one sperm from fertilizing an egg and that underlie the contraction cycle in rhythmically beating heart muscle cells. In the same way, small changes in the concentration of hydrogen ions caused

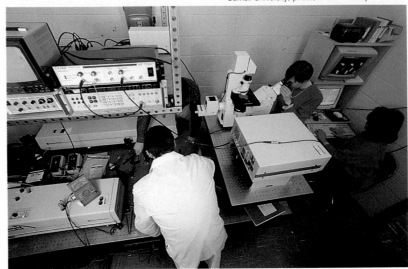

Researchers construct a two-photon laser scanning fluoresence microscope (right), which uses a stream of ultrafast laser pulses to illuminate a living cell. Fluorophores, special molecules that fluoresce when exposed to light, are added to the living tissue. A stream of 100-femtosecond (100 quadrillionths of a second) red visible-light laser pulses focused at a specific level in the cell causes a fluorophore to absorb two photons of red light simultaneously and then emit light. This avoids the problems of cell damage and photobleaching (destruction of the fluorophores) that occur with ultraviolet lasers. On the opposite page, two-photon fluorescence microscopy is used to image internal free calcium ion concentrations in a live fish epidermal cell. Taken at one-minute intervals, top to bottom, left to right, this series shows vertical cross sections through the cell.

by cellular activity can be monitored, as well as the voltage changes in the membranes of nerve cells. One rather unexpected discovery made by such studies is that the supporting cells of the nervous system, the glial cells, also exhibit changes during brain activity although on a much less rapid scale than the nerve cells themselves. This work permits better understanding of the relationship between the neurons themselves and their supporting cohorts of the glia.

The third revolution: Look, no lenses!

All of the microscopes and the ways of using them that have been described are variations on a general theme, one in which lenses are used to illuminate the sample and record the image either in digital or analog modes. The improvements to these microscopes have consisted of ingenious ways of providing contrast and significant, if modest, increases in resolution. There has, however, been a major new development—the introduction of digital imaging devices that do not use lenses at all. This new class of instruments is referred to as "scanned probe microscopes." In such instruments a probe illuminates, touches, or otherwise interacts with the sample, one pixel at a time, and this information, acquired serially, is used to form the image.

The scanned probe microscope most similar to a standard light microscope is the near-field scanning optical microscope, or NSOM. In this instrument light is taken to the specimen down a very fine optical fiber. Placing the fiber in close proximity (10 nanometers) to the sample (near-field condition) ensures that light does not spread out too far and illuminates only an area barely larger than the diameter of the fiber. Farther away from the sample, in the "far field" where standard microscopes operate, the area illuminated would be large and represented by an Airy disk, as described above. In the near-field instrument a detector picks up the light transmitted (or reflected) from each illuminated point. Scanning the fiber across the sample creates a map of the object of

114

Ingrid Brust–Mascher, Rebecca Williams,
Watt W. Webb, Department of Applied Physics, Cornell University

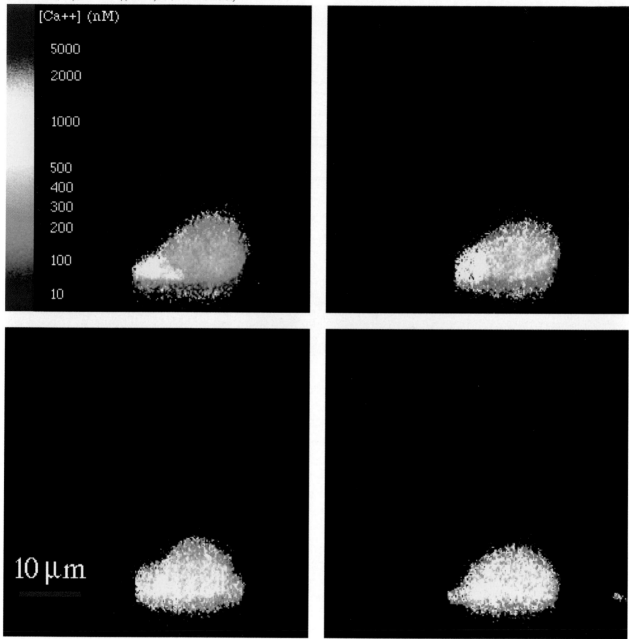

study—a digital micrograph—not limited by diffraction and therefore not limited in resolution by the wave properties of the light. NSOMs are in their infancy but have already shown themselves capable of a resolving power of about $\lambda/40$, much higher than a lensed microscope, which is limited to about $\lambda/2$.

The NSOM is only one of the new lensless instruments. The first to become an important tool was the scanning transmission electron microscope (STEM) devised by Albert Crewe and his colleagues at the University of Chicago. In the STEM the probe is a fine beam of electrons focused on the sample. The electrons emerging from the sample after

Cornell University; photos, © Dan McCoy—Rainbow

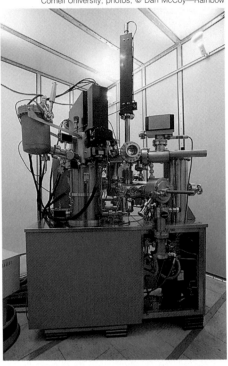

The scanning transmission electron microscope (above right), with its control panel (above), focuses a fine beam of electrons on a sample. The electrons that emerge from the sample after interacting with it are collected by detectors in the image space. No lenses are needed to form the image; instead, it is formed point by point when the beam scans across the sample. This type of microscope was the first to resolve individual atoms.

interacting with it are collected by detectors in the image space. There are no lenses to form an image; instead, the image is formed point by point as a fine beam, produced by a bright source called a field-emission gun, scans across the sample. Since there are no lenses in the imaging path, no aberrations are introduced in the image side of the system. This microscope was the first to resolve individual atoms. It also permitted dynamic studies of large-scale atomic movement.

Credit for scanned probe (lensless) instruments usually goes to the inventors of the scanning tunneling microscope (STM). They were Gerd Binnig and Heinrich Rohrer, scientists at the IBM Zürich Research Center in Switzerland, who shared the 1986 Nobel Prize for Physics with Ruska, the pioneer developer of electron microscopes mentioned above. In the STM the probe consists of a wire with a point that is made to approach an electrically conducting sample. When the probe tip almost touches the sample, a current can be made to flow between the two, even though there is no actual contact. The electrons that flow between the tip and the sample are said to be "tunneling." The flow of electrons is exquisitely sensitive to the distance between sample and probe, increasing rapidly as the two come closer and decreasing as they move apart. A set of piezoelectric crystals, which change shape according to the voltage applied to them, is used to scan the tip in a raster across the sample and also to move the tip up and down. (A raster is a pattern in which an area is scanned from side to side in lines from top to bottom.) Since the current that tunnels across the gap between the sample and the tip is a sensitive indicator of how far the tip and the sample are from each other, one can thus map out the sample.

116

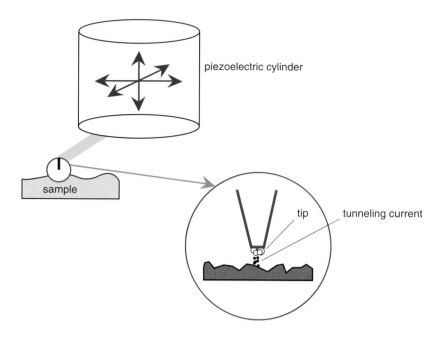

piezoelectric cylinder

sample

tip

tunneling current

In a scanning tunneling microscope (left and below), voltages applied to sectors of a piezoelectric cylinder cause it to bend in the horizontal plane and thereby scan the tip of a wire across the sample. When the wire tip almost touches the sample, electrons flow between structures at the surface of the sample and a single atom exposed at the tip, a phenomenon called "tunneling." The intensity of the tunneling current is proportional to the distance between the tip and the sample. The images that are formed are essentially maps of specific parts of the sample surface that have a given set of characteristics. Scanning tunneling microscopy has permitted the solution of the complex structure of many materials. Below left are Gerd Binnig (left) and Heinrich Rohrer, inventors of the scanning tunneling microscope.

The images obtained are not really topographic maps but maps of the probability of tunneling. In some materials such as gallium arsenide, there is a different probability of tunneling for different atoms at the surface. Viewing a sample in an STM thus does not show an image of every physical bump and cranny but, instead, produces a map of specific parts of the surface that have a given set of characteristics. Other parts of the surface that do not interact with the probe are not detected.

In practice, rather than measuring the tunneling current directly, it is usual to record signals from a feedback circuit that keeps the tip at a constant distance from the surface, thus preventing the tip from actually crashing into the sample surface. This crash-avoidance system

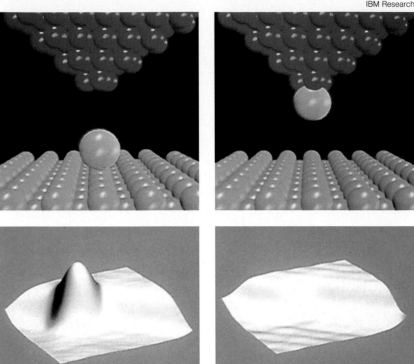

Computer-generated diagrams (right, top row) represent a scanning tunneling microscope tip (red), a single-crystal nickel surface (blue), and a xenon atom (pink). At the top left the xenon atom rests on the nickel surface. An electrical pulse attracts the xenon atom to the microscope tip (top right), which changes the amount of tunneling current that flows between the tip and the surface. Images produced by the scanning tunneling microscope (bottom row) show the presence (left) and the absence (right) of the xenon atom on the nickel surface. Below is a scanning tunneling microscope image of gallium arsenide; the gallium is blue, and the arsenic is red.

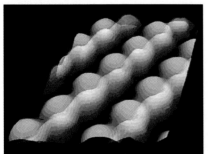

IBM Research

enables the tip to follow the contour of the sample so faithfully that it outlines the bumps made by single tunneling atoms at the surface of the sample. For example, it is common to visualize atoms in carbon or mica just to demonstrate that the apparatus is working properly. In standard microscopy, instead of atoms 0.1–0.2 nanometer in size, it was satisfying to visualize patterns 0.2 micrometer (200 nanometers) in the siliceous skeletons of diatoms (a class of algae) when testing the resolution of the instrument. Scanning tunneling microscopy has permitted the solution of the complex structure of silicon and many other materials. It has even allowed the imaging at atomic resolution of the double strand of DNA.

There is not as yet a complete understanding of the mechanisms by which tunneling takes place. One problem is to figure out why atomic resolution is possible, particularly when the probing tips can be as crude as pieces of stiff wire cut at a bias. The popular explanation for this is that, although overall such a probe is not very sharp, there is an atom at the tip that protrudes farther than all the others, and it is through this atom that the current is carried. In fact, the existence of multiple images suggests that there may well often be many such protruding atoms on different parts of the tip.

There are also problems in understanding the images of biological molecules because by and large biological molecules are insulators. Obviously, for electrons to flow between the sample and the tip, there must be not only a conducting tip but also a sample that conducts electrons. What then is the path of the tunneling current in the case of insulators, such as biological molecules?

118

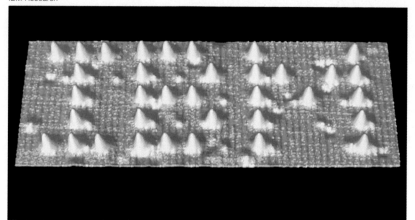

An important feature of scanning tunneling microscopes is that they can be used not just to detect atomic-scale structures but also to move single atoms. This capability has been elegantly exploited, notably by Donald Eigler at the IBM Almaden Research Center in San Jose, Calif., who has displaced atoms so as to form characters. Of greater interest yet are the atomic-scale switches fabricated by moving atoms around and placing them in definite patterns (atomic writing). This feat may open the road to very high-density computer chips.

Many instruments closely related to the STM have now been developed. H. Kumar Wickramasinghe of the IBM T.J. Watson Research Center at Yorktown Heights, N.Y., has listed more than a dozen different types of information that have already been visualized at high resolution by scanned probes. They include the mapping of magnetic domains, of electrostatic forces, and of areas that have different temperatures. A scanning ion conductance microscope is one of many new devices pioneered at the University of California at Santa Barbara. This instrument suggests that it will one day be possible to map the ion channels that traverse cell membranes and are so basic to many of life's processes.

One of the most generally useful scanned probe instruments is the scanned force microscope (also called atomic force microscope). In the most recent version of this device, a laser beam detects the motion of a stylus that scans the surface of the sample. The laser beam is directed at a V-shaped supporting arm (called the cantilever) microfabricated from silicon dioxide. The cantilever is very pliable in the up-and-down direction and relatively stiff in other directions. It bears the stylus at its end. The laser beam reflected from the cantilever is aimed at a split detector so that light falls equally on both halves. When the cantilever holding the stylus moves vertically as it meets obstacles during scanning, light from the laser beam shifts, illuminating one half of the detector more than the other. In this way it is possible to detect motions of a fraction of an angstrom in height with a lateral resolution on the order of one or two angstroms. (The distance between the nuclei of the oxygen atom and that of the hydrogen atoms in water is 0.965 angstrom.) Consequently, atomic topography can be detected in materials.

119

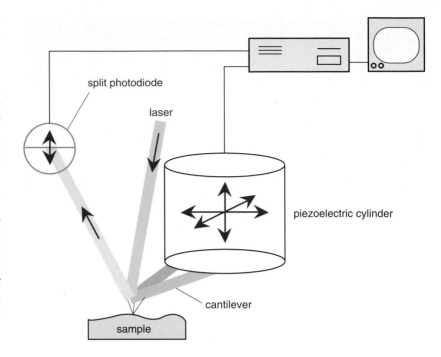

For a scanned force (or atomic force) microscope, voltage applied to the piezoelectric cylinder controls the position of the cantilever and tip, as was the case with the scanning tunneling microscope. Scanning the tip across the sample maps its surface. Up-and-down motions of the tip are detected by deflections of a laser beam that is reflected from the cantilever. The reflected beam is aimed at a photodiode detector that is split so that the light falls equally on both sides. When the cantilever moves vertically as the tip scans the surface, light from the laser beam shifts and illuminates one half of the detector more than the other half. In this way a researcher can detect motions measuring a fraction of an angstrom in height and achieve a lateral resolution of one to two angstroms, thereby detecting the atomic topography of the material.

One of the problems in scanned force microscopy is to make tips that are fine enough to interact with samples so as to produce images with atomic detail. A recent fascinating display of the power of this technique is its use in the dynamic study of the formation and dissolution of calcite. One can see many atomic layers as they become deposited and also study the influence of defects or impurities on the growth of new layers. No doubt this approach will permit a clearer appreciation of the factors affecting the dynamic behavior of materials.

Future prospects

Although the force with which the stylus interacts with the sample is very small, it is likely large enough to distort biological samples. Up to now, even though it is possible to demonstrate atomic resolution on hard samples, there are few reports of resolution greater than molecular. Nevertheless, the scanned force microscope has been used successfully to look at many types of biological molecules. It has resolved details of some ion channels, which were undetected by other imaging techniques. It has also been used successfully in imaging DNA, and there are many who hope that it will be a useful tool in the great quest for sequencing the human and other genomes.

While the high-resolution work is tremendously exciting, the ultimate value of the scanned force microscope may in fact lie at another level entirely since it is essentially equivalent to a scanning electron microscope but can also operate on live cells in an aqueous environment. As a result, it may be possible with this instrument to study living cells at a resolution that is far greater than is possible with the light microscope, opening the way for the dynamic study of changes of macromolecular aggregates at cell surfaces.

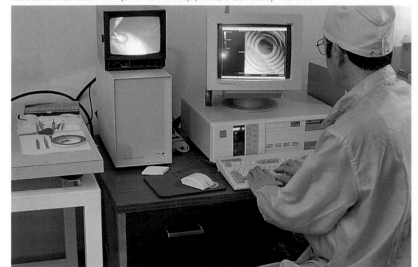

David Lilienfield at the Nanofabrication Facility of Cornell University, Ithaca, New York, operates a scanned (or atomic) force microscope (top) as part of a project integrating microfabrication and biology. The aim of the project is to gain a better understanding of how the plant disease rust might be controlled. By microfabricating specific surface topographies of a bean leaf in silicon, quartz, and other material (bottom), Lilienfield and his colleagues were able to identify those features on the leaf that signal the bean rust fungus to attack the plant.

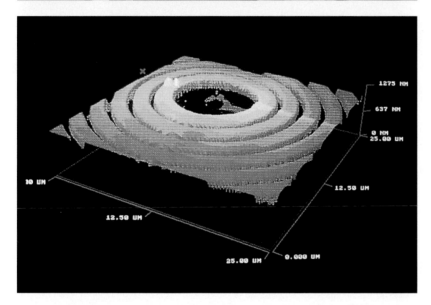

One cannot conclude better than by quoting Wickramasinghe: "The invention of the STM has stimulated the development of several novel scanned probe superresolution microscopies capable of measuring physical properties of objects on an unprecedented scale, *i.e.*, down to nanometer resolution. New scanned probes are emerging at a faster rate than time permits for their key applications to be determined. From the work performed to date it is clear that this new class of microscopies will have major impact on future science and technology."

Abbe, the designer of the modern light microscopes whose work was mentioned at the beginning of this article, keenly felt the limitations to resolution due to the diffraction of light (and other waves). He predicted that future microscopes would, in ways not clear in his day, allow circumvention of this barrier. He would have been happy to see the revolutions in microscopy that are taking place today.

121

DEAD MEN'S
MOLECULES

by William W. Hauswirth

Once the old bones and withered flesh were bypassed for the treasures buried with them. Now the human remains *are* the treasures as the new field of molecular archaeology digs for the DNA still locked inside, which holds secrets about who our ancestors were and how they lived.

We humans are naturally curious. Our inquisitiveness ranges from scientific questions regarding the nature of our physical world to gossipy ones about the private affairs of our neighbors. Among the most universally held desires, independent of nationality or culture, is the wish to know who our ancestors were, where and how they lived, and what they were like. The recent and ongoing revolution in DNA biotechnology has created a new discipline aimed at directly solving these age-old puzzles. This new field, molecular archaeology, is the result of a fusion of the techniques and principles of molecular biology with classical archaeology and anthropology and can be defined as the molecular study of ancient human biological material, principally DNA. Molecular archaeology is therefore a subdiscipline of molecular anthropology, the molecular study of all humans, past or present.

Contributions of genetics and molecular biology

Molecular biology has made possible the genetic study of ancient human populations in at least two fundamental ways. First, new molecular techniques have allowed scientists to conduct rapid genetic analyses of large segments of modern societies. With such data about the specific genetic characteristics of different populations in hand, it has been possible to begin reconstructing ancient relationships between neighboring native populations and even between distant populations located on separate continents. This type of approach, which uses modern population genetics to deduce ancient human behavior, for example, population migrations and intermixing, has led to many interesting but as yet controversial ideas regarding the origin of ancestral humans. Most notable among them is the so-called Eve hypothesis, which is discussed later in the article. In some cases these inferences of ancient behavior can now be tested rather directly by the genetic analysis of human DNA that has been preserved from ancient times. This, then, is one primary focus of molecular archaeology.

A second way in which molecular biology has made molecular archaeology possible is technical in nature. The first molecular studies of preserved DNA in the early 1980s found the material to be chemically damaged and available in exceedingly low concentration. Conventional molecular techniques at that time required high-quality, intact DNA for analysis. Fortunately, the invention of a DNA-amplification technique called the polymerase chain reaction (PCR) solved problems of both quantity and quality of ancient DNA in a single step. In fact, it is quite certain that without the advent of PCR, which became widely available to scientists in the late 1980s, the emergent field of molecular archaeology would have remained nearly dormant—and dependent on the fortuitous, extraordinary preservation of an occasional human DNA sample. Therefore, to appreciate how molecular archaeology was born and now thrives, it is important to understand both how DNA analysis can describe the genetic nature of a population and how PCR technology has allowed scientists the opportunity to study a broad range of preserved human remains.

DNA is a linear, two-stranded, chainlike molecule made up of a specific arrangement of four small units called bases that are carried on a molecular backbone. As the genetic material of a cell, long chains of DNA function as a code for making all cellular proteins. The segment of DNA that codes for a protein is called a gene and is typically 2,000–20,000 bases long. In human DNA there are approximately three billion bases arrayed in a specific and heritable way in each cell. Perhaps half of that DNA comprises the 200,000 genes thought to exist in the human genome; *i.e.,* the total genetic endowment of the human species. The remainder is noncoding DNA, whose function is currently not fully understood, although a portion of it is involved in telling the cell when and under what circumstances to use each of the genes.

All DNA within a cell from an individual human is derived approximately equally from that individual's mother and father. Because some of the bases in a chain of DNA can be different without fundamentally altering its protein-coding function, the specific sequence of bases in one individual human's DNA—determinable by genetic analysis—is a distinctive record of the mother's and father's DNA. Similarly, the analysis of DNA from an ancient individual found, for instance, in a prehistoric burial site provides a record of the kinds of genes present at one time in prehistory. In addition, and more importantly, through comparisons with the DNA of other ancient humans, such an analysis provides a record of genetic interactions between ancient tribes and of their migrations. Once sufficient genetic data are available on a number of geographically separated societies, it is possible to deduce large-scale relationships between populations and, hence, migration patterns and the origin of founding populations.

Fortunately, a useful genetic profile of an individual does not require the determination of the entire three billion-base genome. It is not even necessary to determine the DNA sequence, the precise order of base units, of a single gene in order to gain a valid picture of a person's

WILLIAM W. HAUSWIRTH is Professor in the Department of Medical Microbiology and Ophthalmology, University of Florida College of Medicine, Gainesville.

(Overleaf) Photograph by Eric Pasquien—Sygma

genetic ancestry. Rapid progress in human genetics over the past decade has uncovered many small DNA regions that can vary quite distinctively between unrelated individuals. Hence a targeted analysis of this so-called hypervariable DNA, which is usually found among noncoding DNA, can lead to a definitive picture of genetic descent. The approach is particularly powerful when several hypervariable regions are analyzed simultaneously from one individual. This sort of analysis forms the current basis for so-called DNA-fingerprint identification of suspects at a crime scene. For archaeology the same techniques of genetic identification apply. The only difference is that the time scale is significantly expanded, to thousands or even tens of thousands of years, rather than focused on a single moment in the recent past.

The problem of analyzing ancient DNA is therefore threefold. First, one needs to target the analysis on a selected hypervariable DNA segment of the human genome, one often only a few hundred bases in length. Second, one needs to repair the damage that has accumulated in ancient samples of DNA over the centuries. Third, the analysis needs to be done on the very small amounts of DNA typically found in archaeological remains. None of these requirements could be met until the advent of PCR in the mid-1980s. PCR begins with a sample of DNA and, by means of the enzyme DNA polymerase, copies it over and over to produce millions of exact replicas. As its name implies, PCR is a chain-reaction process in which each cycle of the process doubles the amount of DNA previously present. After 25 to 40 successive cycles carried out automatically by machine, a test tube that originally contained a minute amount of damaged archaeological DNA now contains an analyzable quantity of intact DNA from that portion of the genome targeted by the

The 140-year-old skin of a quagga (below left), a type of zebra that became extinct in the 19th century, was the first tissue of any species to yield preserved genetic material for molecular analysis. In 1984 a team led by Allan Wilson at the University of California at Berkeley cloned and sequenced a small segment of the animal's DNA. The next year Svante Pääbo, then of the University of Uppsala, Sweden, reported recovering the first DNA sequences from a human specimen, the skin of a 4,400-year-old Egyptian mummy (below).

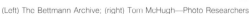

(Opposite page) In the late 1980s the identification and later molecular analysis of DNA from 8,000-year-old human brains preserved in a nonacidic, water-saturated peat bog at Windover, Florida, showed that wet archaeological tissue samples, as well as dry ones, could contain useful genetic material. A human skull (top left) from the Windover site is examined with magnetic resonance imaging to determine whether brain tissue is encased. Skulls are also assessed by X-ray (top right) before the brain mass (in foreground) is removed. The film to the right of the X-ray depicts sequences of mitochondrial DNA that was obtained from Windover brain tissue and sorted by means of a technique called gel electrophoresis. A portion of a film record of a gel electrophoresis analysis (bottom right) identifies corresponding 120-base-long sequences (bright bands in center and right vertical lanes) in PCR-amplified DNA from a sample of Windover brain tissue (center lane) and from a modern human (right lane). The left lane, generated without a sample of DNA from ancient or modern tissue, serves as a control. Not all bodies preserved in peat have produced analyzable DNA. Attempts to isolate DNA from bodies like that of a "bog man" (bottom left) from Iron Age England, whose tissues were preserved in acidic peat, have been unsuccessful.

PCR reaction. Because DNA polymerase uses preexisting DNA to make new DNA and can generally copy only undamaged DNA, PCR in effect repairs ancient DNA by selecting for amplification only those few DNA molecules in a sample that have remained undamaged. In this way the biotechnology of the 1980s has eliminated virtually all practical barriers to the genetic analysis of ancient humans.

Recovering ancient human DNA

Given a field as young as molecular archaeology, some very basic questions regarding the field as a whole initially needed to be answered. First, under what archaeological conditions could human DNA be expected to be preserved? Second, what regions of the human genome would be the most informative for relating ancient humans and societies to each other?

After about 10 years of experience worldwide, there appear to be no hard and fast guidelines as to what type of tissue or preservation site will yield the highest quality ancient DNA. Published reports from the 1970s of chemical analysis of mummy skin and internal organs indicated that DNA and related compounds were present. Nevertheless, the first molecular analysis of preserved DNA from any species did not appear until 1984, when a small DNA segment from the 140-year-old skin of a quagga, a now-extinct type of zebra, was cloned and its DNA sequence determined. The next year Svante Pääbo, currently of the University of Munich, Germany, reported the first DNA sequences from an ancient human specimen, the skin of a 4,400-year-old Egyptian mummy. The resulting opinion that human DNA would be most easily recovered from dried archaeological samples, particularly skin, changed quickly when, a year later, DNA was identified from 8,000-year-old human brain tissue preserved in a water-saturated peat bog at the Windover, Florida, archaeological site, an ancient Indian burial ground. Not all bodies preserved in peat have proved genetically useful, however. Attempts to isolate DNA from human tissues preserved in acidic European peat bogs have been unsuccessful. The main reason for DNA preservation at the Windover site is likely related to the nonacidic nature of its peat and its high mineral content, both of which distinguish it from European bogs.

Realizing the value of genetic studies of prehistoric populations, investigators in the mid-1980s used the best molecular techniques of the time in an attempt to amplify ancient genetic material. They inserted DNA fragments into bacteria, which were then grown in large quantity and the DNA extracted. Damaged DNA, however, proved to be very poor material for such a direct approach, and further progress awaited development of PCR. The first application of PCR to ancient human DNA was reported in 1988: an analysis of 7,000-year-old brain DNA from another Florida peat bog by Pääbo and Allan Wilson at the University of California at Berkeley. This success was followed just a year later by simultaneous reports from England and Japan documenting PCR amplification of human DNA from preserved bone samples. Soon thereafter, workers in France added ancient human teeth to the list of sources. Other potential sources of human DNA from, for instance, dried blood on weapons or

126

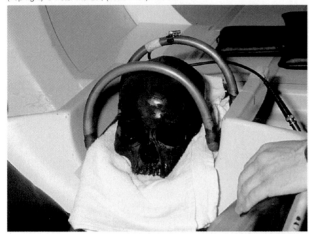

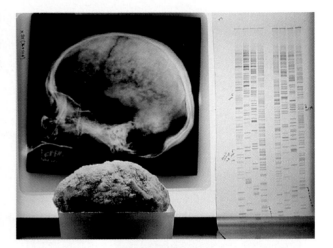

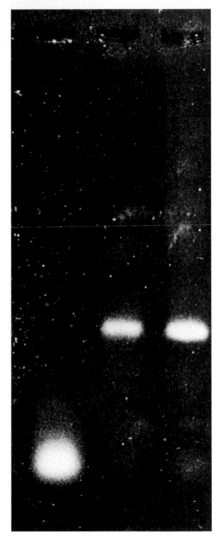

blood ingested by insects have yet to prove viable. Nevertheless, reports of DNA from preserved skeletal material greatly expanded the potential sources for genetic analysis because of the prodigious amount of human bone and teeth available from ancient burial sites throughout the world in all types of environments.

Problems of analysis

Early excitement over the application of PCR to archaeological samples was quickly tempered by the realization that PCR amplification of ancient DNA could mislead an unwary investigator. By its nature PCR could give rise to DNA that was not representative of the human who was being tested. This outcome would be particularly devastating for an investigator attempting to reconstruct ancient genetic histories. One problem relates to the high sensitivity of PCR; *i.e.,* its ability to detect extremely small amounts of DNA. Therefore, even normally acceptable levels of contaminating DNA, if they are in an archaeological sample, might be amplified in preference to the true ancient DNA. In the early 1990s a series of precautionary steps to be taken by laboratory personnel were informally agreed upon. When rigorously followed, they appear to reduce significantly the chance of contamination from past handling of archaeological

127

Researcher takes a tissue sample from the foot of a 2,000-year-old mummy (above) for PCR amplification of the DNA fragments in the tissue. PCR is a chain reaction process in which a specific DNA fragment is repeatedly copied by means of enzymes, each cycle doubling the amount of DNA previously present. After 25 to 40 successive copying cycles, which can be carried out in a matter of hours by automated laboratory equipment (above right), even a minute amount of archaeological DNA from a single human cell exists in sufficient quantity to be analyzed by standard techniques. In PCR analysis of archaeological DNA, care must be taken to avoid contaminating the sample with modern DNA and to recognize and sort out copying errors introduced by the PCR process.

material by modern humans, from introduction of DNA by laboratory personnel themselves, or from other sources of DNA in the laboratory.

Another kind of misleading result from PCR amplification arises not from outside contamination but from the fact that ancient DNA, virtually always badly damaged, is an imperfect starting material for PCR amplification. A PCR-generated DNA fragment may not be an accurate copy of the target sequence because the PCR reaction can occasionally introduce errors related to the damage within the ancient DNA. This was initially demonstrated in theory in tests of DNA samples of modern origin. Later, in 1991, such error-prone PCR products were uncovered in analyses of ancient DNA by collaborating groups from the University of Florida and Stanford University. Importantly, this work also demonstrated that it was possible to distinguish accurate PCR products from PCR artifacts by careful analysis of the frequency and kinds of sequences encountered. Therefore, with careful laboratory technique to avoid contamination from modern DNA sources and careful analysis of PCR products themselves to sort out PCR errors, it appears that a good portion of the world's current collection of preserved human tissue, mostly bone, may be amenable to genetic analysis.

Nuclear and mitochondrial DNA

Having the ability to rescue ancient DNA and amplify it sufficiently for modern genetic analysis led to the next major question: what human DNA sequences would be the most informative to analyze in order to reconstruct ancient genetic history? To this end, it is useful to consider the properties of a DNA sequence that would be optimal for the purpose. First, the sequence should be well characterized in modern human populations so that its distribution and behavior in ancient societies can be validly analyzed. Second, the sequence should differ enough between unrelated individuals to serve as a unique genetic marker of an individual and his or her relatives. These criteria eliminate the vast majority of known human DNA sequences from consideration because most of them are within genes and thus code for the proteins that determine

128

the structure and function of each cell of the body. Since the functions of genes are so essential for each cell, only limited variation among individuals can be tolerated without serious effects. Therefore, most gene sequences are useless for genetic analysis because they are necessarily identical or nearly identical for all individuals in all populations. Fortunately, a good part of the human genome is nongenic DNA, which is where useful hypervariable DNA resides. Such DNA does not encode proteins and is frequently quite different among unrelated individuals. Hypervariable DNA regions therefore genetically distinguish the lineage of a given individual and can readily be used to begin reconstructing the genetic history of ancient societies.

There are two distinct classes of DNA within a normal human cell—nuclear DNA and mitochondrial DNA. Nuclear DNA, which is found in the cell nucleus and which comprises more than 99.99% of the genetic information, is inherited equally from the nuclear DNA of the mother and father. It therefore traces both maternal and paternal lineages simultaneously. Recently, a particularly informative kind of hypervariable nuclear DNA has been identified in the human genome, collectively termed microsatellite sequences. They are short DNA segments containing repeated units of only two, three, or four bases. Microsatellites occur several hundred thousand times throughout the human genome and are useful markers of lineage because a specific microsatellite sequence at a specific location frequently will vary between unrelated individuals in the number of times a repeat unit is reiterated within the microsatellite region. Consequently, they can be used to fingerprint ancient humans genetically and to trace human lineages within an archaeological site.

One disadvantage of nuclear DNA markers is that, because they come from both the maternal and paternal lines, analysis over many generations becomes very complicated if the size of a population being studied is large. For such purposes mitochondrial DNA has a distinct advantage. Mitochondrial DNA exists not in the nucleus but in the mitochondrion, the cellular structure responsible for providing the energy needed to carry out most cellular functions. Although the amount of mitochondrial DNA is very small relative to nuclear DNA, it is genetically unique because mitochondria are transmitted only in the mother's egg cells, not the father's sperm cells. Hence, mitochondrial DNA sequences trace only the maternal line of descent in a population. This difference makes mitochondrial DNA analysis extremely useful for relating individuals within and between populations. Within a small noncoding region of the mitochondrial DNA, a large amount of sequence diversity has been found to exist within the world's population. The range of current variation has been well established, and computer techniques for relating mitochondrial lineages have been developed over the past decade. Therefore, in conjunction with microsatellite nuclear sequences, mitochondrial sequence analysis allows refined genetic analysis of ancient populations.

There are several exceptions to the general rule that DNA sequences within genes are unusable for genetic analysis. Important among them are the human leukocyte antigen (HLA) genes, a family of genes that

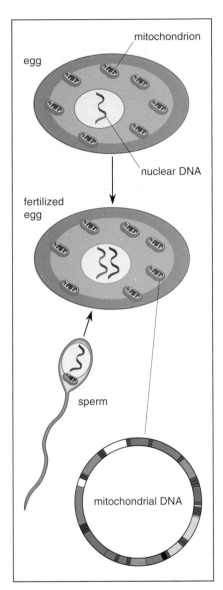

Two kinds of DNA exist within the normal human cell. Nuclear DNA, found in the cell nucleus and comprising the vast majority of an individual's genes, is inherited equally from the mother and father through the uniting of an egg and a sperm cell. Nuclear DNA, therefore, simultaneously traces maternal and paternal lines of descent. Mitochondrial DNA, which is found in specialized cell structures called mitochondria, carries a small number of genes arranged on a ring-shaped molecule. All the mitochondria of an individual derive from the egg cell. Mitochondrial DNA is thus inherited uniquely from the mother and traces only the maternal lineage.

code for proteins vital to the human immune response to infectious disease. The world's population today exhibits a large number of slightly different versions of HLA genes, probably reflecting the great diversity of infectious agents that humans encounter. Any one individual, however, will possess only a small subset of these gene variants. Hence, that gene subset, as determined by DNA analysis, defines an individual's genetic lineage in much the same way that microsatellite and mitochondrial sequences do. The interesting advantage of HLA gene analysis in ancient populations is that the genes are related to resistance and susceptibility to infectious diseases. Their analysis in these populations eventually will allow inferences regarding the types of diseases that were widespread in ancient societies. Thus, a combination of such well-studied human DNA sequences, rescued and amplified by PCR from a variety of ancient archaeological remains, provides the opportunity to begin reconstructing genetic relationships and possibly even deduce the health status of ancient civilizations.

Molecular archaeology today

Although systematic genetic studies of ancient human populations are just beginning, preliminary insights as to the behavior of ancient civilizations are emerging. Genetic analyses at the Windover archaeological site have taken advantage of a frequent aspect of prehistoric sites that is absent for modern human populations: ancient burial sites were often used for extended times. Therefore, human remains may represent a genetic record covering many generations. Radiocarbon dating of human bone at Windover suggests that the first individuals were interred about 8,200 years ago and the last about 6,900 years ago—a 1,300-year time span. With the assumption of a 25-year generation period, therefore, genetic analysis of the kinds of target sequences summarized above may be able to reconstruct the continuous genetic history of about 50 generations of humans at this single burial site.

Already some interesting trends are becoming apparent. For example, mitochondrial DNA analysis has shown that the Windover site is composed of a very limited number of maternal lineages. That is, individuals interred nearly 8,000 years ago have mitochondrial sequences identical to those interred more than 1,000 years later, suggesting that continuous lines of female ancestry existed throughout the period. This could mean that tribal females tended to remain within the tribe to bear children and that few females from genetically distinct neighboring societies entered the tribe. Of course, until it is known whether ancient neighboring populations indeed had distinct mitochondrial DNA sequences, it is risky to speculate on how much the Windover females intermixed with other tribes and how far-ranging they were. Because nuclear HLA genes trace both maternal and paternal lineages, their analysis offers an interesting contrast to that of mitochondrial DNA. The Windover bones contain more types of HLA genes than would be expected from the limited number of mitochondrial types. This result suggests that more exchanges of males than females took place between genetically distinct neighboring

L. Agler, B. Barton, D. Dickel, and R. Brunck

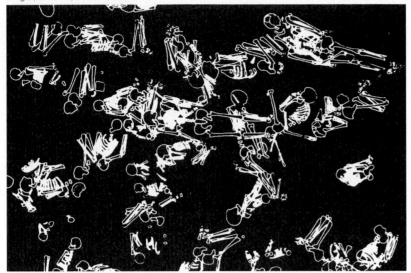

Part of a map of the Windover archaeological site shows the placement of some of the full and partial skeletons that have been uncovered at the ancient Indian burial ground. Radiocarbon dating of the remains suggests a 1,300-year use of the site beginning about 8,200 years ago. With the assumption of a 25-year generation period, molecular analysis of the DNA in the bones thus has the potential to reconstruct the continuous genetic history of as many as 50 generations of individuals.

populations. The emerging picture is that Windover males were more mobile than their female contemporaries—not unexpected in a prehistoric society but the first genetic evidence for such differential behavior.

Another way in which genetic analysis of ancient societies can be used is in a comparison with the genes of modern groups inhabiting the same or nearby locations. In the case of Windover, the modern relatives of these early Florida residents are unknown. Nevertheless, a comparison can be made with mitochondrial sequences known from modern North American Indian groups. Analysis of several North American tribes by Doug Wallace of Emory University, Atlanta, Georgia, and Rik Ward of the University of Utah suggests that a limited number of maternal lineages (possibly only four) initially entered the Americas from Asia. Comparison of these data with Windover mitochondrial DNA reveals a close relationship of the ancient Windover people to only one of these founding lineages. This would imply that the original groups migrating from Asia may have settled different portions of the New World. Certainly, large-scale conclusions of this sort will require much additional substantiation by further analysis of ancient and modern native American Indians, but the potential to understand ancient migrations becomes apparent from this one example.

The concept that HLA genes are related to susceptibility and resistance to infectious diseases gives the comparison of HLA genes between Windover and modern humans heightened interest. The HLA genes found within Windover are very similar to those in modern humans. Ancient human societies were likely to have been exposed to many of the same infectious agents that cause diseases today, and the possession of common HLA genes provides some of the first experimental evidence supporting this view.

The precise disease resistance conferred by specific HLA genes is currently a major focus of immunologic research. When such mechanistic links between HLA genes and disease are more fully understood, scientists will be able to reconstruct the genetic predisposition of Windover and other ancient populations to specific infectious agents. According to popular theory, many serious diseases like smallpox and influenza were unknown in the New World before Western contact by Columbus and his successors. HLA analysis could provide a direct genetic test of the idea. Additionally, HLA analysis of Windover has uncovered at least one novel HLA gene not currently recognized in the modern human population. This may be an extinct gene, or it may yet be present but be undiscovered. In either case, tracking a novel HLA gene through ancient populations to subsets of modern society provides an exciting way to trace human lineages over many millennia.

Studies of other ancient populations are currently in progress at several sites throughout the world. In Japan, Satoshi Horai and co-workers, who have studied ancient and modern Asian mitochondrial DNA sequences, suggest that Japan was populated by a subset of Asian people. Interestingly, their work also hints that American Indians derived from a different subset of the original Asians. As with Windover, the data base for making such broad conclusions is rapidly expanding in both Asia and the United States, and more detailed conclusions are expected to test and expand the initial inferences.

At the University of Oxford, Robert Hedges, Erika Hagelberg, James Clegg, and colleagues are focusing on medieval European burial sites in order to reconstruct European settlement patterns over the past several thousand years. In this regard the discovery in 1991 of the body of a late-Stone Age man, dubbed the Iceman, preserved in an Austro-Italian glacier for about 5,300 years offers the prospect for an interesting genetic comparison with medieval and modern genetic data. This case

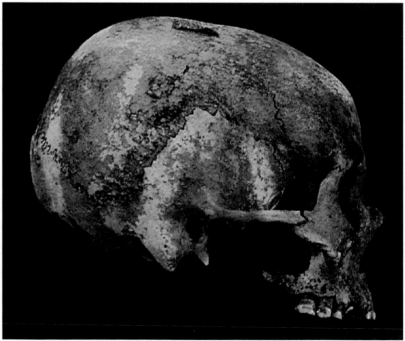

A 5,800-year-old human skull from prehistoric Japan provided mitochondrial DNA for a study that compared ancient and modern DNA sequences. The rectangular hole at the top of the skull marks the volume of bone removed for DNA analysis. The results of the study, carried out by Satoshi Horai and colleagues of the National Institute of Genetics, Mishima, Japan, suggest that at least some people who lived in Japan 6,000 years ago had an origin in common with contemporary Southeast Asians.

Satoshi Horai, National Institute of Genetics, Japan

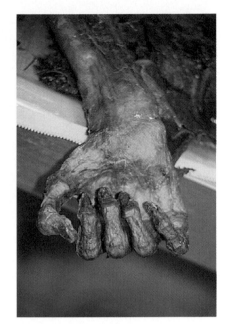

brings up an important cautionary point: genetic conclusions based on a single sample need to be viewed carefully, since human populations are most accurately characterized by the range of genetic types they possess. Populations are best compared by their particular distributions of genetic types and not against the genetic type of any one individual. Thus, heavy reliance on a DNA analysis of the Iceman, were he to be genetically unrepresentative of his contemporaries, could lead molecular archaeologists to the wrong conclusion. On the other hand, analysis of any 5,000-year-old European would add a significant page to scientists' understanding of European settlement and migration.

Molecular archaeology is not limited to the few studies discussed above. Results presented at several recent scientific meetings show that analysis of ancient North American, South American, Middle Eastern, North African, and Western Pacific populations are under way. Such widespread interest portends an explosive growth in our understanding of the ancient world.

Prospects for the future

It is clear that molecular archaeology is in its infancy. Attempts to anticipate what lies ahead are limited by the fact that not all ancient preserved material will have analyzable human DNA and by the current level of understanding of human genetics. Molecular archaeology should significantly influence ideas about human migrations. Today the most detailed information regarding ancient migrations is based on patterns of present-day linguistic groups in defined geographic areas and on analysis of blood-group proteins, both of which serve to broadly classify modern populations. Detailed genetic analysis of both modern and ancient native populations in corresponding geographic locations, based on the kinds of genetic targets noted above, will considerably expand these ideas.

The discovery in 1991 of the body of a late-Stone Age man preserved in rich anatomic detail in an Austro-Italian glacier (above left and above) offers scientists the chance to conduct a unique genetic comparison between a 5,300-year-old European and medieval and modern humans. Nevertheless, genetic conclusions based on a single ancient individual, who may well be genetically unrepresentative of his contemporaries, must be viewed carefully. Populations are best compared by their particular distributions of genetic types and not against the genetic type of any one sample.

133

The mummified remains of people who lived along the northern coast of Chile 3,000–4,000 years ago, part of the Chinchorro Tradition, are providing molecular archaeologists with DNA for genetic lineage studies. Genetic comparisons between different ancient South American societies should help answer basic questions about the southward patterns of human migration into South America during the peopling of the New World.

Neanderthal bone found with a skull from Iraq, which dates to about 50,000 years ago, is the focus of DNA recovery and analysis efforts by several European and U.S. laboratories. If DNA can be analyzed from sufficiently old human samples, the results may help scientists test theories about the genetic and geographic origin of humans more directly than ever before.

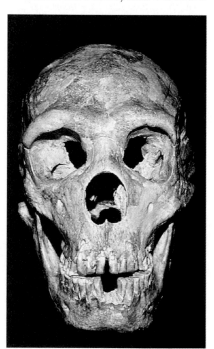

Although it is unlikely that the already established general patterns of human migration between continents will be altered significantly by new information, it is clear that because of its ability to resolve details of ancient genetic relationships and migrations, molecular archaeology will add a richness unavailable from a more conventional analysis of modern societies alone. For instance, although few disagree that Asians initially peopled the New World or about how they came, conflicting theories persist regarding patterns of migration once humans settled the Americas. Movement southward into South America rests on a large body of archaeological evidence. But once humans reached South America, did they settle the eastern and western coasts simultaneously, or did they migrate from one coast to the other across the Andes mountain chain? Genetic comparisons between ancient South American societies, many of which left well-preserved burial sites with copious skeletal remains, should bear significantly on this question and related ones.

One of the most important questions in human evolution, the geographic and genetic origin of the human species, is a topic of intense controversy. Contributing to the turmoil is the idea put forward in the late 1980s by Wilson that all modern humans are descended from one female who lived in Africa about 200,000 years ago—the Eve, or out-of-Africa, hypothesis. Wilson's assertion is based on a study of several hundred modern mitochondrial DNA samples from individuals worldwide. By means of computer analysis it was found that all types of mitochondrial DNA sequences could be related to one another and that the types of mitochondrial DNA from which all others were derived exist only in Africa today. Fossil evidence and a limited amount of nuclear DNA evidence also support the idea that the deepest roots of the human species reside in Africa.

However, recent reanalysis of the computerized approach to constructing relationships between DNA sequences found alternative, equally probable ways of grouping and relating these human mitochondrial DNA sequences. Significantly, many of the alternatives do not lead to the out-

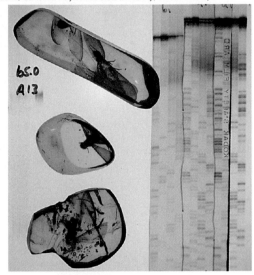

of-Africa conclusion. Given the timing of the proposed initial migrations from Africa to the rest of the Old World, molecular archaeology may play a key role in resolving the issue if DNA can be rescued and analyzed from human samples of sufficient antiquity. Currently, several laboratories in Europe and the United States are attempting such an analysis based on 50,000-year-old Middle Eastern Neanderthal bone.

The idea of determining the genetics of Neanderthal humans raises an important unanswered question in molecular archaeology. How old can an archaeological sample be and still yield useful human DNA? As of early 1993 the oldest human successfully analyzed for DNA sequence lived about 10,000 years ago. Clearly, however, DNA can be preserved for much longer periods of time. Until 1992 the record was DNA from a 17 million-year-old leaf of a species of magnolia preserved in Idaho shale, but in that year new reports documented DNA from termites and bees preserved in amber for about 30 million years or more. Such records indicate that the time limit on human DNA preservation has not yet been reached, and the scientific community eagerly awaits results of Neanderthal bone analysis. Again, it is important to remember that conclusions about human relationships based on genetic studies are most convincing when numerous samples from a population are available. Thus, there may be severe limitations on archaeological remains older than 10,000 years since rarely, if ever, would there be large numbers of samples available for rigorous analyses.

Another archaeological theory that can be directly tested by molecular archaeology is the idea of a post-Columbian genetic bottleneck. On the basis of American Indian population data of the 16th and 17th centuries, it appears that the native population in the Western Hemisphere declined precipitously after European contact. The reasons are thought to be related to a combination of extensive warfare, starvation, and, most importantly, infectious diseases like smallpox, influenza, and measles, which were apparently not endemic to the Americas before Columbus.

Although the most ancient human DNA successfully analyzed to date is about 10,000 years old, molecular archaeologists do not know the maximum age of genetic material that can be recovered and studied. Until 1992 the record for the preservation of nonhuman DNA was 17 million years, held by specimens of magnolia leaf (top left) found in waterlogged Idaho shale. In that year separate research teams reported DNA from amber-preserved termites 30 million years old (top right, shown with DNA sequence analyses) and bees between 25 million and 40 million years old (above). Such discoveries are indications that the age limit for human DNA preservation has not yet been reached.

135

The bottleneck idea asserts that, if sufficiently few native Americans survived this catastrophic period, there should be far fewer versions of a given hypervariable DNA present today than before Columbus because many ancient genes would have become extinct. When more ancient populations have been genetically characterized, an estimate of pre-Columbian versus post-Columbian genetic diversity will directly test the idea and magnitude of the bottleneck.

Progress in understanding the molecular basis of human diseases, particularly inherited diseases, will directly affect the ability of molecular archaeology to determine the health status of ancient societies. As large regions of the human genome are characterized in the next decade by the current international human genome projects, many of the approximately 4,000 human genetic diseases will be related to specific types of DNA. When each such link between DNA and a disease is made, it becomes a fascinating target for analysis within ancient populations. Conversely, the remains of ancient populations may hold clues for understanding the evolution of human disease. For instance, a lack of ancient evidence worldwide for a certain genetic disease at some point in the past may imply a more recent origin. Additionally, the history of recent diseases, such as AIDS, may be traced over much shorter time scales by PCR analysis of human tissue specimens preserved from the late 19th and early 20th centuries. Thus, in its broadest sense, molecular archaeology includes genetic analysis of any preserved human tissue, even if only a few decades old.

Finally, molecular archaeology offers the possibility, heretofore thought impossible, of studying the continuous evolution of human DNA over thousands of years. The existence of ancient burial sites spanning 50 or more human generations would be unique resources for following a rapidly evolving DNA sequence through time. When continuous human

Aztec Indians dying from smallpox contracted from the Spaniards are shown in an illustration from a 16th-century treatise on the New World. According to the genetic bottleneck idea, the post-Colombian decimation of the American Indian population by introduced European diseases, warfare, and starvation should have resulted in a reduction in genetic diversity in the native population, accompanied by the extinction of many ancient genes. When enough ancient Indian remains have been genetically characterized, comparisons of genetic diversity in pre- and post-Columbian populations will directly test the idea and magnitude of the bottleneck.

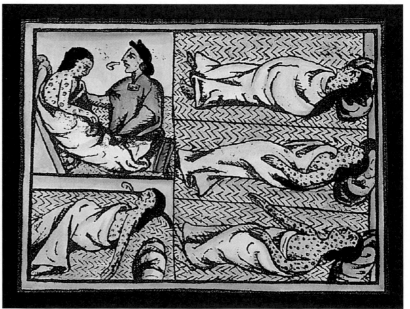

James Sugar—Black Star

As more and more human remains of different ages are unearthed from sites around the world, molecular archaeologists will have better opportunities to study the evolution of DNA over thousands of years. When continuous human lineages spanning many generations can be constructed from individual burial sites and individuals within those lineages accurately dated by radiocarbon techniques, it will be possible to establish absolute rates of evolution for DNA.

lineages are established at such burial sites and individuals within that lineage accurately dated by radiocarbon techniques, absolute rates of DNA evolution will be possible.

The new field of molecular archaeology is just beginning to establish its scientific underpinnings and is a long way from realizing its ultimate potential. Nevertheless, the recent marriage of molecular techniques and classical archaeology promises fascinating new answers to many of our oldest questions about our origin and nature.

FOR ADDITIONAL READING

Luigi Luca Cavalli-Sforza, "Genes, Peoples, and Languages," *Scientific American* (Nov. 1991, pp. 104–110).

Ann Gibbons, "Mitochondrial Eve: Wounded, but Not Dead Yet," *Science* (Aug. 14, 1992, pp. 873–875).

William W. Hauswirth, Cynthia D. Dickel, and David A. Lawlor, "Genetic Analysis of Human Tissue Preserved in a Wet Environment," *Ancient DNA* (Springer-Verlag, 1992).

David A. Lawlor *et al.*, "Ancient HLA genes from 7,500-Year-Old Archaeological Remains," *Nature* (Feb. 28, 1991, pp. 785–788).

Philip E. Ross, "Eloquent Remains," *Scientific American* (May 1992, pp. 114–125).

"Where Did Modern Humans Originate?" *Scientific American* (April 1992, pp. 66–83).

The Chemistry of Ultrasound

by Kenneth S. Suslick

Ultrasound can produce temperatures as high as those on the surface of the Sun and pressures as great as those at the bottom of the ocean. In some cases it can also increase chemical reactivities by nearly a millionfold.

Ultrasound is simply sound pitched above human hearing. It has found many uses in many areas. At home it is used for dog whistles, burglar alarms, and jewelry cleaners. In hospitals physicians employ ultrasound to remove kidney stones without surgery, treat cartilage injuries (such as "tennis elbow"), and image fetal development during pregnancy. In industry it is important for emulsifying cosmetics and foods, welding plastics, cutting metals, and accomplishing large-scale cleaning. None of these applications, however, takes advantage of the effects that ultrasound can have on chemical reactivity.

The chemical applications of ultrasound, "sonochemistry," have become an exciting new field of research during the past decade. The history of sonochemistry, however, begins in the late 1800s. During field tests of the first high-speed torpedo boats in 1894, Sir John I. Thornycroft and Sydney W. Barnaby discovered severe vibrations from and rapid erosion of the ship's propeller. They observed the formation of large bubbles (or cavities) formed on the spinning propeller and postulated that the formation and collapse of these bubbles were the source of their problems. By increasing the propeller size and reducing its rate of rotation, they could minimize this difficulty of "cavitation." As ship speeds increased, however, this became a serious concern, and the Royal Navy commissioned Lord Rayleigh to investigate. He confirmed that the effects were due to the enormous turbulence, heat, and pressure produced when cavitation bubbles imploded on the propeller surface. In the same work he explained that cavitation was also the origin of teakettle noise!

This phenomenon of cavitation occurs in liquids not only during turbulent flow but also under high-intensity ultrasonic irradiation. It is responsible for both propeller erosion and the chemical consequences of ultrasound. Alfred L. Loomis noticed the first chemical effects of ultrasound in 1927, but the field of sonochemistry lay fallow for nearly 60 years. The renaissance of sonochemistry occurred in the 1980s, soon

KENNETH S. SUSLICK is a Professor of Chemistry and Professor at the Beckman Institute at the University of Illinois at Urbana-Champaign.

after the advent of inexpensive and reliable laboratory generators of high-intensity ultrasound.

Scientists now know that the chemical effects of ultrasound are diverse and include substantial improvements in chemical reactions. In some cases, ultrasonic irradiation can increase reactivities by nearly a millionfold. The chemical effects of ultrasound fall into three areas: homogeneous sonochemistry of liquids, heterogeneous sonochemistry of liquid-liquid or liquid-solid systems, and sonocatalysis (which overlaps the first two). Because cavitation can take place only in liquids, chemical reactions do not generally occur during the ultrasonic irradiation of solids or solid-gas systems.

Ultrasonic irradiation differs from traditional energy sources (such as heat, light, or ionizing radiation) in duration, pressure, and energy per molecule (Figure 1). Because of the immense temperatures and pressures and the extraordinary heating and cooling rates generated by cavitation bubble collapse, ultrasound provides an unusual mechanism for generating high-energy chemistry. As in photochemistry, very large amounts of energy are introduced in a short period of time, but it is thermal rather than electronic excitation. High thermal temperatures are reached. Furthermore, sonochemistry has a high-pressure component, which suggests that it might be possible to produce on a microscopic scale the same large-scale conditions produced during explosions or by shock waves (a shock wave is a compressional wave formed whenever the speed of a body or fluid relative to a medium exceeds that at which the medium can transmit sound).

Sound, ultrasound, and cavitation

Sound is nothing more than waves of compression and expansion passing through gases, liquids, or solids. We can sense these waves directly through our ears if they have frequencies from about 20 Hertz to 16 kiloHertz (the Hertz unit is cycles of compression or expansion per second; kiloHertz is thousands of cycles per second). These frequencies are similar to those of low-frequency radio waves, but sound is intrinsically different from radio or other electromagnetic radiation. For example, electromagnetic radiation (radio waves, infrared, visible light, ultraviolet, X-rays, gamma rays) can pass through a vacuum without difficulty; on the other hand, sound cannot because the compression and expansion waves of sound must be contained in some form of matter.

High-intensity sound and ultrasound are generally produced in a similar fashion; electric energy is used to cause the motion of a solid surface, such as a speaker coil or a piezoelectric ceramic. Piezoelectric materials expand and contract when an electric field is applied. For ultrasound a high-frequency alternating electric current is applied to a piezoelectric ceramic attached to the wall of a metal container (as in an ultrasonic cleaning bath of the kind used, for example, by jewelers) or to a rod of metal immersed in the liquid to be irradiated (Figure 2).

Ultrasound has frequencies pitched above human hearing (above roughly 16 kiloHertz). Scientists can make narrow beams of "silent" ultrasound far more intense than the roar of a jet engine but completely unheard by humans' ears. Ultrasound has wavelengths between successive compression waves measuring roughly between 10 and 10^{-3} centimeters. These lengths are not comparable to molecular dimensions. Because of this mismatch, the chemical effects of ultrasound cannot result from a direct interaction of sound with molecular species.

Nonetheless, the ultrasonic irradiation of liquids does produce a plethora of high-energy chemical reactions. This occurs because ultrasound causes other physical phenomena in liquids that create the conditions necessary to drive chemical reactions. The most important of these is cavitation: the formation, growth, and implosive collapse of bubbles in a liquid. The dynamics of cavity growth and collapse are strikingly dependent on the local environment. Cavity collapse in a homogeneous liquid is very different from cavitation near a liquid-solid interface, which will be considered later.

As ultrasound passes through a liquid, the expansion cycles exert negative pressure on the liquid, pulling the molecules away from one another. If the ultrasound is sufficiently intense, the expansion cycle can create cavities in the liquid. This will occur when the negative pressure exceeds the tensile strength of the liquid, which varies according to the type

Figure 1. Chemistry: the interaction of energy and matter. The three axes represent duration of the interaction, pressure, and energy per molecule. The labeled islands represent the nature of the interaction of energy and matter in various kinds of chemistry.

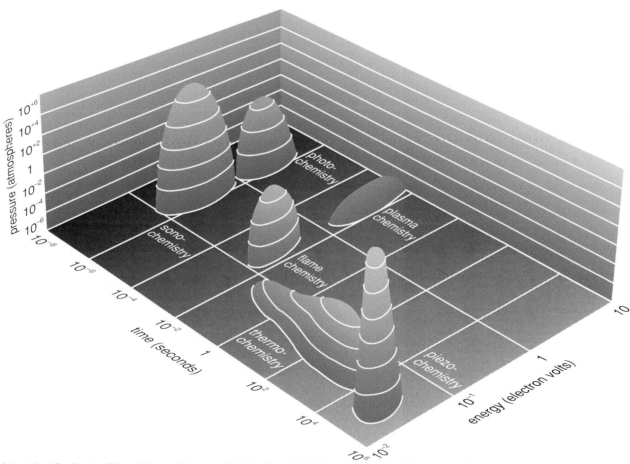

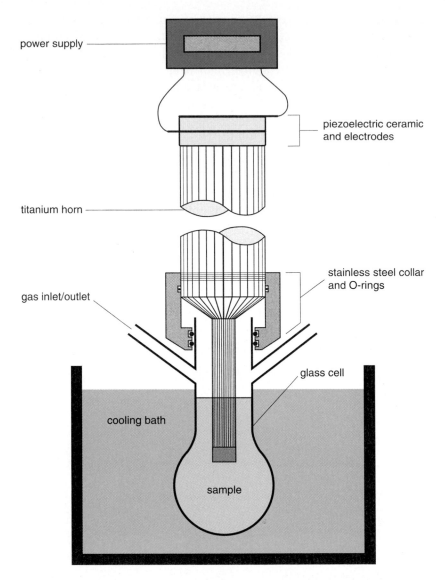

*Figure 2. Diagram shows a typical
sonochemical apparatus. Ultrasound
can easily be introduced into a chemical
reaction in which there is good control of
temperature and ambient atmosphere. The
usual piezoelectric ceramic is PZT, a lead
zirconate titanate material.*

Adapted from information supplied by Kenneth S.
Suslick and Edward B. Flint

power supply

piezoelectric ceramic
and electrodes

titanium horn

stainless steel collar
and O-rings

gas inlet/outlet

glass cell

cooling bath

sample

and purity of the liquid. (Tensile strength is the maximum stress that a material can withstand from a stretching load without tearing.) Normally, cavitation is a nucleated process; that is, it occurs at preexisting weak points in the liquid, such as gas-filled crevices in suspended particulate matter or transient microbubbles from previous cavitation events. Most liquids are sufficiently contaminated by small particles that cavitation can be readily initiated at moderate negative pressures.

Once formed, small gas bubbles irradiated with ultrasound will absorb energy from the sound waves and grow. Cavity growth depends on the intensity of the sound. At high intensities a small cavity may grow rapidly through inertial effects. If cavity expansion is sufficiently rapid during the expansion half of a single acoustic cycle, it will not have time to recompress during the compression half of the cycle.

At lower acoustic intensities cavity growth can also occur by a slower process called rectified diffusion (Figure 3). Under these conditions a cavity will oscillate in size over many expansion and compression cycles. During such oscillations the amount of gas or vapor that diffuses in or out of the cavity depends on the cavity's surface area, which is slightly larger during expansion than during compression. Cavity growth during each expansion is, therefore, slightly larger than shrinkage during the compression. Thus, over many acoustic cycles the cavity will grow. The growing cavity can eventually reach a critical size where it can efficiently absorb energy from the ultrasonic irradiation. Called the resonant size, this critical size depends on the liquid and the frequency of sound; at 20 kiloHertz, for example, it is roughly 170 micrometers. At this point the cavity can grow rapidly during a single cycle of sound.

Once the cavity has overgrown, either at high or low sonic intensities, it can no longer absorb energy as efficiently. Without the energy input the cavity can no longer sustain itself. The surrounding liquid rushes in, and the cavity collapses. It is this implosion of the cavity that creates an unusual environment for chemical reactions.

The sonochemical hot spot

Compression of a gas generates heat. On a macroscopic scale, one can feel this when pumping a bicycle tire; the mechanical energy of pumping is converted into heat as the tire is pressurized. The compression of cavities when they implode in irradiated liquids is so rapid that little heat can escape from the cavity during collapse. The surrounding liquid, however, is still cold and will quickly quench the heated cavity. Thus, one generates a short-lived, localized hot spot in an otherwise cold liquid. Such a hot spot is the source of homogeneous sonochemistry; it has a temperature of roughly 5,000° C (9,000° F), a pressure of about 1,000 atmospheres, a lifetime considerably less than a microsecond, and heating and cooling rates above 10 billion° C per second. For a rough comparison, these are, respectively, the temperature of the surface of the Sun, the pressure at the bottom of the ocean, the lifetime of a lightning strike, and a million times faster cooling than a red-hot iron rod plunged into

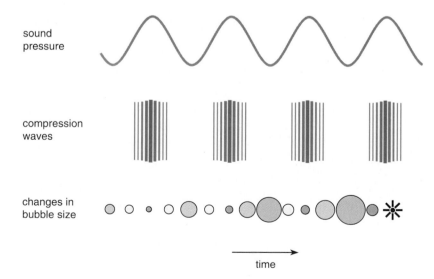

Figure 3. Liquids irradiated with ultrasound can produce bubbles. These bubbles oscillate, growing a little more during the expansion phase of the sound wave than they shrink during the compression phase. Under the proper conditions, the bubbles can undergo a violent collapse, which generates very high pressures and temperatures. This process is called cavitation.

Adapted from information supplied by Kenneth S. Suslick

water. Thus, cavitation serves as a means of concentrating the diffuse energy of sound into a chemically useful form. Alternative mechanisms involving electrical microdischarge have been proposed (most recently by M.A. Margulis of the Russian Institute for Organic Synthesis), but they do not appear fully consistent with observed data.

Determination of the temperatures reached in a cavitating bubble has remained a difficult experimental problem. The transient nature of the cavitation event precludes direct measurement of the conditions generated during bubble collapse. Chemical reactions themselves, however, can be used to probe reaction conditions. The effective temperature of a system can be determined with the use of competing unimolecular reactions whose rate dependencies on temperature have already been measured. This technique of "comparative-rate chemical thermometry" was used by K.S. Suslick, D.A. Hammerton, and R.E. Cline, Jr., at the University of Illinois to determine the effective temperature reached during cavity collapse. For a series of organometallic reactions, the relative sonochemical rates were measured. In combination with the known temperature behavior of these reactions, the conditions present during cavity collapse could then be determined. The effective temperature of these hot spots was roughly 5,200 K. Of course, the comparative rate data represent only a composite temperature; during the collapse the temperature has a highly dynamic profile, as well as a spatial gradient in the surrounding liquid.

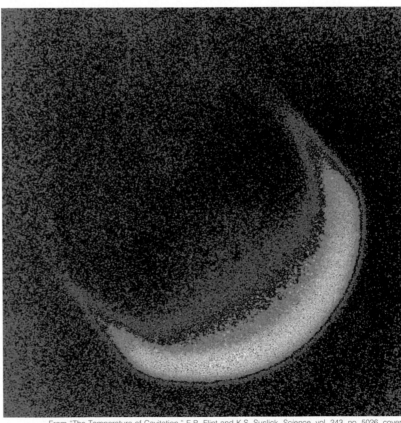

Figure 4. High-intensity ultrasound creates localized hot spots in liquids through the process of cavitation. Local heating produces excited states of molecules that emit light, just as they do in a flame. The image shown is such sonoluminescence from a vibrating titanium rod that is one centimeter (about 0.4 inch) in diameter. False color is used to enhance contrast.

From "The Temperature of Cavitation," E.B. Flint and K.S. Suslick, *Science*, vol. 243, no. 5026, cover, Sept. 20, 1991, © 1991 AAAS

Figure 5. A bubble in a liquid irradiated with ultrasound implodes near a solid surface. The presence of the solid causes the implosion to be asymmetrical, forming a high-speed jet of liquid that impacts the surface. The cavity is spherical at first, but as it collapses the jet develops opposite the solid surface and moves toward it.

When a liquid is subjected to ultrasound, not only does chemistry occur but light is also produced (Figure 4). Such "sonoluminescence" provides an alternate measure of the temperature of the high-energy species produced during cavitation. High-resolution sonoluminescence spectra were recently reported and analyzed by E.B. Flint and Suslick. From a comparison of synthetic to observed spectra, the effective cavitation temperature of the emitting species is about 5,100 K. The agreement between this spectroscopic determination of the cavitation temperature and that made by comparative rate thermometry of sonochemical reactions is surprisingly close.

Cavitation in liquid-solid systems

When cavitation occurs in a liquid near a solid surface, the dynamics of cavity collapse change dramatically. In pure liquids the cavity remains spherical during collapse because its surroundings are uniform. Close to a solid boundary, however, cavity collapse is very asymmetrical and generates high-speed jets of liquid (Figure 5). The potential energy of the expanded bubble is converted into kinetic energy of a liquid jet that moves through the bubble's interior and penetrates the opposite bubble wall. Werner Lauterborn at the Technische Hochschule in Darmstadt, Germany, observed liquid jets driving into the surface with velocities of roughly 400 kilometers per hour (Figure 6). These jets hit the surface with tremendous force. This process can cause severe damage at the point of impact and can produce newly exposed, highly reactive surfaces; it has great importance for understanding the corrosion and erosion of metals observed in propellers, turbines, and pumps, where cavitation is a continual technological problem.

Distortions of bubble collapse depend on a surface several times larger than the resonant size of the bubble. The presence of fine powders, therefore, does not induce jet formation. In the case of liquid-powder

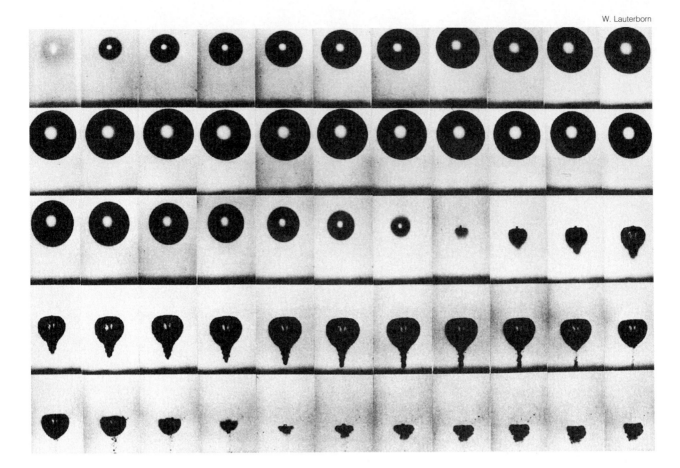

slurries, the shock waves created by homogeneous cavitation can create high-velocity interparticle collisions. The turbulent flow and shock waves produced by intense ultrasound can drive metal particles together at sufficiently high speeds to cause effective melting at the point of collision (Figure 7). Such interparticle collisions are capable of inducing striking changes in surface texture, composition, and reactivity, as discussed below.

S.J. Doktycz and Suslick used metal powders to estimate the effective maximum temperatures and speeds reached during interparticle collisions (Figure 8). When chromium, molybdenum, and tungsten powders of a few micrometers in size are irradiated in decane at 20 kiloHertz and 50 watts per square centimeter, one observes agglomeration and welding of particles for the first two metals but not for the third. On the basis of the melting points of these metals, the effective transient temperature reached at the point of impact during interparticle collisions is estimated at roughly 3,000° C. On the basis of the volume of the melted region of impact, the amount of energy generated during collision was determined. From this, the velocity of impact was estimated to be roughly 1,800 kilometers per hour, which is half the speed of sound in liquids. It should be noted that the conditions reached during interparticle collisions are not directly related to the temperatures reached during cavitational collapse of bubbles.

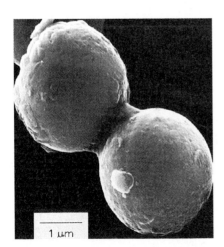

1 μm

146

Before Ultrasound   **After Ultrasound**

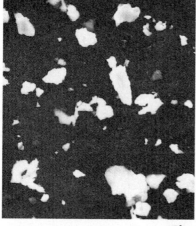
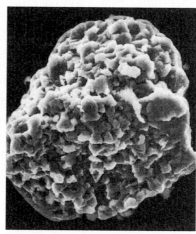

Chromium

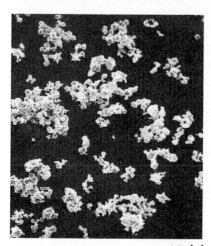

Molybdenum

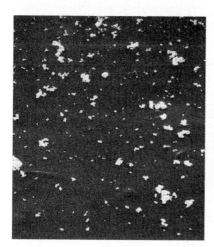
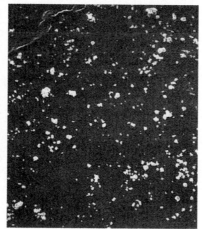

Tungsten

Figure 6. (Opposite page, top) High-speed microcinemagraphic sequence of laser-induced cavitation near a solid surface shows the formation of a microjet impact with a velocity of approximately 400 kilometers (250 miles) per hour.

Figure 7. (Opposite page, bottom) Scanning electron micrograph reveals zinc powder after ultrasonic irradiation. The neck formation from localized melting or plastic deformation was caused by high-velocity collisions of the zinc particles.

Figure 8. (left) Scanning electron micrographs reveal slurries of metal powders before and after ultrasonic irradiation. Chromium has a melting point of 1,857° C (3,374.6° F), and its particles both agglomerate and are deformed; molybdenum melts at 2,617° C (4,742.6° F), and its particles are slightly agglomerated but not smoothed or deformed; tungsten melts at 3,410° C (6,170° F) and is unaffected.

(Opposite page, bottom, and this page) Stephen J. Doktycz and Kenneth S. Suslick in the Center for Microanalysis of Materials, University of Illinois at Urbana–Champaign

Sonochemistry in homogeneous liquids

High-intensity ultrasonic probes (10 to 500 watts per square centimeter) are the most reliable and effective sources for laboratory-scale sonochemistry. A typical laboratory apparatus permits easy control over ambient temperature and atmosphere (Figure 2). Lower acoustic intensities can often be used in liquid-solid heterogeneous systems because of the reduced liquid tensile strength at the liquid-solid interface. For such reactions a common ultrasonic cleaning bath will often be adequate. The low intensity available in these devices (about one watt per square centimeter) can, however, prove to be a limitation. On the other hand, ultrasonic cleaning baths are easily accessible, comparatively inexpensive, and usable on moderately large scales. Finally, for large-scale irradiations, flow reactors with high ultrasonic intensities are commercially available in modular units as powerful as 20 kilowatts.

The chemical effect of ultrasound on aqueous solutions has been studied for many years. The primary products are molecular hydrogen (H_2) and hydrogen peroxide (H_2O_2). Other high-energy intermediates may include HO_2 (superoxide), $H\cdot$ (atomic hydrogen), $OH\cdot$ (hydroxyl), and $e^-_{(aq)}$ (solvated electrons). Peter Riesz and collaborators at the U.S. National Institutes of Health demonstrated definitively the generation of $H\cdot$ and $OH\cdot$ during ultrasonic irradiation. The extensive recent work in Arne Henglein's laboratory at the Hahn-Meitner Institute involving aqueous sonochemistry of dissolved gases established analogies to combustion processes. As one would expect, the sonolysis of water, which produces both strong reductants and oxidants, is capable of causing secondary oxidation and reduction reactions, as often observed by Margulis and co-workers.

In contrast, the ultrasonic irradiation of organic liquids has been little studied. Suslick and co-workers established that, as long as the total vapor pressure is low enough to allow effective bubble collapse, almost all organic liquids will generate free radicals (uncharged, reactive intermediates possessing an unpaired electron) when they undergo ultrasonic irradiation. The sonolysis of simple hydrocarbons creates the same kinds of products associated with very-high-temperature pyrolysis. Most of these products—H_2, CH_4 (methane), and the smaller 1-alkenes)—derive from a well-understood radical chain mechanism. Relatively large amounts of acetylene (C_2H_2) are also produced, which is explained by the stability of this gas at very high temperatures.

The sonochemistry of solutes dissolved in organic liquids also remains largely unexplored, though that of metal carbonyl compounds is an exception. In 1981 P.F. Schubert, J.W. Goodale, and Suslick reported the first sonochemistry of discrete organometallic complexes and demonstrated the effects of ultrasound on metal carbonyls. Detailed studies of these systems led to important understandings of the nature of sonochemistry. Unusual reactivity patterns have been observed during ultrasonic irradiation, including novel metal cluster formation and the initiation of homogeneous catalysis at low ambient temperature, with rate enhancements greater than 100,000-fold.

148

Polymers and biomaterials: bond making and breaking

The effects of ultrasound on polymers (giant molecules formed by the coupling of small molecules—monomers) have been thoroughly studied during the past 30 years. The controlled cleavage of polymers in solutions irradiated with ultrasound has been examined in detail. Polymer degradation produces chains of smaller lengths with relatively uniform molecular weight distributions, with cleavage occurring primarily in the center of the polymer chain. Several mechanisms have been proposed for this sonochemical cleavage, which is usually described as a mechanical breakage of the chains induced by shock waves or by solvent flow created by cavitation during the ultrasonic irradiation of liquids.

This polymer fragmentation was used by G.J. Price at the University of Bath, England, to synthesize block copolymers of various sorts. Block copolymers are long-chain polymers with two different, but linked, parts. As an analogy, one can imagine a train made up in front by passenger cars and in back by freight cars. In addition, Peeter Kruus at Carleton University, Ottawa, reported the use of ultrasound to initiate polymerization in solutions of various monomers.

Applications of ultrasound to the synthesis of biomaterials are under rapid development. While the chemical effects of ultrasound on aqueous solutions have been studied for many years, the development of aqueous sonochemistry for the synthesis of biomaterials is very recent. The area of protein microencapsulation has proved especially interesting. Microencapsulation, the enclosing of materials in capsules a few micrometers in size, has diverse important applications: these include uses with dyes, flavors, and fragrances; as drug-delivery systems; and as medical diagnostic agents.

One recent example is the use of high-intensity ultrasound to make aqueous suspensions of long-lived proteinaceous microspheres filled with air or with water-insoluble liquids for medical applications (Figure 9). By itself, emulsification is insufficient to produce these long-lived microspheres; chemical reactions requiring oxygen are critical in forming them. Specifically, the sonolysis of water produces hydrogen atoms that react with oxygen to produce superoxide. Suslick and M.W. Grinstaff demonstrated that the proteinaceous microspheres are held together by disulfide bonds between protein cysteine residues and that superoxide is the cross-linking agent.

Sonoluminescence: microscopic thunder and lightning

A few years after the discovery of sonochemical reactions, H. Frenzel and H. Schultes in 1934 first observed sonoluminescence from water. As with sonochemistry, sonoluminescence derives from acoustic cavitation. Although sonoluminescence from aqueous solutions has been studied in some detail, only recently has significant work been reported on sonoluminescence from liquids containing no water. In both cases the emission of light results from the high-temperature formation of reactive chemical species in electronic excited states. The emitted light from these excited states provides a spectroscopic probe of the cavitation event.

149

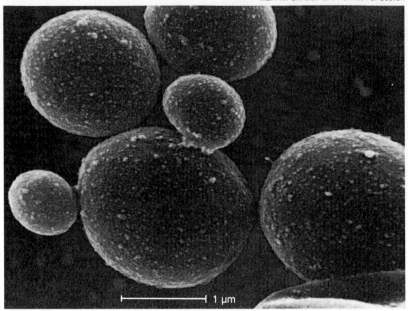

Figure 9. Proteinaceous microspheres filled with the oily hydrocarbon dodecane were formed by the ultrasonic irradiation of albumin solutions. Such microspheres may prove useful for drug delivery and medical diagnostic imaging.

High-resolution sonoluminescence spectra from hydrocarbons and silicone oil were recently analyzed by Flint and Suslick. The observed emission comes from excited-state diatomic carbon, which are the same transitions responsible for the blue color of a hydrocarbon flame (from a kitchen stove, for example). The details of this emission depend on the temperature of the excited states of C_2 and can be accurately modeled with synthetic spectra as a function of presumed temperature. From a comparison of synthetic to observed spectra, the average effective temperature of the excited state of C_2 is about 5,100 K, as mentioned above.

Recently it was discovered that sonoluminescence can be observed, quite remarkably, in a single, oscillating gas bubble. In 1990 D.F. Gaitan and L.A. Crum at the University of Mississippi discovered conditions under which a single, stable gas bubble could produce sonoluminescent emission on each acoustic cycle and could continue this process essentially indefinitely. Seth J. Putterman at the University of California at Los Angeles examined these bubbles with a time resolution in picoseconds. Gaitan, Crum, and Putterman were able to use sophisticated light-scattering techniques to measure the radius-time curve of the luminescing bubble and to correlate the optical emissions with a particular phase of the sound field. As expected, the emissions occurred during cavity collapse. Quite surprisingly, the duration of the sonoluminescence emissions was less than a hundred picoseconds, roughly one-millionth the duration of the acoustic cycle used. This very short emission appears to originate from the formation of shock waves within the collapsing bubble during the first stages of compression.

Heterogeneous sonochemistry: reactions of solids and liquids

The use of high-intensity ultrasound to enhance the reactivity of metals has become an important synthetic technique for many heterogeneous

150

organic and organometallic reactions, especially those involving reactive metals, such as magnesium, lithium, and zinc. This development originated in the early work of Pierre Renaud in France in the 1950s and continued with the more recent breakthroughs of J.-L. Luche at the University of Grenoble, France. This application of sonochemistry grew rapidly during the past decade in a large number of laboratories throughout the world. The effects are quite general and apply to reactive inorganic salts as well. Reactivity rate enhancements of more than 10-fold are common; yields are often substantially improved; and by-products are avoided. A few simple examples of the sonochemistry of reactive reagents are shown in the reactions below (where))) indicates ultrasonic irradiation), taken from the work of Takashi Ando, Philip Boudjouk, Luche, Timothy J. Mason, and Suslick, among others.

$$C_6H_5Br + Li \xrightarrow{\text{)))}} C_6H_5Li + LiBr$$

$$RBr + Li + R'_2NCHO \xrightarrow[\text{2. H}_2\text{O}]{\text{1.)))}} RCHO + R'_2NH$$

$$2 \text{ o-C}_6H_4(NO_2)I + Cu \xrightarrow{\text{)))}} \text{o-}(O_2N)H_4C_6 - C_6H_4(NO_2) + 2 \text{ CuI}$$

$$RR'HC - OH + KMnO_{4 \, (s)} \xrightarrow{\text{)))}} RR'C{=}O$$

$$C_6H_5CH_2Br + KCN \xrightarrow[\text{Al}_2\text{O}_3]{\text{)))}} C_6H_5CH_2CN$$

The mechanism of the rate enhancements in reactions of metals has been unveiled by monitoring the effect of ultrasonic irradiation on the kinetics of the chemical reactivity of the solids, examining the effects of irradiation on surface structure and size distributions of powders and solids, and determining depth profiles of the surface elemental composition. The power of this three-pronged approach has been demonstrated in studies of the sonochemistry of transition metal powders. Doktycz and Suslick found that ultrasonic irradiation of liquids containing nickel, zinc, and copper powders leads to dramatic changes in structure. The high-velocity interparticle collisions produced in slurries cause smoothing of individual particles (Figure 10) and agglomeration of particles into extended aggregates (Figure 8). Surface composition was probed by Auger electron spectroscopy and mass spectrometry to generate depth profiles of the elements in these powders; they revealed that ultrasonic irradiation effectively removed the inactive surface oxide coating. The removal of such coatings dramatically improved reaction rates.

Considerably less work has been done on the activation of less reactive metals. This goal continues to attract major efforts in both synthetic organometallic chemistry and heterogeneous catalysis. Ultrasound can be used at room temperature and pressure to promote heterogeneous reactions that normally occur only under extreme conditions of hundreds of atmospheres of pressure and hundreds of degrees. For example, R.E. Johnson and Suslick found good results with the use of ultrasound to drive some of the most difficult reactions known for transition metals:

D.J. Casadonte and K.S. Suslick
in the Center for Microanalysis of Materials, University of Illinois at Urbana–Champaign

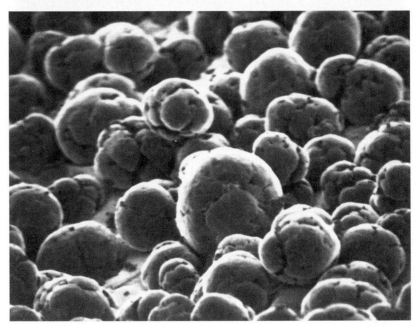

Figure 10. Electron micrograph reveals the effect of ultrasonic irradiation on the surface texture of nickel powder. High-velocity collisions caused by the ultrasonic irradiation of slurries are responsible for these effects. Before the irradiation (top) the particles were rough and measured about 160 micrometers in diameter; after one hour of irradiation (bottom) they had become smooth and were about 80 micrometers in diameter.

the attack of carbon monoxide on the very unreactive early transition metals such as vanadium, tantalum, molybdenum, and tungsten.

Another application of ultrasound in materials chemistry involves the process of intercalation, which is the adsorption of organic or inorganic compounds as guest molecules between the atomic sheets of layered solid hosts, such as graphite or molybdenum sulfide. Intercalation permits the systematic change of optical, electronic, and catalytic properties. Such materials have many technological applications (for example, lithium batteries, hydrodesulfurization catalysts, and solid lubricants). The kinetics of intercalation, however, are generally extremely slow, and syntheses usually require high temperatures and very long reaction times. M.L.H. Green at the University of Oxford, Suslick, and their students discovered that high-intensity ultrasound dramatically increases the rates of intercalation of a wide range of compounds (including amines, metallocenes, and metal-sulfur clusters) into various layered inorganic solids (such as ZrS_2, V_2O_5, TaS_2, MoS_2, and MoO_3). Scanning electron microscopy of the layered solids in conjunction with studies of chemical kinetics demonstrated that the origin of the observed rate enhancements comes from particle fragmentation (which dramatically increases surface areas) and to a lesser extent from surface damage. Because high-intensity ultrasound can rapidly form uniform dispersions of micrometer-sized powders of brittle materials, it is useful for a wide range of liquid-solid reactions.

Another application of heterogeneous sonochemistry involves the preparation of amorphous metals. If one can cool a molten metal alloy quickly enough, it can be frozen into a solid before it has a chance to crystallize. Such amorphous metallic alloys lack long-range crystalline order and have unique electronic, magnetic, and corrosion-resistant properties. The production of amorphous metals, however, is difficult because extremely rapid cooling of molten metals is necessary to prevent crystallization. Cooling rates of approximately 10^6 K per second are required; for comparison, plunging red-hot steel into water produces cooling at only about 2,500 K per second. Very recently the use of ultrasound to synthesize amorphous metal powders by using the sonochemical decomposition of volatile organometallics was reported by Suslick, S.-B. Choe, A.A. Cichowlas, and Grinstaff. This exciting discovery opens new applications of ultrasound for the low-temperature synthesis of unusual phases. For example, the sonolysis of iron pentacarbonyl produces nearly pure amorphous iron, which was characterized by a variety of techniques to prove its lack of long-range order. Scanning electron micrographs show conchoidal fractures (those with smoothly curved surfaces, which are typical of an amorphous material) and at higher magnification reveal a coral-like porosity resulting from the agglomeration of small clusters of iron (Figures 11 and 12).

The sonochemically synthesized amorphous powders may have important technological applications. For example, the amorphous iron powder is an active catalyst for several important reactions, including the synthesis of liquid fuels from CO and H_2 (which can be produced from coal). In addition, magnetic measurements reveal amorphous iron to be a very soft ferromagnet; that is, a material that very quickly forgets its magnetization once an imposed magnetic field has been turned off. While such materials would be very bad for making permanent magnets, they are very good for making magnetic shielding, electrical transformer cores, or magnetic media recording heads.

Sonocatalysis

Catalytic reactions are of great importance in both laboratory and industrial applications. Catalysts increase the rates of chemical reactions without being consumed themselves; they are generally divided into two

Photos, Mark W. Grinstaff and Kenneth S. Suslick
in the Center for Microanalysis of Materials, University of Illinois at Urbana–Champaign

 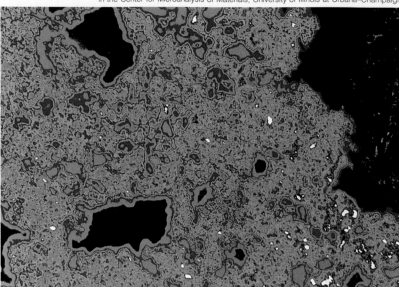

Figure 11. Amorphous iron powder is formed from the ultrasonic irradiation of iron carbonyl (above). As shown in the electron micrograph, the heating and cooling produced by cavitation are so rapid that the iron atoms cluster and solidify before they can form a well-ordered crystal.

Figure 12 (above right) is a transmission electron micrograph of such powder, in false color to enhance contrast. Because of their excellent magnetic properties, amorphous metals have important technological applications; these can include electrical transformer cores and magnetic tape recorder heads.

types. If the catalyst is a molecular or ionic species dissolved in a liquid, then the system is "homogeneous"; if the catalyst is a solid, with the reactants in either a percolating liquid or gas, then it is "heterogeneous." In both cases it is often a difficult problem either to activate the catalyst or to keep it active.

Ultrasound has potentially significant applications in both homogeneous and heterogeneous catalytic systems. Heterogeneous systems are generally more important industrially than are homogeneous systems. For example, virtually all of the petroleum industry is based on a series of heterogeneous catalytic transformations. Heterogeneous catalysts often require rare and expensive metals. The catalytic converters used on automobiles to lessen pollution, for example, use platinum or rhodium, which are enormously expensive; rhodium costs about $1,500 per ounce!

Using ultrasound offers some hope of activating less reactive, but also less costly, metals. Some early investigations of the effects of ultrasound on heterogeneous catalysis can be found in the Soviet literature. In this early work, increases in reaction rates were usually observed upon ultrasonic irradiation, but they were rarely more than 10-fold. In the case of modest rate increases, it appears likely that the cause is increased effective surface area; this is especially important in the case of catalysts supported on brittle solids.

More impressive accelerations, however, were recently reported, including hydrogenations (catalytic reactions of hydrogen with unsaturated organic compounds) by nickel, palladium, or platinum. For example, D.J. Casadonte and Suslick discovered that hydrogenation of alkenes by nickel powder is enormously enhanced (about 100,000-fold) by ultrasonic irradiation. A very interesting effect on the surface structure was observed (Figure 10). Ultrasonic irradiation smooths, at a macroscopic scale, the initially crystalline surface and causes agglomeration of small particles. Both effects are probably due to interparticle collisions caused

154

by cavitation-induced shock waves. Auger electron spectroscopy reveals that there is a considerable decrease in the thickness of the oxide coat after ultrasonic irradiation. The removal of this layer is probably responsible for the great increase observed in catalytic activity.

A sound future

Acoustic cavitation results in an enormous concentration of energy. If the energy density in an acoustic field that produces cavitation is compared with that in the collapsed cavitation bubble, there is an amplification factor of almost one trillion. The enormous local temperatures and pressures of cavitation result in sonochemistry and sonoluminescence. Cavitation produces an unusual method for fundamental studies of chemistry and physics under extreme conditions, and sonochemistry provides a unique interaction of energy and matter.

In addition, ultrasound is well suited to industrial applications. Since the reaction liquid itself carries the sound, there is no barrier to its use with large volumes. In fact, ultrasound is already heavily used industrially for the physical processing of liquids, such as emulsification, solvent degassing, and solid dispersion. It is also extremely important in solids processing, including cutting, welding, cleaning, and precipitation.

The extension of ultrasound to the chemical processing of liquids is under way. The future uses of ultrasound to drive chemical reactions will be diverse. It is becoming a common tool in nearly any case where a liquid and a solid must react. In the synthesis of pharmaceuticals, for example, ultrasound may permit improved yields and facilitate reactions run on a larger scale. In the development and use of catalysts, ultrasound also has potential applications. Its ability to create highly reactive surfaces and thereby increase their catalytic activity has only just now been established. Ultrasound can produce materials with unusual properties. The extraordinary temperatures and pressures reached during cavitational collapse, combined with the exceptionally high rates of cooling, may allow researchers to synthesize novel solid phases difficult to prepare in other ways. One may be optimistic that the unusual reactivities caused by ultrasound will find important industrial applications in the years to come.

FOR ADDITIONAL READING

B.P. Barber and S.J. Putterman, "Observation of Synchronous Picosecond Sonoluminescence," *Nature* (July 25, 1991, pp. 318–320).

C. Einhorn, L. Einhorn, and J.L. Luche, *Synthesis* (November 1989, pp. 787–813).

T.J. Mason (ed.), *Advances in Sonochemistry,* vol. 1–3 (JAI Press, 1990–93).

K.S. Suslick (ed.), *Ultrasound: Its Chemical, Physical, and Biological Effects* (VCH Publishers, 1988).

K.S. Suslick, "Sonochemistry," *Science* (March 23, 1990, pp. 1439–45).

K.S. Suslick, S.-B. Choe, A.A. Cichowlas, and M.W. Grinstaff, "Sonochemical Synthesis of Amorphous Iron," *Nature* (Oct. 3, 1991, pp. 414–416).

THE ANIMAL THAT WALKS BY ITSELF

by Juliet Clutton-Brock

"I'll love you always," pledges the dog to its owner, while the cat's commitment often seems more like "Leave me a memo." Part of the difference lies in the way each animal came to associate with humans. The cat, nevertheless, is more social than its stereotype suggests.

Rudyard Kipling's *Just So Stories* are allegories about the interactions between humans and animals. Published in 1902 and intended for children, they possess an elegance and alliteration that, once heard, stick in the mind for life. One of the most memorable of the stories is "The Cat That Walked by Himself." It is a tale about the origin of domestic animals, a subject that has intrigued writers since the time of the ancient Greeks and was central to the development of Charles Darwin's theories of evolution.

Kipling's views were based on his general knowledge of natural history at the end of the 19th century, in particular on his experiences with people and animals in India, where he lived for much of his life. "The Cat That Walked by Himself" ends as follows:

He [the cat] will kill mice, and he will be kind to Babies when he is in the house, just as long as they do not pull his tail too hard. But when he has done that, and between times, and when the moon gets up and night comes, he is the Cat that walks by himself, and all places are alike to him. Then he goes out to the Wet Wild Woods or up the Wet Wild Trees or on the Wet Wild Roofs, waving his wild tail and walking by his wild lone.

In Kipling's time there was no scientific discipline of animal behavior, now known as ethology, but even so it is probably fair to say that individuals who spent their lives with animals knew as much about their behavior as scientists do today. This is particularly true for domestic animals, which have been considered to be outside the natural world and therefore not worthy of scientific observation. Since the early 1980s this neglect has begun to be reversed as biologists have realized the value of studying the natural behavioral patterns of domestic species. Such study is vitally important not only for understanding the relationships between humans and animals but also for improving the welfare of animals that are increasingly subjected to intensive methods of breeding and control.

Kipling formed his story around the seemingly independent, aloof personality of the domestic cat. In a fanciful way he explained how the

JULIET CLUTTON-BROCK *is Archaeozoologist at The Natural History Museum, London, and has written more than 70 publications on mammalian osteology and the history of domesticated mammals.*

(Opposite page) Illustration by Tim Jonke

156

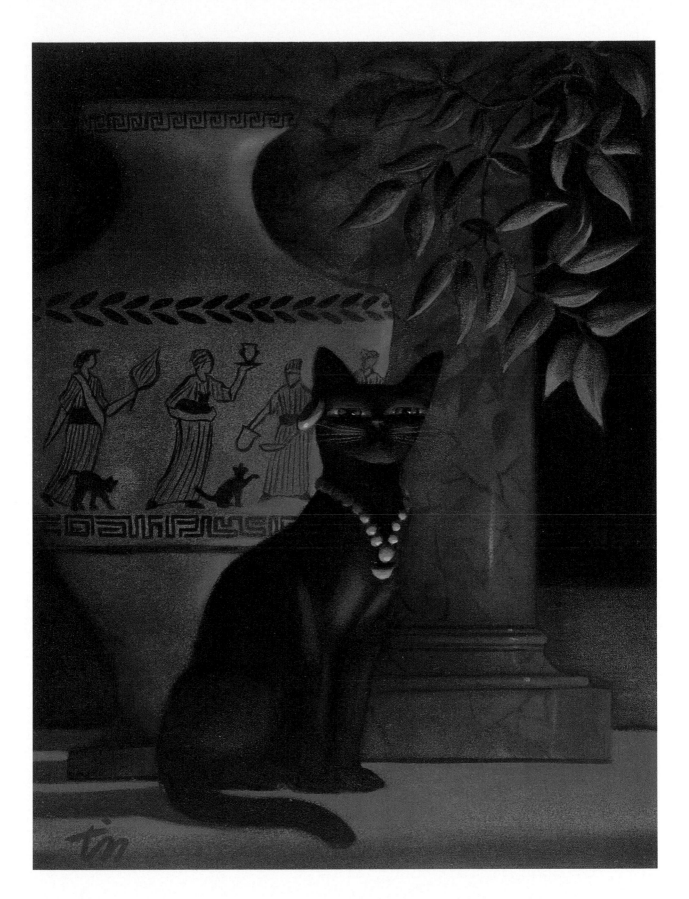

"He will kill mice, and he will be kind to Babies when he is in the house. . . . But when he has done that, and between times, and when the moon gets up and night comes, he is the Cat that walks by himself." Kipling's imaginative account of the domestication of animals captured what people all seem to sense—that the domestic cat lives a life of mysterious ambivalence, not wild yet not fully the devoted servant of humans that the dog, horse, and other domesticated animals have become.

cat was never persuaded to give the same unconditional allegiance to humans as were the dog, horse, and cow. But why should the cat have fared differently from other domesticated animals? And how accurate is that portrait of self-reliance and latent wildness as a description of the cat? By looking at all aspects of the domestic cat, its wild relatives, ancestry, and behavior as a free-ranging domestic animal and as a closely guarded pet, it is possible to assess the level at which Kipling's allegory is based on fact, as well as to better understand the nature of the cat as an animal companion whose history has been marked by the extremes of human love and hate.

The family of cats

The wild cats are the most exclusive meat eaters of all the carnivores. They have few enemies apart from humans, who have killed them in enormous numbers for sport and for their skins. The cat family, or Felidae, ranges in size from the huge Siberian tiger, which weighs as much as 260 kilograms (570 pounds), to the little black-footed cat (*Felis nigripes*) of South Africa, which weighs only 1–2 kilograms (about 2¼–4½ pounds). It is this diversity in size that allows the cat family to be so successful, for all over the world there is a cat for every niche where there are prey animals to feed on. In terms of numbers, the most successful member of the family is the domestic cat (*F. catus*), whose niche is the human environment.

158

A commonly used system of classification divides the cat family into four groups, or genera. The domestic cat and 27 other species of small cat fall within the genus *Felis*, whose largest representative is the puma (also called the cougar or mountain lion). Five species of large cat make up the genus *Panthera*, these being the lion, jaguar, leopard, tiger, and snow leopard. Two species stand on their own: the cheetah (*Acinonyx jubatus*) and the clouded leopard (*Neofelis nebulosa*). The small cats differ from the large cats not only in size but also in their inability to roar and in the way they rest with the tail curled round the body.

Nearly all cats hunt by night, and all but the lion are generally considered to be solitary predators, killing animals smaller than themselves. Lions live in family groups, or prides, and hunt large herd animals. The cheetah usually hunts by day, and it does not roar. Cheetahs differ from all other cats in having large, rather doglike paws with unsheathed claws, which enable these cats to be the fastest running of all animals. Over a short distance the cheetah can reach 110 kilometers (70 miles) per hour.

The senses of all cats are extremely highly developed as adaptations for nocturnal hunting. Cats can move with great silence and stealth, see everything around them, hear the slightest noise, and smell other animals that are out of sight. The eyes of the cat are perhaps its most distinctive feature. In bright light the pupils narrow to a slit or a small circle, depending on the species; in the dark they become large and circular. Not only do cat's eyes see stereoscopically but, like other nocturnal animals, they also have an extra layer of reflecting cells, the tapetum lucidum, which give light entering the eye a second chance to stimulate the light-detecting cells of the retina. It is the tapetum lucidum that shines in the night when a cat's eyes are caught by a bright light such as the beams of a car's headlights. It is probably the seemingly mystical characteristic of their eyes that has been the basis of the belief, since the time of the ancient Egyptians, that domestic cats have some special alliance with the Moon. A cat can see about six times better than a human in dim light, while in total darkness it can still feel its way about with the highly sensitive whiskers around its face and with the sensitive guard hairs of its fur.

In addition to the five senses of sight, hearing, smell, taste, and touch, in which cats excel over humans, cats have another sense of "smell-taste" from the vomeronasal, or Jacobson's, organ in the roof of the mouth. The functioning of this organ is associated with a characteristic lifting of the head and curling of the upper lip, a grimace known by the German word *flehmen*. The vomeronasal organ is used to test the excreta and secretions of other animals and, in the domestic cat at least, to analyze many other odors such as that from the catnip, or catmint, plant.

Nearly all the species of small cats are forest dwellers that must be able to pounce on their prey at speed whether from the end of a thin branch or the edge of a rock. They are, therefore, excellent climbers with the well-known ability, inherited by the domestic cat, to right themselves in a fall so that they land on their feet. This ability, which develops within a few weeks of life, operates through the conjunction of the balancing

The cat family, according to one classification system, comprises four groups, or genera. Making up the genus *Panthera* are five so-called big, or roaring, cats: the leopard (this page, top), lion (center), and tiger (bottom), along with the jaguar and snow leopard. Twenty-eight species of small cats, the domestic cat among them, are assigned to the genus *Felis*. They include (opposite page) the little spotted cat (top left; *F. tigrinus*), a rare species found in Central and South American rain forests; Pallas's cat (top right, *F. manul*) of the Central Asian steppes; bobcat (center left, *F. rufus*) of North American forest, brush, and desert regions; and black-footed cat (center right, *F. nigripes*) of South Africa, the smallest species of cat. Two genera have only one member each: *Acinonyx*, represented by the cheetah (bottom left), and *Neofelis*, represented by the clouded leopard (bottom right). It is the diversity in the size of its members that has allowed the cat family to succeed in every niche throughout the world where there are prey animals to feed on.

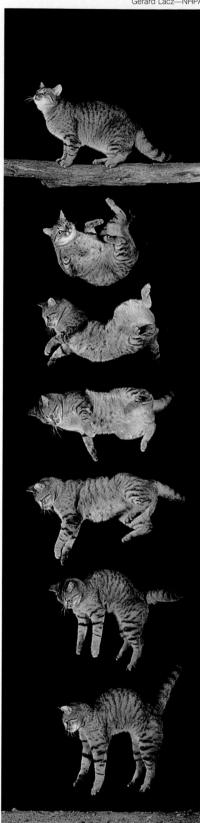

Gérard Lacz—NHPA

mechanism of the inner ear, the sense of sight, and the fast movement of the neck muscles, which rotate the head into an upright position as the animal falls.

All cats have a considerable repertoire of vocalizations, of which the purr is particularly appealing to humans. In the small cats the hyoid bones at the root of the tongue are fully ossified, a state that enables the animals to purr but not to roar. In the large cats the hyoid bones are part cartilage and vibrate in the roar. All cats communicate by yowling, hissing, and mewing. Male cats caterwaul when about to fight, and female cats may "scream" when mating.

The cats are all territorial, and all mark their home ranges by spraying and depositing excreta as well as by rubbing their fur against trees or other objects. They also exchange personal scents by rubbing and licking each other.

The young of both small and large cats are born blind and helpless. A litter usually comprises about four kittens, or cubs, in whose rearing the father plays little or no part. The young are usually fully independent at six months of age, but they may remain with their mother for as long as two years.

Every cat, whether it is a lion or a domestic pet, is an individual whose behavior is adapted for grasping opportunities and dealing with unexpected situations. It is hardly ever a scavenger but is first and foremost a hunter and has the hunter's skills of quick reactions and fast movements. How is it then that the domestic cat is so very successful at living as a pampered companion in the human environment? To answer this question one needs to examine why the wild cat first became associated with humans and how it became domesticated.

Routes to domestication

The early domestication of the dog and all livestock animals, including the horse, is generally believed to have followed a course that was both cultural and biological. The cultural process of domestication began when animals that had become tame—*i.e.*, no longer fearful of being handled by humans—were incorporated into the social structure of a human community and became objects of ownership, inheritance, purchase, and exchange. The biological changes in body form and structure that took place in the newly domesticated animals came second to this integration into human society. The biological process of domestication resembled evolution. It began when a small number of parent animals were separated from the wild species and became habituated to humans. These animals formed a founder group, which was changed over successive generations both in response to natural selection under the new regime imposed by the human community and its environment and by artificial selection for economic, cultural, or aesthetic reasons.

Domestication of most animal species probably began independently in many different places where young animals were kept in captivity in a more or less haphazard way. Sometimes these animals remained tame into adult life and then bred in captivity to produce the founders of a domestic stock. This process could happen, however, only when the natural behavioral patterns of the animal species matched those of humans. To have the potential to be domesticated, a species must be gregarious, must be a daytime feeder that can eat a variety of foods, must breed readily in captivity, must flee only a short distance from a perceived threat before its fear diminishes, and must have a wide home range. The wolf has all these characteristics, and it is easy to see why the dog became the first domestic animal, but the wild cat has none of them. The cat is more or less solitary, is an obligatory carnivore, is nocturnal, and is territorial.

There is, however, a rather different alternative to taming by which wild animals can become associated with human societies—that is, through commensalism. Commensalism is an association between individuals of two species in which one species benefits from the other. The commensal bond may be either temporary or permanent. The commensal animal of longest standing that is associated with humans is probably the house mouse (*Mus musculus*). Fossil records show that, from the end of the last ice age until 4,000 years ago, this species of mouse was restricted in its distribution to Anatolia and western Asia. It was found first in association with Epipaleolithic (Middle Stone Age) human settlements in what is now Israel, dated to 10,000 years ago. The house mouse spread slowly into western Europe, where its remains are uncommon until the Bronze Age (about 1500 BC); in Britain it is recorded first from the Iron Age (500 BC). All the evidence indicates that the westward spread of the house mouse was closely followed by that of the cat.

Karl Rütimeyer, a Swiss scientist who in 1866 described the animal remains from the famous Neolithic (New Stone Age) lake villages in Switzerland (about 3000 BC), clearly believed that the role of the cat in those ancient times was to kill rodents, for he wrote:

The little animals which are so inconvenient in our modern houses, rats and mice, do not seem to have troubled the inhabitants of the lake dwellings, so that they could the more easily do without cats, of which no remains whatever are found.

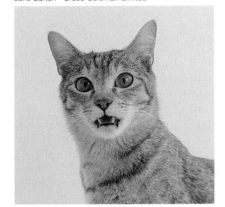

The small cats are predators that must be able to pounce quickly on their prey from tree branches, rocky ledges, and other precipitous locations. They are thus excellent climbers and balancers with the ability, inherited by the domestic cat (photo sequence on opposite page), to right themselves as they fall so as to land on their feet. Like its wild relatives, the domestic cat also possesses a special sense of "smell-taste" from the vomeronasal organ in the roof of the mouth. After the animal tastes or smells a substance of particular interest, such as the urine of another cat, it raises its head and sucks in air through a partly open mouth (above) to bring the chemicals to the vomeronasal organ. The characteristic head lift and grimace associated with vomeronasal sampling is known as flehmen.

The natural behavioral patterns of animal species are believed to have played a major role in the way they became associated with early humans. Species that were incorporated into human society through a process of taming and captive breeding were those whose behavior had much in common with that of humans. The wolf, for example (left), is gregarious, feeds during the day and on a wide variety of foods, and has a wide home range. It is thus no surprise that the dog became the first domestic animal. The wild cat, by contrast, has none of the wolf's characteristics. Instead, it is likely that cats formed their first link with humans as tolerated commensal animals.

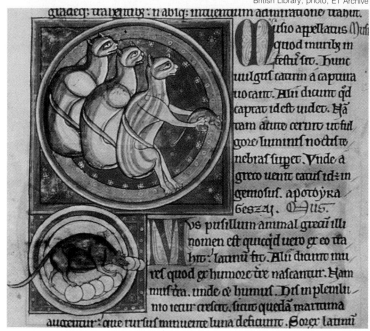

Three cats practice their ancient role as mouse catcher on an illuminated page of a 13th-century bestiary. Fossil records show that beginning about 4,000 years ago the house mouse (Mus musculus) migrated slowly into Europe from Asia as a commensal animal associated with human settlements. All evidence indicates that the westward spread of the mouse was closely followed by that of the cat, which became accepted by humans as a pest destroyer.

The most plausible explanation for the early associations of the wild cat with humans is that it became a tolerated commensal animal, having been attracted to settlements and food stores by small animals already established there as pests. Several of Aesop's fables, which could have had their origins as early as the 6th century BC, are about cats and mice, showing that the function of the cat as a pest destroyer was already well known in ancient Greece. About 44 BC the Sicilian historian Diodorus Siculus wrote about the sacred cats of Egypt: "The cat is likewise useful against asps with their deadly bite and the other reptiles that sting."

The crucial difference between commensalism and domestication is that the commensal animal benefits from the human environment but lives and breeds in the wild, while the domesticated animal is owned and its breeding controlled. Nevertheless, the same species can live either as a commensal or as a fully domesticated animal, common examples being black and brown rats, house mice, pigeons, cats, and dogs. All of these species have a dual role in human societies. Wild rats and mice living as commensals are agricultural and urban pests that destroy vast quantities of human resources and carry diseases, while domestic rats and mice can be cherished pets and are of great importance as laboratory animals. Feral cats—cats derived from domestic stock that live in self-sustaining populations—can exist wild as commensals, yet under domestication cats can be so highly bred that they cannot survive without human protection.

The wild ancestor

Of all the species of small wild cats, only one has a serious claim to being the ancestor of the domestic cat. It is *F. silvestris*, the most widespread of wild cats, still to be found, although in ever diminishing numbers, in Europe, Africa, and southern Asia. Over this huge region *F. silvestris*,

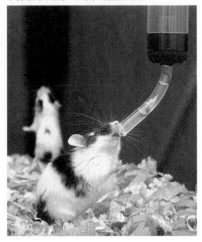

Mice—as well as cats, dogs, and other animals—can live either as commensal animals (far left) or as fully domesticated ones (left). The crucial difference is that the former benefits from the human environment but lives and breeds in the wild, while the latter is owned and its breeding is controlled.

which is commonly called the wildcat, differs greatly in appearance. In the north it is typified by the European wildcat, *F. silvestris silvestris*, which has a broad head, heavy body, rather short legs, and a thick coat. In Africa *F. silvestris lybica* is long legged and much more elegant, with big ears and a thin coat, while in India *F. silvestris ornata* is smaller and has a spotted coat. All these forms will interbreed, however, and today they are generally considered to belong to a single species.

Linnaeus, the pioneer 18th-century classifier of plants and animals, who probably had never seen a wildcat and may have been looking at his own blotched tabby, described both the wildcat and the domestic cat as having a blotched tabby coat and gave them the same name, *F. catus*. However, as was pointed out in 1907 by the well-known taxonomist of mammals R.I. Pocock, the European wildcat has a striped rather than a blotched coat, so the name for the wildcat was changed to *F. silvestris*, a name that had first been applied to it in the late 1700s.

The species of wild cat with by far the strongest claim to being the ancestor of the domestic cat is Felis silvestris, *commonly called the wildcat. In Europe it is found as the subspecies* F. silvestris silvestris *(left), which has a broad head and heavily built body. In Africa the subspecies is* F. silvestris lybica *(center), a long-legged, big-eared animal. The Asian form is* F. silvestris ornata *(right), which is smaller and has small spots, rather than stripes, on the body coat.*

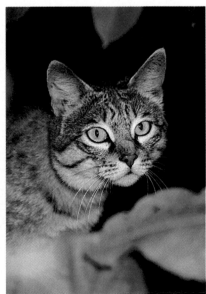

It occasionally has been suggested that Pallas's cat (*F. manul*) and the sand cat (*F. margarita*) could be ancestors of the Persian cat, while the Asian golden cat (*F. temmincki*) and the leopard cat (*F. bengalensis*) have been proposed as ancestors of the Siamese. No sound evidence exists, however, for giving separate ancestries to the Persian and Siamese breeds; they are probably descended from small founder groups or mutants of domesticated cats bred in western and eastern Asia within the last few hundred years.

It appears that the aboriginal progenitor of all domestic cats worldwide was a wildcat most closely resembling today's *F. silvestris lybica*, the African form. In later stages of its development as a species, what is now the domestic cat probably interbred locally with both European and Asian forms of wildcat. This is suggested by the coat pattern of the common domestic striped tabby in Europe, which has a combination of the characters of the European and the African wildcats, and by the spotted coat, suggestive of the Asian wildcat, that sometimes appears in domestic cats in India.

First associations with humans
The bones of cats are often found at archaeological sites from the early prehistoric period, but it is probable that they are from cats that were killed for their pelts, as the bones are usually together with those of other fur-bearing mammals such as fox or bear. One example is a cat's tooth found in the prepottery Neolithic levels of Jericho and dating to around 9,000 years ago; another is from Harappa in the Indus Valley of modern Pakistan dating to 4,000 years ago. A more significant find comes from the earliest Neolithic levels of Cyprus (8,000 years ago), where, remarkably, the house mouse also appears. These finds are important because there are no records of cat or mouse from Cyprus earlier than the known date for the first human immigration to this eastern Mediter-

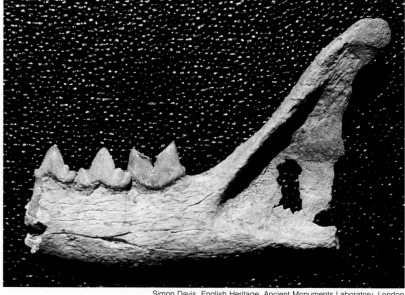

Part of a mandible, or lower jawbone, identified as that of Felis silvestris *comes from an 8,000-year-old Neolithic site in southern Cyprus. Because no fossil records of cats—or of mice—exist prior to the earliest appearance of humans on Cyprus, the find implies that the first cats to reach the island must have been taken there purposefully, possibly in an effort to deal with the introduced mice.*

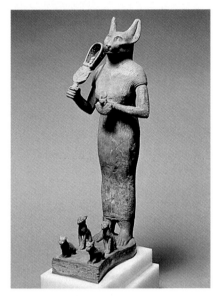

Detail of a wall painting (left) from an Egyptian tomb dating from 1400 BC depicts a cat helping a hunter retrieve birds. All such pictorial representations show the cat of ancient Egypt as a striped, large-eared animal closely resembling the modern Felis silvestris lybica, the African wildcat. In ancient Egyptian society the cat was worshiped as one of the sacred animals, and the cat goddess Bast (above) had a major temple at the city of Bubastis. The bronze statue shown, from the 22nd dynasty (950–730 BC), represents Bast as a woman with a cat's head.

ranean island. The two species, therefore, must have been carried to the island by ship. It can easily be accepted that the mice traveled as unknown passengers, but the first cats to reach Cyprus must have been at least captives if not pets. It thus raises the question of whether the cat was purposefully taken to the island, 8,000 years ago, in an effort to deal with a plague of mice.

The ancient Egyptian cat

It is widely believed that the ancient Egyptians were the first to domesticate the cat but, in fact, there is little pictorial evidence of cats before the New Kingdom (18th dynasty, about 1600 BC). All the ancient Egyptian depictions of cats show them as being closely similar to the modern African wildcat, with its striped coat, neat head, large ears, and long legs. The paintings, statuettes, and mummy cases in the shapes of seated cats from ancient Egypt show the animals in a nearly vertical position, which is anatomically impossible for any modern domestic cat but is identical to the posture of the African wildcat when sitting upright.

As is well known, the cat held a special place in the society of ancient Egypt. It was worshiped as one of the sacred animals, and the cat goddess Bast, or Bastet, had a huge temple devoted to her at Bubastis. The Greek writer Herodotus visited Bubastis about 450 BC, when the status of the cat was at its height. He described how the Egyptians held an annual festival, attended by 700,000 people, at which more wine was consumed than at any other Egyptian festival. Herodotus also described how thousands of cats were kept in the temple as sacred animals and

167

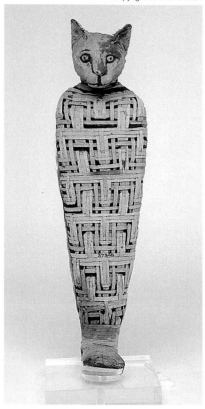

Cat mummy, found at the sacred Egyptian city of Abydos, is from the Roman period. In the 5th century BC the Greek writer Herodotus described how thousands of cats kept in the sacred temple at Bubastis were mummified when they died.

were mummified when they died. Uncountable numbers of these cat mummies have been preserved in the dry air of the tombs. There were so many that at the end of the 1800s a boatload of 19 tons was taken to England with the idea that the mummies could be used as fertilizer.

It is often quoted from Herodotus that when a cat died a natural death in an Egyptian household, all the inmates shaved their eyebrows. Four hundred years later Diodorus Siculus described seeing a crowd of Egyptians outside a house demanding the death of a Roman soldier who had accidentally killed a cat. Nevertheless, the temple priests who looked after the sacred cats seem to have run a side business, as it were, as suggested by the results of an X-ray study of 55 mummified and wrapped cats in London's Natural History Museum. The X-rays show that the cats were nearly all less than one year old when they died and that several of them had broken necks. Apparently the cats were specially bred by the priests, who then killed them and sold the mummified bodies as votive offerings to be placed in the sacred repositories.

One reason for the slow spread of the domestic cat around the Mediterranean before Roman times may have been that it was forbidden to export cats from Egypt. On the other hand, some traditions that surround the modern domestic cat may well have originated in ancient Egypt. For example, there would seem to be no particular reason why the diet of farm cats should be supplemented with bowls of bread and milk, as is common in England, or why house cats should be fed on fish except that these were the customs of the guardians of the sacred cats in ancient Egypt, as described by Diodorus:

For the cats and ichneumons [mongooses] they break up bread into milk and calling them with a clucking sound set it before them, or else they cut up fish caught in the Nile and feed the flesh to them raw.

The early associations of the cat with humans in North Africa and western Asia are supported by linguistic evidence. The word *cat* is thought to have come from the Nubian word *kadiz*. It was first used in the Latin *cattus*, which replaced the older name *feles* when the domestic cat was introduced to Rome. *Puss* is believed to be derived from Pasht, a variant of Bast, and *tabby* from *attabiya*, the name of a quarter of Baghdad where a special kind of striped silk was first manufactured in the Middle Ages.

The domestic cat

Like other species of animals whose historical relationship with humans has been as a commensal animal rather than as a fully domesticated one, the cat has been subjected to much less artificial selection for favored characters than, say, the dog or the pig. At least that was true until very recently, for during the past 50 years the development of new breeds of domestic cat has begun to catch up with that of the dog.

Another difference between the cat and other domestic animals is probably related to the amount of interbreeding that occurred over the millennia between free-ranging cats and *F. silvestris,* which was a much more common wild animal in the past than it is today. The cat, therefore, has retained closer links in body form and behavior with the wild species than have other fully domesticated animals. And, conversely, domestic genes have been introduced into the wild species, a fact particularly evident over the continent of Africa, where interbreeding between wild and domestic cats still takes place in localities that are inhabited by both species.

Even so, the cat has not escaped the physical and behavioral changes that accompany the process of domestication. The wildcat is a solitary, nocturnal hunter of small prey. The fully domesticated cat is a companion animal that may live its whole life indoors, sleeping most of the time, feeding on milk and boneless foods, and pining when its owner is away. How have such extraordinary changes been brought about?

The domestic animal, whether it is a cow or a cat, differs from its wild progenitor in a number of similar characteristics. The reason is that the selective pressures of breeding in captivity and the rearing of young mammals in close association with humans causes an imbalance and disruption of growth in different parts of the organism, irrespective of species. The mechanisms of this process are not well understood, but they are likely to be due to dietary changes, stress, and hormonal changes resulting from the extension of the young animal's dependence on humans into its adult life.

The first stages of domestication are almost always accompanied by a reduction in size of the body and shortening of the jaws. This is so generally true that reduction in size is the main criterion used to distinguish domestic from wild animal remains at archaeological sites. Then there are changes in the distribution of the fat in the body, in the carriage of the tail and ears, and in the texture and color of the coat. Over many generations natural selection for survival in the new, human environment and artificial selection by humans for favored characteristics combine to produce new races or breeds of animals that look quite different from their wild progenitors.

The perceptual world of the domestic animal is also very different from that of its wild progenitor. The livestock animal, for example, does not have to be constantly on guard against predators, while the house cat does not have to find and kill prey. In addition, it is advantageous from the human's point of view to have animals that are placid and social and that have a low response to stress. In all domestic species that have been examined, it appears that humans have unconsciously selected for reduction in size and weight of the brain with ensuing reduction in the total functional capacity of the sensory organs. In the domestic cat the average weight of the brain can be up to 27% less than that of the European wildcat. Moreover, the auditory bullae of the domestic cat are very much reduced in size so that its hearing is less acute. (The auditory bulla is the thin-walled bony projection at the base of the skull that encases the middle ear.) In the farm cat or feral cat, although it may live by its wits, the brain and auditory bullae are still within the size range of the domestic cat rather than of the wildcat.

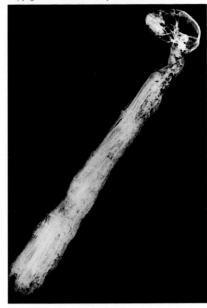

A broken neck is evident in an X-ray of a mummified and wrapped cat, part of a radiological study of 55 cat mummies in London's Natural History Museum. The X-rays showed that the cats were nearly all less than a year old at the time of death and that several had broken necks. The cats seem to have been specially bred by the temple priests, who then sacrificed them for mummification and sold the mummies to the public as votive offerings.

169

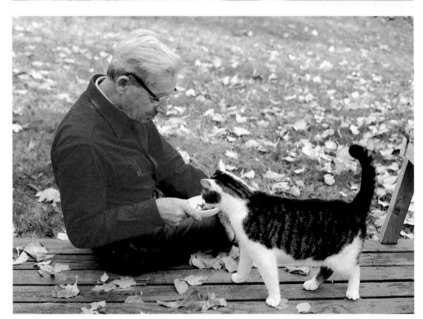

In the niche of the human environment, the cat has come to depend on its owner for shelter, comfort and attention, and a steady food supply. By a process that remains to be fully understood, this intimate association with humans together with selective pressures of breeding in captivity has brought about a number of physical and behavioral changes characteristic of domestication. Such changes include a reduction in body size, the size of the auditory bullae, and the size and weight of the brain; modifications in fat distribution, carriage of the ears and tail, and texture and color of the coat; and a more placid and social temperament.

The hunting cat

Many surveys have been made of the feeding habits and diet of feral cats. One of the earliest, in 1951, was conducted by the zoologist Earl L. Hubbs on the feral cats that lived along California's Sacramento Valley. His study was based not on the behavior of living cats, as it would be today, but on the stomach contents of 219 animals that were killed for the project—an illustration of how different were the attitudes toward biological studies a few decades ago.

Although all free-ranging cats benefit humans by killing rodent pests, they also kill enormous numbers of birds and other wild animals. In one survey carried out in a single Bedfordshire village in England by biologists P.B. Churcher and J.H. Lawton in 1987, it was found that the bodies of 22 species of birds and 15 species of mammals were brought

170

into people's homes by their cats in one year, the most important species being wood mice (17%), house sparrows (16%), and bank voles (14%). A total of 1,090 prey animals were caught during the year, for an average of 14 per cat.

In some parts of the world, particularly on oceanic islands such as Aldabra in the Indian Ocean, populations of feral cats survive by feeding on turtle hatchlings and other species of endangered rare animals. The cats on these islands are descendants of ships' cats that either landed by accident or were taken ashore by sailors. Like all cats, they are opportunistic hunters of any small prey they can catch, and they can do irreparable damage to the indigenous fauna.

The cat as a social animal

How the solitary hunter can also live as a social animal, either in a community of feral cats or in a human family, is an anomaly that is only just beginning to be understood. Unfortunately, very little is known about the natural behavioral patterns of either the European or the African wildcat. Many studies, however, have been carried out on the behavior of free-ranging and feral cats in different parts of the world. From them a picture has been built up showing that the cat is remarkably versatile in its behavior.

The observations have been reviewed by the German animal behaviorist Paul Leyhausen, who has worked for many years on the ethology of the domestic cat. In the 1960s Leyhausen concluded that the behavior of feral cats followed a pattern that can be summarized as follows: Both male and female cats are territorial, having a defended territory of around 100 meters (330 feet) in diameter and a wider home range, which can be as much as 2 kilometers (1.2 miles) across. Males have larger home ranges than females, and they fight more for supremacy, while females fight to defend their territories. Cats avoid encounters by having individual timetables when traveling through or staying in border

Free-ranging cats benefit humans as destroyers of rodent pests, but they also kill enormous numbers of small animals. For all their millennia of domestication, cats remain opportunistic hunters, and when inadvertently or thoughtlessly introduced to a new environment, they can do great harm to the indigenous fauna.

The sequestered ruins of the Roman Forum (above) make a popular gathering place for the feral cats of Rome. In recent decades studies of feral and free-ranging cats have contributed to a picture of the cat as being capable of a remarkable diversity of social activities. In different groups feral female cats may be territorial or cooperative, solitary or gregarious, and individual or communal in rearing their young. Feral males may share territories and females or may compete for total dominance; they may tolerate kittens or drive them away.

areas. Neighbors come to tolerate each other at close quarters, and at certain times all the cats in a neighborhood assemble in what appears to be a social gathering on neutral ground. When there are several males of equal strength in a neighborhood, they stop fighting and form loose associations, which Leyhausen called brotherhoods.

Twenty years later, in the 1980s, Leyhausen had to revise his description entirely about the behavior of feral cats, for they were found to show an amazing diversity of social activities. Females may be strictly territorial in one group but tolerant or even cooperative in another, and they may or may not tolerate dominant males in their territories. They may be gregarious or solitary, share homes and dens or defend them, and nurse and raise their young individually or communally. Males may share territories and females, or one dominant male may drive out all the others. Kittens may be tolerated or chased away or even killed by males. In short, the cat has ceased to be the stereotyped "animal that walks by itself." Its true personality is now recognized to be that of an individual that can adapt its behavior to its circumstances.

The early experiences of the kitten have been found, not unexpectedly, to be of great importance in the development of its social or solitary behavior. Farm kittens that are brought up communally will grow into social cats, whereas those that are on their own or that have frequent negative experiences with a few adult cats will likely become solitary. Between two and seven weeks of age, kittens go through a sensitive phase in which they can be socialized to humans (or indeed to such other animals as horses, dogs, or even animals that are their natural prey). Kittens that receive a lot of attention and stroking during this period will grow up to be cats that are fully trusting of humans, whereas cats that are left alone with their mothers at this time will tend to be shy and solitary in adult life.

Coat color and temperament

Although cats seem capable of a very high diversity of behavior, each individual cat, as with all organisms, is constrained by its genes. And it appears that temperament in the domestic cat is linked to the inherited color of its coat.

It is a remarkable fact that the coat patterns and colors of cats are not randomly distributed among different populations. The coats of the majority of cats in urban areas differ from those living in the country, and the coats of cats in the inner cites will even differ from those in the suburbs. Furthermore, the most common type of coat and its color in different cities and different countries can be correlated with the movements of people over the centuries, and it has even been used to make deductions about the approximate date that an immigrant group of cats arrived in a new region. Most of this work was carried out by Neil B. Todd in the 1970s at the Carnivore Genetics Center, Newtonville, Massachusetts.

Because they have a worldwide distribution, a number of coat colors were probably derived from genetic mutations that occurred early in the

In the first few weeks of life, kittens go through a sensitive phase in which they can be socialized to humans and other animals, including those that are their natural prey. Kittens that receive much attention and stroking during this period will grow up trusting of humans, while those that are left with their mothers will tend to be shy and solitary as adults.

history of cat domestication. They are the striped tabby, black, blue, orange, white-spotted, and white. All of these coat colors can appear in either short- or long-haired form, the latter being a mutation that is probably also of ancient origin. To a certain extent the color and pattern of the coat and the length of the hair are self-perpetuating, but they are also affected by human selection for favored kittens. Today, throughout the world, the most common coat colors are blotched tabby, black, and orange, the last of which is sex-linked and gives rise to male ginger cats and female tortoiseshell cats (including calico, which is tortoiseshell with white).

For his investigations into the genetics of cat populations, Todd collated the numbers of cats showing each of the three coat colors in a great many localities in Europe, western Asia, and North Africa and then drew maps showing their geographic distributions. The highest numbers of black cats were found in Britain and northwestern Africa, with slightly

173

Map drawn from the work of population geneticist Neil B. Todd plots the frequency with which the gene mutation for the blotched tabby coat appears in Europe and parts of Asia and Africa. Contour lines give percentages in increments of 10, with spot locations showing more precise numbers. Making use of the fact that the coat patterns and colors of cats are not randomly distributed, Todd showed that the most common types—blotched tabby, black, and orange—can be correlated with the movements of cats and their human owners over the centuries. The map shown indicates a focus in Britain for the blotched tabby coat, an idea supported by the presence of the blotched tabby pattern in varied numbers in the countries that received colonists from Britain during the past 300 years.

lower numbers around the Mediterranean and in the Italian cities of Venice and Rome. Todd suggested that black cats originated in the eastern Mediterranean region in the classical period. The single-colored coat, especially black, appears to be particularly successful in cities, perhaps because this mutation is linked through the hormonal system with a rather placid temperament, one that is more tolerant of crowding than that of the wild type, the striped tabby.

The blotched tabby is very widespread and appears to have a temperament even better suited to the urban environment than the black cat. Todd postulated that the blotched tabby coat first occurred as a mutation in Britain about 300 years ago, with a secondary place of origin in Iran. The idea of Britain as a focus is supported by the presence of the blotched tabby pattern in varying numbers in North America, Canada, Australia, New Zealand, and Tasmania, all of which received colonists from Britain in the past 300 years.

The distribution of cats with orange in their coats is very different from those of the black and blotched tabby. Besides being most common in eastern Asia, very high numbers of ginger and tortoiseshell cats exist

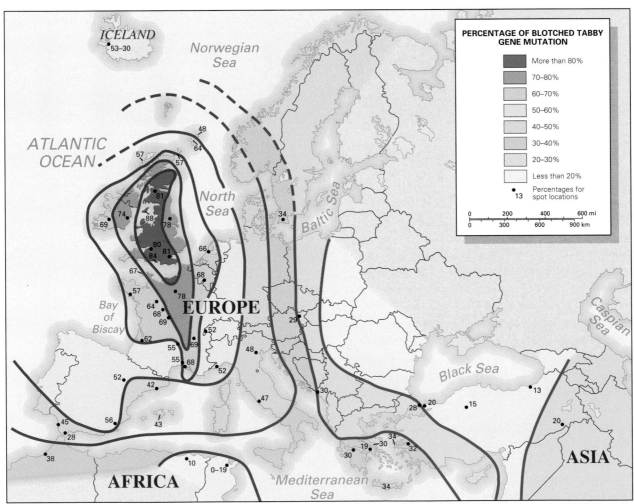

Adapted from "Cats and Commerce" by Neil B. Todd. Copyright © November 1977 by Scientific American, Inc. All rights reserved

The temperament of a cat, and thus the kind of environment to which it is best suited, appears linked to the inherited color of its coat. The single-colored cat, especially black (top left), seems particularly successful in cities; its coat mutation may be related through the hormonal system with a disposition tolerant of crowding. The blotched tabby (bottom) appears even better suited to urban life than the black cat. By contrast, the cat with orange in its coat (top right, a male ginger) is most common in the countryside, where cats are less concentrated, and does not seem to do especially well in cities.

in Turkey, along the north coast of Africa, and in the western isles of Scotland. Todd suggested that orange cats originated in Asia Minor and then spread westward to Africa and Europe. For reasons that can only be guessed at, they do not have an especially high survival value in cities and are most commonly found in the countryside, where cats are less concentrated.

The sacred cat today

There may always be cats that walk by themselves, but there are also growing numbers that serve their human owners as a status symbol or a decorative appendage to the home. Many are dearly loved, and their deaths are mourned. They often belong to one of the new breeds, having an unusual coat color, folded ears, hairless bodies, or coats so long-haired that they must be groomed every day. The faces of long-haired cats are often bred to be so short and flat that there is no room for their teeth, and they cannot breathe without snuffling. Furthermore, the claws of cats that are kept indoors are often surgically removed to prevent them from scratching the furniture. There is no doubt that should a clawless-

175

The proclivity for humans to perpetuate and amplify novel animal mutations is apparent in some of the more "exotic" breeds of cats. The Scottish fold's peculiar ears (top left), which probably do not aid the animal's hearing, arose from a single mutated kitten that appeared among a litter in Scotland in the 1960s. Cats of long-haired breeds like the blue Persian (above) can have faces so flat that their breathing and chewing are impaired. The virtually hairless sphynx (top right), which originated in Canada in the late 1960s, would be disadvantaged in any but a protected human environment. Another cat better suited for indoor life is the ragdoll (bottom right), selected for its tendency to go limp when handled and its silky mat-resistant coat.

cat mutation ever appear, breeders would waste little time in developing it for the market.

An example of the effect of human whim can be seen in a comparatively new breed called the ragdoll. These cats were selected for their tendency to become limp and floppy when handled and for their silky coat, which mats less than is usual for long-haired cats. Although the peculiar characteristics of ragdolls do not enhance, and probably diminish, the ability to survive outdoors in the natural environment, they are not liabilities in the human environment of the apartment, where the animals receive constant protection.

It is possible that the ancient Egyptians would have approved of cats like ragdolls, for their own sacred cats received no less attention in life and after death. Nevertheless, in the process of domestication a breed of animal can be changed out of all recognition from its wild progenitor. Surely the cat is worth more as a companion than to be transformed into an icon to human vanity.

176

FOR ADDITIONAL READING

P.B. Churcher and J.H. Lawton, "Predation by Domestic Cats in an English Village," *Journal of Zoology* (July 1987, pp. 439–455).

Juliet Clutton-Brock, *The British Museum Book of Cats Ancient and Modern* (British Museum Publications, 1988).

Simon J.M. Davis, *The Archaeology of Animals* (Batsford, 1987).

Helmut Hemmer, *Domestication: The Decline of Environmental Appreciation* (Cambridge University Press, 1990).

Rudyard Kipling, *Just So Stories for Little Children* (Macmillan, 1902).

R.I. Pocock, "On English Domestic Cats," *Proceedings of the Zoological Society of London* (1907, pp. 143–168).

Roger Tabor, *The Wild Life of the Domestic Cat* (Arrow Books, 1983).

Neil B. Todd, "Cats and Commerce," *Scientific American* (November 1977, pp. 100–107).

Dennis C. Turner and Patrick Bateson (eds.), *The Domestic Cat: The Biology of Its Behaviour,* which includes a chapter by Paul Leyhausen, "The Tame and the Wild—Another Just-So Story" (Cambridge University Press, 1988).

Mary Evans Picture Library

Kipling drew several illustrations for his Just So Stories, *including one for "The Cat That Walked by Himself." Recent research has shown that the idea of the cat as an aloof loner is, like all stereotypes, oversimplified. The cat's true personality is now recognized to be that of an individual that can adapt its behavior with amazing flexibility in response to its circumstances.*

INTELLIGENT VEHICLE-HIGHWAY SYSTEMS

by Michael J. Cassidy

Increasingly heavy traffic on highways has made driving ever more time-consuming and hazardous. Offering a promising solution to this problem are advanced electronic technologies that can be applied to both roads and vehicles.

Roadway traffic congestion has become an important concern in virtually all major urban centers of the world. Delays created by congestion contribute to significant economic losses as commuters are prevented from using their time effectively and the distribution of goods and services is impeded. The added fuel consumption and engine emissions resulting from congestion are sources of serious environmental concern. Traveler frustration caused by congestion imparts a significant social cost to societies. And, finally, safety problems associated with congested highway operations continue to inflict costs that are often too great to measure in monetary terms.

For many regions of the world, highway congestion is not a recently occurring phenomenon. Early attempts to deal with it typically centered on the construction of new highway facilities. Building more roads in an effort to escape congestion has generally become an inefficient, if not infeasible, approach, however. The growing costs of construction in most of the world, coupled with the scarcity of available right-of-way in urban areas, have greatly increased the expense associated with highway construction. In much of the world, environmental and social priorities discourage new construction, as the installation of large highways often increases automobile ridership and physically divides communities.

Moreover, because of a phenomenon known as "latent demand," building additional infrastructure is often not an effective long-term solution for minimizing congestion. Stated simply, latent demand reflects the tendency of a motoring public to make use of available roadways. Over an extended time period, surface transport demand invariably rises to meet, and eventually exceed, roadway capacity.

Given the high costs and limited returns yielded from efforts to manage congestion through added construction, current trends in transportation engineering involve strategies to minimize congestion through the improved "management" of existing highway facilities. In recent years a variety of traffic management strategies have sought to control

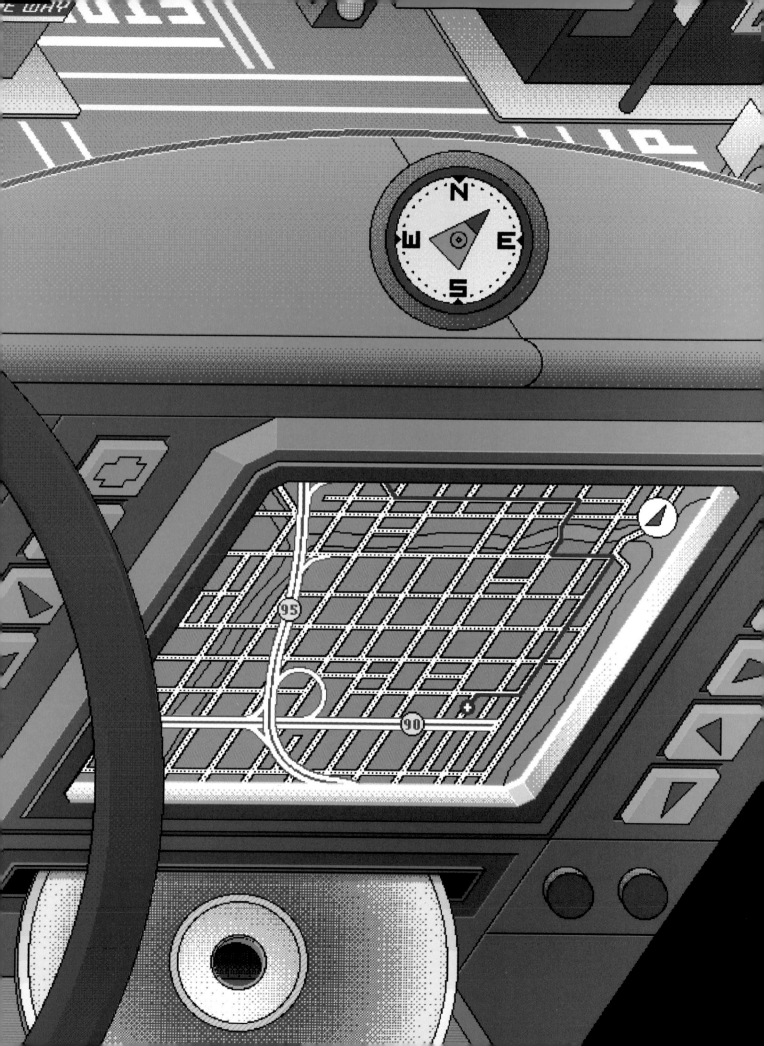

Traffic congestion, as seen on a Los Angeles freeway (above), has become a major problem for cities throughout the world. A traditional response to the problem has been to build new highways, as in Pennsylvania (above right).

the demand for roadway use. Examples include the promotion of public mass transportation and of car pools. In many communities employment centers have initiated "flexible" working hours in an attempt to reduce highway demand during the daily rush hours. Some countries have even instituted so-called congestion pricing, which places a surcharge on motorists using downtown highways during rush-hour periods.

Other types of traffic management strategies have sought to improve the capabilities of highway facilities to better accommodate existing traffic demands. Such strategies include the improved utilization of highway traffic signals and the employment of emergency service patrols that quickly respond to and remove the causes of congestion.

In many instances these traffic management strategies have indeed reduced congestion problems. However, they have improved highway operating conditions by relatively small percentages. The increasing demands for transport and the growing importance of surface transportation in the world economy dictate that major improvements be made.

The deployment of advanced electronic technologies provides the potential to significantly enhance mobility, productivity, and roadway safety by improving existing capabilities in the areas of highway surveillance, motorist communications, and vehicle control. Advanced technology systems would be implemented in both the highway and the vehicle. Consequently, the term Intelligent Vehicle-Highway Systems (IVHS) has been adopted in the United States to describe those technologies that might be appropriate for deployment on surface transportation systems. IVHS comprises four elements: Advanced Traffic Management Systems, Advanced Traveler Information Systems, Commercial Vehicle Operations, and Advanced Vehicle Control Systems. These elements describe and characterize the objectives of IVHS.

Advanced Traffic Management Systems

Conventional traffic management systems have existed for a number of years on major highway networks throughout the world. Advanced Traffic

MICHAEL J. CASSIDY *is an Assistant Professor of Civil Engineering at Purdue University, West Lafayette, Indiana.*

(Overleaf) Illustration by John Craig

180

Management Systems, however, represent considerable enhancements of these traditional systems. Advanced Traffic Management Systems monitor traffic flow in "real time"; that is, flow characteristics and changes in these characteristics are measured and evaluated as they actually occur. As operating problems are identified, the Advanced Traffic Management System implements control strategies to remove the source of the problem and to manage the resulting congestion. Identifying operating problems promptly requires the development of advanced detection technologies.

The traditional technology used for traffic surveillance is the inductive loop. This type of detector generally consists of twisted wire cable that is formed into a rectangular or diamond shape and buried beneath individual highway lanes. It forms a tuned circuit that searches for a vehicle by "scanning" the roadway above it 30–60 times per second. As vehicles travel over the detector, their metal interrupts the tuned circuit and thereby indicates their presence. Loop detectors measure the frequency

Efforts to reduce congestion on the highways include the promotion of buses and car pools (above left) and the construction of subways (above).

Automatic Eagle/Eagle Signal; photo, Ray Bohannon

A traffic engineer attends a workstation of MONARC (Master Office Network Adaptive Real-Time Control), an Advanced Traffic Management System (ATMS) that offers such features as monitoring of traffic flow in real time, surveillance of intersections, and advisories to motorists. It can also be used as an ATMS for the Intelligent Vehicle-Highway Systems of the future.

Courtesy of Commonwealth Virginia, State Department of Transportation, City of Richmond, New Traffic Signal System, Traffic Control Center

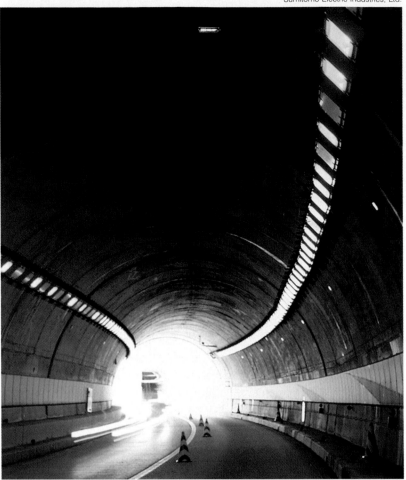

Sumitomo Electric Industries, Ltd.

A television camera mounted on the ceiling of a highway tunnel provides images that are combined with image-processing technology developed by Sumitomo Electric Industries, Ltd., in Japan to measure both the speed of the cars in the tunnel and the distances between them. The system can also measure traffic volume over a period of five minutes and the degree of congestion in a traffic jam. The information is transmitted to monitor/control systems and traffic information boards.

of the vehicles (the flow) and the amount of time they spend crossing the loop (vehicle speed). Advanced computer algorithms (step-by-step procedures for solving problems) are being developed and tested to enhance the reliability of the predicted occurrences of congestion based on measurements using inductive loops.

Pattern recognition and correlation techniques are also being used in an effort to improve traffic monitoring capabilities. As vehicles pass over inductive loops, the detector transforms voltage changes into a voltage signal that characterizes the undercarriage of each individual vehicle. These digitized patterns (or "signatures") are compared over successive inductive loops located at fixed points along the roadway. Where patterns are matched, traffic flow conditions are inferred from measured vehicle travel times over known roadway distances (that is, loop detector locations).

Efforts are also under way to improve surveillance capabilities using technologies other than inductive loop detectors. In many areas of the world, video-image processing is being utilized to monitor highway conditions automatically. Traffic flow is captured on video images via closed-circuit cameras located along the roadside. "Machine vision algorithms"

182

then identify the changing position of vehicles by evaluating color or shade changes in the individual pixels (elements) of the video image. Thus, image-sensing software can identify the real-time trajectories of individual vehicles and thereby measure characteristics of the traffic stream that characterize roadway operating quality.

Yet another approach for monitoring traffic conditions involves the use of a vehicle-mounted "tag" or transponder that identifies only the individual vehicle onto which it is installed. (A transponder is a radar or radio set that, upon receiving a designated signal, emits a signal of its own and that is used for the detection, identification, and location of objects.) An adhesive decal displaying a bar code is one type of commonly used vehicle identification tag. As a "tagged" vehicle passes by roadside reading devices, the vehicle's tag is read and recorded. The information, which is immediately processed by a master computer, can be used for evaluating roadway operating conditions. Moreover, the simple technology of these so-called automatic vehicle identification systems is already being used in many cities of the world for automatic toll collection.

The improved ability to monitor roadway operating conditions continually provides the capability to identify the occurrence of operating problems promptly and reliably. Data from the Advanced Traffic Management System are continuously transmitted to remote operations centers, where trained personnel monitor highway conditions. Once the Advanced Traffic Management System has reported a problem, traffic schemes can be quickly implemented to remove the source of the problem and to minimize the resulting congestion. Examples of such control schemes may include the dispatching of emergency vehicles or the automatic adjustment of traffic signals. Of perhaps even greater importance, improved surveillance technologies will facilitate the transmission of information concerning highway operating problems to the driving public.

Advanced Traveler Information Systems

Advanced Traveler Information Systems are designed to provide motorists with real-time information on roadway operating problems and on alter-

A transponder mounted on the front license plate bracket (below left) operates in conjunction with in-pavement antennas and a roadside reader (below) to provide electronic identification for the vehicle. The laptop computer on top of the roadside reader cabinet is connected to it temporarily for on-site diagnostic activity. Two-way communication takes place between the transponder and the roadside reader even while tagged vehicles travel by the reader at up to 160 kilometers (100 miles) per hour. A single reader can monitor freely flowing highway traffic, in multiple lanes, through the use of antennas. Transactions recorded by the roadside reader are typically relayed to a central computer.

Photos, Mark IV Industries Ltd., I.V.H.S. Division, Ontario, Canada

A driver inserts his personal "smart card" into a small radio transponder as he approaches a toll-collection area. Receivers located either above the road or in the pavement communicate with the transponder, recording the locations where the car enters and exits the expressway and where the tolls are paid. Toll amounts are transmitted back to the transponder, and records of the transactions are entered onto the smart card.

nate routes to avoid those problems. The information may be transmitted by audio and visual means within the vehicle, along the roadside, and even in private homes and places of business.

Informing drivers of the potential danger of "downstream" operating problems can significantly improve highway safety. Moreover, providing sufficient navigation information to the driver so as to facilitate diversion around problem areas via parallel roadways can dramatically reduce congestion and delays.

In addition to transmitting relevant information on roadway conditions via traditional commercial radio broadcasts, many cities have established radio stations for the exclusive purpose of continuous traffic reporting. Likewise, many cities have implemented roadside changeable message signs that electronically display motorist advisories.

A changeable message sign, at the entrance to a tunnel in Newport News, Virginia, provides motorists with lane-control signals and other necessary advisories.

One of the more advanced strategies for the transmission of motorist information is the onboard vehicle navigation system. These systems make use of data storage technologies (typically compact discs) to display digitized road map and/or navigation information to the motorist inside the vehicle. The visual information, which can be augmented with voice-synthesized navigation commands, is typically displayed via a dashboard-mounted television monitor or through the use of so-called head-up displays that project "directional arrows" or brief text messages onto the lower portion of the vehicle's windshield. The onboard navigation system monitors the precise location of the vehicle over time by the use of either directional and distance measuring instrumentation mounted on the vehicle itself or geographic positioning systems that communicate with satellite or roadside transponders.

A number of demonstration projects are attempting to evaluate the potential of these onboard navigation systems to utilize real-time data on highway conditions in order to identify optimal diversion routes and display the detour information to the motorist. As operating problems (identified through the Advanced Traffic Management System) are transmitted to personnel located in the operations center, this information can be formatted and further relayed to the in-vehicle microprocessors that are a component of the onboard navigation systems. Possible technology for providing two-way, real-time communications between vehicles and the operations center include radio data communications, cellular systems, satellite communications, and roadside broadcasts used in conjunction with microwave transmissions or low-powered radio signals.

Ongoing research is also concerned with formulating algorithms for identifying optimal diversion routes subject to conditions prevailing on

Sumitomo Electric Industries, Ltd.

A woman inserts a compact disc into her car navigation system. Such discs can provide displays inside the vehicle of digitized road maps and other information useful to motorists.

A motorist uses a hand-held controller to ask for route guidance from Ali-Scout, a traveler information system developed by Siemens Automotive. The system employs infrared signals to send and receive data from a central computer via roadside beacons like that seen in the background. The information received by the driver is displayed on the Ali-Scout screen.

the roadway network. Coupled with this is research directed at such human issues such as how motorists respond to routing advisories and how such advisories can be best presented to the motorist. And, finally, systems to adjust traffic signals automatically so as to accommodate diverted vehicles are currently being deployed and tested.

In the future, increased emphasis is likely to be placed on transmitting traveler information to homes, businesses, and transportation terminals via teletext machines, electronic displays, and cable television. In this way, route planning can occur prior to departure as well as while the trip is under way.

Commercial Vehicle Operations

IVHS technology is being rapidly deployed for enhanced efficiency and safety in Commercial Vehicle Operations. Data communication networks between dispatchers and individual commercial vehicles are rapidly becoming standard equipment for many trucking fleets. These networks often make use of mobile satellite communications to facilitate two-way transmission of simple coded messages and to provide for continuous monitoring of vehicle location over large regions. The communication networks, along with onboard navigators, facilitate adaptive routing strategies. They allow routing decisions to be modified and updated while shipments are in transit. Dispatchers can adjust delivery routes to accommodate time-dependent customer demands. Vehicle operators can select detours to avoid unforeseen travel delays caused by accidents or other roadway incidents. This latter consideration becomes especially important in the transport of hazardous materials.

IVHS technologies extend to other aspects of commercial vehicle operations as well. Automatic vehicle identification technologies, coupled with instrumentation in the roadway for weighing and classifying commercial vehicles, are currently being used to significantly reduce delays associated with traveling through weigh stations or ports of entry (jurisdictional boundaries).

As part of demonstration projects in a number of regions, truck operators equipped with identification tags installed on their vehicles are able to drive through traditional bottlenecks with virtually no delay. They are able to do this because the required operational data are automatically processed. Such data include weight and classification information, the vehicle's safety and inspection history, and invoice data associated with goods delivery.

Regulatory agencies charged with the administrative management of interstate trucking operations are also able to take advantage of IVHS deployment. Computerized record systems improve the accessibility of data needed for assessing tariffs and for evaluating commercial transport safety issues. Moreover, the automated collection of routine commercial vehicle data will reduce manpower requirements at jurisdictional borders, weigh stations, and other checkpoints. Thus, the application of IVHS technology for commercial vehicle operations promises to reduce costs greatly while improving transport safety and efficiency.

The application of IVHS may also result in considerable improvements for bus and paratransit operations such as dial-a-ride bus service and van pools. Dynamic routing and scheduling can occur via onboard vehicle navigators. Communication between the transit vehicle, the fleet management center, and transit patrons at depots can lead to greater access and efficiency in public transportation. Likewise, communication and navigation technologies will likely prove useful with police, fire, and other emergency services.

Advanced Vehicle Control Systems

In essence, the previous three elements of IVHS can serve to enhance transportation safety and efficiency by monitoring highway operations and providing information on prevailing conditions to motorists and highway management agencies. The fourth element of IVHS, Advanced Vehicle Control Systems, will serve to improve roadway capacity and safety by assisting in and/or automating the driving task itself. Initial implementation of technology for advanced vehicle control will include systems that aid the driver in operating the vehicle. Such technologies include warning systems that activate automatically when a vehicle moves too close to an object, automatic braking systems that activate in emergencies, and onboard systems to enhance driver visibility at night or during bad weather.

Future technologies might well include adaptive systems that automatically regulate vehicle speed, acceleration, and braking. The physical space between vehicles, and those vehicles' relative velocities, might be regulated by onboard radar systems or by the transmission of information signals from one vehicle to the next.

Considerable research is also being undertaken to develop lateral guidance systems, which actually control the position of a vehicle within its travel lane. One such system under development utilizes video-image-processing techniques to carry out the lane-keeping task. A camera

Sumitomo Electric Industries, Ltd.

The bus location system developed by Sumitomo Electric Industries, Ltd., utilizes onboard vehicle navigators to obtain and display information concerning the movement of buses along their routes. Such systems are expected to help bus operators improve their scheduling and routing.

VORAD Safety Systems, Inc.

The small black square on the front of the bus houses an antenna transmitter and receiver assembly that is part of VORAD, a high-frequency radar system that warns drivers with tones and lights if their vehicles are too close to those ahead of them.

mounted on the vehicle's front bumper sends to an onboard computer a video image of the vehicle's location relative to a reference stripe painted on the roadway pavement. Image-processing algorithms continually measure the distance between the vehicle and the reference stripe. Signals generated by the computer are then transmitted to the vehicle's steering controller for automatic lateral adjustment.

A somewhat related approach to automatic lateral control involves a laser beam transmitter mounted atop a vehicle and receiver units installed at the roadside. The transmitter and receivers communicate information on lateral distance to the vehicle's onboard computer for automatic steering control. Yet another possible technology system for automatic lane keeping seeks to control lateral position by magnetic or electronic probes installed in the highway itself.

As vehicle control technologies advance, implementation will likely occur gradually. Some lanes may be set aside for automated operation only. These automated sections of highway would facilitate high-speed travel with short spacings between vehicles, allowing highway capacity to be increased significantly. At the same time, partially or fully automated control would dramatically reduce the consequences of driver error and thereby provide for safer operations.

Future directions

The deployment of IVHS is not without significant hurdles. Considerable work remains before its full implementation can become a reality. At a recent seminar addressing issues in automatic vehicle control, for example, a traffic engineer expressed outrage at the suggestion of using video images to monitor the lateral position of a vehicle relative to a painted reference stripe—"How can such a system work if snow is on the road?"

188

Indeed, the deployment of IVHS will require a great deal of additional research and technological refinement. IVHS must be fail-safe, even under the harsh environmental conditions to which highway facilities are often subjected. But barriers to IVHS implementation extend beyond needed advancements in technology. There are a considerable number of so-called institutional issues that must be addressed before the broad-based deployment of IVHS can occur.

For example, there are serious concerns regarding liability. As automated vehicle and highway systems are gradually deployed, there is a potential shift in liability for highway accidents from the driver to equipment manufacturers and operating agencies. If left unresolved, these liability issues could significantly impede IVHS deployment.

Also, the IVHS industry currently lacks protocols and standards for technology. For full benefits to be achieved from IVHS, standards must be established for hardware and software systems to ensure compatibility from one jurisdiction to the next. Manufacturing companies must be willing to cooperate to produce compatible equipment. Yet, if private companies are to be expected to invest in research and development, they will naturally desire a return on their investments. Thus, an operating environment that will encourage the sharing of innovations and still protect the proprietary right of developers must be established.

The operation and maintenance of IVHS will also necessitate changes in the manner in which the public sector currently operates. Deploying and operating IVHS will require an unprecedented amount of multi-jurisdictional cooperation. New areas of technical expertise will be required for operating and maintaining complex technology systems associated with IVHS. And, very importantly, there is a pressing need for new and innovative funding mechanisms by which to pay for the development, deployment, and maintenance of IVHS.

Despite the obstacles that currently exist, the utilization of IVHS appears to be on the horizon. Fundamental research efforts, as well as actual demonstration projects, are ongoing throughout the world. In North America, Europe, East Asia, and Australia, efforts are being directed at developing advanced technology systems to improve surface transportation. Thus, the opportunity to make significant improvements in highway operation and safety is now within our grasp.

FOR ADDITIONAL READING

"Applications of Advanced Technologies in Transportation Engineering," *Proceedings from the First International Conference* (American Society of Civil Engineers, 1989).

"Applications of Advanced Technologies in Transportation Engineering," *Proceedings from the Second International Conference* (American Society of Civil Engineers, 1991).

Institute of Transportation Engineers, *Traffic Engineering Handbook,* 4th ed. (Prentice Hall, 1992).

Institute of Transportation Engineers Journal, Special Issue, "Intelligent Vehicle-Highway Systems" (1990).

CLIMATE

IN THE ICE

by Michael C. Morrison

Scientists are drilling three kilometers into the Greenland ice cap to recover an unprecedented 200,000-year record of the Earth's climate. Their findings will aid in understanding past climate changes and the potential for human activity to affect climate in the decades ahead.

As the end of the 20th century approaches, predicting the weather not only days ahead but also years and decades into the future has taken on new importance. Growing concern about the influence of human activity on global temperatures and on large ecosystems like rain forests has raised questions about the changes humans may be making to the climate of the Earth. The more dire predictions of climate change, which include catastrophic sea-level rise, desertification, and severe disturbance to existing ecosystems, make it imperative that the causes of climate change be better understood.

Behind the question of climate change lies a dynamic and still poorly understood system involving land, air, sea, life, ice, and sun. These parts form a web of complex interactions and feedbacks called the climate system. Changes in any one part of the system affect all the others and ultimately result in a change in what is known as climate. The aim of climatology is to understand how this system works and which components are important in producing the climate on Earth.

Critical to an understanding of climate and the effects that human activity may be having on it is a record of how climate has behaved in the past. Scientists know that the ice ages have come and gone in 100,000-year cycles, and they have long recognized patterns of change in climate on much shorter, seasonal time scales. What they do not understand, however, are how climate changes take place—and why—on scales longer than the seasons. Records of direct observations of climate extend back only a few hundred years, with spotty accounts of exceptional events going back as much as a few thousand years. To understand why climate undergoes changes over long time periods, it is necessary to start by knowing how it has changed over those periods. In

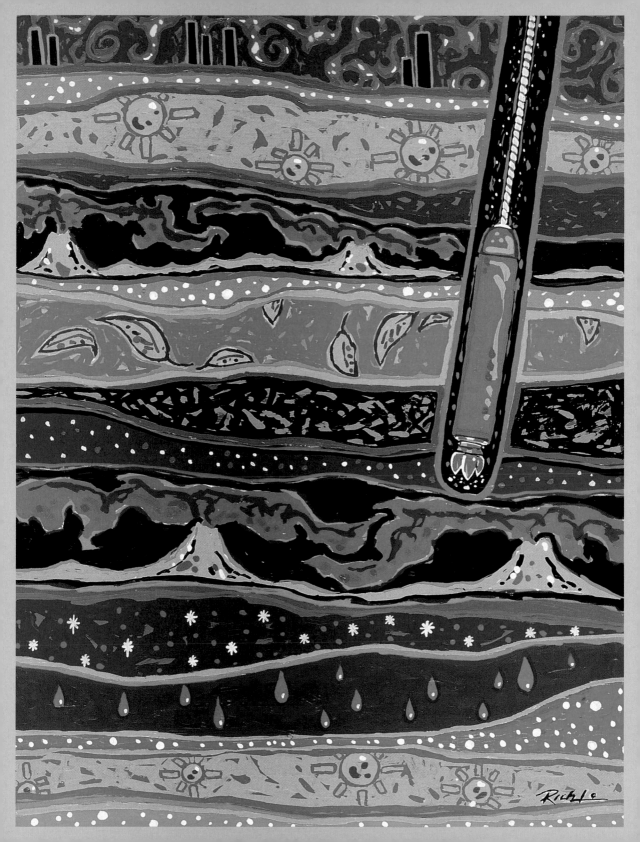

the absence of human records, scientists must look for natural records of climate change.

Examples of records that researchers have found useful are deep-sea and lake-bottom sediments and tree rings. These have provided some information about climate history, including the cycle of ice ages. Sediment records often contain very long histories, sometimes millions of years, but they are not detailed. Conversely, tree rings provide detailed records but of limited duration—a few thousand years at most. Further, both tree rings and sediments record climate only indirectly. For instance, how well a tree thrives and grows in a given year is affected by climate, so the thickness of a tree's annual growth rings allows inferences to be made about climate. That information, however, is "filtered" through the physiology of the tree.

Ice cores, cylinders of ice drilled from polar ice sheets and high-altitude glaciers around the world, can provide not only a very detailed record of climate—one capable of annual and even seasonal resolution—but also a continuous record hundreds of thousands of years long. Unlike sediments and tree rings, ice cores carry a relatively direct record of atmospheric conditions stored in the ice itself. Thus, information obtained from ice cores complements that obtained from indirect sources.

The objective of the Greenland Ice Sheet Project Two (GISP2) is to recover the longest, most detailed continuous record of climate history available from the Northern Hemisphere from a 3,000-meter ice core drilled from the Greenland ice sheet. (One meter is about 3.3 feet.) The core is anticipated to yield a 200,000-year history of climate. That history should allow scientists to better understand the important causes of climate change and thus provide a context for assessing the potential for human activities to affect the natural course of climate change.

How ice sheets record climate

In places where the snow that falls from year to year does not completely melt or evaporate, each new year's snowfall adds to what already exists. It is this process that creates the glaciers, ice sheets, and ice caps of the world in polar regions and at high altitudes. An ice sheet consists of successive annual layers of snow, each preserved in order, one layer beneath the next.

When snow falls on an ice sheet, it carries with it dust and chemicals from the atmosphere. In effect, the ice sheet preserves samples of the atmosphere's chemistry from times well before direct records began to be taken, storing them in sequential layers. As each snow layer piles atop previous ones, the layers below become compressed under the accumulating weight, and eventually they turn into ice. This transition from snow to ice occurs at a characteristic depth for each site and depends on the average annual snow accumulation and the average temperature. The depth at which snow turns to ice is known as the firn-ice transition.

A characteristic of the firn-ice transition is that spaces between snow crystals above the transition turn into bubbles—small pockets of trapped air—below the transition. As a result, ice below the transition contains

MICHAEL C. MORRISON is Associate Director, GISP2 Science Management Office, Institute for the Study of Earth, Oceans, and Space, University of New Hampshire.

(Overleaf) Illustration by Rich Lo

(Top left) Amy Tchao, University of New Hampshire;
(top right) Michael Morrison; (bottom) Debra A. Meese, CRREL

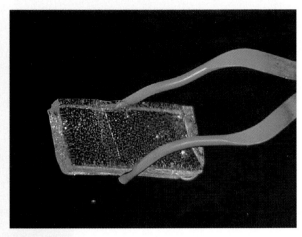

The layered nature of Greenland's accumulated snowfall is apparent in a backlit vertical slice of the top meter of snow at the GISP2 site (top left). Each annual snow layer preserves samples of the atmosphere and its chemistry for the year in which the snow fell. Small air spaces in the snow eventually become ice-embedded bubbles (top right), each a tiny sample flask containing air from hundreds to hundreds of thousands of years ago. Each layer also contains atmospheric dust and chemicals, which appear in the ice as a visible band, sometimes quite prominently (left).

not only dust and chemicals but also samples of the atmosphere from the time that the bubbles formed. In essence, the bubbles are small sample flasks that can be analyzed to learn the composition of the atmosphere hundreds to hundreds of thousands of years ago.

Previous ice-core records and the need for GISP2

Over the past few decades, many ice cores have been drilled to obtain climate history information. The predominant drilling sites have been the Antarctic and Greenland ice sheets. Ice cores have also been re-trieved from lower-latitude, high-altitude locations in Asia and North and South America.

Prior to current Greenland drilling activities, the Vostok ice-core project in Antarctica, conducted by a French-Soviet collaboration in the 1980s, provided the longest history of climate. The approximately 2,500-meter Vostok ice core represented 160,000 years and encompassed one full ice-age (glacial) cycle, which began about 120,000 years ago and ended about 11,000–12,000 years ago, and the two warm (interglacial) periods at either end of the glacial cycle. Among other findings the Vostok record revealed a strong correlation between temperature and carbon dioxide concentration in the atmosphere, further supporting the predicted role of carbon dioxide in influencing climate.

Researchers with the Vostok project unload a length of ice core retrieved from the Antarctic ice sheet. Prior to the current Greenland drilling activities, the French-Soviet Vostok effort provided the longest history of climate, about 160,000 years. Among its important findings the Vostok record revealed a strong correlation between temperature and atmospheric carbon dioxide concentration.

The Vostok record also suggested that the recent history of climate was characterized by long cooling periods followed by a relatively rapid transition to the warmer interglacial periods. But because of low annual snow accumulation rates, the level of detail in the Vostok core was insufficient to reveal the processes at work during these rapid-warming events. Nor could it determine the true cause-and-effect relationship between temperature and carbon dioxide; *i.e.,* whether temperature was the factor causing changes in carbon dioxide concentrations or vice versa. Further, the timing of the glacial-interglacial cycle appeared to be synchronous with small, long-term cyclical changes in the Earth's orbit (the so-called Milankovitch effect) that affect the solar heating of the Northern Hemisphere but not the Southern Hemisphere. It thus appeared from the Vostok record that solar heating variations in the Northern Hemisphere might be controlling the 100,000-year glacial cycle around the world.

The Vostok results stimulated significant interest in studying the potential importance of the Northern Hemisphere in controlling climate change. For example, Wallace Broecker of the Lamont-Doherty Geological Observatory, Palisades, New York, who is presently chairman of the GISP2 Advisory Committee, proposed that the North Atlantic may be controlling circulation of the world's oceans, perhaps partially explaining the Northern Hemisphere's role in climate change.

The Greenland ice sheet provides a unique opportunity to recover a climate history of the Northern Hemisphere and, because Greenland has greater annual snowfall than Antarctica, a much more detailed record than the Vostok record. Two-thirds of Greenland lies within the Arctic Circle, and its ice sheet, the island's major physical feature, blankets nearly 85% of the land. In the late 1970s a deep ice core was retrieved from the Greenland ice sheet in a U.S.-Danish-Swiss study named GISP (later called GISP I to distinguish it from GISP2). Much was learned from the core, including remarkable evidence that the climate may have changed from glacial to interglacial conditions in as little as 50 years. But, while the GISP I core was drilled in a logistically convenient location

194

on the southeastern part of the ice cap near an existing defense radar station, the site was not ideal from a scientific standpoint.

For recovery of as complete and accurate a record as possible, the best place in Greenland to drill was thought to be near the highest point of the ice sheet, an area about 650 kilometers north of the Arctic Circle known as Summit. (A kilometer is about 0.62 miles.) There the ice exhibits the least lateral movement, reducing the possibility that ice that had migrated in at some level from a different site with different characteristics could be misinterpreted as a rapid change in climate. In addition, the ice at Summit was estimated to be 3,000 meters thick, containing in unparalleled detail a 200,000-year record of climate and perhaps encompassing two full glacial and interglacial cycles.

In the late 1980s European and U.S. scientists met and concluded that the best way to recover the climate record available at Summit was to extract two cores. One core would be drilled directly at Summit and the other 20 or 30 kilometers away on the flank. Two cores would address many concerns and provide many benefits. A primary concern was determining whether the rapid climate change suggested by the GISP I record was the result of an actual climate event or only lateral ice movement. Further, the two Summit cores would be located far enough apart that the degree of ice movement at each core site would be different. Thus, an event detected in both cores could be confidently attributed

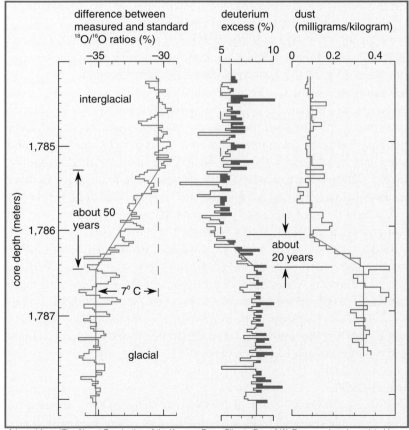

The GISP I ice core, retrieved during the late 1970s from a site in southeastern Greenland, contained intriguing evidence that the climate may have shifted extremely rapidly from glacial to interglacial conditions at the end of the last glacial cycle. The graph at left traces portions of three separate measurements from the GISP I core—oxygen-18/oxygen-16 ratio, deuterium excess, and dust content— at a depth corresponding to the end of the last ice age. All three measurements show sudden shifts indicative of warming over a 20–50-year time span, while the magnitude of the change in the $^{18}O/^{16}O$ ratio, which can be read as an "isotopic thermometer," indicates a temperature increase of as much as 7° C (12.6° F).

Adapted from "The Abrupt Termination of the Younger Dryas Climate Event," W. Dansgaard et al., reprinted by permission of Nature, vol. 339, no. 6225, pp. 532–533, June 15, 1989, © Macmillan Magazines Ltd.

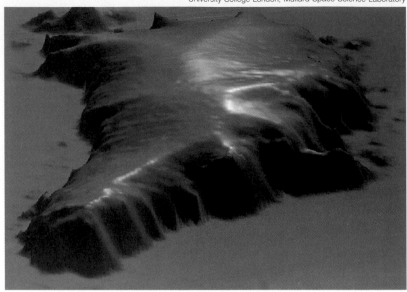

The ice sheet that entombs Greenland's actual landmass is depicted in a three-dimensional map (right) synthesized by computer from satellite altimeter data. The highest point, known as Summit, lies about 3,000 meters above bedrock near the center of the sheet. A contour map (below), giving elevations in meters, locates the GISP2 and GRIP drill sites as well as the earlier GISP I site.

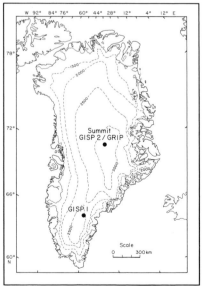

GISP2 Science Management Office

to the climate rather than to ice movement. In general, two records would allow more certain interpretation of the recovered climate history than one. The different methods used to analyze each core and different scientific approaches would further assure that conclusions about the climate could be trusted. Finally, on a practical level, two cores drilled independently would provide some insurance that, in case of difficulties, at least one core would be successfully recovered.

In the fall of 1988 the U.S. National Science Foundation (NSF) funded GISP2. About the same time, an eight-nation European collaborative funded drilling of the companion site, an effort called the Greenland Icecore Project (GRIP). The plan for GISP2, which would work at the flank location, included a large array of analyses on the core in order to maximize the information that could be obtained from the record. Over the next few years, 25 different research projects at 17 universities and other institutions across the U.S. would participate in GISP2. The European GRIP endeavor made similar plans to include as many analyses as possible. The diversity of research and level of collaboration between researchers for these two cores represent a milestone in ice-core research and promise to produce the richest history of climate ever.

In May 1989 a ski-equipped LC-130 aircraft operated by the 109th Air National Guard from Schenectady, New York, touched down on the Greenland ice sheet near Summit and dropped off five people with 4,100 kilograms (9,000 pounds) of navigation equipment and supplies. Within a day these five had located the exact spot chosen for GISP2 drilling and had established the beginnings of the camp that would support scientists and drilling personnel for the project. GISP2 had begun.

Life at GISP2

During the summer months of the Northern Hemisphere, between 40 and 60 people live and work at the GISP2 camp. The field season typically begins in late April or early May and ends in late August or early September. From about May 9 to August 5, the Sun does not set, giving 24 hours of daylight. Temperatures at Summit for most of the Greenland summer range from −20° to 0° C (−4° to 32° F) but may drop as low as −40° C (−40° F) at the beginning or end of the season. Cold air does not hold much moisture, and if there is no wind or cloud cover to block the Sun, it is not unusual to find people working outside in T-shirts.

People travel to the GISP2 camp by ski-equipped LC-130 aircraft operated by the Air National Guard. New arrivals step off the plane to a cold, flat, white world punctuated with red and blue camp buildings and the geodesic dome that houses the drill. At an altitude of 3,200 meters above sea level, newcomers find themselves gasping for air with slight exertion. When the wind is low and clouds are few, the icescape is brilliant. The snow surface sparkles with light reflected from snowflakes, and the horizon is featureless in all directions save the campsite. When there are clouds and wind, snow fills the air, often making it impossible to tell where the sky and the snow surface meet. Flag lines along all major routes of travel around the camp prevent people from becoming lost during such whiteouts.

Although annual accumulation of snow is less than a meter, a structure on the snow surface rapidly gathers large drifts during windstorms, and camp personnel work hard to keep buildings clear of snow. Before each winter some structures are taken down and stored to reduce snow-removal efforts when the field season resumes the following spring. The two permanent buildings are designed to minimize drifting effects. One, the drill dome, because of its shape, induces a scouring effect that greatly reduces snow-removal requirements. While some drifting still occurs, there is a drift-free area around the dome. The other permanent building is the galley and social area, known as the "Big House." This structure is erected on stilts, which offer little wind resistance and thus do not cause drifting. Someday the annual snowfalls will bring the snow surface up to the base of the Big House, and the usual drifting process will begin. All structures left on the surface ultimately will be buried by drifting processes and snow accumulation.

People sleep in either weatherports or tents. Weatherports at the camp are red half-cylinder structures made from tubular aluminum arches and a canvas cover. Equipped with plywood floors and oil heaters, they lodge up to 15 people. Some team members who prefer more private, though colder, accommodations live in unheated tents. Every year a small, thriving "tent city" springs up. Everyone takes meals in the Big House, which is staffed by a full-time cook, and all look forward to "flight periods" when aircraft bring in supplies, mail, and "freshies"—fresh fruit and vegetables. Electricity for the camp comes from a diesel generator, the heat from which is also used to melt snow for the camp's water supply.

Drilling

Until GISP2, typical ice-core drills produced cores no larger than 10 centimeters in diameter. (A centimeter is about 0.4 inch.) Because of

197

The "Big House" (top, at left), erected on stilts to prevent snowdrift accumulation, is one of the GISP2 camp's two permanent structures and serves as mess hall, social area, and administration building. Nearby are the red half-cylinder weatherports used as sleeping accommodations by some of the scientific team. Flag lines between structures keep people from becoming lost during whiteouts. The other permanent camp building is the dome (above left) that houses the drill and the lower part of its 37-meter tower. In favorable weather team members (above right) find inventive ways outdoors to relieve the monotony of the drilling work and the icy environment.

the number of researchers involved in GISP2, a greater quantity of ice was required; thus, a larger drill was developed. The NSF contracted with the University of Alaska's Polar Ice Coring Office, which provides logistic and drilling support for NSF-funded ice-coring efforts, to build a drill that would recover a core 13.2 centimeters in diameter, producing almost twice as much ice as the 10-centimeter drill.

With each drill run the GISP2 drill typically cuts a five-to-six-meter length of ice core. The drill itself is approximately 20 meters long and is lowered down the borehole on a four-kilometer-long Kevlar cable. The cable contains electrical conductors that take power to the drill and return information about the drill back to the operators at the surface. Because ice deforms easily under pressure, the hole formed by drilling would close on itself from the pressure of the surrounding ice if there was nothing in the hole to supply back pressure. Many fluids, including jet fuel, diesel fuel, specialized petroleum-based fluids, and ethylene glycol antifreeze, have been used for this purpose. A new drilling fluid, the organic compound butyl acetate, is being used in the GISP2 hole because it is one of the few fluids that have a low viscosity and low freezing point and are relatively safe to work with. The entire borehole is filled with butyl acetate to within 100 meters of the surface to keep the drill hole open.

The leading section of the drill consists of a cutter head, the component that actually does the cutting, and a hollow tube called the core sleeve, which accepts the ice core that the cutter head carves out. The drill section above the core sleeve comprises a pump, which pulls drilling fluid and ice chips from the cutter head around the outside of the core sleeve and into a screen section above the pump. The chips are trapped in the screen section, while the fluid returns to the hole. Above the screen section are the motor that turns the cutter head and the instrument package that controls the drill motor and measures temperature, current to the motor, weight on the drill cutters, and speed of the motor. At the very top, or trailing section, of the drill are three pieces of spring steel known as antitorque blades. The blades press against the side of the borehole, preventing the drill body from spinning as the cutter head turns against the ice. At the surface a carousel holding a fresh empty core sleeve and screen section waits for the drill to arrive with a new section of core. The full core sleeve and screen section are loaded on the carousel, the new waiting sections are loaded on the drill, and the drill returns down the hole for another core section. In late 1992, when the drill was working at a depth of 2,250 meters, it produced 30 meters of core per day during two shifts of drilling.

Once a new section of ice core is in the drill dome, it is extruded from the core sleeve, placed in trays, and cut into two-meter-long sections. To prevent microscopic cracks from forming in the core and thus allowing the trapped gas bubbles to mix with present-day air, the temperature of the ice is never allowed to rise above − 15° C (5° F). During the summer the temperature is often higher than this, so once the ice is cut, it is immediately moved to a network of trenches below the snow surface.

Processing the core

Excavated out of the snow surface is a trench 50 meters long and 3–4 meters wide. The trench connects a large subsurface room—essentially a snow cave—where core is stored before processing, another trench

The supporting superstructure for GISP2's 20-meter-long drill is housed inside the drill dome. Made of aluminum and reinforced fiberglass pipe, it includes an innovative carousel system that allows drilling operations to continue as ice-core sections are unloaded. After the drill is hauled to the surface, the core-filled sleeve is rotated out of the drill assembly to be emptied, while a fresh sleeve is swung into the assembly and the drill returned down the hole for another core section.

(Top and bottom) Bruce Koci, Polar Ice Coring Office, University of Alaska, Fairbanks

GISP2 workers, dressed in clothing that protects them from butyl acetate drilling fluid, handle a freshly cut six-meter-long ice-core section inside the dome. Temperature in the dome is kept near − 15° C to prevent thermal shock to the core after it is extracted from the ice sheet.

Richard B. Alley, Pennsylvania State University, University Park

GISP2 researcher cuts ice samples in the core-processing line, a subsurface trench that receives the new cores from the drill dome. Once extracted, the ice core is sectioned to allow for a variety of continuous and occasional on-site measurements, including visual appearance, electrical conductivity, sampling for isotopes, and analyses for major ions and dust.

known as the core-processing line (CPL), and a second large storage room where processed core and samples are kept before shipment to the U.S. It is in this complex that the core is first processed and sampled. Many researchers leave the field with prepared samples to be analyzed in the U.S., while others complete their analyses in the field.

The CPL trench is 30 meters long by 4 meters wide and has six alcoves off the side. The air temperature in the trench ranges from −35° C (−31° F) in the early part of the field season to −20° C (−4° F) near the end. An average of 15 scientists work 10 or more hours per day in the trench processing core. Even though there is no wind in the trench to contend with, working in its extreme temperatures requires heavy clothing and occasional warm-up breaks. Some researchers must also wear special "clean suits" and gloves to prevent contamination of the core samples.

The CPL plays a critical role beyond just processing the core. Many analyses are performed there directly on the core, and discussion of the results among the researchers guides the course of subsequent sampling and analysis. When one researcher detects an interesting feature in the core, others are notified and can focus their efforts on the section of interest. The discussion also serves to break up tasks that are otherwise tedious and cold.

Movement in the ice sheet

Central to all measurements is the nature of the motion of ice in the ice sheet. The ice near Summit is moving vertically downward as new snow falls each year. The ice near the edges of the ice sheet is moving horizontally, carrying away ice mass as new snow falls on the surface. Surface snowfall initially has a low density, usually about three-tenths that of liquid water. With the continual addition of new snow, the snow below the surface becomes increasingly compressed and dense until it reaches the firn-ice transition, where it achieves a density of about nine-tenths that of water.

200

At GISP2 the firn-ice transition lies about 90 meters down, where the layers are formed from snow that fell about AD 1700. Below this point the density of the ice does not change appreciably. But the horizontal movement at the edges of the ice sheet stretches and thins the ice at Summit so that, as a given layer of ice moves downward, it becomes thinner and thinner. Consequently, a layer of snow that starts out nearly a meter thick at the surface is thinned first by compression and then by stretching. Toward the bottom of the ice sheet, the amount of thinning increases rapidly. Thus, whereas the ice at a depth of about 1,700 meters—a little more than halfway to the bottom—marks the glacial-to-interglacial transition, which took place 11,000–12,000 years ago, the bottom of the ice sheet, at 3,000 meters, is expected to be about 200,000 years old.

Dating the record

For the climate record contained in the GISP2 core to be useful, scientists must know the age of the core at different depths. Accurate knowledge of these ages is critical to understanding the processes involved in the rapid climate transitions observed so far in the Vostok and GISP I records.

Several ice-core properties studied by GISP2 researchers have an annual signal; that is, there is a peak in the property (for example, in the concentration of dust) every year. By counting these peaks, each year can be identified and the age of the core determined. Because of thinning and other processes, however, counting layers in other cores has proceeded only to ages of a few thousand years. For older ages theoretical models of the ages and specialized but less accurate measurements have been made. At GISP2, because of the high annual snowfall and because many measurements that detect annual peaks are made and can be compared, counting has dated the core to unprecedented ages, about 40,000 years before the present. GISP2 thus promises to be an exceptionally well-dated record.

Ice-core measurements

Most of the chemical elements that are found naturally in the Earth's crust and atmosphere are mixtures of two or more forms called isotopes. Each isotope of a given element is characterized by a different atomic mass, reflecting differing numbers of neutrons in the atomic nucleus. While each isotope of an element behaves essentially the same chemically, its slightly different mass gives it slightly different physical properties. Two elements whose stable isotopes are important in ice-core research are oxygen and hydrogen, and they provide scientists with information on the history of temperature.

By far the most common isotope of oxygen is oxygen-16 (^{16}O), with an atomic mass of 16. The next most common oxygen isotope is oxygen-18 (^{18}O), whose two additional neutrons in the nucleus give it an atomic mass of 18. Most water molecules contain ^{16}O and thus have the formula $H_2^{16}O$. Water that contains ^{18}O, and has the formula $H_2^{18}O$, condenses more readily than ^{16}O-containing water. The ratio of ^{18}O to ^{16}O in a given sample of water depends primarily on the temperature at which the water condensed from a vapor. Thus, measuring the $^{18}O/^{16}O$ ratio in the ice core makes it possible to calculate the temperature at the time the snow fell. The ratio in water of the two primary isotopes of hydrogen—hydrogen-1 (^1H) and hydrogen-2 (deuterium; ^2H)—also depends on temperature and provides additional temperature information.

This "isotopic thermometer" records seasonal variations in temperature as well as longer-term climate changes and is one of the measurements used in counting annual layers. Measurements on the isotopes of oxygen and hydrogen in the GISP2 core are being carried out by researchers at the University of Colorado and the University of Washington.

One· of the more pressing questions about how the climate may change over the next few decades concerns the role of the atmospheric "greenhouse gases" and the effects of human-caused increases in their concentrations. Greenhouse gases, which include carbon dioxide, water vapor, methane, and chlorofluorocarbons, are so named because they trap solar heat that is reradiated from the Earth's surface and thus influence global temperatures and climate patterns. The main naturally occurring greenhouse gases are carbon dioxide and water vapor. Without their presence during much of the Earth's history, the planet would have been a frozen world. On the other hand, concentrations of greenhouse gases much higher than actually exist might have made the Earth's surface an inferno like that of the planet Venus.

A key to a detailed understanding of the role of these gases in the climate system is a record of their concentrations in the past. Very accurate atmospheric measurements of carbon dioxide concentrations have been made in Hawaii since 1958, but no earlier records exist. The trapped bubbles of air contained in the ice core provide a unique opportunity to analyze the composition of the atmosphere before the late 1950s. Measurements on the gases in the ice core are being carried out by researchers at the Scripps Institution of Oceanography, San Diego, California; the University of Arizona; and the University of Rhode Island.

The special head of a laser-scattering device melts a strip of ice from a core section for continuous dust-concentration measurements, which are made from the collected water. The light-scattering properties of the dust allow readings of relative concentrations from core lengths as thin as one centimeter, sufficient to reveal annual peaks in dust concentrations.

Michael Morrison

Dust in the air is deposited on the ice sheet along with snow. The amount of dust delivered to the ice sheet depends on how much dust is available to become airborne and how much of that dust the winds transport to Greenland. Volcanoes are a major but short-lived source of dust, and volcanic eruptions are routinely observed in the GISP2 record as high levels of dust. For recent times, when volcanic dust peaks in the core can be compared with known eruptions, the peaks aid in dating the core. By identifying volcanic dust with known sources around the world, scientists can deduce atmospheric circulation patterns.

Dust concentrations in the GISP2 core are being measured by researchers at the University of New Hampshire and the State University of New York at Buffalo. The researchers at Buffalo use the light-scattering properties of dust to obtain readings of the relative concentrations of dust in core lengths as thin as one centimeter. This level of detail is sufficient to reveal annual peaks in dust concentrations. Current thinking suggests that greater wind strength in the spring takes more dust to the GISP2 site and thus is responsible for the yearly peaks in the core. As mentioned above, the dust peaks are also used to count annual layers and date the core at different depths. Because of the unparalleled resolution of the dust analyses in the GISP2 core, the annual dust peaks are a mainstay of core dating.

Concentrations of chemical constituents depend on source strength and transport efficiency, as do dust concentrations. However, the major ions found in the ice core have a wide range of sources and thus can provide a wide range of information about climate. The major soluble chemical constituents found in ice are sodium, magnesium, calcium, potassium, chloride, ammonium, nitrate, and sulfate.

Emissions from volcanic eruptions account for some of the largest concentrations of chemical constituents in the ice core. Volcanic emissions

Mark Twickler, University of New Hampshire

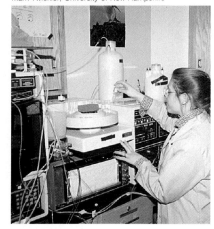

Laboratory researcher at the University of New Hampshire prepares a sample of ice core that has been shipped to the U.S. for analysis. The instrument, an ion chromatograph, is used to measure major ions in core samples.

Prominent peaks in the dust and sulfate record from the GISP2 core at a depth of 147 meters reflect the volcanic eruption of Mt. St. Helens in Washington state in AD 1479. The dust reached Greenland first and the sulfate shortly thereafter. Identifying such peaks with known eruptions and sources helps scientists date the core and deduce atmospheric circulation patterns.

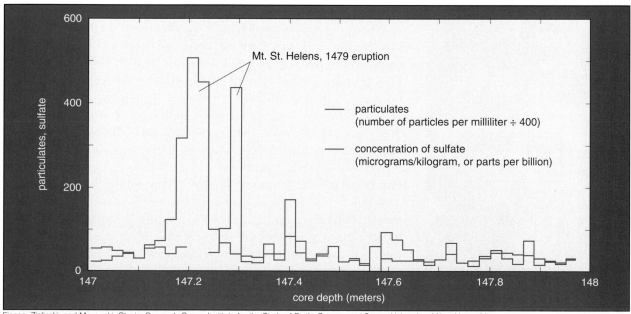

Fiacco, Zielinski, and Mayewski, Glacier Research Group, Institute for the Study of Earth, Oceans, and Space, University of New Hampshire

(Right) GISP2 investigator tends an electrical conductivity measurement (ECM) device as it draws a pair of electrodes along a length of core while measuring the electrical resistance between them. ECM analysis provides a rapid overview of the chemical content and the amount of dust in the core and thus aids in planning further sampling and analysis.

Amy Tchao, University of New Hampshire

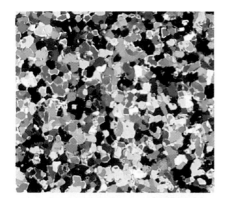

Photos, CRREL

have different compositions but commonly include sulfate or chloride ions. Another important source of atmospheric ions is human activity. The burning of fossil fuels, which contain sulfur, appears in the GISP2 core as a dramatic increase in sulfate concentrations since the beginning of the 20th century. Published studies by Paul Mayewski, chief scientist of GISP2 and director of the GISP2 Science Management Office, and his colleagues have shown that sulfate levels in core layers representing the years of the 1900s have risen as high as three times the "background" level of the past 1,000 years. Chemical concentrations in the core provide a window on a wide variety of important source and transport processes active in the climate system and thus a detailed view of its important changes. Chemical analyses are being performed at the University of New Hampshire and the University of Miami, Florida.

Electrical conductivity measurement (ECM) is an extremely rapid analysis performed in the field by researchers from the Desert Research Institute, Reno, Nevada. Two electrodes are drawn along the surface of the ice core while the electrical resistance between them is measured. ECM provides a rapid overview of the signal in the ice core. Electrical resistance is affected primarily by chemical composition and the amount of dust. Thus, the technique reveals annual peaks as well as volcanic events and general climate transitions. ECM gives a high-resolution "road map" of the core that aids in planning further sampling and analysis. In addition, it provides an overview, with superb resolution, of climate history and is another of the mainstays of core dating.

Researchers at Pennsylvania State University and at the Cold Regions Research and Engineering Laboratory, Hanover, New Hampshire, study the physical properties of the ice core. Ice crystal size and orientation, ice density, annual layer thicknesses, and temperature of the borehole at the time of drilling all reveal information about the processes that acted on the ice during its formation or during its stay in the ice sheet. Larger ice crystals are formed during summer than during winter, and crystal

204

size can be observed with the eye, allowing annual layers to be counted. Counting these visible annual layers is a third mainstay of core dating.

Snow accumulation is believed to have been less during the colder glacial periods than during the warm interglacial. To calculate the actual annual accumulation at the time the snow fell, researchers must measure the annual layer thickness in the ice core and determine the amount of thinning that occurred. Once accumulation rates have been derived, they provide information about the climate directly and are essential for interpreting other ice-core measurements.

Portents of the future

The promise of the climate record of GISP2, as well as that of the GRIP core, is becoming reality. In July 1992 the GRIP team reached bedrock at 3,028.6 meters, and the GISP2 core is expected to be completed by the end of the Greenland summer of 1993. Already both drilling efforts have yielded intriguing information. Early results from GRIP as well as an overview of the European project are discussed in the accompanying Sidebar, while three papers published in early 1993 and discussed below

(Opposite page, lower left) Thin sections of GISP2 core ice from (top to bottom) 92, 314, and 1,330 meters depth, photographed in a polarizing microscope, demonstrate the progressive increase in size of the ice crystals with increasing depth. Ice crystal size and orientation give scientists clues about the processes that acted on the ice during its formation or its stay inside the ice sheet. The small rounded, light-colored inclusions— particularly prominent in the middle photo—are compressed air bubbles that contain samples of past atmospheric composition.

GRIP—Partner Project of GISP2
by Bernhard Stauffer

When scientists concluded that two ice cores would be needed from the ice cap in central Greenland to obtain all the wanted information about the climate and environment of the past, it was a difficult task to convince the funding agencies in the U.S. and Europe of the merits of their plan. The arguments in favor of two drilling efforts were strong, however, and ultimately persuasive. The top of Summit was selected for GRIP and a location 32 kilometers downslope for GISP2.

The European project is coordinated by the European Science Foundation. Scientists from eight nations—Belgium, Denmark, France, Germany, Iceland, Italy, Switzerland, and the United Kingdom—have collaborated in the field work and in the analyses of the ice core. GRIP is funded by the participating nations and by the European Communities. During the summer of 1989 the project's camp was erected and drilling preparations started. All logistic tasks including camp construction, drilling, and maintenance and transportation are coordinated by the GRIP Operation Center at the Geophysical Institute of the University of Copenhagen. All personnel and all material needed at Summit are flown in from Søndre Strømfjord in southwestern Greenland over

Bernhard Stauffer is Professor of Physics at the University of Bern, Switzerland.

a distance of 800 kilometers either by chartered ski-equipped U.S. Air Force Hercules aircraft or, in the case of light cargo and passengers, by a Twin Otter aircraft put at GRIP's disposal by the British Antarctic Survey.

The skyline of Summit is dominated by three seven-meter-high black domes. One lodges the electric generator, the communications facilities, the kitchen, and the dining hall; another, the workshop; and the third, the drill platform. It is surprising for a drill camp that no drill tower is visible from the surface, but the drill, called ISTUK, lies in a trench five meters below the snow surface. ISTUK is an updated version of the same drill used in the U.S.-Danish-Swiss GISP I operation. The 11-meter-long electromechanical drill is lowered on a thin steel cable into the borehole. Electrical conductors in the cable allow control of downhole activity from the surface and provide the power for drilling. The drill cuts an ice core 10 centimeters in diameter and recovers a 2.5-meter length in a typical run. At the surface, drill and drill tower can be tipped to a horizontal position to aid in extracting the core and preparing the drill for a new run. Only two operators are needed in a shift. Three shifts work around the clock, allowing recovery of about 150 meters of core per week. Many of the drillers and the maintenance people at GRIP are the scientists involved in ice-core

View (above) from the top of the GRIP camp's utility dome at Summit includes (left to right) the main dome, drill dome, and parcholtents used as sleeping quarters. (Right) A GRIP scientist prepares the drill, which has been tipped from its vertical position, for another ice-coring run.

Photos, Andreas Fuchs

analysis; their potential lack of technicians' skills is compensated by high motivation.

A characteristic feature of GRIP is the analyses performed in the field. Some on-site tests are made to help select samples for special analyses, while others, like analyses for hydrogen peroxide, ammonium, and organic acids, are done to avoid problems with ice that could become contaminated during transport and storage. Continuous measurements are made of the core's electrical properties (related to content of hydrogen ion and total neutral salt) and of concentrations of dust particles, ammonium, nitrate, hydrogen peroxide, formaldehyde, and calcium. The seasonal variations in many of these properties and constituents have allowed scientists to count annual layers in the core well into the last glaciation and to date the core accurately.

In the summer of 1990 GRIP reached a depth of 769 meters, and in the next summer, 2,321 meters. In July 1992 drilling hit bedrock at a depth of 3,028.6 meters, where the age of the ice is more than 200,000 years. The core has been shipped to Europe and stored in cold rooms in different laboratories for numerous analyses, some of which will last several years. Nevertheless, early results from on-site and laboratory analyses have been published.

The stable-isotope record down to 2,321 meters, representing the climate of the past 40,000 years, confirms earlier findings of several mild climate periods during the mid and late parts of the last glaciation, or glacial cycle. The episodes start abruptly, last 500 to 2,000 years, and terminate gradually. Furthermore, the end of the last glaciation, the last global climatic change of the same order as that predicted for the near future from enhanced greenhouse effects, also occurred in dramatic steps. A warm period starting 14,500 years ago was followed by a cold period starting about 12,700 years ago. This final cold period came to an abrupt end 11,500 years ago, when the temperature in Greenland increased about 7° C (12.6° F) in less than 50 years. At Summit the ice representing this transition is found halfway between surface and bedrock, where any irregularities of the stratigraphy can be excluded and where the thickness of an annual layer is still more than five centimeters.

Results have also been obtained with new analytic techniques, one example being the measurements of ammonium and organic acids. Ammonium was measured for the first time continuously along the core, and GRIP scientists were quite surprised to find sporadic occurrences in the record of very high ammonium concentrations. Further chemical analyses suggest that they represent large forest fires that arose somewhere in the Northern Hemisphere.

Some of the more exciting results emerging from GRIP concern the warm period, called the Eem, before the last glaciation. Although the information is still too scanty to be interpreted with confidence, the ice core from Summit is certain to reveal secrets about this previous interglacial, which was on average about 2° C (3.6° F) warmer than today.

are harbingers of the insight into climate that the GISP2 record will offer.

Mayewski and colleagues reported evidence that the sharp increase in atmospheric sulfate concentrations during the past century may be having a cooling effect on temperatures of the North Atlantic. Whereas increases in carbon dioxide may raise average temperatures, increased sulfate may reduce average temperatures. The researchers compared concentrations of sulfate in the ice core with historical temperature records before and after the onset of the modern industrial period (about AD 1885). For the North Atlantic region they found that, for the millennium prior to 1885, changes in sulfate concentrations did not appear to have a major influence on long-term temperature changes. On the other hand, during the industrial period the high levels of sulfate resulting from human activity may have acted to reduce temperatures significantly and to mask the warming effects of increasing carbon dioxide.

Richard Alley of Pennsylvania State University and colleagues reported new information that takes advantage of the exceptional accuracy of dating made possible by counting annual layers in the GISP2 core. Knowing the thickness of each annual layer, in conjunction with ice deformation models, allowed the investigators to estimate the amount of snow that fell during each year; in other words, the accumulation rate. The accumulation rate is thought to be determined in part by temperature, with increased accumulation implying higher temperature. In examining the GISP2 core, not only did Alley's team find the same rapid change from glacial to interglacial periods that had been seen in the GISP I core, but they also discovered that this change, as reflected in the accumulation rate, occurred in just three years and may have involved a temperature change of as much as 7° C (12.6° F). In addition, they found evidence for rapid transitions between other periods.

Ken Taylor of the Desert Research Institute and colleagues also reported that the rapid change indicated in the GISP I core is real and that such changes were more common and more rapid than previously thought. In their paper they described climate fluctuations, as reflected in the ECM signal, that occur in less than 5 to 20 years. They likened the transitions between cold and warm periods to a "flickering switch"—that is, the climate flips rapidly back and forth between the two states before finally settling down into the new state. Alley's and Taylor's conclusions focus the search for mechanisms responsible for climate change on ones capable of such swift change and flickering behavior. Atmospheric circulation and mechanisms with "trigger" responses must be weighed as important components of climate change.

In the next few years, studies of the GISP2 and GRIP cores will broaden the view of the climate system and perhaps reveal the important factors controlling climate change. Research to date has provided evidence that the climate may change rapidly. The new core studies promise to shed light on just how fast the changes may occur and what causative processes are involved. They may well uncover new mechanisms previously unsuspected. And for the sake of the future, people may understand, and be able to predict, the result of human activity on the climate system.

Greenland Ice Sheet Project Two is funded by the U.S. National Science Foundation and coordinated by the GISP2 Science Management Office, University of New Hampshire. Logistic and drilling support is provided by the Polar Ice Coring Office, University of Alaska, and aircraft support is provided by the 109th TAG, Schenectady, New York.

207

Baikal
The Greatest Great Lake

by Charles R. Goldman

*The "pearl" of Siberia's
natural resources, Lake Baikal
is the world's deepest and oldest freshwater
ecosystem. With the coming of democratization in
Russia, local and foreign scientists have joined forces to
study the lake and the growing threats to it from human activities.*

*CHARLES R. GOLDMAN is Professor of
Limnology, Division of Environmental
Studies, University of California at Davis.
He has participated in six research visits
to Lake Baikal, including the 1990 Unesco
delegation to consider designating the lake
a World Heritage site.*

*(Opposite page) Photograph © Boyd
Norton—Comstock*

Located in southern Siberian Russia just to the north of the Mongolian border, Lake Baikal is unique among the world's large freshwater lakes. It is the deepest, oldest, and most unspoiled among them, and it is home to 2,500 plants and animals, of which perhaps two-thirds are found nowhere else. It is this diversity of predominantly endemic wildlife that makes Baikal truly the "Galapagos Islands" of the world's lakes. An impressive, oft-quoted statistic is that the lake contains 20% of the Earth's unfrozen surface freshwater. In fact, its three contiguous basins could hold all five of the Great Lakes of North America. It actually contains enough water to cover the entire state of Texas to a depth of more than 30 meters. (A meter is about 3.3 feet.)

Lake Baikal has a distant marine origin that dates back over 20 million years. Its basins occupy part of a rift zone in which two enormous pieces of the Earth's crust are separating. At its deepest the lake bottom is more than 1,600 meters below the water surface. Although Baikal's waters are subject to some degradation from human activity, they are currently of very high quality, the exceptions being in the immediate vicinity of a few point sources of pollution. Since water resources worldwide are threatened with increasing degradation and already limit human habitability in many parts of the world, the lake's 23,000 cubic kilometers (six million billion gallons) of clean water may well represent Russia's single most valuable natural resource.

Lakes can no longer be treated as isolated bodies of water. Each is part of the landscape and as such must be viewed in the context of its location and evolution, both geographically and geologically. Moreover, the climate and the local plant and animal life—particularly human beings—profoundly influence the physics, chemistry, and biology of the lake itself.

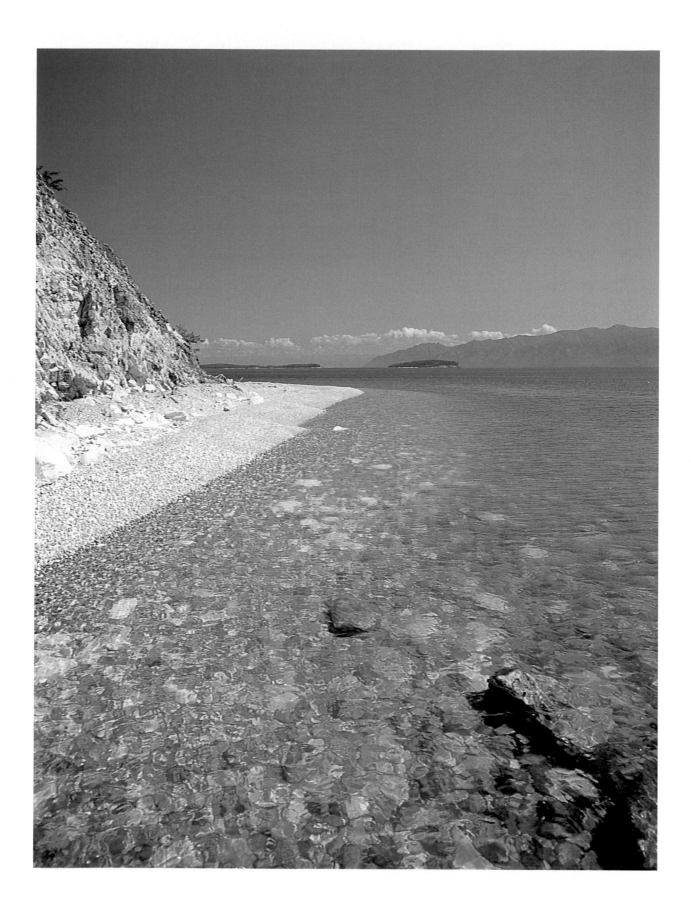

The Baikal basin

The Central Asian lake forms a gentle crescent extending 636 kilometers from southwest to northeast roughly between latitude 51° and 56° N and longitude 104° and 110° E. (A kilometer is about 0.62 mile.) Baikal's width varies to a maximum of 80 kilometers, and its surface covers an area of 31,500 square kilometers (12,200 square miles). The lake was formed, like Lake Tanganyika in Africa, in a giant rift between two separating tectonic plates. The rift continues to widen at 1.5 centimeters per year and may, millions of years hence, eventually split the continent. (A centimeter is about 2.54 inches.)

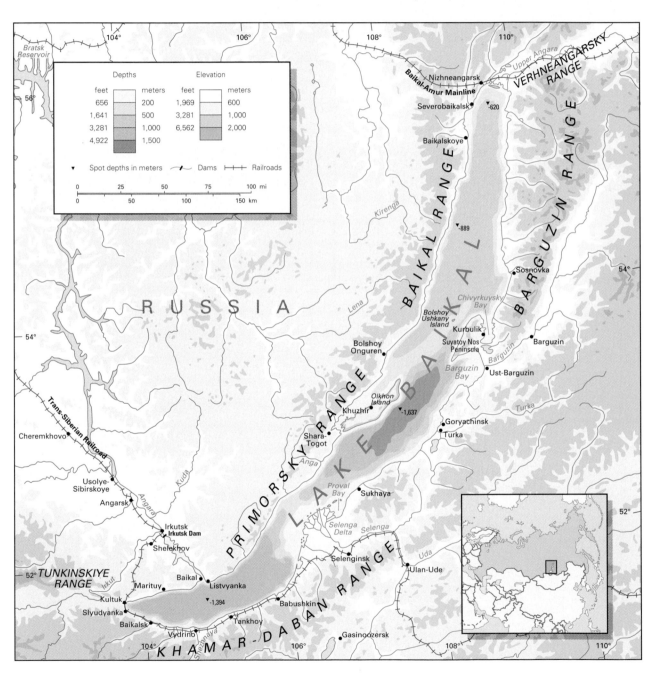

According to acoustic (sonar) soundings made by the Soviet Academy of Sciences, Baikal has a maximum depth of 1,637 meters, making it the deepest continental body of freshwater on Earth. The lake's triple basin resides at the top of the much deeper rift, which is thought to descend more than seven kilometers below the lake level. Between two and a half and an estimated six kilometers of accumulated sediment fill the rift. Although the age of the lake is in the range of 20 million years, it has probably existed in its present form for the past two million to three million years.

Baikal's shore slopes steeply down from the bald alpine and subalpine mountain ranges that border the lake. The region shows considerable evidence of glaciation, including typical U-shaped valleys and cirques, although the lake itself probably was never covered during the last ice age. Previous volcanic and seismic activity is evident, and there are reported to be record numbers of small earthquakes each year. Thermal fields along the eastern shoreline support a hot-springs-bathing industry. In 1990 an expedition sponsored by the National Geographic Society discovered warm-water seeps, similar to the hydrothermal vents found at

Lake Baikal's shores, which comprise the visible, upper portion of a deep rift valley, are diverse in topography and vegetation. Slopes both gentle and steep support a great variety of plant life, from low-growing species (left) and mixed covers of trees and shrubs (top right) to the subarctic taiga, or boreal forest (above). The reindeer herd among the trees belongs to the Evenks, a minority population of the Baikal region.

211

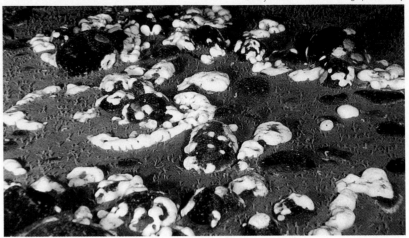

Freshwater sponges thrive more than 400 meters down in the vicinity of warm-water seeps that were discovered beneath Lake Baikal in 1990. The seeps, heated by geothermal energy from the rifting crust, are similar to the life-supporting hydrothermal vents that exist on the ocean bottom at the sites of seafloor spreading.

rift zones on the seafloor, near the bottom of the lake in the vicinity of the hot springs. I was fortunate to dive to the site in the Russian submersible *Pisces* to film the proliferation of deepwater sponges in the seepage zone. Fish, snails, and transparent shrimp also live near the seeps, where the temperature at the mud-water interface was found to be as much as 13° C (24° F) warmer than the near-freezing bottom water.

Geography, climate, and life of the watershed

The watershed, covering more than 500,000 square kilometers (200,000 square miles), lies largely to the east and south of the lake. It is drained by more than 300 streams that deliver an average of about 60 cubic kilometers (16 trillion gallons) of water to the lake each year. Of these, the Selenga is by far the largest, flowing into the south basin from its source about 1,500 kilometers to the east in the Khingan Range in Mongolia. The river provides 40–50% of the annual inflow to the lake. It also brings in a great deal of sediment, forming a brown plume as it enters the lake and creating a massive delta about 40 kilometers wide. The wetlands of the Selenga delta are important breeding sites for ducks, geese, and other aquatic birds and serve as a nursery area for the warmer-water fish. They also provide a measure of biological treatment for the water pollution from the city of Ulan-Ude, located about 100 kilometers upstream at the confluence of the Selenga and Uda rivers.

Baikal's other major tributaries are the 650-kilometer-long Upper Angara, whose estimated annual inflow is 15% of the total, and the 670-kilometer-long Barguzin, which delivers about 7%. The latter's inflow, however, is sufficiently rich in nutrients to make Barguzin Bay one of the most productive areas of the lake, where in July the water becomes green with photosynthetic algae. Most of the lake's outflow is through the Angara River in the southwest. The Angara is about a kilometer wide until it reaches the dam at Irkutsk, about 50 kilometers downstream, where it provides the energy for a major hydroelectric power plant.

The climate of the basin, though typically Siberian with long, cold winters and short summers, is moderated by the lake, which keeps air

212

temperatures in its immediate vicinity significantly warmer in winter and cooler in summer. Minimum winter temperatures can fall near −40° C (−40° F), but average January-February temperatures are at least 20° C (36° F) warmer. Although the warmest months of July and August reach only about 13° C (55° F) at the lake, the air warms with increasing distance from the water, reaching 25° to 30° C (77° to 86° F) at Irkutsk.

Vegetation varies greatly, from treeless alpine areas at higher elevations to the vast, economically important taiga (boreal forest) of mixed coniferous and deciduous trees and shrubs that covers the lakeshore, often to the water's edge. Extensive tree cutting in and around the Baikal basin has supported two large pulp and cellulose mills, one at Baikalsk on the southern shore and the other at Selenginsk on the Selenga River. Cutting is now restricted to dead trees for firewood in many areas, and forest practices are receiving greater scrutiny. Forest fires erupt from time to time, and the local authorities use helicopters to ferry teams of fire fighters to suppress them.

The great variety of habitats in the Baikal area, ranging from the high mountains through the tundra areas to the taiga, abounds with more than 200 species of birds, most of which are migratory, and a remarkable diversity of northern mammals. The latter were the main attraction for early European settlers, who sought the skins of martin, sable, mink, fox, wolverine, and wolf. The Russian brown bear (*Ursus arctos*) still roams the lakeshores and mountain forests and is considered dangerous, particularly in the early spring. In the tundra areas are found lemming, ground squirrels, and northern reindeer. During a lake site visit in 1990 by a delegation of Unesco, it was noted that no comparable landscapes exist in other regions of what was then the U.S.S.R.

The human element

Archaeological investigations of the Lake Baikal region by the Academy of Sciences and Irkutsk State University indicate that humans were present in the basin as early as the late Paleolithic (Old Stone Age). Ethnic Mongols settled the region long before Genghis Khan, whose birthplace is said to be near the lake, consolidated the nomadic tribes into a unified Mongolia in the early 13th century. The first Russian explorer of the

The diverse habitats of the Baikal area abound with more than 200 species of birds. Ruffs (below left; Philomachus pugnax), shown engaging in display and courtship behavior, live on the delta of the Selenga River, an important breeding site for shorebirds. The wolverine (below; Gulo gulo) numbers among mammals that make their home along the Baikal watershed.

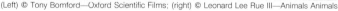

(Left) © Tony Bomford—Oxford Scientific Films; (right) © Leonard Lee Rue III—Animals Animals

The completion of the Trans-Siberian Railroad at the beginning of the 20th century brought an influx of settlers to the Baikal region. The railroad, which winds around the southern end of the lake on its way between Moscow on the west and Vladivostok on the Pacific shore, also opened the area to the large-scale farming, timbering, and urban and industrial development that now threatens the watershed and the lake ecosystem.

area, who left a settlement in 1643, was Kurbat Ivanov, the leader of a Cossack detachment. Many followed in the ensuing centuries, particularly after the opening of the Trans-Siberian Railroad at the beginning of the 20th century. Others came unwillingly, having been exiled to the area during the Stalin era. In the early 1990s there were more than 100,000 inhabitants of the shores of Baikal, with several times as many tourists visiting the lake each year. Although hunting, fishing, and sheep and cattle raising are traditional in the region, modern industrial, forestry, and agricultural activities on the watershed now support 1.2 million inhabitants, including a number of important ethnic minorities.

The region has long been an area of ethnic contact between Russian Europeans, who now comprise about 72% of the population, and Buryats and other Mongols, who maintain Central Asian culture and make up about 24%. The Buryats in particular, who are largely involved in agriculture and fisheries, have a deeply religious reverence for Lake Baikal, calling it the "sacred sea," and are often leaders among activist conservation groups working to limit or reverse the damage being done to the lake. They retain a form of Buddhist religion called Lamaist, for which the Baikal region is the main center in Russia. In addition, Ukrainians, Armenians, Jews, Belorussians, Evenks, and Tatars provide diversity to the rest of the minority population. An interesting group in the eastern Baikal region is the Staroobryads, who have managed to maintain aspects of ancient Russian culture since the 18th century.

The growth in the number of tourists visiting the "Pearl of Siberia," as the lake is proudly known, has been limited only by transportation. A road along the Angara River connects Irkutsk to the lake. Several large tour boats ply its waters. Fast hydrofoils, taking about 10 hours, run from south to north on Baikal every morning and back the next day, providing the main transportation on the lake. The rail system is limited to the passage of the Trans-Siberian around the south end of

214

the lake and the Baikal-Amur Mainline (BAM) at the north end. Ice on the lake is sufficiently thick to support heavy truck traffic in late winter. During times of war the Trans-Siberian Railroad has been run on rails laid across the frozen south basin to speed the flow of materials across Siberia. As additional airline routes open to Irkutsk, tourism is expected to become an even more dominant industry. The construction of the BAM in the 1970s and '80s brought in about 40,000 immigrants, and the rich natural resources of Siberia are likely to attract more inhabitants to this still sparsely populated region.

The lake's physical environment

Baikal is a very cold lake with a great north-south extension as well as re-markable depth. It is in every sense a mecca for the world's limnologists. These lake scientists, the freshwater counterparts of oceanographers, have joined Russian scientists in recent years to study the unique lake. To promote cooperative lake and watershed studies, a new Baikal In-

A Buryat family (above left) and an Evenk woman (above) represent two of the ethnic minorities that live in the Baikal region. Buryats, a Mongol people involved in farming, fishing, and timbering, possess a deep religious reverence for the lake and are often leaders among activist conservation groups. Evenks, traditional inhabitants of the northern taiga, are engaged in hunting, farming and herding, and industrial occupations.

In summer the main transportation on Baikal is by high-speed hydrofoil, which traverses the north-south length of the lake in about 10 hours.

Limnologists on Lake Baikal raise a sediment trap from the deepest point of the lake, more than 1,600 meters below the surface. The lake's depth, age, geology, and endemic plant and animal life have made it a center of interest for lake scientists around the world.

ternational Center for Ecological Research (BICER) was opened in late 1991. A number of countries have already joined BICER, and more are expected.

Because of the lake's great length, the north basin is the first to freeze each winter and the last to thaw. After the ice melts in the spring, the Sun's heat is absorbed in the near-surface layer of water, developing thermal stratification. This effect occurs first in the south basin in June and moves gradually north to the central and north basins in July and August. Individual embayments and some nearshore areas warm more quickly from solar heating of their shallow waters, warmer stream inflows, or both. These areas stratify sooner than the main body and are thus prime recreational sites where people can swim in summer in relative comfort, insulated from the otherwise extremely cold water. (I first swam in the lake in the summer of 1971 with Canadian and Scandinavian colleagues. The 12° C [54° F] water made the experience both stimulating and a bit painful.)

Because strong winds can blow across such a great expanse of water surface, the waters of Baikal mix to great depth, particularly when lake temperatures are low and resistance to mixing is minimal. The cooler north and central basins mix longer in summer than the warmer south basin. At times the friction of the wind is sufficient to produce large waves that pile up the water on the windward side while reducing the water level to the lee. This phenomenon, called a seiche, is reported to raise the water level as much as 20 centimeters in the south basin during a prolonged period of northerly winds. When the winds cease, the lake water rocks back and forth with an oscillation period of almost six hours in the south basin.

As in the oceans of the Northern Hemisphere, currents in the lake tend to flow counterclockwise. Fronts of upwelling water develop at the underwater ridges between the basins. In this inland sea there are, in fact, distinct similarities to upwelling in marine systems. In early September,

216

when air temperatures begin their rapid descent toward winter, vertical convection currents form as the colder, denser surface water sinks. Surface cooling and sinking continues through the fall and into the winter until the entire water mass has cooled to its maximum density at 4° C (39° F). An important aspect of this process is an annual replenishment of oxygen in the deepest waters of the lake.

Next, as the water drops below 4°, it becomes slightly less dense, enabling it to float above the 4° water until it reaches freezing temperature and turns to ice. In a sense, the surface layer of ice insulates the main body of water from the extremely cold winter air. It is for this reason that lakes do not freeze to their bottoms. Instead, a good deal of chemical and biological activity occurs, although at a reduced rate, under the winter cover of ice and snow. As winter progresses and heat continues to be lost from the ice surface, additional ice forms at the undersurface. Even in the warmer south basin, the ice reaches a meter or more in thickness and persists for four to five months. Variation in temperature and friction of the wind on the enormous ice cover cause expansion and contraction, resulting in cracking and upthrusts that give vent to a variety of unnerving sounds.

Lake life

The waters of Baikal are extremely soft in the sense that mineral content is very low. Although the deeper water may contain as much as 100 milligrams per liter of dissolved solids, most of the lake water is below 95 milligrams per liter (compared with, for example, 160 milligrams per liter for Lake Michigan). The waters are bicarbonate in nature and contain the important cations (positive ions) calcium, magnesium, sodium, and potassium in descending order of concentration—a pattern typical of the soft-water composition of many of the world's lakes. The important plant nutrients nitrogen and phosphorus occur in sufficient quantities to support a healthy population of algae. These free-floating photosynthetic microorganisms constitute Baikal's primary producers, the base of the lake's food chain. Bioassay experiments support the idea that algal growth in the lake is actually colimited by nitrogen and phosphorus, except where these essential elements are provided by inflow in a quantity sufficient to

© Art Wolfe—Allstock

Ice fishing on Baikal in winter provides both food and sport for the local population. Because of the lake's great north-south extension, its north basin is the first to freeze in winter and the last to thaw. Even in the warmer south basin, the ice reaches a meter or more in thickness, enough to support heavy truck traffic.

produce crops of algae large enough to reduce light penetration and thus shade out the algae below. It is the combination of light, temperature, water movement, and the nutrients essential for plant and animal growth that fuels and controls the dynamics of life in Lake Baikal.

The transparency of the lake water is important since it determines the depth to which light and heat penetrate and the depth to which photosynthetic organisms of the lake can live. A standard way to measure transparency is to record the depth to which a special 20-centimeter white disk, called a Secchi disk, can be seen. Secchi-depth transparency varies greatly in different regions of the lake. Although readings of 40 meters have been reported for the clear winter waters of Baikal, 25 meters appears to be the maximum during the ice-free periods of summer, with only a few centimeters of visibility in the productive Barguzin Bay in July. In fact, light limitation eventually occurs in the deep waters of all lakes. Even in the clearest regions of Baikal, algae seldom have been found growing vigorously below 50 meters.

Another limiting factor for algae is water movement. During the annual mixing period, algae may not stay in the lighted zone of the lake long enough to produce much growth, being constantly carried out of the best-lighted zone by vertical currents. Some of these algal cells are lost to the abyssal depths, while others are returned to the lighted surface waters during upwelling.

The major portion of Baikal is what the limnologist and oceanographer alike call the pelagic zone, the open water that is isolated by its depth from both the bottom and the shore. Early in the 20th century, Baikal's pelagic zone was recognized to be populated by older, "Baikalian" animal life, which had little relationship to the more modern, "Euro-Siberian" coastal life. It is in this offshore region of the lake that most of the primary production occurs. There, as in the northern oceans, the algae known as diatoms dominate the phytoplankton, the community of tiny floating plant and plantlike organisms. They serve, particularly in the early spring, as the most important food for copepod crustaceans, part of the population of tiny animal organisms, or zooplankton, of the lake. Among the phytoplankton, in addition to the diatoms, are green algae and cyanobacteria (blue-green algae).

Farther along the food chain, the zooplankton are consumed by small fish and also by a pelagic shrimplike amphipod, *Macrohectopus branickii*. Larger fish feed on *Macrohectopus* and a host of other amphipod species, some of which live on the bottom even to great depths. Most of the amphipods, however, dwell in the lighted littoral zone, the shore and nearshore areas of the lake, where they are found among the rocks, on the sponges, or in the sediment. Speciation is particularly well developed in Baikal's amphipods. The more than 240 species represent 80% of the world's freshwater amphipod species. By contrast, only a single isopod crustacean inhabits Baikal's waters.

Because of the rapid drop-off of shoreline, Baikal's littoral zone of shallow water is very limited, yet in this relatively narrow zone are found remarkable fields of sponges and their associated symbiotic algae, which

Lake Baikal's relatively narrow zone of shallow water harbors remarkable fields of green sponges, their color deriving from associated symbiotic photosynthetic algae. Such light-dependent life can be affected by human activities that result in the addition of excessive sediment and nutrients to the lake water, reducing its transparency.

color the sponges green. The area also supports species of large, macroscopic algae (macro algae), which look like higher plants. A slippery green coating of attached algae, called periphyton, often grows like moss on the submerged rocks along the shore. Snails, insect larvae, aquatic worms, and other associated invertebrates, in addition to the amphipods, live on the warmer, fertile nearshore bottom. At times, during what fly fishermen refer to as a hatch, the nearshore surface waters swarm with newly emerging flies. Large areas of macro algae and aquatic plants sway in the littoral currents, giving the bottom a look of both beauty and high fertility.

Lake Baikal contains at least 50 different species of fish. The most important commercially is omul (*Coregonus autumnalis migratorius*), a type of whitefish, which typically accounts for about 70% of the catch. Omul reach about a half kilogram (a pound) in weight, and larger female individuals may lay as many as 40,000 eggs apiece during spawning runs up the lake's tributaries. The young hatch in April or May and are carried by the stream current to the lake, where they begin feeding on the smallest of the zooplankton. Perch and pike are found near river mouths. Siberian sturgeon also inhabit the lake, as do four members of the salmon family.

One salmonid, the Baikalian grayling, is frequently taken along the lakeshore by a technique that involves running the bow of a large vessel up on the bank and then turning the propellers to create a current behind the ship. Standing on the ship's stern, the crew drop artificial flies, which are attached beneath a large visible float, to drift out with the current. The fish, attracted to the current and displaced bottom-dwelling organisms, bite readily on the artificial bait.

Commercial fisherman on the lake use nets, and enough fish have been available to support a cannery. Like many of the world's fisheries, overexploitation and changing environmental conditions have reduced both the catch and the average size of the fish taken.

219

While diving in the *Pisces* in Baikal's north basin, I observed and filmed the pelagic sculpin golomyanka, the name given to either *Comephorus baicalensis*, or the smaller, closely related *C. dybowskii*. This small, nearly translucent fish has a huge mouth for its size and feeds voraciously on *Macrohectopus* and other small animals. It is so full of oil that, once dried, it can be burned like a candle. From the submersible, golomyanka were observed near the thermal seeps among colorless deepwater sponges. When frightened, they dived into the soft sediment and disappeared. Golomyanka occasionally have been collected at great depths during plankton net tows. They are believed to be an important food for the endemic freshwater seals that inhabit Baikal.

The Baikal seal, or nerpa (*Phoca sibirica*), is an attractive animal with large brown eyes, a silver gray back, and a whitish-yellow belly. It reaches about a meter and a half in length and weighs as much as 130 kilograms. Thoroughly adapted to freshwater, the seals are most abundant in the north and central basins but may be observed anywhere in the lake. During winter, when ice covers the lake, they maintain open holes like their Arctic marine relatives. Their pups are born on the ice, and they are hunted on a controlled basis. The herd is estimated to number about 30,000, although it suffered serious losses in recent years from a distemper epidemic of the kind that decimated seal populations in the Baltic.

In recent decades Baikal has experienced a major water-level change that, according to some investigators, has had serious consequences on the aquatic life. When the large hydroelectric dam on the Angara River outflow at Irkutsk was completed in the 1950s, the lake's nearshore spawning areas, which had been warmed sufficiently by sunlight, were flooded by a meter of deeper, colder water. It took years for waves to cut new shallow areas along the steep shoreline. During this period catches of omul declined drastically. At the same time, however, the lake also saw a drop in populations of *Epischura*, a copepod member of the zooplankton community and an important food item for fish. To further complicate analysis of cause and effect, populations of the yellow-winged sculpin, which had comprised 50% of the omul diet, also declined drastically.

Commercial fishing on the lake (below) has been large enough to support a cannery, but overfishing and alterations to the environment have reduced both catch and the size of the fish taken. To maintain populations of the depleted omul (Coregonus autumnalis migratorius), Baikal's commercially most important fish, stock is reared on a large scale and released via trough into the lake's tributaries (below right).

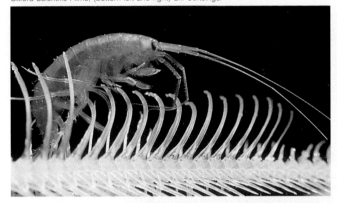

A moratorium on omul harvest, instituted between 1969 and 1975, undoubtedly helped the partial recovery of this extremely important fishery.

Threats to Baikal's future

A variety of environmentally destructive human enterprises menace almost all of the world's watersheds, and the Baikal region is no exception. At Baikal these activities pose immediate or future dangers to the watershed and the lake ecosystem. Within the lake basin the threats include excessive influx of sediment from tributary streams. The increased sediment in turn results from the erosion of watershed land that has been disturbed by lumbering, sheep and cattle grazing, mink and sable farms, road construction, and urban and industrial development. The sediment carried in by snowmelt during spring runoff and rainstorms is temporarily suspended in the water column, causing a short-term loss of transparency. In addition, the nutrients carried in the sediment stimulate algal growth, lowering transparency for a longer term. Whereas some nutrient and sediment transport to the lake is essential to maintenance of the existing fertility, excessive transparency loss in the littoral zone can shade out or cover with sediment the unique sponge community and its associated symbiotic algae. Aquatic plants that depend on light penetration in the typically clear waters of the littoral zone are also harmed or eliminated by shading and sedimentation. The alteration of tributary

Deepwater amphipod (top left), scavenging on a fish skeleton, is a representative of the more than 240 amphipod species found in Baikal's waters. The exceptionally high speciation in the lake offers scientists the opportunity to look at the evolution of species in a way never before studied. The golomyanka (top right), a small deep-dwelling fish endemic to Baikal, is a voracious feeder on amphipods and other small animals. This fish in turn is an important food for the Baikal seal, or nerpa (above), the only species of seal that lives in freshwater all year around. A sculpin (above left), one of 30 known species of sculpin that evolved in the lake, protects an egg mass laid on a sponge.

221

Shrouded in smog, a hydroelectric station stands at Irkutsk, about 50 kilometers downstream from Lake Baikal on the Angara River. When the dam at Irkutsk was completed in the 1950s, the impounded water raised the lake level and flooded nearshore spawning areas with colder and deeper water. Some investigators believe that the environmental alteration adversely affected both the lake's ecology and its commercial fisheries. Irkutsk and its neighboring industrial towns also lie in the path of prevailing westerly winds, which carry airborne pollution from the urban centers to the lake and its watershed.

stream discharge due to new impoundments on the watershed may also threaten the balance of life in this fragile ecosystem.

Chemical pollution within the basin is both an old problem and a new threat. Transportation of oil and chemicals by boat in summer and by truck over ice in winter is a potential danger to the lake. Baikal, known for severe storms, offers the same opportunity for accidental spills that tanker traffic creates on the world's oceans. The BAM and Trans-Siberian railways, which promote industrialization of the Baikal basin, also pose risks for spills of toxic chemicals.

Point sources of pollution include the sewage discharge from villages and ships as well as discharges into the water and air from the pulp mills. Small settlements around Baikal still lack sewage-treatment facilities, and many boats on the lake release their wastes directly into the water without treatment. One standard measure of domestic pollution is based on counts of coliform bacteria, the bacteria of the intestinal tract of humans and other warm-blooded animals. Counts of the intestinal bacterium *Escherichia coli* in the Selenga River show a gradual increase from a low count at the entrance of the river into Russia at the Mongolian border to a maximum of almost 20,000 bacterial cells per liter (about a quart) downstream of Ulan-Ude and Selenginsk. The Selenga delta, acting as a huge sponge, reduces the count by about two-thirds before the river waters enter Baikal. Although bacterial content is excessive for water contact sports, it is well below that of polluted European rivers like the Danube, Volga, and Dnieper.

The pulp mill at Baikalsk, which discharges 240,000 cubic meters (63 million gallons) of wastewater per day into the south basin, has been the subject of great controversy since its construction. Smoke from the plant, also a source of pollution, is visible on a clear day from Listvyanka, about 70 kilometers across the lake. Plans have been made for conversion of the plant to a furniture factory, but this has not yet taken place. About 50 small industries also exist on the Selenga River at Ulan-Ude. They include electronics factories as well as lead-battery and galvanizing plants and are certain to expand with the growing Siberian economy.

222

The wastewater discharges into Lake Baikal's south basin from the pulp and cellulose mill at Baikalsk (left) have been strongly controversial since the plant's construction in the 1960s. The smoke from the plant is another source of pollution.

Nonpoint sources of chemical pollutants typically come from forest practices, agriculture, livestock grazing, and some types of development such as railroads, roads, urbanization, and industrial activity. Certain forest practices, particularly clear-cutting (removing all the trees from an area), greatly increase erosion and sediment transport to the lake. That sediment may also bury spawning habitat along the stream courses and near shore in the receiving waters of the lake. Sunken logs and forest debris are detrimental to fish-spawning areas. Although the transport of rafts of logs on the lake is prohibited and barge loads have become more common, rafting was still observed as recently as 1990. Agriculture in the lake basin for the most part is limited to small gardens, but sheep grazing is important, and overgrazing can create serious soil loss and erosion.

In addition to local pollution, airborne hazardous substances that originate outside the basin are sometimes transported considerable distances to the lake and its watershed. For example, the five-town industrial complex of Irkutsk-Cheremkhovo and the large 6,000-megawatt Kansk Achinsh coal-fired power plant are located to the west of Baikal, but they lie in the path of often strong prevailing westerly winds.

The logging practice of rafting cut trees from forest to factory (below left) results in sunken logs that clog rivers and remove oxygen from the water as they decay. Though rafting is now banned in the Baikal region and barge loads are more common, the lake and its tributaries sustained considerable damage from logging activities in past decades. Sheep raising (below) is practiced in the Baikal basin, and overgrazing can create serious erosion, which in turn increases the amount of sediment in streams feeding to the lake and in the nearshore receiving waters of the lake itself.

Mikhail Grachev, director of the Limnological Institute of the Siberian division of the Academy of Sciences at Irkutsk, reported on the present state of Baikal's ecosystem as part of the documentation for the lake's qualifications as a World Heritage site. He cited the presence of a number of organic pollutants, including concentrations of organic chlorine compounds encompassing DDT and its metabolites. Chlorinated hydrocarbons have been carried by the winds to all parts of the globe. They can be detected in both polar regions, and despite the fact that they have never been used in the Baikal region, they appear in small amounts in the fat of Baikal seals. The concentrations are only slightly higher than those reported for West Greenland and Arctic Canada, although they are much lower than those for England.

Baikal scientists have also been concerned about mercury, zinc, lead, and other trace elements that have been detected in the lake, the Selenga River, and the snow that falls on the watershed. Measured zinc levels are especially high for all three sources, as are mercury levels for both the snowmelt and the Selenga. Baikal researchers are attempting to develop mathematical models of the pollution status of the lake under current conditions of atmospheric transport and known sources of contaminants. This is particularly important, since even minute quantities of some pollutants can become greatly concentrated as they pass up the aquatic food chain.

Because of the high proportion of endemic plants and animals in the lake, the introduction of exotic, or imported, species represents an ever present peril that could disrupt native life disastrously. Introducing any kind of plant or animal may bring new diseases to which native species lack resistance, or it may bring in competitors strong enough to reduce populations of native species or even cause their extinction. Overfishing of lake species is yet another danger. Overfishing of the omul, for example, has already reduced the average size of the fish and has the potential to severely alter the structure and function of the food web.

The future: to study and protect

Modern scientific study of the Baikal area began about the time of the Russian Revolution of 1917 with the establishment of a permanent

Using a barge-mounted drilling rig frozen in place on the surface of Lake Baikal, scientists successfully recovered a core of the upper 100 meters of undisturbed lake-bottom sediment during the 1992–93 winter. The achievement, the work of the Baikal Drilling Project, is part of a multidisciplinary, multinational effort to decipher the ancient climatic and limnological record of the lake.

Douglas F. Williams, University of South Carolina, Baikal Drilling Project

© Fred Mayer—Magnum

"Save Lake Baikal" proclaims a poster at a bus station in Baikalsk, an injunction that the world must attend if the greatest great lake is to be conserved for future generations.

station, which has since evolved into the Limnological Institute. In the ensuing decades, more than a thousand papers on Baikal have been published, the great majority by Soviet researchers. With the reforms of perestroika in the U.S.S.R. in the late 1980s and the country's subsequent breakup and democratization, scientists worldwide have been given an unprecedented opportunity to join their Russian colleagues in studying the lake. With the support of the Siberian division of the Academy of Sciences, Grachev and his colleagues established BICER, which promises to open up research on the lake and its environment to foreign participation as never before. Current and envisaged projects range from studies of Baikal's food web and of the evolution and speciation of its endemic organisms to a better understanding of its enormously deep vertical mixing and to a project to drill into the lake's underlying sediment. The latter effort, which includes scientists from the former Soviet Union and six other countries, involves extracting cores of the sediment that fills the deep rift in order to clarify knowledge of the lake's ecosystem and of the climatic history of north-central Asia perhaps as far back as 30 million years.

Adding impetus to the drive to research the lake is the realization that the time to survey Baikal, to piece together the workings of its complex ecosystem, and to act wisely to preserve it could be short. Baikal's unique cold freshwater environment has taken millions of years to reach its current evolutionary state. By contrast, the time for human beings to undo what nature has accomplished may be measured in decades. The precarious sensitivity of the lake to disturbance means that it must be guarded jealously for the welfare of the present generation and the heritage of future ones. In recognition of its many unique characteristics, Unesco is currently considering assigning it official status as the Baikal World Heritage Area. That designation, it is hoped, will give Lake Baikal the global attention it needs for its ultimate salvation.

FOR ADDITIONAL READING

Don Belt, "The World's Great Lake" *National Geographic* (June 1992, pp. 2–39).

Mikhail Kozhov, *Lake Baikal and Its Life* (W. Junk, 1963).

Peter Matthiessen, *Baikal: Sacred Sea of Siberia* (Sierra Club Books, 1992).

Report on the Fact-Finding Mission of Unesco to Irkutsk and Lake Baikal (Unesco, 1990).

Chaos, Quarks, and Quantum Leaps
What's in a Scientific Name?

by Stephen S. Hall

When scientists invent catchy names for their discoveries, they indeed may be helping to communicate scientific ideas to a larger public. But they also run a considerable risk of incurring the wrath of their colleagues.

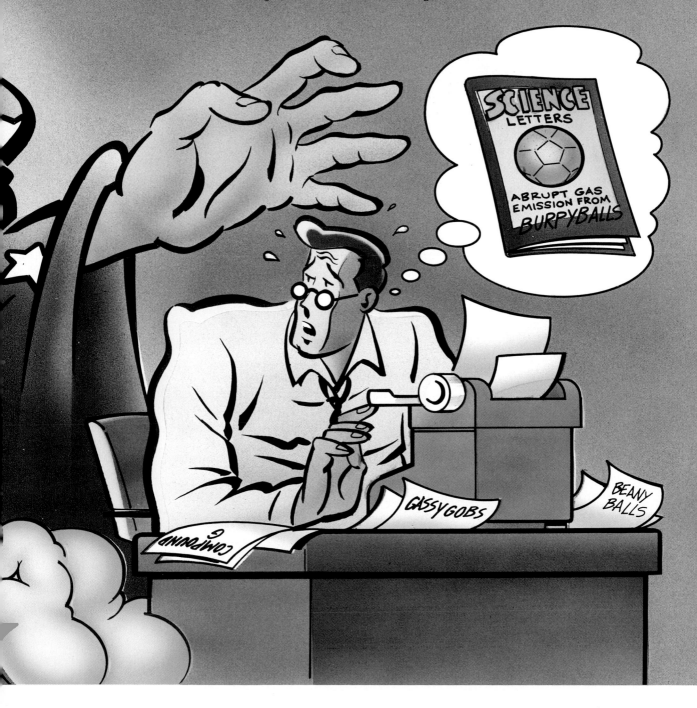

STEPHEN S. HALL is an author and science writer. His books include Mapping the Next Millennium, *an account of the new computer-driven cartography of contemporary biology, astronomy, and other disciplines.*

Illustrations by Ron Villani; concepts by Charles Cegielski

It was in the mid-1970s that Tien-Yien Li, a graduate student in mathematics at the University of Maryland, politely tried to dissuade his faculty adviser, James A. Yorke, from using a vivid, unusual, and disturbingly figurative word in the title of a scientific paper the two of them were writing. This now-famous article explored an obscure mathematical concept known as period three, and Yorke recalls how his junior colleague suggested that the senior author's proposed title "might not be the professionally wise thing to do."

Nonetheless, Yorke went ahead and published the article in a 1975 issue of *American Mathematical Monthly* under the title "Period Three Implies Chaos." Thus did the word *chaos* enter the scientific vocabulary, says Yorke, who has heard about it ever since.

Chaos represents an example of how one well-chosen, resonant word or phrase can echo like a sonic boom far beyond the bounds of science, rattling windows in many other neighborhoods of contemporary culture. Everyone has heard of chaos; some even understand the concept, which involves a paradoxical mathematical orderliness that lies at the heart of unpredictable behavior in dynamic physical systems like turbulence in water flow or, on a grander scale, the weather. But chaos has become much more than the concept embodied in Yorke and Li's 1975 paper, thick as a brick with equations, impenetrable to all but specialists.

Chaos now belongs to the culture at large, an all-purpose metaphor for the unpredictability of things. It has inspired a best-selling book. It has become recreational software. It has become a symbol of the modern condition. As often happens with the most suggestive of scientific terms, society has purloined an intriguing insight from basic research and repackaged it for broader consumption. And like the catchiest terms, the popularity and expanded use of the word *chaos* has riled a considerable number of people, most of them scientists. And therein lies the fundamental paradox in the scientific game of "naming": even as the public hungers for terms that make science accessible and meaningful, the scientific community as a rule does not reward the use of colorful language—and in some cases punishes the perpetrators of linguistic innovation.

"Basically, *large* numbers of people have taken *large* exception to the name *chaos*," says Yorke, who directs the Institute for Physical Science and Technology at the University of Maryland's College Park campus. "This is the name everyone loves to hate." But, he quickly points out, the term helped attract the attention of physicists to an unusual concept known for quite some time to mathematicians and thus gave a transforming boost to the study of chaos in real-world situations—the behavior of a mountain stream hitting a boulder, for example, or blood flowing through the human heart.

Allusion or precision?

In selecting that one controversial term, Yorke reminds us that science involves not only the discovery of new concepts and phenomena but also the subtler task of choosing words that promote rather than impede the

228

communication of those discoveries to a larger public—and understanding of them by that public—a public that increasingly includes not just interested lay onlookers but also scientists in adjoining fields, who tend to be as befuddled as any nonscientist. And in so doing, he rekindles a centuries-old debate, as hoary as Hobbes and Locke, as fresh as last week's issue of *Science* or *Nature*, about the propriety of scientific terminology. Should it cleave to tradition, even at the expense of excluding a potential audience? Or should it play on allusion and metaphor, even at the expense of absolute precision? "What science is about is enabling people to think about scientific concepts by coming up with *words*," Yorke argues. "Words empower us to think about other things, and we must think of the words that allow us to do that."

Choosing words has become all the more important in the past 30 or 40 years if one is to believe a complicated "lexical analysis" of professional scientific writing by Donald P. Hayes of Cornell University, Ithaca, New York, who published his findings in the journal *Nature* in April 1992. Using a computer-based text-analysis system, Hayes compared general scientific journals like *Science, Nature,* and *Scientific American* with an average newspaper, which he classified at a baseline reading level, and concluded that until roughly the end of World War II, such journals were

as accessible as the daily paper to general readers. Since then, however, general journals, especially basic journals in chemistry, biology, physics, and geology, have become many times more inaccessible and difficult to read, Hayes reported. According to the analysis, *Nature*'s increased difficulty dates to around 1947, *Science*'s to around 1960, and *Scientific American*'s to around 1970.

Hayes writes:

"What . . . are the consequences of the drift toward inaccessibility? Specialization in science has produced unprecedented levels of knowledge, but the unwelcome side-effects are clear. These days, more expertise than ever is required to understand published research and theory in other fields and to referee papers and proposals in one's own discipline. The broad consequences are that ideas flow less freely across and within the sciences, and the public's access to (and maybe trust in) science is diminished."

Whatever flow occurs is usually lubricated with figurative language, and consequently, while there may not actually be a trend toward catchy names, it is clear that a public benumbed by leaden, polysyllabic, Latinate, and largely unparsable words fairly lunges for terms that sound even faintly whimsical or friendly. And that attraction has created a dilemma for scientists who dare to invent more adventurous terminology.

Coining a catchy phrase can be a high-stakes enterprise, with all sorts of ramifications for scientists. They include heightened attention for the new discovery or invention, the attendant resentment from scientific colleagues, notoriety (and sometimes infamy) for the namer, and possibly a slight edge in winning the attention of funding agencies. For better or—sometimes—worse, a flashy name for a scientific concept cuts like a weed eater through the thicket of jargon and often stirs great public interest. Astronomer John P. Huchra of the Harvard-Smithsonian Center for Astrophysics, Cambridge, Massachusetts, speaks for many scientists when he says, "It's all in a name. A rose by any other name may *not* smell as sweet."

Although the Enlightenment philosopher John Locke was something of a scold about the use of metaphors, declaiming that they were good for "nothing else but to insinuate wrong ideas, move the passions, and thereby mislead the judgment," metaphoric terminology seems if anything to insinuate a link between scientific insight and public appreciation. There is no dearth of colorful language in contemporary science. Even a cursory spin through contemporary journals reveals an abundance of suggestive, metaphoric names. Chemistry has its *buckyballs* (spherical organic molecules, also known as *buckminsterfullerenes*, named after Buckminster Fuller), and astrophysics has its *WIMPs* (for *weakly interacting massive particles*) and its *MACHOs* (for *massive compact halo objects*, which is not necessarily an improvement on one of the terms it seeks to supplant; namely, *brown dwarfs*).

Cell biology boasts its *chaperone* molecules, which oversee the proper manufacture of proteins in cells. Certain proteins that interact with DNA mesh with each other via *leucine zippers*, and genes are segregated into *exons* (the portions of DNA that are translated into proteins, or expressed) and *introns* (the intervening portions that are not). Physicists recently invoked a *baked Alaska* model to describe concentric "hot" and "cold" layers observed in superfluid helium-3, and biologists like to wield *optical tweezers* (combinations of laser beams that can push and pull around the contents of living cells). Reaching beyond common words into classical mythology, a group of molecular biologists recently dubbed a molecule *Ikaros*.

There are powerful forces in contemporary science opposing the use of such figurative language. John Maddox, editor of the journal *Nature*, recently inveighed against what he called "portmanteau adjectives" in the literature, meaning beads of jargon strung together with hyphens into turgid freight trains of prose, such as *DNA-dependent cytosol-controlled polymerase*. He also pointed out that, while English is the lingua franca of contemporary science, it is not the mother tongue of many scientists, and he thus argued for a limit to the amount of allusive language in the literature (he concedes, though, that "it is not possible to go too far in this direction without making prose sound like baby-talk"). As a rule, scientific bureaucracies—space agencies, multinational collaborations, and the like—tend to oblige the traditional approach. They are cautious hatcheries for terms of such doggedly literal precision that they might easily have been dreamed up for a Monty Python routine. Europe's response to the need for a next-generation ground-based telescope, for example, is a very large instrument formally called . . . the Very Large Telescope. Although not quite baby talk, neither is it Shakespeare.

The naming of the quark

Probably the most successfully suggestive name in recent history is *quark,* coined in 1964 by physicist Murray Gell-Mann of the California Institute of Technology to describe a component of subatomic particles. Though it has been frequently written that he borrowed the term from James Joyce's novel *Finnegans Wake,* Gell-Mann insists that Joyce merely provided its spelling. "During the spring and summer of 1963, I thought of them as *quarks,* but I didn't know how I was going to spell it," he explained recently. "I considered spelling it k-w-o-r-k. Then during the fall I was paging through *Finnegans Wake* and saw the line 'Three quarks for Muster Mark!' " Joyce's pronunciation, rhyming with *lark,* was not quite right, but through a "feeble" chain of reasoning, Gell-Mann convinced himself that he could pronounce it to rhyme with *fork.*

'I thought it wasn't necessary to use pretentious scientific language," Gell-Mann explains, "especially since the terms people usually make up don't look so apt after a period of years. The word *atom* is a very good example. It was an ancient Greek term, meaning 'you can't cut it.' But of course you *can* cut it. So why call it an atom?"

Not only did the word *quark* catch on, but it also set off a dizzying round of subatomic etymological one-upmanship. Gell-Mann added the concepts of *strangeness* and *color* to help tell quarks apart. University of Chicago theorist Yoichiro Nambu conceived of *flavor,* and Harvard University physicist Sheldon Glashow described certain quarks as having *charm.* Quarks now come in a six-pack of metaphoric designations: *up, down, strange, charm, bottom* (or *beauty*), and (still to be discovered) *top* (or *truth*). So pervasively has quark penetrated the language that the term has now become slang for someone who studies too much—"derived from the fact," says a chuckling Gell-Mann, reading from a newspaper clipping, "that such a person might actually know what a quark is."

Jargon for the masses

The graduation of a technical term to the level of slang, or at least an idiomatic expression pregnant with metaphoric meaning, marks the ultimate success of such a word. Everyday speech is full of examples: *meltdown, fax* (the verb), *nuke* (the culinary technique, perpetrated with a microwave), *memory* (digital, not cranial), *brain-dead,* and *access* (one of many synthetic verbs cooked up by computer engineers). The point is, once loosed upon an unsuspecting but verbal public, a technical term assumes a life of its own beyond the control of scientific proctors.

Consider how thoroughly the adjective *quantum* has penetrated the culture from its humble beginnings in theoretical physics: a New Age self-help book (*Quantum Healing*), a hit TV show ("Quantum Leap"), an idiomatic expression (*a quantum jump*), numerous businesses (Quantum Health Resources, Inc., Quantum Securities Inc., and hundreds more), and an all-purpose high-tech adjective to jazz up a business-as-usual

232

noun (*quantum politics* or *quantum golf*). Quasar, a word once limited to the astronomical description of a quasi-stellar object in space, now refers to a brand of television set. Metaphors, of course, travel a two-way street. Two recent American novels (among many examples) borrow from the scientific lexicon for their titles: Russell Banks's *Continental Drift* and Lisa Grunwald's *The Theory of Everything*.

Following the lead of theoretical physics, certain scientific subcultures tend to incubate interesting and whimsical terminology. Developmental biologists, flashing a playfulness not always apparent in other precincts of biology, have taken to coining amusing, idiosyncratic names for genes that play roles in the embryological maturation of the fruit fly. Hence the field is thick with labels like *runt, hairy, Toll, zen, even-skipped, odd-paired, swallow, oskar, gooseberry, twist, snail, sevenless,* and *single-minded,* to note but a few. Similarly, biochemists have long had a flair for giving clever names to enzymes, like *swivelase, decapitase, transferase, cocoonase,* and *luciferase* (for the protein that puts the fire in fireflies). And chemists fond of synthesizing unusual molecular structures have christened their creations with suggestive names like *propellane, basketene,* and *bowtiediene.*

"It has caused more problems in my career"

Given the clear success of terms like *quark* and concepts like *quantum,* why are there not more metaphoric terms? Why do comparatively few

233

fields provide a fertile ground for imaginative terminology while so many others remain doggedly literal and Latinate? The probable reason is that there exists considerable resistance in the scientific community to the colorful, allusive phrase. Anne Eisenberg, a professor at Polytechnic University, Brooklyn, New York, says that, from the point of view of scientists, "there's something suspect about it if you make it understandable. There's tremendous snobbery against the comprehensible." "The bad side of that is the snobbery," says Eisenberg, who writes frequently about the language of science. "The good side of that is that it reflects the desire for scientific precision."

Alan Dressler is an astrophysicist who became rudely introduced to that kind of snobbery. Based at the Observatories of the Carnegie Institution of Washington, Pasadena, California, Dressler joined a now-defunct seven-person collaboration known informally as the Seven Samurai in the mid-1980s to study the "peculiar motions" of hundreds of galaxies in the universe ("peculiar" in the sense that they depart from the predicted motion of the expanding universe). Dressler happened to be fielding questions from the press at a 1987 meeting of the American Physical Society when he was asked to characterize an unusually dense aggregation of matter in the universe that he and his colleagues had suggested as being the gravitational influence toward which many of these galaxies appeared to be streaming. "I was waving my arms, looking for some way to explain how all these galaxies were moving," Dressler recalls, "and as sort of an unintentional ad lib I used the term *great attractor*."

In a few short years *Great Attractor* has achieved upper-case authority in scientific journals and captured the public imagination as a way to convey a puzzling and important astronomical phenomenon. But, to Dressler's consternation, the term has proved perhaps greatest as an attractor of criticism and ridicule. "It has caused more problems in my career than any other thing I have ever done," he said recently, referring to "pot shots" from fellow astronomers and accusations of grandstanding. "It shocks me. There is such resentment against the idea that a scientist might be playing to the audience that, if any, we really should be playing to—namely, the public." One of the unfortunate casualties of the controversy, Dressler suggests, is the hypothesis underlying the Great Attractor. "It's been very destructive to the scientific discussion."

Some of science's other more enduring terms have, like the *Great Attractor,* been conceived on the spur of the moment for public consumption. British astronomer Fred Hoyle is said to have coined the term *big bang* in the late 1940s while derisively trying to explain a theory about the origin of the universe on a BBC radio show. Princeton University physicist John Archibald Wheeler introduced the phrase *black hole* at a public lecture in 1967. The term itself, Wheeler said in an interview, was actually suggested by someone else—he does not remember whom—during a 1967 meeting at the Institute for Space Studies, New York City, and was intended as a substitute for *gravitationally completely collapsed star.* "After you get around to saying that about ten times," Wheeler recalled, "you look desperately for something better."

234

It was at a similarly informal lunchtime colloquy in 1977 that Harvard molecular biologist Walter Gilbert, Massachusetts Institute of Technology professor Susumu Tonegawa, and Salk Institute scientist Melvin Cohn sat at a cafeteria table in Basel, Switzerland, and cooked up several terms that still rankle some biologists. Gilbert gets credit for thinking up *intron*, but negative reaction was swift, and it began at that same lunch.

"*I* coined the term *exon*," Cohn recalls of the lunch. "I was actually thinking of *exxon*, with two x's, like the oil company. It was a joke. I was making fun of Gilbert because I didn't think those were the best possible terms. They were too slangy and didn't best describe what was going on." Nonetheless, Gilbert dutifully wrote down the two words, *intron* and *exxon*, on a napkin, and thus they appeared (with the second x in *exon* excised) when Gilbert introduced the terms in a 1978 *Nature* commentary. He says now that he preferred *intron* to a rival term, *intervening sequence*, because *intron* implied greater impartiality about the biological function of such segments of DNA.

Rarely have newly minted scientific terms triggered such raw and widespread hostility. The terms were so unpopular, Gilbert admits, that Benjamin Lewin, editor of the journal *Cell*, "forbade the term *intron* to be used" for several years. *Intron* was even put to a nonbinding straw vote conducted by biologist Argiris Efstratiadis, now at Columbia University, New York City, at a 1978 Gordon Conference meeting, and *intervening sequence* resoundingly defeated *intron*. But, as one participant recalls, "everybody used *intron* because it was easier," and therein lies a lesson about scientific terminology. For all the Hobbesian bluster about accuracy and precision, scientists are pragmatists, too. They appreciate terms that are easy to use and remember.

Molecule, thy name is . . .

The vagaries and perils of nomenclature are readily apparent in the fascinating semantic histories of three biological molecules that have played leading roles in the biomedical revolution: tumor necrosis factor, interferon, and interleukin-2.

Tumor necrosis factor represents the stolid, old-school approach to naming things. The molecule was first isolated in 1975 by Elizabeth Carswell of the Memorial Sloan-Kettering Cancer Center, New York City, who was searching for a cancer-destroying substance that was known to be produced naturally by the body after exposure to certain bacterial toxins. When the substance was induced experimentally in laboratory animals, tumors in the animals essentially stopped growing, turned black, and died (or "necrosed" from hemorrhaging)—hence, *tumor necrosis factor*. Ironically, the very same molecule happened to have been studied by different scientists interested in a completely different physiological effect, namely cachexia, the syndrome of appetite loss and wasting that occurs with aging and chronic disease. Converging on the same molecular treasure from a totally different route, they isolated the identical molecule and called it something else: *cachectin*. The molecule still travels by both names.

Interferon, once hailed as a potential cure for cancer, was discovered in 1957 by Alick Isaacs and Jean Lindenmann at the National Institute for Medical Research in England. The name derives from a phenomenon that had interested Isaacs for years. When cells in laboratory dishes were infected with one type of virus (influenza virus, for example), the infected cells mysteriously gained the ability to resist infection when subsequently exposed to a different strain of the virus. The phenomenon was known as interference, and after many years of effort, Isaacs isolated a factor that seemed responsible for it. His lab notes indicate that even before he found it, he was referring to it as *interferon*. Purists, however, objected to what they perceived as a promiscuous mixing of Greek and Latin in the term, the first part (*interfer*, from *interference*) being Latin and the suffix (*on*, from *ion*) being Greek.

Many biologists, biochemists in particular, protested against *interferon* on purely scientific grounds. They were so skeptical about the molecule's existence that they coined a different set of terms to describe the discovery: *imaginon, hypotheticon,* and *misinterpreton.* One of Isaacs' colleagues, Joseph Sonnabend, has suggested that Isaacs may have invited some of those doubts by naming the object before it had been isolated and characterized. "By using the word *interferon*, Alick made a mistake that was not pointed out at the time, although it should have been," Sonnabend says. "By saying *interferon* is a singular noun, just

236

the interferon, he assumed that the antiviral activity he was measuring resided in a unique and single molecule, which as we know now is not true." In fact there are about 20 different types of interferon, and they achieve their effects as part of larger biochemical cascades. A number of interferons, incidentally, have now been genetically engineered and approved as pharmaceuticals. And what was the trade name for one of the first? Intron.

One of the most serendipitous episodes of "naming" involves interleukin-2. The molecule was originally discovered by Doris Morgan, Frank Ruscetti, and Robert Gallo of the U.S. National Institutes of Health. It was isolated from a broth used to sustain white blood cells in culture because it seemed to stimulate in particular the proliferation of immune cells known as T lymphocytes. Indeed, Morgan and her colleagues named this new molecule *T-cell growth factor* in a 1976 paper in the journal *Science*.

Unbeknownst to the discoverers, T-cell growth factor was merely one of a burgeoning family of molecules that carry signals between white blood cells, or leukocytes. At the time there appeared to be hundreds of these molecules, with names like *MAF* (for *macrophage activating factor*) and *BAF* (for *B-cell activating factor*), and it was not until some young researchers overhauled the nomenclature of the field in a Swiss bar that it became clear that many of the BAFs and MAFs were in fact a few molecules with multiple names.

The reorganization took place in May 1979, when a group of biologists gathered for a conference at the small village of Ermatingen in Switzerland. Many researchers convened at a bar after the formal workshop sessions for what became a highly informal nomenclature meeting. Many names were bandied about, according to Joost J. Oppenheim, chief of the U.S. National Cancer Institute's laboratory of molecular immunoregulation, who attended both the conference and the beer-hall deliberations. (He recalls that the scientists, after much discussion— and many beers—considered naming this family of molecules *heidikines* in honor of the barmaid who waited on their table.) But it was Verner Paetkau of the University of Alberta who ultimately christened the family. "It came to me in a flash," Paetkau recalls. "These are messages that go between leukocytes. Okay, so it's *interleukin*. Then I had another flash immediately after that, that I was mixing Greek and Latin roots. But I thought, what the hell, we're scientists. We're not classical scholars." At the time only interleukin-1 and interleukin-2 were known; now there are a dozen interleukins. (Paetkau, incidentally, denies a story, still in circulation, that *interleukin* was partly inspired by Interlaken, the name of another Swiss town.)

As spontaneous and haphazard as the "naming" process sometimes seems, there is more aforethought than meets the eye. Oppenheim, who has served on a number of nomenclature committees, says the trick of naming families of molecules, for example, is "to promote communication and yet not put any restrictive connotations that would artificially foretell that that family of molecules was going to be this and that. You have to allow some leeway, because you never know what you're going to discover." He also says that the inevitable arguments over the right word are intellectually productive. "When people hear about a fight over terminology, they become very interested and very focused on the issues," according to Oppenheim. "It really galvanizes scientific interest."

Just say the word—the right word

Though it seems at best a side dish to the meat of discovery, the naming of scientific objects and theories can have an important bearing on the reception of new intellectual ideas. Many scientists learn early in their careers the subtle difference a turn of phrase can make. "In my thesis, I described what I called *bursts of star formation*," John Huchra recalls. "The words that became famous, one year later, were *starburst galaxies*." In 1981 astronomer Daniel Weedman, now at Pennsylvania State University, described essentially the same phenomenon as Huchra but with slightly more felicitous and economical phrasing. "It's a contributing factor in name recognition, and whether the public finds it interesting," Huchra says. "Not just the public at large, but the astronomical community. It's certainly true that when something has a name that is catchy or descriptive, it will hold more interest in the field."

Yorke, coiner of *chaos*, says his group deliberates for months before coming up with new terms to describe physical phenomena—*shy, crisis,* and *metamorphosis* are among their more recent creations. He believes that the well-chosen name helps scientists visualize behavior in physical systems. "It's a specific phenomenon that's going to occur, and it's got features you can study," he says. "If you don't have a name for it, you can't see it. Once you have a name for it, you can see it. And the name has to be suggestive. I tell people that it's terrible to name something using a person's name, like the *Mandelbrot set*. It doesn't help you *see* it. *Gravitational lens* is a better name than an *Einstein lens*. And *chaos* is a better name than *Yorke-like behavior*."

What about the converse? Can a bland or neutral name blunt enthusiasm for the scientific idea behind it? There was much biological palaver in the 1980s involving *transposons* and *jumping genes*—alternate names for segments of genetic material that moved promiscuously from chromosome to chromosome. Yet the phenomenon, now a cornerstone of 20th-century genetics, had been reported decades earlier by Barbara McClintock of Cold Spring Harbor (New York) Laboratory, first with the term *mutable loci* and later *movable elements*. In that case the marriage of an unexciting term to an unexpected observation may have retarded acceptance of the idea; McClintock received a Nobel Prize in 1983 for work done in the 1940s and 1950s.

Physicists point to another example in the case of the scanning tunneling microscope (STM), for which IBM researchers Gerd Binnig and Heinrich Rohrer received a Nobel Prize in 1986. In the late 1960s, about a decade before the IBM scientists published their first findings, a team of researchers at the U.S. National Bureau of Standards (NBS) headed by Russell D. Young developed an instrument that was remarkably similar to the STM in its ability to image landscapes of packed atoms. Scientists cite several reasons why the instrument failed to achieve widespread acceptance, including the persuasive fact that the NBS terminated the project and assigned Young to another task. But in choosing the difficult name *Topografiner*—from the Greek *topographein,* meaning "to describe a place"—the NBS may have subtly biased the scientific community against a superb discovery.

"How would *you* pronounce it?" asked a physicist who spelled it out once for a writer. After hearing a halting attempt to locate an accentable syllable, he continued, "Probably a good try. The instrument was *very, very* similar to the STM, but it never caught on," says the physicist, who asked not to be named because of lingering hard feelings about credit for the invention. "I think the fact that the name was impossible to pronounce for most people certainly didn't help its popularity compared to Binnig and Rohrer's scanning tunneling microscope, or STM. That was a real easy term to understand and an easy acronym to pronounce. No ambiguity there."

Even Young rues the name. "That was kind of a committee decision, I'm afraid," he concedes now. "People would try to pronounce it and stumble over the word, so we knew we didn't have a good name." The correct pronunciation, he added, is Ta-POG-ra-fine-er. Young believes, however, that cancellation of the project and not its tongue-tying name killed the machine.

A catchy name can also attract attention to an object that still awaits discovery—in inverse proportion, some argue, to the scientific vigor of the idea. In 1984 astronomer Richard A. Muller and colleagues of the University of California at Berkeley ventured a theory in the journal *Nature* that the Sun was being shadowed by a companion "death star," which periodically kicked up a swarm of killer comets hurtling toward Earth and causing massive extinctions every 26 million years or so. From a list of possible names appended to a tongue-in-cheek footnote, an editor at *Nature* selected *Nemesis,* for the Greek goddess who tormented the excessively rich, proud, and powerful. The name as much as the theory captivated the public, and the death star even landed on the cover of *Time* magazine in 1985.

Nemesis has yet to be located, and to some in the astronomical community, the name seems to have proved far more captivating than the theory. "It was a cute idea, and the name just made it cuter," says Paul Weissman, an expert in solar system dynamics at the Jet Propulsion Laboratory, Pasadena. "But very few people believe in it anymore." And that statement says more about the sociology of science, Muller replies, than about the Nemesis theory. "Most people think the theory is wrong. It is not wrong," he insists, "and is in good shape." The Berkeley team of Nemesis hunters recently launched a revamped search for a candidate death star.

"The whole reason we put in the footnote was to be somewhat playful, so that people *wouldn't* resent it," Muller explains. "I did get some comments, like 'Why are you naming it before you've found it?' There is a prejudice in science against people seeking publicity, and that's a good prejudice. Making up names is part of the job in terms of communication. But it subverts the scientific merit system, so both sides are right."

It would all be a matter of modest extracurricular interest except that some scientists believe the catchy name, all things being equal, can favorably influence grant applications. Muller does nothing to undermine that theory. "Everyone has heard of the Nemesis theory," says Muller. "It has made it easier to get funding to do the search." That confirms the sense in other quarters; a name that passes peer review on Madison Avenue will probably also play well at the National Science Foundation or National Institutes of Health.

While Yorke, Dressler, and other "namers" have taken their lumps, consider what the literary landscape of science would look like without them. Instead of *chaos,* we would have *stochasticity* or *nonlinear dynamic systems theory.* Instead of *black holes,* we would have *Schwarzchild singularities.* And if Dressler's term *Great Attractor* had not caught the fancy of reporters, we might instead have been left with the name championed by one of his collaborators, the University of Oxford theoretician Donald Lynden-Bell. Nimbly dodging the pitfalls of colorful, controversial, or playful language, he boldly proposed the term *VMO,* which stood for, he explained, *very massive object.*

Finally, the effort required for thinking up a good figurative name may work against another scientific imperative: priority and credit. The point was made by Joel E. Cohen, a population biologist at Rockefeller University, New York City, who in a recent issue of *Science* cited what he called "Stigler's Law" in attempting to claim credit for a witty remark attributed to someone else. "Stigler's Law," Cohen wrote, "asserts that a discovery is named after the last person to discover it, because once a discovery has been named, no one else claims it as a discovery." "Stigler's Law," Cohen added, "was discovered many times before Stigler named it."

FOR ADDITIONAL READING

Anne Eisenberg, "Metaphor in the Language of Science," *Scientific American* (May 1992, p. 144), and "Quantum English," *Scientific American* (October 1991, p. 134).

Donald P. Hayes, "The Growing Inaccessibility of Science," *Nature* (April 30, 1992, pp. 739–740).

John Maddox, "Language for a Polyglot Readership," *Nature* (Oct. 8, 1992, p. 475).

Scott L. Montgomery, "Codes and Combat in Biomedical Discourse," *Science as Culture* (vol. 2, part 3, 1991, pp. 341–390).

Encyclopædia

Britannica

Science Update

Major Revisions from the 1993 *Macropædia*

The purpose of this section is to introduce to continuing *Yearbook of Science and the Future* subscribers selected *Macropædia* articles or portions of them that have been completely revised or written anew. It is intended to update the *Macropædia* in ways that cannot be accomplished fully by reviewing the year's events or by revising statistics annually, because the *Macropædia* texts themselves—written from a longer perspective than any yearly revision—supply authoritative interpretation and analysis as well as narrative and description.

Three articles have been chosen from the 1993 printing: ANALYSIS AND MEASUREMENT (in part), SOLAR SYSTEM (in part), and TREES. Each is the work of distinguished scholars, and each represents the continuing dedication of the *Encyclopædia Britannica* to bringing such works to the general reader.

Analysis and Measurement

RADIATION MEASUREMENT

In science and technology, it is often necessary to measure the intensity and characteristics of ionizing radiation such as alpha, beta, and gamma rays or neutrons. The term ionizing radiation refers to those subatomic particles and photons whose energy is sufficient to cause ionization in the matter with which they interact. The ionization process consists of removing an electron from an initially neutral atom or molecule. For many materials, the minimum energy required for this process is about 10 electron volts (eV), and this can be taken as the lower limit of the range of ionizing radiation energies. The more common types of ionizing radiation are characterized by particle or quantum energies measured in thousands or millions of electron volts (keV or MeV, respectively). At the upper end of the energy scale, the present discussion will be limited to those radiations with quantum energies less than about 20 MeV. This energy range covers the common types of ionizing radiation encountered in radioactive decay, fission and fusion systems and the medical and industrial applications of radioisotopes. It excludes the regime of high-energy particle physics in which quantum energies can reach billions or trillions of electron volts. In this field of research, measurements tend to employ much more massive and specialized detectors than those in common use for the lower-energy radiations.

RADIATION INTERACTIONS IN MATTER

For the purposes of this discussion, it is convenient to divide the various types of ionizing radiation into two major categories: those that carry an electric charge and those that do not. In the first group are the radiations that are normally viewed as individual subatomic charged particles. Such radiation appears, for example, as the alpha particles that are spontaneously emitted in the decay of certain unstable heavy nuclei. These alpha particles consist of two protons and two neutrons and carry a positive electrical charge of two units. Another example is the beta-minus radiation also emitted in the decay of some radioactive nuclei. In this case, each nuclear decay produces a fast electron that carries a negative charge of one unit. In contrast, there are other types of ionizing radiation that carry no electrical charge. Common examples are gamma rays, which can be represented as high-frequency electromagnetic photons, and neutrons, which are classically pictured as subatomic particles carrying no electrical charge. In the discussions below, the term quantum will generally be used to represent a single particle or photon, regardless of its type.

Only charged radiations interact continuously with matter, and they are therefore the only types of radiation that are directly detectable in the devices described here. In contrast, uncharged quanta must first undergo a major interaction that transforms all or part of their energy into secondary charged radiations. Properties of the original uncharged radiations can then be inferred by studying the charged particles that are produced. These major interactions occur only rarely, so it is not unusual for an uncharged radiation to travel distances of many centime-

Alpha particles

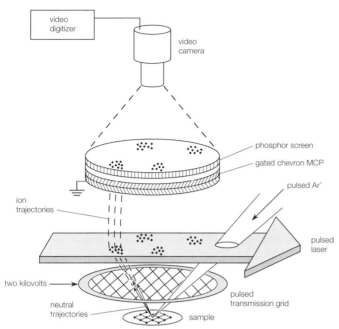

Figure 49: *RIS apparatus for basic studies of surface physics and chemistry.*
A multichannel plate (MCP) is used to measure angular distributions of energy-selected neutral atoms emitted from surfaces irradiated with argon ions (Ar^+).
By permission of Pennsylvania State University

tres through solid materials before such an interaction occurs. Instruments that are designed for the efficient detection of these uncharged quanta therefore tend to have relatively large thicknesses to increase the probability of observing the results of such an interaction within the detector volume.

Interactions of heavy charged particles. The term heavy charged particle refers to those energetic particles whose mass is one atomic mass unit or greater. This category includes alpha particles, together with protons, deuterons, fission fragments, and other energetic heavy particles often produced in accelerators. These particles carry at least one electronic charge, and they interact with matter primarily through the Coulomb force that exists between the positive charge on the particle and the negative charge on electrons that are part of the absorber material. In this case, the force is an attractive one between the two opposite charges. As a charged particle passes near an electron in the absorber, it transfers a small fraction of its momentum to the electron. As a result, the charged particle slows down slightly, and the electron (which originally was nearly at rest) picks up some of its kinetic energy. At any given time, the charged particle is simultaneously interacting with many electrons in the absorber material, and the net result of all the Coulomb forces acts like a viscous drag on the particle. From the instant it enters the absorber, the particle slows down continuously until it is brought to a stop. Because the charged particle is thousands of times more massive than the electrons with which it is interacting, it is deflected relatively little from a straight-line path as it comes to rest. The time that elapses before the particle is stopped ranges from a few picoseconds (1×10^{-12} second) in solids or liquids to a few nanoseconds (1×10^{-9} second) in gases. These times are short enough that the stopping time can be considered to be instantaneous for many purposes, and this approximation is assumed in the following sections that describe the response of radiation detectors.

Several characteristics of the particle-deceleration process are important in understanding the behaviour of radiation detectors. First, the average distance traveled by the particle before it stops is called its mean range. For a given material, the mean range increases with increasing initial kinetic energy of the charged particle. Typical values for charged particles with initial energies of a few MeV are tens or hundreds of micrometres in solids or liquids and a few centimetres in gases at ordinary temperature and pressure. A second property is the specific energy loss at a given point along the particle track (path). This quantity measures the differential energy deposited per unit path-length (dE/dx) in the material; it is also a function of the particle energy. In general, as the particle slows down and loses energy, the dE/dx value tends to increase. Thus, the density with which energy is being deposited in the absorber along the particle's track tends to increase as it slows down. The average dE/dx value for charged particles is relatively large because of their short range, and they are often referred to as high dE/dx radiations.

Interactions of fast electrons. Energetic electrons (such as beta-minus particles), since they carry an electric charge, also interact with electrons in the absorber material through the Coulomb force. In this case, the force is a repulsive rather than an attractive one, but the net results are similar to those observed for heavy charged particles. The fast electron experiences the cumulative effect of many simultaneous Coulomb forces, and undergoes a continuous deceleration until it is stopped. As compared with a heavy charged particle, the distance traveled by the fast electron is many times greater for an equivalent initial energy. For example, a beta particle with an initial energy of 1 MeV travels one or two millimetres in typical solids and several metres in gases at standard conditions. Also, since a fast electron has a much smaller mass than a heavy charged particle, it is much more easily deflected along its path. A typical fast-electron track deviates considerably from a straight line, and deflections through large angles are not uncommon. Because a fast electron will travel perhaps 100 times as far in a given material as a heavy charged particle with the same initial energy, its energy is much less densely deposited along its track. For this reason, fast electrons are often referred to as low dE/dx radiations.

There is one other significant difference in the energy loss of fast electrons as compared with that of heavy charged particles. While undergoing large-angle deflections, fast electrons can radiate part of their energy in the form of electromagnetic radiation known as bremsstrahlung, or braking radiation. This form of radiation normally falls within the X-ray region of the spectrum. The fraction of the fast-electron energy lost in the form of bremsstrahlung is less than 1 percent for low-energy electrons in light materials but becomes a much larger fraction for high-energy electrons in materials with high atomic numbers.

Interactions of gamma rays and X rays. Ionizing radiation also can take the form of electromagnetic rays. When emitted by excited atoms, they are given the name X rays and have quantum energies typically measured from 1 to 100 keV. When emitted by excited nuclei, they are called gamma rays, and characteristic energies can be as high as several MeV. In both cases, the radiation takes the form of photons of electromagnetic energy. Since the photon is uncharged, it does not interact through the Coulomb force and therefore can pass through large distances in matter without significant interaction. The average distance traveled between interactions is called the mean free path and in solid materials ranges from a few millimetres for low-energy X rays through tens of centimetres for high-energy gamma rays. When an interaction does occur, however, it is catastrophic in the sense that a single interaction can profoundly affect the energy and direction of the photon or can make it disappear entirely. In such an interaction, all or part of the photon energy is transferred to one or more electrons in the absorber material. Because the secondary electrons thus produced are energetic and charged, they interact in much the same way as described earlier for primary fast electrons. The fact that an original X ray or gamma ray was present is indicated by the appearance of secondary electrons. Information on the energy carried by the incident photons can be inferred by measuring the energy of these electrons. The three major types of such interactions are discussed below.

Photoelectric absorption. In this process, the incident X-ray or gamma-ray photon interacts with an atom of the absorbing material, and the photon completely disappears; its energy is transferred to one of the orbital electrons of the atom. Because this energy in general far exceeds the binding energy of the electron in the host atom, the

Stopping time

Brems-strahlung

Creation of secondary electrons

electron is ejected at high velocity. The kinetic energy of this secondary electron is equal to the incoming energy of the photon minus the binding energy of the electron in the original atomic shell. The process leaves the atom with a vacancy in one of the normally filled electron shells, which is then refilled after a short period of time by a nearby free electron. This filling process again liberates the binding energy in the form of a characteristic X-ray photon, which then typically interacts with electrons from less tightly bound shells in nearby atoms, producing additional fast electrons. The overall effect is therefore the complete conversion of the photon energy into the energy carried by fast electrons. Since the fast electrons are now detectable through their Coulomb interactions, they can serve as the basis to indicate the presence of the original gamma-ray or X-ray photon, and a measurement of their energy is tantamount to measuring the energy of the incoming photon. Because the photoelectric process results in complete conversion of the photon energy to electron energy, it is in some sense an ideal conversion step. The task of measuring the gamma-ray energy is then reduced to simply measuring the equivalent energy deposited by the fast electrons. Unfortunately, two other types of gamma-ray interactions also take place that complicate this interpretation step.

Compton scattering. An incoming gamma-ray photon can interact with a single free electron in the absorber through the process of Compton scattering. In this process, the photon abruptly changes direction and transfers a portion of its original energy to the electron from which it scattered, producing an energetic recoil electron. The fraction of the photon energy that is transferred depends on the scattering angle. When the incoming photon is deflected only slightly, little energy is transferred to the electron. Maximum energy transfer occurs when the incoming photon is backscattered from the electron and its original direction is reversed. Since in general all angles of scattering will occur, the recoil electrons are produced with a continuum of energies ranging from near zero to a maximum represented by the backscattering extreme. This maximum energy can be predicted from the conservation of momentum and energy in the photon-electron interaction and is about 0.25 MeV below the incoming photon energy for high-energy gamma rays. After the interaction, the scattered photon has an energy that has decreased by an amount equal to the energy transferred to the recoil electron. It may subsequently interact again at some other location or simply escape from the detector.

Pair production. A third gamma-ray interaction process is possible when the incoming photon energy is above 1.02 MeV. In the field of a nucleus of the absorber material, the photon may disappear and be replaced by the formation of an electron-positron pair. The minimum energy required to create this pair of particles is their combined rest-mass energy of 1.02 MeV. Therefore, pair production cannot occur for incoming photon energies below this threshold. When the photon energy exceeds this value, the excess energy appears as initial kinetic energy shared by the positron and electron that are formed. The positron is a positively charged particle with the mass of a normal negative electron. It slows down and deposits its energy over an average distance that is nearly the same as that for a negative electron of equivalent energy. Therefore both particles transfer their kinetic energy over a distance of no more than a few millimetres in typical solids. The magnitude of the deposited energy is given by the original photon energy minus 1.02 MeV. When the positron member of the pair reaches the end of its track, it combines with a normal negative electron from the absorber in a process known as annihilation. In this step both particles disappear and are replaced by two annihilation photons, each with an energy of 0.511 MeV. Annihilation photons are similar to gamma rays in their ability to penetrate large distances of matter without interacting. They may undergo Compton or photoelectric interactions elsewhere or may escape from detectors of small size.

Role of energy and atomic number. The probability for each of these three interaction mechanisms to occur varies with the gamma-ray energy and the atomic number of the

absorber. Photoelectric absorption predominates at low energies and is greatly enhanced in materials with high atomic number. For this reason, elements of high atomic number are mostly chosen for detectors used in gamma-ray energy measurements. Compton scattering is the most common interaction for moderate energies (from a few hundred keV to several MeV). Pair production predominates for higher energies and is also enhanced in materials with high atomic number. In larger detectors, there is a tendency for an incident photon to cause multiple interactions, as, for example, several sequential Compton scatterings followed by pair production followed by the interaction of an annihilation photon. Since little time separates these events, the deposited energies add together to determine the overall size of the output pulse.

Interactions of neutrons. Neutrons represent a major category of radiation that consists of uncharged particles. Owing to the absence of the Coulomb force, neutrons may penetrate many centimetres through solid materials before they interact in any manner. When they do interact, it is primarily with the nuclei of atoms of the absorbing material. The types of interaction that are important in the detection of neutrons are again catastrophic since the neutrons may either disappear or undergo a major change in their energy and direction.

In the case of gamma rays, such major interactions produce fast electrons. In contrast, the important neutron interactions result in the formation of energetic heavy charged particles. The task of detecting the uncharged neutron is thus transformed into one of measuring the directly observable results of the energy deposited in the detector by the secondary charged particles. Because the types of interaction that are useful in neutron detection are different for neutrons of different energies, it is convenient to subdivide the discussion into slow-neutron and fast-neutron interaction mechanisms.

Slow neutrons. These are conventionally defined as neutrons whose kinetic energy is below about 1 eV. Slow neutrons frequently undergo elastic scattering interactions with nuclei and may in the process transfer a fraction of their energy to the interacting nucleus. Because the kinetic energy of a neutron is so low, however, the resulting recoil nucleus does not have enough energy to be classified as an ionizing particle. Instead, the important interactions for the detection of slow neutrons involve nuclear reactions in which a neutron is absorbed by the nucleus and charged particles are formed. All the reactions of interest in slow neutron detectors are exoenergetic, meaning that an amount of energy (called the Q-value) is released in the reaction. The charged particles are produced with a large amount of kinetic energy supplied by the nuclear reaction. Therefore, the products of these reactions are ionizing particles, and they interact in much the same way as previously described for direct radiations consisting of heavy charged particles. Some specific examples of nuclear reactions of interest in slow-neutron detection are given below in the section *Active detectors: Neutron detectors.*

Fast neutrons. Neutrons whose kinetic energy is above about 1 keV are generally classified as fast neutrons. The neutron-induced reactions commonly employed for detecting slow neutrons have a low probability of occurrence once the neutron energy is high. Detectors that are based on these reactions may be quite efficient for slow neutrons, but they are inefficient for detecting fast neutrons.

Instead, fast neutron detectors are most commonly based on the elastic scattering of neutrons from nuclei. They exploit the fact that a significant fraction of a neutron's kinetic energy can be transferred to the nucleus that it strikes, producing an energetic recoil nucleus. This recoil nucleus behaves in much the same way as any other heavy charged particle as it slows down and loses its energy in the absorber. The amount of energy transferred varies from nearly zero for a grazing angle scattering to a maximum for the case of a head-on collision. Hydrogen is a common choice for the target nucleus, and the resulting recoil protons (or recoiling hydrogen nuclei) serve as the basis for many types of fast-neutron detectors. Hydrogen provides a unique advantage in this application since a fast neutron can transfer up to its full energy in a single

Margin notes:
Recoil electrons

Annihilation photons

Heavy charged particle formation

Q-value

scattering interaction with a hydrogen nucleus. For all other elements, the heavier nucleus limits the maximum energy transfer in a single scattering to only a fraction of the neutron energy. In any elastic-scattering interaction, the energy that is not transferred to the recoil nucleus is retained by the scattered neutron which, depending on the dimensions of the detector, may interact again or simply escape from the detector volume.

Applications of radiation interactions in detectors. A number of physical or chemical effects caused by the deposition of energy along the track of a charged particle are listed in the first column of Table 5. Each of these effects can serve as the basis of instruments designed to detect radiation, and examples of specific devices based on each effect are given in the second column.

One category of radiation-measurement devices indicates the presence of ionizing radiation only after the exposure has occurred. A physical or chemical change is induced by the radiation that is later measured through some type of processing. These so-called passive detectors are widely applied in the routine monitoring of occupational exposures to ionizing radiation. In contrast, in active detectors a signal is produced in real time to indicate the presence of radiation. This distinction is indicated for the examples in Table 5. The normal mode of operation of each detector type is also noted. These include pulse mode, current mode, and integrating mode as defined below (see *Active detectors: Modes of operation*). An indication is also given as to whether the detector is normally capable of responding to a single particle or quantum of radiation or whether the cumulative effect of many quanta is needed for a measurable output.

In the descriptions that follow, emphasis is placed on the behaviour of devices for the measurement of those forms of ionizing radiation consisting of heavy charged particles, fast electrons, X rays, and gamma rays. Techniques and devices of primary interest for the measurement of neutrons are discussed separately in a later section because they differ substantially in operation or composition or both. The detection methods that are included also are limited to those that are relatively sensitive to low levels of radiation. There are a number of other physical effects resulting from exposure to intense radiation that can also serve as the basis for measurements, many of which are important in the field of radiation dosimetry (the measurement of radiation doses). They include chemical changes in ionic solutions, changes in the colour or other optical properties of transparent materials, and calorimetric measurement of the heat deposited by intense fluxes of radiation.

(margin note) Effects of intense radiation

PASSIVE DETECTORS

Photographic emulsions. The use of photographic techniques to record ionizing radiations dates back to the discovery of X rays by Röntgen in the late 1800s, but similar techniques remain important today in some applications. A photographic emulsion consists of a suspension of silver halide grains in an inert gelatin matrix and supported by a backing of plastic film or another material.

If a charged particle or fast electron passes through the emulsion, interactions with silver halide molecules produce a similar effect as seen with exposure to visible light. Some molecules are excited and will remain in this state for an indefinite period of time. After the exposure is completed, this latent record of the accumulated exposure can be made visible through the chemical development process. Each grain containing an excited molecule is converted to metallic silver, greatly amplifying the number of affected molecules to the point that the developed grain is visible. Photographic emulsions used for radiation detection purposes can be classified into two main subgroups: radiographic films and nuclear emulsions. Radiographic films register the results of exposure to radiation as a general darkening of the film due to the cumulative effect of many radiation interactions in a given area of the emulsion. Nuclear emulsions are intended to record individual tracks of a single charged particle.

Radiographic films. Radiographic films are most familiar in their application in medical X-ray imaging. Their properties do not differ drastically from those of normal photographic film used to record visible light, except for an unusually high silver halide concentration. Thickness of the emulsion ranges from 10 to 20 micrometres, and they contain silver halide grains up to 1 micrometre in diameter. The probability that a typical incident X ray will interact in the emulsion is only a few percent, and so methods are often applied to increase the sensitivity so as to reduce the intensity of the X rays needed to produce a visible image. One such technique is to apply emulsion to both sides of the film base. Another is to sandwich the photographic emulsion between intensifier screens that consist of thin layers of light-emitting phosphors of high atomic number, such as calcium tungstate, cesium iodide, or rare earth phosphors. If an X ray interacts in the screen, the light that is produced darkens the film in the immediate vicinity through the normal photographic process. Because of the high atomic number of the screens, they are more likely to cause an X ray to interact than the emulsion itself, and the X-ray flux needed to achieve a given degree of darkening of the emulsion can be decreased by as much as an order of magnitude. The light is produced in the normal scintillation process (see below *Active detectors: Scintillation and Čerenkov detectors*) and travels in all directions from the point of the X-ray interaction. This spreading causes some loss of spatial resolution in X-ray images, especially for thicker screens, and the screen thickness must therefore be chosen to reach a compromise between resolution and sensitivity.

(margin note) Intensifier screens

Nuclear emulsions. In order to enable visualization of single particle tracks, nuclear emulsions are generally made much thicker than ordinary photographic emulsions (up to 500 micrometres) and they have an even higher silver halide content. Special development procedures can reveal the tracks of individual charged particles or fast electrons as a nearly continuous trail of developed silver grains that is visible under a microscope. If the particle is stopped in the emulsion, the length of its track can be measured to give its range and therefore an estimate of its initial energy.

Table 5: Applications of Radiation Interactions in Detectors

results of interaction of incident radiation	detector category	active or passive	single quantum sensitivity	mode type (for active detectors)
Sensitized silver halide grains in photographic emulsion	radiographic film	passive	no	
	nuclear emulsion	passive	yes	
Trapped charges in crystalline materials	thermoluminescent dosimeter	passive	no	
	memory phosphor	passive	no	
Damaged track in dielectric materials	track-etch film	passive	yes	
Radioactivity induced by neutrons	activation foil	passive	no	
Vaporized superheated liquid drop	bubble chamber	active and passive	yes	pulse
Ion pairs in a gas	ion chamber pocket dosimeter	(integrating)	no	
	current-mode ion chamber	active	no	current
	proportional tube	active	yes	pulse
	Geiger-Müller tube	active	yes	pulse
Mobile electron-hole pairs in semiconductor	silicon diode	active	yes	current and pulse
	coaxial germanium detector	active	yes	pulse
Prompt fluorescence in transparent materials	scintillation detector	active	yes	current and pulse
Čerenkov radiation	Čerenkov detector	active	yes	pulse

The density of the grains along the track is proportional to the dE/dx of the particle, and therefore some distinction can be made between particles of different type.

Film badge dosimeters.   Small packets of photographic emulsions are routinely used by workers to monitor radiation exposure. The density of the developed film can be compared with that of an identical film exposed to a known radiation dose. In this way, variations that result from differences in film properties or development procedures are canceled out. When used to monitor exposure to low-energy radiation such as X rays or gamma rays, emulsions tend to overrespond owing to the rapid rise of the photoelectric cross section of silver at these energies. To reduce this deviation, the film is often wrapped in a thin metallic foil to absorb some of the low-energy photons before they reach the emulsion.

One of the drawbacks of photographic film is the limited dynamic range between underexposure and overexposure. In order to extend this range, the holder that contains the film badge often is fitted with a set of small metallic filters that cover selected regions of the film. By making the filters of differing thickness, the linear region under each filter corresponds to a different range of exposure, and the effective dynamic range of the film is extended. The filters also help to separate exposures to weakly penetrating radiations (such as beta particles) from those due to more penetrating radiations (such as gamma rays).

Thermoluminescent materials.   Another technique commonly applied in personnel monitoring is the use of thermoluminescent dosimeters (TLDs). This technique is based on the use of crystalline materials in which ionizing radiation creates electron-hole pairs (see below *Active detectors: Semiconductor detectors*). In this case, however, traps for these charges are intentionally created through the addition of a dopant (impurity) or the special processing of the material. The object is to create conditions in which many of the electrons and holes formed by the incident radiation are quickly captured and immobilized. During the period of exposure to the radiation, a growing population of trapped charges accumulates in the material. The trap depth is the minimum energy that is required to free a charge from the trap. It is chosen to be large enough so that the rate of detrapping is very low at room temperature. Thus, if the exposure is carried out at ordinary temperatures, the trapped charge is more or less permanently stored.

After the exposure, the amount of trapped charge is quantified by measuring the amount of light that is emitted while the temperature of the crystal is raised. The applied thermal energy causes rapid release of the charges. A liberated electron can then recombine with a remaining trapped hole, emitting energy in the process. In TLD materials, this energy appears as a photon in the visible part of the electromagnetic spectrum. Alternatively, a liberated hole can recombine with a remaining trapped electron to generate a similar photon. The total intensity of emitted light can be measured using a photomultiplier tube and is proportional to the original population of trapped charges. This is in turn proportional to the radiation dose accumulated over the exposure period.

The readout process effectively empties all the traps, and the charges thus are erased from the material so that it can be recycled for repeated use. One of the commonly used TLD materials is lithium fluoride, in which the traps are sufficiently deep to prevent fading, or loss of the trapped charge over extended periods of time. The elemental composition of lithium fluoride is of similar atomic number to that of tissue, so that energy absorbed from gamma rays matches that of tissue over wide energy ranges.

Memory phosphors.   A memory phosphor consists of a thin layer of material with properties that resemble those of TLD crystals in the sense that charges created by incident radiation remain trapped for an indefinite period of time. The material is formed as a screen covering a substantial area so that it can be applied as an X-ray image detector. These screens can then be used as an alternative to radiographic films in X-ray radiography.

The incident X rays build up a pattern of trapped charges over the surface of the screen during the exposure period.

As in a TLD, the screen is then read out through the light that is generated by liberating these charges. The energy needed to detrap the stored charges is supplied in this case by stimulating the crystal with intense light from a laser beam rather than by heating. The luminescence from the memory phosphor can be distinguished from the laser light by its different wavelength. If the amount of this luminescence is measured as the laser beam scans across the surface of the screen, the spatial pattern of the trapped charges is thereby recorded. This pattern corresponds to the X-ray image recorded during the exposure. Like TLDs, memory phosphors have the advantage that the trapped charges are erased during readout, and the screen can be reused many times.

Track-etch detectors.   When a charged particle slows down and stops in a solid, the energy that it deposits along its track can cause permanent damage in the material. It is difficult to observe direct evidence of this local damage, even under careful microscopic examination. In certain dielectric materials, however, the presence of the damaged track can be revealed through chemical etching (erosion) of the material surface using an acid or base solution. If charged particles have irradiated the surface at some time in the past, then each leaves a trail of damaged material that begins at the surface and extends to a depth equal to the range of the particle. In the materials of choice, the chemical etching rate along this track is higher than the rate of etching of the undamaged surface. Therefore, as the etching progresses, a pit is formed at the position of each track. Within a few hours, these pits can become large enough so that they can be seen directly under a low-power microscope. A measurement of the number of these pits per unit area is then a measure of the particle flux to which the surface has been exposed.

There is a minimum density of damage along the track that is required before the etching rate is sufficient to create a pit. Because the density of damage correlates with the dE/dx of the particle, it is highest for the heaviest charged particles. In any given material, a certain minimum value for dE/dx is required before pits will develop. For example, in the mineral mica, pits are observed only from energetic heavy ions whose mass is 10 or 20 atomic mass units or greater. Many common plastic materials are more sensitive and will develop etch pits for low-mass ions such as helium (alpha particles). Some particularly sensitive plastics such as cellulose nitrate will develop pits even for protons, which are the least damaging of the heavy charged particles. No materials have been found that will produce pits for the low dE/dx tracks of fast electrons. This threshold behaviour makes such detectors completely insensitive to beta particles and gamma rays. This immunity can be exploited in some applications where weak fluxes of heavy charged particles are to be registered in the presence of a more intense background of gamma rays. For example, many environmental measurements of the alpha particles produced by the decay of radon gas and its daughter products are made using plastic track-etch film. The background to omnipresent gamma rays would dominate the response of many other types of detectors under these circumstances. In some materials the damage track has been shown to remain in the material for indefinite periods of time, and pits can be etched many years after the exposure. Etching properties are, however, potentially affected by exposure to light and high temperatures, so some caution must be exercised in the prolonged storage of exposed samples to prevent fading of the damage tracks.

Automated methods have been developed to measure the etch pit density using microscope stages coupled to computers with appropriate optical-analysis software. These systems are capable of some degree of discrimination against "artifacts" such as scratches on the sample surface and can provide a reasonably accurate measurement of the number of tracks per unit area. Another technique incorporates relatively thin plastic films, in which the tracks are etched completely through the film to form small holes. These holes can then be automatically counted by passing the film slowly between a set of high-voltage electrodes and electronically counting sparks that occur as a hole passes.

(margin notes)

Trapping of charges

Use as an X-ray image detector

Thresholds for pit development

Measurement of etched tracks

Neutron-activation foils. For radiation energies of several MeV and lower, charged particles and fast electrons do not induce nuclear reactions in absorber materials. Gamma rays with energy below a few MeV also do not readily induce reactions with nuclei. Therefore, when nearly any material is bombarded by these forms of radiation, the nuclei remain unaffected and no radioactivity is induced in the irradiated material.

Among the common forms of radiation, neutrons are an exception to this general behaviour. Because they carry no charge, neutrons of even low energy can readily interact with nuclei and induce a wide selection of nuclear reactions. Many of these reactions lead to radioactive products whose presence can later be measured using conventional detectors to sense the radiations emitted in their decay. For example, many types of nuclei will absorb a neutron to produce a radioactive nucleus. During the time that a sample of this material is exposed to neutrons, a population of radioactive nuclei accumulates. When the sample is removed from the neutron exposure, the population will decay with a given half-life. Some type of radiation is almost always emitted in this decay, often beta particles or gamma rays or both, which can then be counted using one of the active detection methods described below. Because it can be related to the level of the induced radioactivity, the intensity of the neutron flux to which the sample has been exposed can be deduced from this radioactivity measurement. In order to induce enough radioactivity to permit reasonably accurate measurement, relatively intense neutron fluxes are required. Therefore, activation foils are frequently used as a technique to measure neutron fields around reactors, accelerators, or other intense sources of neutrons.

Materials such as silver, indium, and gold are commonly used for the measurement of slow neutrons, whereas iron, magnesium, and aluminum are possible choices for fast-neutron measurements. In these cases, the half-life of the induced activity is in the range of a few minutes through a few days. In order to build up a population of radioactive nuclei that approaches the maximum possible, the half-life of the induced radioactivity should be shorter than the time of exposure to the neutron flux. At the same time, the half-life must be long enough to allow for convenient counting of the radioactivity once the sample has been removed from the neutron field.

Bubble detector. A relatively recent technique that has been introduced for the measurement of neutron exposures involves a device known as a superheated drop, or bubble detector. Its operation is based on a suspension of many small droplets of a liquid (such as Freon [trademark]) in an inert matrix consisting of a polymer or gel. The sample is held in a sealed vial or other transparent container, and the pressure on the sample is adjusted to create conditions in which the liquid droplets are superheated; *i.e.,* they are heated above their boiling point yet remain in the liquid state. The transformation to the vapour state must be triggered by the creation of some type of nucleation centre.

This stimulus can be provided by the energy deposited from the recoil nucleus created by the scattering of an incident neutron. When such an event occurs, the droplet suddenly vaporizes and creates a bubble that remains suspended within the matrix. Over the course of the neutron exposure, additional bubbles are formed, and a count of their total number is related to the incident neutron intensity. The bubble detector is insensitive to gamma rays because the fast electrons created in gamma-ray interactions have too low a value of dE/dx to serve as a nucleation centre. Bubble detectors have found application in monitoring the exposure of radiation personnel to ionizing radiation because of their good sensitivity to low levels of neutron fluxes and their immunity to gamma-ray backgrounds. Some types can be recycled and used repeatedly by collapsing the bubbles back to droplets through recompression. The same type of device can be made into an active detector by attaching a piezoelectric sensor. The pulse of acoustic energy emitted when the droplet vaporizes into a bubble is converted into an electrical pulse by the sensor and can then be counted electronically in real time.

Super-heating

ACTIVE DETECTORS

In many applications it is important to produce a signal that indicates the presence of ionizing radiation in real time. Such devices are classified as active detectors. Many types of active detectors can produce an observable signal for an individual quantum of radiation (such as a single alpha particle or an X-ray photon). Others may provide a signal that corresponds to the collective effect of many quanta interacting in the detector within its response time.

Modes of operation. In many types of detectors, a single particle or quantum of radiation liberates a certain amount of charge Q as a result of depositing its energy in the detector material. For example, in a gas, Q represents the total positive charge carried by the many positive ions that are produced along the track of the particle. (An equal charge of opposite sign is carried by the free electrons that are also generated.) This charge is created over a very short time, typically less than a nanosecond, as the particle slows down and stops; it is then collected over a much longer period of time, ranging from a few nanoseconds to several microseconds. In a gas or a semiconductor, the charge is collected through the motion of individual charge carriers in the electric field that is established within the detector. As these moving charges represent an electric current, detector response to a single quantum of radiation can then be modeled as a momentary burst of current that begins with the stopping of the charged particle and ends once all the charge carriers have been collected. If the detector is undergoing continuous irradiation, a sequence of these current bursts will be produced, one for each interacting quantum. In most applications the time of arrival of each quantum of radiation is randomly distributed. For purposes of this discussion, it is assumed that the average time between events in the detector is long compared with the charge collection time. Each burst of current is then distinct, and the integral or area under the current versus time profile for each burst is the charge Q formed for that event. Because the amount of energy deposited may be different for individual events, each of these current pulses may represent a different total charge Q. Furthermore, the charge collection time may also be variable, so the length of each of these current bursts may be different.

Detector current

Current mode. One way to provide an electrical signal from such a detector is to connect its output to an ammeter circuit with a slow response time. If this response time is long compared with the average time spacing between current bursts, then the ammeter will measure a current that is given by the mean rate of charge formation averaged over many individual radiation quanta. This mode of operation is called current mode, and many of the common detector types can be operated in this way. The measured current represents the product of the rate at which quanta are interacting in the detector multiplied by the average charge Q created by a single quantum of radiation. For a given source of radiation, doubling its intensity will double the observed current. However, different currents will result from radiations that have equal interaction rates but deposit a different average energy per interaction.

Integrating mode. There are circumstances in which the current from the detector is simply integrated during the time of exposure, and the accumulated total charge is measured at its completion. This integration mode of operation produces information that is related to the total exposure, but it cannot provide detail on possible variation of the intensity during the exposure time. In that sense, it is similar to the operation of passive detectors. Portable ion chambers are sometimes used in this manner; the total ionization charge is measured by noting the drop in voltage across the chamber after it has been initially charged using a reference voltage source. The integration mode can be useful when a direct measurement of small signal currents may be difficult or impractical.

Pulse mode. In many applications information is sought about the properties of individual quanta of radiation. In such cases, a mode of detector operation known as the pulse mode is employed, in which a separate electrical pulse is generated for each individual radiation quantum that interacts in the detector. The detector output may be connected to a measuring circuit as indicated in Figure

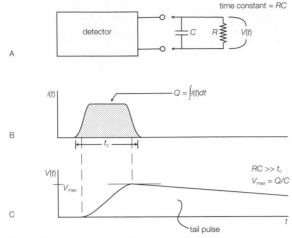

Figure 50: (A) A simple equivalent circuit for the development of a voltage pulse at the output of a detector. R represents the resistance and C the capacitance of the circuit; $V(t)$ is the time (t)-dependent voltage produced. (B) A representative current pulse due to the interaction of a single quantum in the detector. The total charge Q is obtained by integrating the area of the current, $i(t)$, over the collection time, t_c. (C) The resulting voltage pulse that is developed across the circuit of (A) for the case of a long circuit time constant. The amplitude (V_{max}) of the pulse is equal to the charge Q divided by the capacitance C.

Adapted from G.F. Knoll, *Radiation Detection and Measurement*, 2nd ed. (1989), reprinted with permission of John Wiley and Sons, Inc., New York City

Time constant

50. This circuit could represent, for example, the input stage of a preamplifier unit. The basic signal is the voltage observed across the circuit consisting of a load resistance (R) and capacitance (C). This type of configuration has an associated time constant given by the product of the resistance and capacitance values (RC). For simplicity, it will be assumed that this time constant is long compared with the charge collection time in the detector but small relative to the average time between interactions of individual quanta in the detector.

Under these circumstances each interacting quantum gives rise to a voltage pulse of the form sketched in Figure 50C. The voltage pulse rises over the charge collection time, reaches its maximum when all the charge has been collected, and then exponentially decays back to zero with a characteristic time set by the time constant of the measuring circuit. This type of signal pulse is called a tail pulse, and it is observed from the preamplifier used with many kinds of common radiation detectors.

The most important property of the tail pulse is its maximum size, or amplitude. Under the conditions described, the amplitude is given by $V_{max} = Q/C$, where Q

Amplitude of tail pulses

is the charge produced by the individual quantum in the detector and C is the capacitance of the measuring circuit. Under typical conditions tail pulses are then amplified and shaped in a second unit known as a linear amplifier in a manner that preserves the proportionality of the pulse amplitude to the charge Q produced in the detector.

Counting and spectroscopy systems. Detector systems operating in pulse mode can be further subdivided into two types: simple counting systems and more complex spectroscopy systems. The basic elements of both types of pulse-processing systems are shown in Figure 51.

Counting systems. In simple counting systems, the objective is to record the number of pulses that occur over a given measurement time, or alternatively, to indicate the rate at which these pulses are occurring. Some preselection may be applied to the pulses before they are recorded. A common method is to employ an electronic unit known as an integral discriminator to count only those pulses that are larger than a preset amplitude. This approach can eliminate small amplitude pulses that may be of no interest in the application. Alternatively, a differential discriminator (also known as a single-channel analyzer) will select only those pulses whose amplitudes lie within a preset window between a given minimum and maximum value. In this way, the accepted pulses can be restricted to those in which the charge Q from the detector is within a

specific range. When the number of pulses meeting these criteria are accumulated in a digital register over the measurement time, the measurement consists of reporting the total number of accepted events over the time period.

One property that must be considered in counting systems is the concept known as dead time. Following each event in a detector, there is a period of time in which the measurement system is processing that event and is insensitive to other events. Because radiation events typically occur randomly distributed in time, there is always some chance that a true event will occur so soon after a previous event that it is lost. This behaviour is often accounted for by assigning a standard dead time to the counting system. It is assumed that each accepted event is followed by a fixed time period during which any additional true event will be ignored. As a result, the measured number of counts (or the counting rate) is always somewhat below the true value. The discrepancy can become significant at high radiation rates when the dead time is a significant fraction of the average spacing between true events in the detector. Corrections for dead-time losses can be made assuming that the behaviour of the counting system and length of its dead time are known.

Dead time

As an alternative to simply registering the total number of accepted pulses over the counting time, the rate at which the accepted events are occurring in real time can be indicated electronically using a rate meter. This unit provides an output signal that is proportional to the rate at which accepted pulses are occurring averaged over a response time that is normally adjustable by the user. Long response times minimize the fluctuations in the output signal due to the random nature of the interaction times in the detector, but they also slow the response of the rate meter to abrupt changes in the radiation intensity.

Spectroscopy systems. The pulse-mode counting systems described above provide no detailed information on the amplitude of the pulses that are accepted. In many types of detectors, the charge Q and thus the amplitude of the signal pulse is proportional to the energy deposited by the incident radiation. Therefore, an important set of measurement systems are based on recording not only the

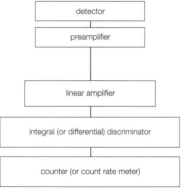

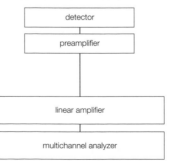

Figure 51: (Top) Pulse-processing units commonly used in a pulse-counting system. (Bottom) The units constituting spectroscopy system.

number of pulses but also their distribution in amplitude. They are known as spectroscopy systems, and their main application is to determine the energy distribution of the radiation that is incident on the detector.

In spectroscopy systems the objective is to sort each pulse according to its amplitude. Every pulse from the linear amplifier is sorted into one of a large number of bins or channels. Each channel corresponds to signal pulses of a specific narrow amplitude range. As the pulses are sorted into the channels matching their amplitude, a pulse-height spectrum is accumulated that, after a given measurement time, might resemble the example given in Figure 52. In this spectrum, peaks correspond to those pulse amplitudes around which many events occur. Because pulse amplitude is related to deposited energy, such peaks often correspond to radiation of a fixed energy recorded by the detector. By noting the position and intensity of peaks recorded in the pulse-height spectrum, it is often possible to interpret spectroscopy measurements in terms of the energy and intensity of the incident radiation.

This pulse-height spectrum is recorded by sending the pulses to a multichannel analyzer, where the pulses are electronically sorted out according to their amplitude to produce the type of spectrum illustrated in Figure 52. Ideally, every incoming pulse is sorted into one of the channels of the multichannel analyzer. Therefore, when the measurement is completed, the sum of all the counts that have been recorded in the channels equals the total number of pulses produced by the detector over the measurement period. In order to maintain this correspondence at high counting rates, corrections must be applied to account for the dead time of the recording system or the pileup of two pulses spaced so closely in time that they appear to be only one pulse to the multichannel analyzer.

One important property of spectroscopy systems is the

energy resolution. This concept is most easily illustrated by assuming that the detector is exposed to radiation quanta of a single fixed energy. (A radioisotope emitting a single gamma-ray energy in its decay comes very close to this ideal.) Many radiation quanta then deposit the same energy in the detector and ideally should produce exactly the same charge Q. Therefore, a number of pulses of precisely the same amplitude should be presented to the multichannel analyzer, and they all should be stored in a single channel. In actual systems, however, some fluctuations are observed in the amplitude of these pulses, and they are actually spread out over a number of channels in the spectrum, as illustrated in Figure 53. A formal definition of energy resolution is shown in the figure, expressed as the ratio of the full-width-at-half-maximum (FWHM) of the peak divided by the centroid position of the peak. This ratio is normally expressed as a percentage, and small values correspond to narrow peaks and good energy resolution. If the incident radiation consists of multiple discreet energies, good energy resolution will help in separating the resulting peaks in the recorded pulse-height spectrum.

Some potential causes of fluctuations that broaden the peaks include drifts in the detector-operating parameters over the course of the measurement, random fluctuations introduced by the noise in the pulse-processing electronics, and statistical fluctuations due to the fact that the charge Q consists of a finite number of charge carriers. This latter statistical limit is in some ways the most fundamental determinant in energy resolution since, as opposed to the other sources of fluctuation, it cannot be reduced by more careful experimental procedures. Poisson statistics predicts that the fractional standard deviation that characterizes these fluctuations about the average number of charge carriers N should scale as $1/\sqrt{N}$. Therefore, detectors that produce the largest number of carriers per pulse show the best energy resolution. For example, the charge Q from a scintillation detector normally consists of photoelectrons in a photomultiplier tube. The average number produced by a 1-MeV particle is normally no more than a few thousand, and the observed energy resolution is typically 5–10 percent. In contrast, the same particle would produce several hundred thousand electron-hole pairs in a semiconductor, and the energy resolution is improved to a few tenths of a percent.

Detection efficiency. The intrinsic detection efficiency of any device operated in pulse mode is defined as the probability that a quantum of radiation incident on the detector will produce a recorded pulse. Especially for radiations of low intensity, a high detection efficiency is important to minimize the total time needed to record enough pulses for good statistical accuracy in the measurement. Detection efficiency is further subdivided into two types: total efficiency and peak efficiency. The total efficiency gives the probability that an incident quantum of radiation produces a pulse, regardless of size, from the detector. The peak efficiency is defined as the probability that the quantum will deposit all its initial energy in the detector. Since there are almost always ways in which the quantum may deposit only part of its energy and then escape from the detector, the total efficiency is generally larger than the peak efficiency.

For a given detector, efficiency values depend on the type and energy of the incident radiation. For incident charged particles such as alpha particles or beta particles, many detectors have a total efficiency that is close to 100 percent. Since these particles begin to deposit energy immediately upon entering the detector volume, a pulse of some amplitude is inevitably produced if the particle reaches the active volume of the device. Very often, any departure from 100 percent efficiency in these cases is due to absorption or scattering of the incident particle before it reaches the active volume. Furthermore, if the detector is thick compared with the range of the incident particle, most particles are fully stopped in the active volume and deposit all their energy. Under these circumstances, the peak efficiency also will be near 100 percent.

For incident gamma rays, the situation is quite different. Except for low-energy photons, it is quite possible for an incident gamma-ray photon to pass completely through

Adapted from G.F. Knoll, *Radiation Detection and Measurement*, 2nd ed. (1989), reprinted with permission of John Wiley and Sons, Inc., New York City, after J.C. Philippot, *IEEE Transactions on Nuclear Science* NS-17(3), 446, © 1970 IEEE

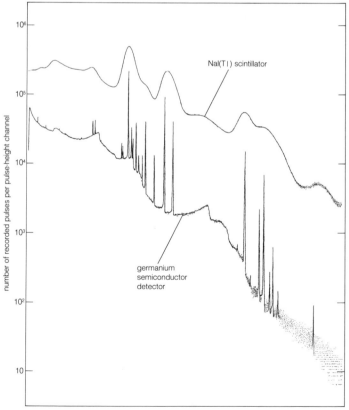

Figure 52: *Representative pulse-height spectra for a source emitting gamma rays of many different energies.* The top spectrum is from a scintillation detector, and the bottom is from a germanium semiconductor detector. The superior energy resolution of the germanium is evident from the much narrower peaks, allowing separation of gamma-ray energies that are unresolved in the scintillator spectrum.

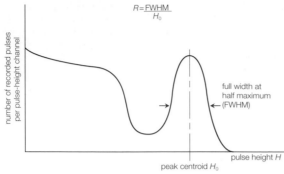

$$R = \frac{FWHM}{H_0}$$

number of recorded pulses per pulse-height channel

full width at half maximum (FWHM)

peak centroid H_0

pulse height H

Figure 53: A simple pulse-height spectrum (such a spectrum might be recorded from a scintillator for a single energy gamma-ray source) showing the definition of energy resolution R.

Factors that enhance efficiency

the detector without interacting. In such cases, the total efficiency will then be substantially less than 100 percent. Furthermore, many of the gamma-rays may deposit only a fraction of their energy in the detector. These events do not contribute to the peak efficiency so, although they produce pulses, their amplitude does not indicate the initial energy of the incident gamma ray. Thus the peak efficiency values incorporate only those gamma-ray photons that interact one or more times in the detector and eventually deposit all their energy. The total efficiency for gamma rays may be enhanced by increasing the detector thickness in the direction of the incident gamma-ray flux. For a given thickness, the peak efficiency is enhanced by choosing a detector material with a high atomic number to increase the probability that all the energy of the original photon will eventually be photoelectrically absorbed. Full energy absorption could take place in a single photoelectric interaction but, more likely, it happens after the incident photon has Compton-scattered one or more times elsewhere in the detector. Alternatively, full absorption is also observed if pair production is followed by subsequent full absorption of both annihilation photons. Since these multiple interactions are enhanced in detectors of large volume, the peak efficiency for gamma-ray detectors improves significantly with increasing size.

Timing characteristics. One of the added benefits of pulse-mode operation is the fact that the arrival time of an individual quantum of radiation is closely related to the time of appearance of a pulse at the detector output. In many nuclear measurements, it is advantageous to be able to determine that two quanta are emitted in the same nuclear process and therefore may be sensed by two separate detectors in virtual time coincidence. Another example of the application of timing information is in the determination of the velocity or energy of a particle by measuring its flight time between its point of origin and a distant detector.

The timing information is carried by the leading edge or rising portion of the detector output pulse. The precision of timing measurements is enhanced in detectors that produce a prompt output pulse with a fast rise time. The time characteristics of the leading edge are related to the charge collection time from the detector, and the best timing performance is generally obtained from detectors in which the charges are collected most rapidly. For example, timing precision of less than one nanosecond can be obtained using organic scintillators for which the light (that is subsequently converted to charge in a photomultiplier tube) is emitted within a period of several nanoseconds following the deposition of the particle energy. On the other hand, timing measurements from gas-filled detectors may have an imprecision of up to one microsecond or more owing to the relatively long and sometimes variable charge-collection time of these devices.

Gas-filled detectors. The passage of a charged particle through a gas results in the transfer of energy from the particle to electrons that are part of the normal atomic structure of the gas. If the charged particle passes close enough to a given atom, the energy transfer may be sufficient to result in its excitation or ionization. In the

excitation process, an electron is elevated from its original state to a less tightly bound state. Energy levels in typical gas atoms are only spaced a few electron volts apart, so that the energy needed for excitation is a small fraction of the kinetic energy of typical radiation quanta. The excited state exists for a specific lifetime before the atom decays back to the original ground energy state. Typical mean lifetimes for excited atomic states in gases are normally only a few nanoseconds. When the atom spontaneously returns to the ground state, the excitation energy is liberated, generally in the form of an electromagnetic photon. The wavelength of electromagnetic radiation for typical gases is in the ultraviolet region of the spectrum. Thus, for every excited gas atom that is formed, the observable result is the appearance of an ultraviolet photon. As a typical charged particle will create thousands of excited atoms along its track, a resulting flash of ultraviolet photons appears, originating along the track of the particle. Some detectors, based on directly sensing this ultraviolet light and known as gas scintillators, are described below (see *Scintillation and Čerenkov detectors*). Similar ultraviolet photons also play an important part in the generation of a pulse from a Geiger-Müller tube.

Release of ultraviolet radiation

For close encounters between an incident charged particle and a gas atom, enough energy may be transferred to totally remove an electron. This is the process of ionization, and it results in the creation of an ion pair. Because the ionized atom is electron-deficient, it carries a net positive electric charge and is called a positive ion. The other member of the ion pair is the electron that is no longer bound to a specific atom and is known as a free electron. Most free electrons are formed with low kinetic energy, and they simply diffuse through the gas, taking part in the random thermal motion of all the atoms. Some free electrons are formed with enough kinetic energy to cause additional excitation and ionization. These are called delta rays, and their motion follows short branches away from the primary ionization and excitation that is created directly along the track of the incident charged particle.

The ionization potential, or the minimum energy required to remove an electron, is about 10 eV for the gases typically used in radiation detectors. Approximately 30 eV of energy loss by the incident charged particle is needed on average to create one ion pair. The remainder of the energy is expended in various excitation processes. For a 1-MeV charged particle that transfers all its energy to the gas, about 30,000 ion pairs will be formed along its track. Both the positive ions and the free electrons can be made to drift in a preferred direction by applying an external electric field. It is the movement of these charges that serves as the basis for the electrical signal produced by the important category of gas-filled detectors that includes ion chambers, proportional counters, and Geiger-Müller detectors.

Ion chambers. An ion chamber is a device in which two electrodes are arranged on opposite sides of a gas-filled volume. By applying a voltage difference between the two electrodes, an electric field is created within the gas. The ion pairs formed by incident radiation experience a force due to this electric field, with the positive ions drifting toward the cathode and the electrons toward the anode. The motion of these charges constitutes an electric current that can be measured in an external circuit.

Ion chambers are frequently operated as current-mode devices. The current-voltage characteristics of a typical ion chamber under constant irradiation conditions are shown in Figure 54. At low applied voltages, there is some

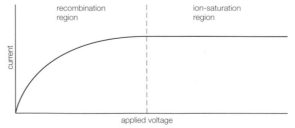

recombination region

ion-saturation region

current

applied voltage

Figure 54: Current-voltage characteristics of an ion chamber.

Ion saturation

tendency for the positive and negative charges to collide and recombine, thereby neutralizing them and preventing their contribution to the measured current. As the voltage is raised, the stronger electric field separates the charges more quickly, and recombination is eventually made negligible at a sufficient applied voltage. This point marks the onset of the ion-saturation region, where the current no longer depends on applied voltage; this is the region of operation normally chosen for ion chambers. Under these conditions the current measured in the external circuit is simply equal to the rate of formation of charges in the gas by the incident radiation.

Air-filled ion chambers operated in current mode are a common type of portable survey meter used to monitor potential personnel exposure to gamma rays. One reason is that the historical unit of gamma-ray exposure, the roentgen (R), is defined in terms of the amount of ionization charge created per unit mass of air. Because of the close connection of the signal produced in an ion chamber with this definition, a measurement of the ion current under proper conditions can give an accurate measure of gamma-ray exposure rate over a wide range of incident gamma-ray energies.

The magnitude of the current observed from a typical ion chamber for a modest gamma-ray exposure rate is quite small. For example, at a gamma-ray exposure rate of 10^{-3} roentgen per hour (a small but significant level for personnel monitoring purposes), the expected ion current from a one-litre ion chamber at atmospheric pressure is about 0.1 picoampere (pA). These low currents require the use of sensitive electrometers for their accurate measurement.

Ion chambers are sometimes operated in a manner similar to passive detectors in integration mode. In this case, the ion chamber is first connected to a constant voltage source V_0. The chamber has an inherent capacitance C, and this initial charging step has the effect of storing an electrical charge on it equal to CV_0. The chamber is then disconnected from the voltage source and exposed to the radiation. During the exposure period, ion pairs are formed in the gas and are swept to their corresponding electrodes by the electric field created by the voltage on the chamber. At the end of the exposure period, the voltage on the chamber will have dropped, as the ionization charge that is collected serves to partially discharge the stored charge CV_0. The chamber is then read out by recording the voltage drop ΔV that has occurred. If there are no other losses (such as leakage current across insulators), the amount of ionization charge created during the exposure is simply given by $C\Delta V$. Small pocket chambers of this type are frequently used to monitor exposure of personnel at radiation-producing facilities.

Ion chambers are rarely operated in pulse mode, and this mode of operation is only considered for high-dE/dx particles that can deposit large amounts of energy in the gas. The main problem is the small size of the voltage pulse that is produced by the interaction of a single quantum of radiation. The deposition of 1 MeV of energy in an ion chamber with a typical capacitance of 100 picofarads (pF) results in a voltage pulse with amplitude of only about 50 microvolts (μV). While it is possible to work with signals of such low level using careful techniques, it is much more common to use gas-filled detectors in pulse mode in the form of proportional or Geiger-Müller counters.

Proportional counters. The small pulse amplitude encountered in ion chambers can be remedied by using gas-filled detectors in a different manner. A proportional counter utilizes the phenomenon of gas multiplication to increase the pulse size by factors of hundreds or thousands. As a result, proportional-counter pulses are in the millivolt rather than microvolt range and therefore can be processed much more easily.

Gas multiplication

Gas multiplication is a consequence of the motion of a free electron in a strong electric-field. When the strength of the field is above about 10^4 volts per centimetre, an electron can gain enough energy between collisions to cause secondary ionization in the gas. After such an ionizing collision, two free electrons exist in place of the original one. In a uniform electric field under these conditions, the number of electrons will grow exponentially as they

are drawn in a direction opposite to that of the applied electric field. The growth of the population of electrons is terminated only when they reach the anode. The production of such a shower of electrons is called a Townsend avalanche and is triggered by a single free electron. The total number of electrons produced in the avalanche can easily reach 1,000 or more, and the amount of charge generated in the gas is also multiplied by the same factor. The Townsend avalanche takes place in a time span of less than one microsecond under the typical conditions present in a proportional counter. Therefore, this additional charge normally contributes to the pulse that is observed from the interaction of a single incident quantum.

In a proportional counter, the objective is to have each original free electron that is formed along the track of the particle create its own individual Townsend avalanche. Thus, many avalanches are formed for each incident charged particle. One of the design objectives is to keep each avalanche the same size so that the final total charge that is created remains proportional to the number of original ion pairs formed along the particle track. The proportionality between the size of the output pulse and the amount of energy lost by the incident radiation in the gas is the basis of the term proportional counter.

Virtually all proportional counters are constructed using a wire anode of small diameter placed inside a larger, typically cylindrical, cathode that also serves to enclose the gas. Under these conditions, the electric-field strength is nonuniform and reaches large values in the immediate vicinity of the wire surface. Almost all of the volume of the gas is located outside this high-field region, and electrons formed at a random position in the gas by the incident radiation drift toward the wire without creating secondary ionization. As they are drawn closer to the wire, they are subjected to the continually increasing electric field, and eventually its value becomes high enough to cause the initiation of a Townsend avalanche. The avalanche then grows until all the electrons reach the wire surface. As nearly all avalanches are formed under identical electric-field conditions regardless of the position in the gas where the free electron was originally formed, the condition that their intensities be the same is met. Furthermore, the high electric-field strength needed for avalanche formation can be obtained using applied voltages between the anode and cathode of no more than a few thousand volts. Near the wire surface, the electric-field strength varies inversely with the distance from the wire centre, and so extremely high field values exist near the surface if the wire diameter is kept small. The size of the output pulse increases with the voltage applied to the proportional tube, since each avalanche is more vigorous as the electric-field strength increases. This behaviour is illustrated in Figure 55.

Electric-field strength

In order to sustain a Townsend avalanche, the negative charges formed in ionization must remain as free electrons. In some gases there is a tendency for neutral gas molecules to pick up an extra electron, thereby forming a negative ion. Because the mass of a negative ion is thousands of times larger than the mass of a free electron, it cannot gain sufficient energy between collisions to cause secondary ionization. Electrons do not readily attach to noble gas molecules, and argon is one of the common choices for the fill gas in proportional counters. Many other gas species also are suitable. Oxygen readily attaches to electrons, however, so air cannot be used as a proportional fill gas under normal circumstances. Proportional counters must therefore be sealed either against air leakage or operated as continuous gas-flow detectors in which any air contamination is swept out of the detector by continuously flowing the fill gas through the active volume.

For proportional counters of normal size, only heavy charged particles or other weakly penetrating radiations can be fully stopped in the gas. Therefore, they can be used for energy measurements of alpha particles but not for longer-range beta particles or other fast electrons. Low-energy electrons produced by X-ray interactions in the gas may also be fully stopped, and proportional counters find application as X-ray spectrometers as well. Even though fast electrons do not deposit all of their energy, the gas-multiplication process results in a pulse that is generally

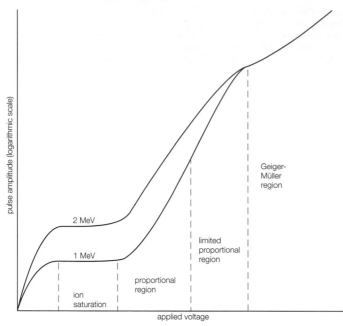

pulse amplitude (logarithmic scale)

2 MeV

1 MeV

ion
saturation

proportional
region

limited
proportional
region

Geiger-
Müller
region

applied voltage

Figure 55: *Regions of operation of gas-filled detectors.*
The two curves represent the observed pulse height for
quanta depositing two different amounts of energy in the gas.

Adapted from G.F. Knoll, *Radiation Detection and Measurement*, 2nd ed. (1989) reprinted with
permission of John Wiley and Sons, Inc., New York City

voltage increases. Finally, at high voltages a transition to the Geiger-Müller mode of operation takes place as the large avalanches inevitably result in their uncontrolled spread. Because the Geiger discharge is self-limiting, radiation that creates only a single ion pair in the gas will result in an output pulse as large as that produced by a particle that deposits a great deal of energy and creates many ion pairs. Therefore, the amplitude of the output pulse carries no energy information, and Geiger tubes are useful only in pulse-counting systems. They will produce a pulse for virtually every charged particle that reaches the fill gas, and many Geiger tubes are fitted with a thin entrance window to allow weakly penetrating radiations such as alpha particles to enter the gas.

Gamma-
ray
detection
efficiency

As with all gas-filled detectors, the detection efficiency for gamma rays is low, only a few percent. Almost no gamma-ray photons interact directly in the gas. A pulse can be produced if the gamma ray interacts in the solid wall of the tube and the secondary electron that is formed subsequently enters the gas before losing all its energy. As typical secondary electrons travel no more than one or two millimetres in solids, only the inner layer of the wall closest to the gas will contribute any secondary electrons. The probability that the incoming gamma ray interacts in this thin layer is small, leading to the low value of detection efficiency.

Nonetheless, Geiger tubes make useful instruments to check for the presence of alpha, beta, or gamma radiation. Despite the fact that the gamma detection efficiency is low, a Geiger tube will respond to single gamma-ray photons and thus can indicate lower levels of gamma radiation than is possible from an ion chamber operated in less sensitive current mode. The output of a portable Geiger survey meter may be displayed using a rate meter to indicate the average rate of pulse production from the tube or through the generation of an audible sound on a loudspeaker for each detected pulse. This is the origin of the stereotypical clicking of the Geiger counter that is often associated with radiation detectors.

Semiconductor detectors. When a charged particle loses its energy in a solid rather than a gas, processes similar to ionization and excitation also take place. In most solids or liquids, however, the resulting electrical charges cannot be transported over appreciable distances and thus cannot serve as the basis of an electrical signal. There is one category of solids that are an exception. These are semiconductor materials, of which silicon and germanium are the predominant examples. In these materials, charges created by radiation can be collected efficiently over distances of many centimetres.

The electronic structure of semiconductors is such that, at ordinary temperatures, nearly all electrons are tied to specific sites in the crystalline lattice and are said to have an energy in the valence band. At any given time, a few electrons will have gained sufficient thermal energy to have broken loose from localized sites and are called conduction electrons; their energy lies in a higher conduction band. Since some energy must be expended in freeing an electron from its normal place in the covalent lattice of a crystal, there is a band gap that separates bound valence electrons from free conduction electrons. In pure crystals no electrons can have an energy within this gap. In silicon the band gap is about 1.1 eV, and in germanium it is about 0.7 eV. In perfect materials held at absolute zero temperature, all electrons would theoretically be bound to specific lattice sites, so that the valance band would be completely filled and the conduction band empty. The thermal energy available at ordinary temperatures allows some electrons to be freed from specific sites and be elevated across the band gap to the conduction band. Therefore, for each conduction electron that exists, an electron is missing from a normally occupied valence site. This electron vacancy is called a hole, and in many ways it behaves as though it were a point positive charge. If an electron jumps from a nearby bond to fill the vacancy, the hole can be thought of as moving in the opposite direction. Both electrons in the conduction band and holes in the valence band can be made to drift in a preferred direction under the influence of an electric field.

Geiger
discharge

large enough to record, and therefore proportional counters can be used in simple counting systems for beta particles or gamma rays.

Geiger-Müller counters. In a Townsend avalanche there are many excited molecules formed in addition to the secondary ions. Within a few nanoseconds, many of these excited molecules return to their ground state by emitting an ultraviolet photon. This light may travel centimetres through the gas before being reabsorbed, either in a photoelectric interaction involving a less tightly bound shell of a gas atom or at a solid surface. If a free electron is liberated in this absorption process, it will begin to drift toward the anode wire and can produce its own avalanche. By this mechanism, one avalanche can breed another, spreading throughout the entire volume of the gas-multiplication region around the anode wire. This uncontrolled spread of avalanches throughout the entire detector is known as a Geiger discharge.

In a proportional counter the spread of avalanches is inhibited through the addition of a small amount of a second gas (for example, methane) that absorbs the ultraviolet photons without producing free electrons. In a Geiger-Müller counter, conditions are such that each avalanche creates more than one additional avalanche, and their number grows rapidly in time. The propagation of avalanches is eventually terminated by the buildup of a cloud of positive charge around the anode wire that consists of the positive ions that were also formed during the avalanches. Ions move thousands of times more slowly than free electrons in the same electric field, and in the short span of a few microseconds needed to propagate the avalanches, their movement is minimal. Because most avalanches are clustered around the anode wire, this positive space charge reduces the electric field in the critical multiplication region below the strength required for additional avalanches to form, and the Geiger discharge ceases. In the process a huge number of ion pairs have been formed, and pulses as large as one volt are produced by the Geiger-Müller tube. Because the pulse is so large, little demand is placed on the pulse-processing electronics, and Geiger counting systems can be extremely simple.

Gas-filled detectors can be operated in several regimes, as illustrated in Figure 55. At low applied voltage, no gas multiplication takes place, and the detector functions as an ion chamber. At some minimum voltage, avalanches begin to form, marking the start of the proportional-counter region, and they become more vigorous as the

The passage of an energetic charged particle through a semiconductor transfers energy to electrons, the vast majority of which are bound electrons in the valence band. Sufficient energy may be transferred to promote a valence electron into the conduction band, resulting in an electron-hole pair. In semiconductor detectors, an electric field is present throughout the active volume. The subsequent drift of the electrons and holes toward electrodes on the surface of the semiconductor material generates a current pulse in much the same manner as the motion of ion pairs in a gas-filled ion chamber.

The minimum energy transfer required for creation of an electron-hole pair is the band-gap energy of about 1 eV. Experimental measurements show that, as in the production of an ion pair in a gas, about three times the minimum energy is required on the average to form an electron-hole pair. Thus, a 1-MeV charged particle losing all its energy in a semiconductor will create about 300,000 electron-hole pairs. This number is about 10 times larger than the number of ion pairs that would be formed by the same particle in a gas. As one consequence, the charge packet for equivalent energy loss by the incident particle is therefore 10 times larger, improving the signal-to-noise ratio as compared with a pulse-type ion chamber. More significant is the improvement in energy resolution. The statistical fluctuations in the number of charge carriers per pulse (that often limit energy resolution) become a smaller fraction as the total number of carriers increases. Thus semiconductor detectors offer the best energy resolution provided by common detectors, and values of a few tenths of a percent are not uncommon.

Another benefit derives from the fact that the detection medium is a solid rather than a gas. In solids, the range of heavy charged particles such as alphas is only tens or hundreds of micrometres, as opposed to a few centimetres in atmospheric pressure gases. Therefore, the full energy of the particle can be absorbed in a relatively thin detector. More importantly, it is practical to fully absorb fast electrons such as beta particles. As opposed to ranges of metres in gases, fast electrons travel only a few millimetres in solids, and semiconductor detectors can be fabricated that are thicker than this range. Therefore, spectroscopic methods can be employed to measure the energies of fast electron radiations.

Silicon detectors. Silicon detectors with diameters of up to several centimetres and thicknesses of several hundred micrometres are common choices for heavy charged particle detectors. They are fabricated from extremely pure or highly resistive silicon that is mildly *n*- or *p*-type owing to residual dopants. (Doping is the process in which an impurity, called a dopant, is added to a semiconductor to enhance its conductivity. If excess positive holes are formed as a result of the doping, the semiconductor is a *p*-type; if excess free electrons are formed, it is an *n*-type semiconductor.) A thin layer of the oppositely doped silicon is created on one surface, forming a rectifying junction—*i.e.,* one that allows current to flow freely in only one direction. If voltage is now applied to reverse-bias this diode so that the free electrons and positive holes flow away from the junction, a depletion region is formed in the vicinity of the junction. In the depletion region, an electric field exists that quickly sweeps out electron-hole pairs that may be thermally generated and reduces the equilibrium concentration of the charge carriers to exceedingly low levels. Under these circumstances the additional electron-hole pairs suddenly created by the energy deposited by a charged particle now become detectable as a pulse of current produced from the detector. Raising the applied voltage increases the thickness of the depletion layer, and fully depleted configurations are commercially available in which the depletion region extends from the front to back surfaces of the silicon wafer. The entire volume of silicon then becomes the active volume of the detector. Silicon diode detectors with thicknesses of less than a millimetre are generally small enough in volume so that the thermally generated carriers can be tolerated, allowing operation of these detectors at room temperature.

These simple silicon diode detectors are presently limited to depletion depths of about one millimetre or less.

In order to create thicker detectors, a process known as lithium-ion drifting can be employed. This process produces a compensated material in which electron donors and acceptors are perfectly balanced and that behaves electrically much like a pure semiconductor. By fabricating *n*- and *p*-type contacts onto the opposite surface of a lithium-drifted material and applying an external voltage, depletion thicknesses of many millimetres can be formed. These relatively thick lithium-drifted silicon detectors are widely used for X-ray spectroscopy and for the measurement of fast-electron energies. Operationally, they are normally cooled to the temperature of liquid nitrogen to minimize the number of thermally generated carriers that are spontaneously produced in the thick active volume so as to control the associated leakage current and consequent loss of energy resolution.

Germanium detectors. Semiconductor detectors also can be used in gamma-ray spectroscopy. In this case, however, it is advantageous to choose germanium rather than silicon as the detector material. With an atomic number of 32, germanium has a much higher photoelectric cross section than silicon (atomic number, Z, of 14), as the probability of photoelectron absorption varies approximately as $Z^{4.5}$. Therefore, it is far more probable for an incident gamma ray to lose all its energy in germanium than in silicon, and the intrinsic peak efficiency for germanium will be many times larger. In gamma-ray spectroscopy, there is an advantage in using detectors with a large active volume. The depletion region in germanium can be made several centimetres thick if ultrapure material is used. Advances in germanium purification processes in the 1970s have led to the commercial availability of material in which the residual impurity concentration is about one part in 10^{12}.

The most common type of germanium gamma-ray spectrometer consists of a high-purity (mildly *p*-type) crystal fitted with electrodes in the coaxial configuration shown in Figure 56. Normal sizes correspond to germanium volumes of several hundred cubic centimetres. Because of their excellent energy resolution of a few tenths of a percent, germanium coaxial detectors have become the workhorse of modern-day high-resolution gamma-ray spectroscopy. The band gap in germanium is smaller than that in silicon, so thermally generated charge carriers are even more of a potential problem. As a result, virtually all germanium detectors, even those with relatively small volume, are cooled to liquid-nitrogen temperature during their use. Typically, the germanium crystal is sealed inside a vacuum enclosure, or cryostat, that provides thermal contact with a storage dewar of liquid nitrogen. Mechanical refrigerators are also available to cool the detector for use in remote locations where a supply of liquid nitrogen may not be available.

Although semiconductor detectors can be operated in current mode, the vast majority of applications are best served by operating the device in pulse mode to take advantage of its excellent energy resolution. The time required to collect the electrons and holes formed along a particle track is typically tens to hundreds of nanoseconds,

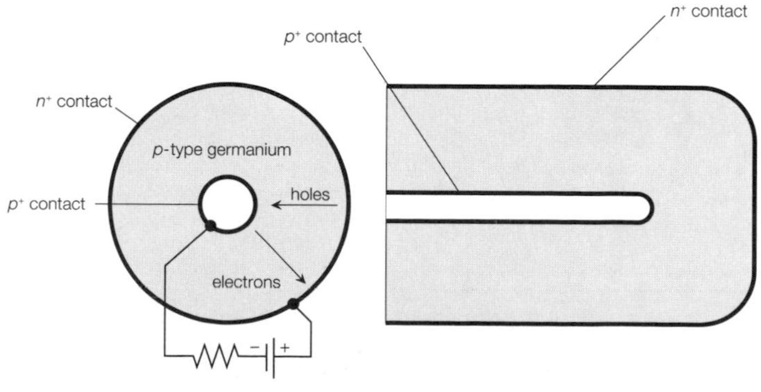

Figure 56: *Configuration of a typical germanium coaxial detector.*
Cross sections oriented (left) perpendicular to and (right) along the cylindrical axis.

depending on detector thickness. The rise time of the output pulse is therefore of the same order, and relatively precise timing measurements are possible, especially for thin detectors.

Scintillation and Čerenkov detectors. One of the overworked images of radiation in popular perception is the idea that radioactive materials glow, emitting some form of eerie light. Most materials when irradiated do not emit light; however, low-intensity visible and ultraviolet light can be detected from some transparent materials owing to the energy deposited by interacting charged particles. The intensity of this light is far too small to be seen with the naked eye under ordinary circumstances, and visible glowing requires radiation fields of extraordinary intensity. One example is the blue luminescence that can be seen in the water surrounding the core of some types of research reactors. This light originates from the Čerenkov radiations (see below) from secondary electrons produced by the extremely intense gamma-ray flux emerging from the reactor core.

Scintillators. In certain types of transparent materials, the energy deposited by an energetic particle can create excited atomic or molecular states that quickly decay through the emission of visible or ultraviolet light, a process sometimes called prompt fluorescence. Such materials are known as scintillators and are commonly exploited in scintillation detectors. The amount of light generated from a single charged particle of a few MeV kinetic energy is very weak and cannot be seen with the unaided eye. However, some early historic experiments by the British physicist Ernest Rutherford on alpha-particle scattering were carried out by manually counting scintillation flashes from individual alpha particles interacting in a zinc sulfide screen and viewed through a microscope. Modern scintillation detectors eliminate the need for manual counting by converting the light into an electrical pulse in a photomultiplier tube or photodiode (see below). A typical scintillator-photomultiplier assembly is illustrated in Figure 57.

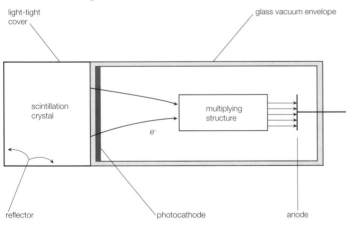

light-tight cover

glass vacuum envelope

scintillation crystal

multiplying structure

e^-

reflector

photocathode

anode

Figure 57: Scintillation detector consisting of a scintillator mounted in optical contact with a photomultiplier tube.

Steps in charge-carrier production

There are four distinct steps involved in the production of a pulse of charge due to a single energetic charged particle:

1. The particle slows down and stops in the scintillator, leaving a trail of excited atomic or molecular species along its track. The particle may be incident on the detector from an external source, or it may be generated internally by the interaction of uncharged quanta such as gamma rays or neutrons. Typical excited states require only a few electron volts for their excitation; thus many thousands are created along a typical charged particle track.

2. Some of these excited species return to their ground state in a process that involves the emission of energy in the form of a photon of visible or ultraviolet light. These scintillation photons are emitted in all directions. The total energy represented by this light (given as the number of photons multiplied by the average photon energy) is a small fraction of the original particle energy deposited in the scintillator. This fraction is given the name scintillation efficiency and ranges from about 3 to 15 percent for

common scintillation materials. The photon energy (or the wavelength of the light) is distributed over an emission spectrum that is characteristic of the particular scintillation material.

The excited species have a characteristic mean lifetime, and their population decays exponentially. The decay time determines the rate at which the light is emitted following the excitation and is also characteristic of the particular scintillation material. Decay times range from less than one nanosecond to several microseconds and generally represent the slowest process in the several steps involved in generating a pulse from the detector. There is often a preference for collecting the light quickly to form a fast-rising output signal pulse, and short decay times are therefore highly desirable in some applications.

3. Some fraction of the light leaves the scintillator through an exit window provided on one of its surfaces. The remaining surfaces of the scintillator are provided with an optically reflecting coating so that the light that is originally directed away from the exit window has a high probability of being reflected from the surfaces and collected. As much as 90 percent of the light can be collected under favourable conditions.

4. A fraction of the emerging light photons are converted to charge in a light sensor normally mounted in optical contact with the exit window. This fraction is known as the quantum efficiency of the light sensor. In a silicon photodiode, as many as 80 to 90 percent of the light photons are converted to electron-hole pairs, but in a photomultiplier tube, only about 25 percent of the photons are converted to photoelectrons at the wavelength of maximum response of its photocathode (see below).

Quantum efficiency

The net result of this sequence of steps, each with its own inefficiency, is the creation of a relatively limited number of charge carriers in the light sensor. A typical pulse will correspond to at most a few thousand charge carriers. This figure is a small fraction of the number of electron-hole pairs that would be produced directly in a semiconductor detector by the same energy deposition. One consequence is that the energy resolution of scintillators is rather poor owing to the statistical fluctuations in the number of carriers actually obtained. For example, the best energy resolution from a scintillator for 0.662 MeV gamma rays (a common standard) is about 5 to 6 percent. By comparison, the energy resolution for the same gamma-ray energy in a germanium detector may be about 0.2 percent. In many applications, the disadvantage of poor energy resolution is offset by other favourable properties, for example, high gamma-ray detection efficiency.

There are many characteristics that are desirable in a scintillator, including high scintillation efficiency, short decay time, linear dependence of the amount of light generated on deposited energy, good optical quality, and availability in large sizes at modest cost. No known material meets all these criteria, and therefore many different materials are in common use, each with attributes that are best suited for certain applications. These materials are commonly classified into two broad categories: inorganic and organic scintillators.

Most inorganic scintillators consist of transparent single crystals, whose dimensions range from a few millimetres to many centimetres. Some inorganics, such as silver-activated zinc sulfide, are good scintillators but cannot be grown in the form of optical-quality large crystals. As a result, their use is limited to thin polycrystalline layers known as phosphor screens.

The inorganic materials that produce the highest light output unfortunately have relatively long decay times. The most common inorganic scintillator is sodium iodide activated with a trace amount of thallium [NaI(Tl)], which has an unusually large light yield corresponding to a scintillation efficiency of about 13 percent. Its decay time is 0.23 microsecond, acceptable for many applications but uncomfortably long when extremely high counting rates or fast timing measurements are involved. The emission spectrum of NaI(Tl) is peaked at a wavelength corresponding to the blue region of the electromagnetic spectrum and is well matched to the spectral response of photomultiplier tubes. Thallium-activated cesium iodide [CsI(Tl)] also produces excellent light yield but has two relatively long decay components with decay times of 0.68 and 3.3 microseconds. Its emission spectrum is shifted toward the longer-wavelength end of the visible spectrum and is a better match to the spectral response of photodiodes. Both NaI(Tl) and CsI(Tl) have iodine, with an atomic number of 53, as a major constituent. Therefore the photoelectric cross section in these materials is large enough to make them attractive in gamma-ray spectroscopy. They are available economically in large sizes so that the corresponding gamma-ray intrinsic peak efficiency can be many times greater than that for the largest available germanium detector. Other inorganic scintillation materials are listed in Table 6. Included are some recently developed materials with much shorter decay times but, unfortunately, also lower light yields. These materials are useful for timing measurements but will have poorer energy resolution compared with the brighter materials.

Organic scintillators A number of organic molecules with a so-called π-orbital electron structure exhibit prompt fluorescence following their excitation by the energy deposited by an ionizing particle. The basic mechanism of light emission does not depend on the physical state of the molecule; consequently, organic scintillators take many different forms. The earliest were pure crystals of anthracene or stilbene. More recently, organics are used primarily in the form of liquid solutions of an organic fluor (fluorescent molecule) in a solvent such as toluene, or as a plastic, in which the fluor is dissolved in a monomer that is subsequently polymerized. Frequently, a third component is added to liquid or plastic scintillators to act as a wave shifter, which absorbs the primary light from the organic fluor and re-radiates the energy at a longer wavelength more suitable for matching the response of photomultiplier tubes or photodiodes. Plastic scintillators are commercially available in sheets or cylinders with dimensions of several centimetres or as small-diameter scintillating fibres.

One of the most useful attributes of organic scintillators is their fast decay time. Many commercially available liquids or plastics have decay times of two to three nanoseconds, allowing their use in precise timing measurements. Organics tend to show a somewhat nonlinear yield of light as the deposited energy increases, and the light yield per unit energy deposited is significantly higher for low dE/dx particles such as electrons than for high dE/dx heavy charged particles. Even for electrons, however, the light yield is two to three times smaller than that of the best inorganic materials.

Because liquids and plastics can be made into detectors of flexible size and shape, they find many applications in the direct detection of charged particle radiations. They are seldom used to detect gamma rays because the low average atomic number of these materials inhibits the full energy absorption needed for spectroscopy. The average atomic number is not greatly different from that of tissue, however, and plastic scintillators have consequently found some useful applications in the measurement of gamma-ray doses. A unique application of liquid scintillators is in the counting of radioisotopes that emit low-energy beta particles, such as hydrogen-3 (^{3}H) or carbon-14 (^{14}C). As these low-energy beta particles have rather short ranges, they can be easily absorbed before reaching the active volume of a detector. This attenuation problem is completely avoided if the sample is dissolved directly in the liquid scintillator. In this case, the beta particles find themselves in the scintillator immediately after being emitted.

Čerenkov detectors. Čerenkov light is a consequence of the motion of a charged particle with a speed that is greater than the speed of light in the same medium. No particle can exceed the speed of light in a vacuum (c), but in materials with an index of refraction represented by n, the particle velocity v will be greater than the velocity of light if $v > c/n$. For materials with an index of refraction in the common range between 1.3 and 1.8, this velocity requirement corresponds to a minimum kinetic energy of many hundreds of MeV for heavy charged particles. Fast electrons with relatively small kinetic energy can reach this minimum velocity, however, and the application of the Čerenkov process to radiations with energy below 20 MeV is restricted to primary or secondary fast electrons.

Čerenkov light is emitted only during the time in which the particle is slowing down and therefore has very fast time characteristics. In contrast with the isotropically emitted scintillation light, Čerenkov light is emitted along the surface of a forward-directed cone centred on the particle velocity vector. The wavelength of the light is preferentially shifted toward the short-wavelength (blue) end of the spectrum. The total intensity of the Čerenkov light is much weaker than the light emitted from equivalent energy loss in a good scintillator and may be only a few hundred photons or less for a 1-MeV electron. Čerenkov detectors are normally used with the same type of light sensors employed in scintillation detectors.

Conversion of light to charge. There are two major types of devices used to form an electrical signal from scintillation or Čerenkov light: the photomultiplier tube and the photodiode. Photomultiplier tubes are vacuum tubes in which the first major component is a photocathode. A light photon may interact in the photocathode to eject a low-energy electron into the vacuum. The quantum efficiency of the photocathode is defined as the probability for this conversion to occur. It is a strong function of wavelength of the incident light, and an effort is made to match the spectral response of the photocathode to the emission spectrum of the scintillator in use. The average quantum efficiency over the emission spectrum of a typical scintillator is about 15 to 20 percent.

The result of sensing a flash of light is therefore the production of a corresponding pulse of electrons from the photocathode. Their number at this point is typically a few thousand or less, so that the total charge packet is too small to be conveniently measured. Instead, the photomultiplier tube has a second component that multiplies the number of electrons by a factor of typically 10^5 or

Čerenkov light

Table 6: Some Properties of Inorganic Scintillators

material	specific gravity	wavelength of maximum emission (nm)	principal decay constant (μs)	total light yield (photons/MeV)	relative gamma-ray pulse height with Bialkali photomultiplier tube
NaI(Tl)	3.67	415	0.23	38,000	1.00
CsI(Tl)	4.51	560	0.68	65,000	0.49
CsI(Na)	4.51	420	0.63	39,000	1.11
LiI(Eu)	4.08	470	1.4	11,000	0.23
BGO	7.13	505	0.30	8,200	0.13
BaF$_2$ slow component	4.89	310	0.62	10,000	0.13
BaF$_2$ fast component	4.89	220	0.0006	—	0.03*
ZnS(Ag) (polycrystalline)	4.09	450	0.2	—	1.30†
CaF$_2$(Eu)	3.19	435	0.9	24,000	0.78
CsF	4.11	390	0.004	—	0.05
Li glass‡	2.5	395	0.075	—	0.10
For comparison, a typical organic (plastic) scintillator:					
NE 102A	1.03	423	0.002	10,000	0.25

*Using an ultraviolet-sensitive photomultiplier tube. †For alpha particles. ‡Properties vary with exact formulation.
Source: Adapted from G.F. Knoll, *Radiation Detection and Measurement*, 2nd ed., copyright © 1989 by John Wiley & Sons, Inc. Reprinted by permission of John Wiley & Sons, Inc.

Photo-
diodes

10^6. The electron multiplication takes place along a series of electrodes called dynodes that have the property of emitting more than one electron when struck by a single electron that has been accelerated from a previous dynode. After the multiplication process, the amplified pulse of electrons is collected at an anode that provides the tube's output. The amplitude of this charge is an indicator of the intensity of the original light flash in the scintillator.

Alternatively, the light can be measured using a solid-state device known as a photodiode. A device of this type consists of a thin semiconductor wafer that converts the incident light photons into electron-hole pairs. As many as 80 or 90 percent of the light photons will undergo this process, and so the equivalent quantum efficiency is considerably higher than in a photomultiplier tube. There is no amplification of this charge, however, so the output pulse is much smaller. When the photodiode is operated in pulse mode, many sources of electronic noise are large enough to degrade the quality of the signal, and for a given scintillator a poorer energy resolution is usually observed with a photodiode than with a photomultiplier tube. However, the photodiode is a much more compact and rugged device, operates at low voltage, and offers corresponding advantages in certain applications. Scintillators coupled to photodiodes can also be conveniently used in current mode, especially for intense radiation fluxes. The current of electron-hole pairs induced by the scintillation light can be large enough to make noise contributions less important.

Neutron detectors. The general principle of detecting neutrons involves a two-step process. First, the neutron must interact in the detector to form charged particles. Second, the detector must then produce an output signal based on the energy deposited by these charged particles. Many of the major detector types that have already been discussed for other radiations can be adapted to neutron measurements by incorporating a material that will serve as a neutron-to-charged-particle converter.

Slow-neutron detectors. For slow neutrons, the principal conversion methods involve one of the nuclear reactions shown in Table 7. In each case, the reaction is characterized by a positive Q-value, meaning that this amount of energy is released in the reaction. Since the incoming slow neutron has a low kinetic energy and the target nucleus is essentially at rest, the reactants have little total kinetic energy. Consequently, the reaction products are formed with a total kinetic energy essentially equal to the Q-value. When one of these reactions is induced by a slow neutron, the directly measurable charged particles appear with the same characteristic total kinetic energy. Since the neutron contributes nothing to the kinetic energy of the reaction products, these reactions cannot be used to measure the energy of slow neutrons; they may only be applied as the basis for counters that simply record the number of neutrons that interact in the detector.

Table 7: Some Reactions Useful for Slow-Neutron Detection

reaction*	Q-value (MeV)	cross section (in barns) for thermal (0.025 eV) neutrons
$^{10}B + n \rightarrow {}^7Li + \alpha$	2.31	3,840
$^6Li + n \rightarrow {}^3H + \alpha$	4.78	940
$^3He + n \rightarrow {}^3H + p$	0.764	5,330
$^{235}U + n \rightarrow X + Y$ (fission fragments)	~200	575

*n represents a neutron, p a proton, and α an alpha particle.

In the lithium-6 (^6Li) and boron-10 (^{10}B) reactions, the isotopes of interest are present only in limited percentage in the naturally occurring element. To enhance the conversion efficiency of lithium or boron, samples that are enriched in the desired isotope are often used in the fabrication of detectors. Helium-3 (^3He) is a rare stable isotope of helium and is commercially available in isotopically separated form.

Boron
trifluoride
propor-
tional tube

One of the common detectors for slow neutrons is a proportional tube filled with boron trifluoride (BF_3) gas. Some incident neutrons interact with the boron-10 in the gas, producing two charged particles with a combined energy

of 2.3 MeV. These particles leave a trail of ion pairs in the gas, and a pulse develops in the normal manner as in any proportional counter. Boron trifluoride performs as an acceptable proportional gas only at pressures of less than one atmosphere, and the detection efficiency is therefore limited by the corresponding low density of boron nuclei at such pressures. Alternatively, a conventional proportional gas can be used, and the boron can be present in the form of a solid layer deposited on the inner surface of the tube.

Proportional counters filled with helium-3 also are based on a neutron interaction in the gas that produces charged particles. In this case, the Q-value of 0.76 MeV imparts this energy to the particles formed in the reaction. Helium works well as a proportional gas even at high pressure; thus helium-3 proportional tubes filled to 20 atmospheres or more provide neutron detection with relatively high intrinsic efficiency.

Also common are slow-neutron detectors in the form of scintillators in which either boron or lithium is incorporated as a constituent of the scintillation material. Europium-activated lithium iodide is one example of a crystalline scintillator of this type, and boron-loaded plastic scintillators are also available.

The fission reaction is often used as a neutron converter in conjunction with ion chambers. The enormous energy released in a fission reaction appears primarily as the kinetic energy of the two fission products. These fission fragments are highly ionizing charged particles, and they result in an unusually large energy deposition in the detector. Uranium-lined ion chambers (fission chambers) are common neutron sensors employed to monitor nuclear reactors and other intense sources of neutrons.

Fast-neutron detectors. The probability of inducing one of the reactions listed in Table 7 is expressed as the magnitude of its neutron cross section. These values are relatively large for slow neutrons but decrease by several orders of magnitude for fast neutrons. Therefore, slow-neutron detectors such as the boron trifluoride tube become inefficient for the direct detection of fast neutrons. One method used to increase this efficiency is to surround the detector with a material that effectively moderates or slows down the fast neutrons. For example, a polyethylene layer with a thickness of 20 to 30 centimetres will cause some incident fast neutrons to scatter many times from the hydrogen nuclei that are present, giving up energy in the process. A fraction of these moderated neutrons may then diffuse to the detector as slow neutrons with a high interaction probability. Since the moderation process obscures any information on the original energy of the fast neutron, these devices are useful only in simple neutron-counting systems.

Fast-
neutron
elastic
scattering

The preferred conversion reaction for the direct detection of fast neutrons tends to be the elastic-scattering interaction. The resulting recoil nuclei can absorb a significant fraction of the original neutron energy in a single scattering and then deposit that energy in a manner similar to that of any other charged particle. The scattered neutron, now with a lower energy, may either escape from the detector or possibly interact again elsewhere in its volume. The most common scattering target is hydrogen, and a fast neutron can transfer up to all its energy in a single collision with a hydrogen nucleus. The amount of energy transferred varies with the scattering angle, which in hydrogen covers a continuum from zero (corresponding to grazing-angle scattering) up to the full neutron energy (corresponding to a head-on collision). Thus, when monoenergetic fast neutrons strike a material containing hydrogen, a spectrum of recoil protons is produced that ranges in energy between these limits. Some information about the original energy of the neutrons can be deduced by recording the pulse height-spectrum from a hydrogen-containing detector. This process generally involves applying a computer-based deconvolution code to the measured spectrum and is one of the few methods generally available to experimentally measure fast-neutron energy spectra.

The result of a fast-neutron scattering from hydrogen is a recoiling energetic hydrogen nucleus, or recoil proton. One type of detector based on these recoil protons is a proportional counter containing a hydrogenous gas. Pure hydrogen can be used, but a more common choice is a heavier hydrocarbon such as methane in which the range of the resulting recoil protons typically is short enough to be fully stopped in the gas. Recoil protons also can be generated and detected in organic liquid or plastic scin-tillators. In instances such as these, many more hydrogen nuclei are present per unit volume than in a gas, so that the detection efficiency for fast neutrons can be many times larger than in a proportional counter.

(Glenn F. Knoll)

Solar System

Venus

Venus, symbol ♀ in astronomy, is the second planet from the Sun and the planet whose orbit is closest to that of the Earth. When visible, Venus is the brightest planet in the sky. Viewed through a telescope, it presents a brilliant, yellow-white, essentially featureless face to the observer. The obscured appearance results because the surface of the planet is hidden from sight by a continuous and permanent cover of clouds. Features in the clouds are difficult to discern and become evident only when the planet is viewed in ultraviolet light (Figure 16). When observed at ultraviolet wavelengths, the clouds of Venus exhibit distinctive dark markings, with complex swirling patterns near the equator and global-scale bright and dark bands that are V-shaped and open to the west. Venus' mean distance from the Sun is 108 million kilometres. Its distance from the Earth varies from a minimum of about 42 million kilometres to a maximum of about 257 million kilometres.

PRINCIPAL CHARACTERISTICS

Venus' orbit is the most nearly circular of that of any planet, with a deviation from perfect circularity of only about 1 part in 150. The period of the orbit—that is, the length of the Venusian year—is 224.7 Earth days.

Rotation   The rotation of Venus is unusual in both its direction and speed. Most of the planets in the solar system rotate in a counterclockwise direction when viewed from above their north poles; Venus, however, rotates in the opposite, or retrograde, direction. Were it not for the planet's clouds, an observer on Venus' surface would see the Sun rise in the west and set in the east. Venus spins on its axis very slowly, taking 243 Earth days to complete one rotation. Venus' spin and orbital periods are synchronized with the Earth's orbit such that Venus always presents the same face toward the Earth when the two planets are at their closest approach. The reasons for this are poorly understood but must have to do with the gravitational influence exerted on Venus by the Earth.

Because Venus is closer to the Sun than is the Earth, it exhibits phases like those of the Moon. In fact, the discovery of these phases by the Italian scientist Galileo in 1610 was one of the most important in the history of astronomy. The prevailing view of Galileo's day was the assertion by the Greek astronomer Ptolemy that the Earth lies at the centre of the solar system. The observation of the phases of Venus is inconsistent with this view but is consistent with the Polish astronomer Nicolaus Copernicus' idea that the solar system is centred around the Sun. Galileo's observation of the phases of Venus provided the first direct observational evidence for Copernicus' theory.

Venus is nearly the Earth's twin in terms of size and mass. Venus' diameter is about 12,102.5 kilometres, or 94.9 percent of the Earth's diameter at the Equator, while its mass is 4.87×10^{24} kilograms, or 81.5 percent that of the Earth. The similarities to the Earth in size and mass also produce a similarity in density; Venus' density is 5.24 grams per cubic centimetre, as compared with 5.52 for the Earth. (See Table 3.)

In terms of its shape, Venus is more nearly a perfect sphere than are most planets. A planet's rotation generally causes a slight flattening at the poles and bulging at the equator, but Venus' very slow rotation rate allows it to maintain its highly spherical shape.

THE ATMOSPHERE

Venus has the most massive atmosphere of all the terrestrial planets. Its atmosphere is composed of 96.5 percent carbon dioxide (CO_2) and 3.5 percent nitrogen (N_2). Trace amounts of a number of other gases have been detected, including carbon monoxide (CO), sulfur dioxide (SO_2), water vapour (H_2O), argon (Ar), and helium (He). The atmospheric pressure at the planet's surface varies with the surface elevation but averages about 90 bars, or 90 times the atmospheric pressure at the Earth's surface. This is the same pressure found at a depth of about one kilometre in the Earth's oceans.

The variation of temperature with height in the Venusian atmosphere is shown in Figure 17. The upper atmosphere, extending from the fringes of space down to about 100 kilometres above the surface, varies in temperature from a maximum of about 298 K (25° C) in the daytime to a minimum of 123 K (−150° C) at night. In the middle atmosphere, temperatures increase smoothly from about 173 K at 100 kilometres above the surface to roughly 263 K at the top of the continuous cloud deck, which lies at an altitude of more than 60 kilometres. Below the cloud tops the temperature continues to increase sharply through the lower atmosphere, or troposphere, reaching 733 K at the planet's surface. This temperature is higher than the melting point of lead.   *Temperature*

The clouds that enshroud Venus are enormously thick. The main cloud deck extends from about 45 kilometres above the surface up to nearly 70 kilometres. There are also thin hazes that extend several kilometres below the lowest clouds and about 20 kilometres above the highest ones. The upper haze is somewhat thicker near the poles than in other regions. The main cloud deck is divided into three layers. All of them are quite tenuous; an observer in even the densest cloud regions would be able to see objects

By courtesy of L.D. Travis and W.B. Rossow

Figure 16: Enhanced photograph of Venus, as obtained in February 1979 in ultraviolet light by the Pioneer Venus orbiter, exhibiting the distinctive V-shaped cloud markings of the planet.

Table 3: Planetary Data for Venus

Mean distance from the Sun	108,000,000 km
Eccentricity of orbit	0.007
Inclination of orbit to ecliptic	3.4°
Sidereal period of revolution (year)	224.7 Earth days
Rotation period	243 Earth days (retrograde)
Mean synodic period	584 Earth days
Mean orbital velocity	35 km/s
Inclination of equator to orbit	177°
Mass	4.87×10^{24} kg (0.815 mass of Earth)
Diameter (atmosphere not included)	12,102.5 km (0.949 diameter of Earth)
Density	5.24 g/cm³
Number of known satellites	none
Surface gravity	860 cm/s²
Atmospheric composition	0.96 CO_2, 0.035 N_2, 0.0002 H_2O; trace quantities of CO, O_2, SO_2, HCl, and other gases
Surface atmospheric pressure	90 bars
Mean surface temperature	735 K
Mean visible cloud temperature	230 ± 10 K

at distances of several kilometres. The clouds are bright when viewed from above, reflecting roughly 85 percent of the sunlight striking them.

The microscopic particles that make up the Venusian clouds consist of liquid droplets and perhaps also solid crystals. The dominant material that has been identified in the clouds is highly concentrated sulfuric acid, H_2SO_4. Other materials that may exist include solid sulfur and nitrosylsulfuric acid ($NOHSO_4$). The cloud particles range in size from less than 0.1 to more than 1 micrometre.

The reasons that some cloud-top regions appear dark when viewed at ultraviolet wavelengths are not fully known. Materials that may be present in minute quantities at the cloud tops and may be responsible for absorbing ultraviolet light in some regions include sulfur dioxide, chlorine, and solid sulfur.

The circulation of Venus' atmosphere is quite remarkable and is unique among the planets. Despite the very slow rotation of the planet, the cloud features high in the atmosphere circle Venus completely in only about four days. The wind at the cloud tops blows from east to west

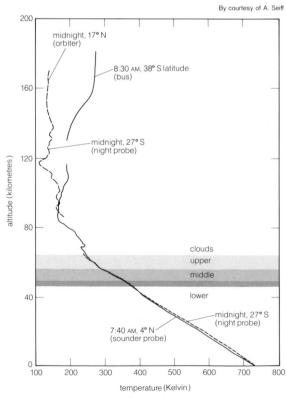

By courtesy of A. Seiff

Figure 17: Temperature profiles in the atmosphere of Venus measured in 1978 by the Pioneer Venus mission. Below 100 kilometres, the atmospheric temperatures are amazingly uniform from day to night and over latitudes up to 60°. Above 100 kilometres, the nightside becomes much cooler than the dayside and is not far above the condensation temperature of carbon dioxide.

at a velocity of about 100 metres per second, or 360 kilometres per hour. The enormous westward wind velocity decreases markedly with decreasing height, and winds at the planet's surface are quite sluggish. Surface winds typically blow at a velocity of no more than one metre per second (less than four kilometres per hour). The cause of the rapid rotation of Venus' upper atmosphere is not well understood and remains a focus of scientific controversy and research.

Not much information is known about wind directions at the planet's surface itself; only a small amount of data has been compiled from observations of wind-blown materials. Despite low surface-wind velocities, the great density of Venus' atmosphere enables these winds to move loose, fine-grained materials, producing features resembling sand dunes that have been seen in some radar images. These features suggest that surface winds are directed dominantly toward the equator in both hemispheres: in the northern hemisphere the surface winds seem to blow primarily toward the south, and in the southern hemisphere they seem to blow primarily toward the north. This pattern is consistent with the idea that hemispheric-scale Hadley cells, or circulation patterns, exist in the Venusian atmosphere. Under this hypothesis, atmospheric gases rise upward owing to heating at the planet's equator, are transported at high altitudes toward the poles, sink to the surface as they cool at higher latitudes, and flow toward the equator along the planet's surface until they warm and rise again. The equatorward flow at the surface may be responsible for the orientations of the wind features that are seen.

A significant consequence of Venus' massive atmosphere is that it produces a greenhouse effect that intensely heats the planet's surface. Because of its bright, continuous cloud cover, Venus actually absorbs less of the Sun's light than does the Earth. However, the sunlight that does penetrate through the clouds is absorbed both in the lower atmosphere and at the surface. The surface and the gases of the lower atmosphere reradiate this energy at infrared wavelengths. On the Earth, reradiated infrared radiation escapes fairly readily into space, allowing the Earth to maintain a comfortably cool surface temperature. On Venus, in contrast, the dense carbon dioxide atmosphere and the thick cloud layers trap much of the infrared radiation. The trapped radiation heats the lower atmosphere further, ultimately raising the surface temperature by hundreds of degrees.

Green- house effect

Above the main body of the Venusian atmosphere lies the ionosphere. As its name implies, the ionosphere is composed of ions, or charged particles, produced both by absorption of ultraviolet solar radiation and by the impact of the solar wind on the upper atmosphere. The primary ions in the Venusian ionosphere are O_2^+ and CO_2^+, and the density of these ions is far greater on the dayside of the planet than on the nightside.

MAGNETIC FIELD AND INTERACTION WITH THE SOLAR WIND

Unlike most planets, Venus has not been found to have its own intrinsic magnetic field. Sensitive measurements by orbital spacecraft have shown that any field originating from within Venus can have a dipole moment of no more than about 10^{19} amperes · square metre, far weaker than the Earth's moment of 8×10^{22} amperes · square metre. The lack of a magnetic field may be related to the planet's slow rotation because, according to the dynamo theory of generation of planetary magnetic fields, rotation helps to drive the motions within the planet's interior that produce the field.

As the solar wind (the flow of charged particles streaming outward from the Sun) impacts a planet at supersonic speeds, it generally forms a bow shock on the sunward side of the planet—that is, a standing wave of plasma that slows down, heats, and deflects the flow around the planet. For some planets the bow shock can lie at a considerable distance from the surface, held off by the planet's magnetic field. Because Venus does not have such a field, however, its bow shock lies only a few thousand kilometres above the surface, held off only by the planet's ionosphere. In fact, the top of the ionosphere, known as the ionopause, lies at a much lower altitude on the dayside of Venus than on the nightside owing to the pressure exerted by the solar wind.

SURFACE

Nature of Venusian rocks

The high atmospheric pressure, the low wind velocities, and, in particular, the extremely high temperatures at the surface of Venus create an environment that is markedly different from any other in the solar system. A series of landings by Soviet spacecraft in the 1970s and early 1980s provided detailed data on the composition and appearance of the surface. A typical view of the surface of Venus, obtained by the lander Venera 13, is shown in Figure 18, in which a rocky plain stretches toward the horizon. Despite the heavy cloud cover, the surface is well illuminated by the light that filters through the clouds. The most striking characteristic of the surface at the site shown in Figure 18, as well as at most other Venera landing sites, is the flat, slabby, layered nature of the rocks. Both volcanic and sedimentary rocks on the Earth can develop such an appearance under appropriate conditions, but the reason that the Venusian rocks exhibit these physical characteristics is not known with certainty. Also present among the rocks is a darker, fine-grained soil. The grain size of the soil is unknown, but some of it was fine enough to be lifted briefly into the atmosphere by the touchdown of the Venera lander, suggesting that some grains are no more than a few tens of micrometres in diameter. Scattered throughout the soil and atop the rocks are pebble-size particles that could be either small rocks or clods of soil.

Surface composition. A number of the Venera landers carried instruments that provided some basic information on the chemical composition of the surface materials of Venus. Only the relative proportions of a few elements were measured, so no definitive information exists concerning the rock types or the minerals that might be present. Two types of techniques were used to measure the content of various elements. Veneras 8, 9, and 10 carried gamma-ray spectrometers that measured the concentrations of radioactive isotopes of elements uranium, potassium, and thorium, while Veneras 13 and 14 also carried X-ray fluorescence instruments that measured the concentrations of a number of major elements. At the Venera 8 site, there were indications that the rock composition may be similar in some respects to that of granite or other igneous rocks that compose the Earth's continents. Because this inference is based on only rather uncertain measurements of the concentrations of a few radioactive elements, however, it must be viewed with caution. Measurements of radioactive elements at the Venera 9 and 10 landing sites suggested that the composition there resembles that of the basalt rocks found on the Earth's ocean floors and in some volcanic regions like Hawaii and Iceland. Along with radioactive isotopes, the Venera 13 and 14 instrumentation measured concentrations of silicon, aluminum, magnesium, iron, calcium, potassium, titanium, and manganese. There were some differences in composition between the two sites; for example, the Venera 13 site was significantly higher in potassium than the Venera 14 site. On the whole, however, the surface composition measured by both the Venera 13 and 14 landers was quite similar to those of terrestrial basalts.

Surface features. A number of Earth-based observatories and Venus-orbiting spacecraft have provided global-scale information on the nature of the planet's surface. All these have used radar systems that can penetrate the Venusian atmosphere and provide a view of the surface otherwise hidden by the thick Venusian clouds.

The entire surface of Venus is dry and rocky; because there is no "sea level," elevations are given as planetary radius—*i.e.,* as the distance from the centre of the planet to the surface. Most of the planet consists of gently rolling plains with elevations that in some areas change by only a few hundred metres over distances of hundreds of kilometres. At several locations on the plains there are broad, gently sloping topographic depressions that may reach several thousand kilometres across; Atalanta Planitia, Guinevere Planitia, and Lavinia Planitia are among these lowlands. Two striking features are the continent-sized highland areas, or terrae: Ishtar Terra in the northern hemisphere, and Aphrodite Terra along the equator. Ishtar is roughly the size of Australia, while Aphrodite is comparable in area to South America. Ishtar possesses the most spectacular topography on Venus. Much of its interior is a high plateau, called Lakshmi Planum, that resembles in configuration the Plateau of Tibet on the Earth. Lakshmi is bounded by mountains on most sides; to the east lie the enormous Maxwell Montes. These mountains extend more than 10·kilometres above the average elevation of Venus and are comparable in size to the Himalayas of Asia. The topography of Aphrodite is more complex than that of Ishtar and is characterized by a number of distinct mountain ranges and several deep, narrow troughs. There also are several smaller elevated regions in addition to the two main terrae, including Alpha Regio, Beta Regio, and Phoebe Regio.

Large-scale topographic features

A radar image of the surface of Venus, assembled from data collected over many months by the U.S. Magellan spacecraft, is shown in Figure 19. The most striking aspect of the surface, as shown in the image, is its enormous geologic complexity and diversity. The planet's crust has been rent by huge faults, thrust upward into mountains, and buried by lavas; and at first glance the similarity to any other planet, including the Earth, appears slight.

Many of the surface features on Venus can be attributed to tectonic activity—that is, to deformational motions within the crust. These include mountain belts, plains deformation belts, rifts, novae, coronae, and tesserae, which are discussed in turn below.

Mountain belts. These are found in the terrae of Venus and are in some ways similar to large mountain belts on the Earth such as the Himalayas of Asia and the Andes of South America. The best examples are the mountains that encircle Lakshmi Planum. Mountain belts typically consist of parallel ridges and troughs with spacings of 5 to 10 kilometres. The mountain belts were most likely formed when blocks of the crust were compressed from the sides and thickened, folding the surface and thrusting it upward. Their formation is thus similar to the orogeny of many mountain ranges on the Earth. A major difference in their appearance, however, arises because there is no liquid water or ice on Venus. Without the flow of rivers or glaciers to carve them, the Venusian mountains have evolved into shapes very different from those of their terrestrial counterparts.

Plains deformation belts. These features are similar in some respects to mountain belts, but they display lower relief and lie primarily in lowland areas such as Lavinia

Figure 18: *View of the surface of Venus obtained by Venera 13.*
Devices from the spacecraft can be seen against the rocky plain: a crescent-shaped camera cover in the centre, a colour calibration standard to the right, and the sawtooth rim of the shock-absorbing ring along the bottom.

and Atalanta Planitae. Like the mountain belts, they may have formed by compression and uplift of the crust.

Rifts. Rifts are among the most spectacular tectonic features on Venus. Most of them lie atop broad, raised areas like Beta Regio. Beta and several other similar regions on Venus appear to be locales where large areas of the crust have been forced upward from below, splitting the surface to form great rift valleys. The rifts are composed of innumerable faults, and their floors lie one to two kilometres below the surrounding terrain. In many ways the rifts on Venus are similar to great rifts on other planets, like the East African Rift on Earth or the Valles Marineris on Mars. For example, volcanic eruptions appear to have been associated with all these features. The Venusian rifts differ from the terrestrial and Martian ones, however, in that little erosion has taken place within them owing to the lack of water on Venus.

Novae. These are landforms apparently unique in the solar system to Venus. They consist of a distinctive radiating pattern of faults and fractures, often lying atop a broad, gently sloping topographic rise. They are typically a few hundred kilometres in diameter and hundreds of metres high. Novae may owe their origin to the effects Diapirs of hot blobs of material, known as diapirs, that originate deep within the interior of Venus. As diapirs rise upward through the planet's interior and approach the surface, they can push the rocks above them upward, fracturing the surface in a radial pattern. Like rifts, many novae have been sites of volcanic eruptions.

Coronae. Coronae (Figure 20) are common on Venus and may be another consequence of the action of diapirs. They consist of circular to oval patterns of faults, fractures, and ridges and, like novae, are typically a few hundred kilometres in diameter. While they may have a raised outer rim, many coronae sag noticeably in their interiors and also outside their rims. Once a diapir has risen near the surface and has cooled, it will no longer be buoyant, and the support that it gave to the surface topography of a nova will be removed. The initially raised topography can then sag under its own weight, producing concentric faulting of the crust as it does so. Coronae may therefore be the ancient scars left by diapirs, whereas novae are the

products of diapirs that are still rising or that otherwise have not yet completed their evolution.

Tesserae. These features are the most geologically complex regions on Venus. Several large elevated regions on the planet, such as Alpha Regio, are composed largely of tessera terrain. Such terrain is extraordinarily rugged and highly deformed, with several different trends of parallel ridges and troughs that cut across one another at a wide range of angles. The deformation in tessera terrain can be so complex that it is difficult to determine what kinds of stresses in the crust were responsible for forming it. Some tesserae may be old terrain that has been subjected to many more episodes of mountain building and faulting than have the materials around it, each one superimposed upon its predecessor to produce the complex pattern that is observed.

Volcanic features. Along with intense tectonic activity, Venus has undergone much volcanism. The largest volcanic outpourings are the huge lava fields that cover most of the rolling plains. These are similar in many respects to fields of overlapping lava flows seen at the surfaces of several other planets, including the Earth, but are far more extensive in area. The individual lava flows are for the most part long and thin, indicating that the lavas were very fluid at the time of their eruption and hence were able to flow for long distances over gentle slopes. Lavas on the Earth and the Moon that flow so readily typically consist of basalts, and so it is probable that basalts are common on the plains of Venus as well.

Of the many types of lava-flow features seen on the Venusian plains, none are more remarkable than the long, sinuous channels. These channels usually have constant widths of about one kilometre but can meander for distances of up to thousands of kilometres across the surface. They probably were carved by flowing lava, but why they have such regular widths and enormous lengths remains unknown. In a few instances, segments of these channels appear to proceed uphill, suggesting that crustal deformation took place after the channels were carved and reversed the gentle downward surface slopes to upward ones.

In some locations on Venus, volcanic outpourings have built mountains similar to the great volcanoes of Hawaii

N.J. Stacy, Cornell University/Jet Propulsion Laboratory

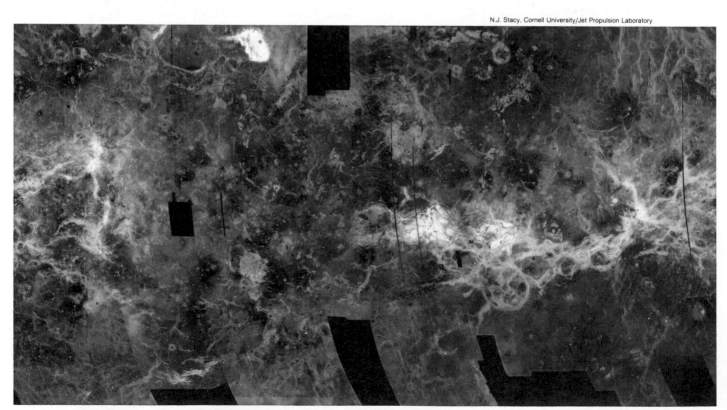

Figure 19: Radar image of the surface of Venus assembled from data collected by the Magellan spacecraft. The image reflects the extensive tectonic and volcanic activity that has produced Venus' complex and diverse geology.

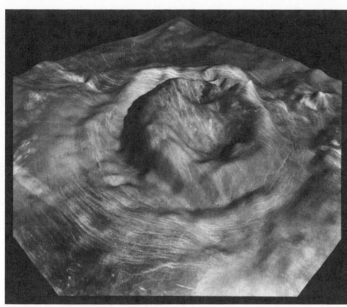

Figure 20: *A corona.*
Magellan altimetry and radar images have been merged to
form this synthetic oblique view, with vertical exaggeration
of the relief. Such circular to oval structures on the Venusian
surface are characterized by complex fracturing and faulting.

Aparna Venkatesan, Cornell University

Shield volcanoes

on the Earth or the Tharsis region on Mars. Sif Mons,
shown in Figure 21, is an example of such a volcano. These
mountains, known as shield volcanoes, reach heights of
several kilometres above the surrounding plains and can
be hundreds of kilometres in diameter. They are made
up of many individual lava flows piled upon one another
in a radial pattern. They develop when a source of lava
below the surface remains fixed and active at one location

long enough to allow the volcanic materials it extrudes to
accumulate above it in large quantities. Like those found
on the rolling plains, the flows comprising the shield volcanoes are generally very long and thin and are likely to
be composed of basalt.

When a subsurface source of lava is drained of its
contents, the ground above it may collapse, forming a
depression called a caldera. Many volcanic calderas are
observed on Venus, both atop shield volcanoes and on the
widespread lava plains. They are often roughly circular in
shape and overall are similar to calderas observed on the
Earth and Mars. The summit region of Sif Mons exhibits
a caldera-like feature 40–50 kilometres in diameter.

Along with the extensive lava plains and the massive
shield volcanoes, there are many smaller volcanic landforms on Venus. Enormous numbers of small volcanic
cones are distributed throughout the plains. So-called pancake domes have a rather unusual appearance (see Figure
22). They are typically a few tens of kilometres in diameter
and approximately one kilometre high and are remarkably
circular in shape. They have flat tops and steep sides, and
appear to have formed when a mass of thick viscous lava
was extruded from a central vent and spread outward for
a short distance before solidifying. The lavas that formed
such domes clearly were much more viscous than most
lavas on Venus. Their composition is unknown, but based
on terrestrial experience they are likely to be much richer
in silica (SiO_2) than the basalts that are believed to predominate elsewhere on the planet.

Impact craters. The surface of Venus has been heavily
modified by forces from within the planet, but it has
been altered by objects from outside as well. Craters dot
the planet, created by impacts with meteorites that have
passed through the planet's atmosphere and struck the
surface. Nearly all solid bodies in the solar system bear
the scars of meteoritic impacts, with small craters typically being more common than large ones. This general
tendency is encountered on Venus as well, but only to a
certain extent. Craters a few hundred kilometres across are

Jet Propulsion Laboratory/National Aeronautics and Space Administration

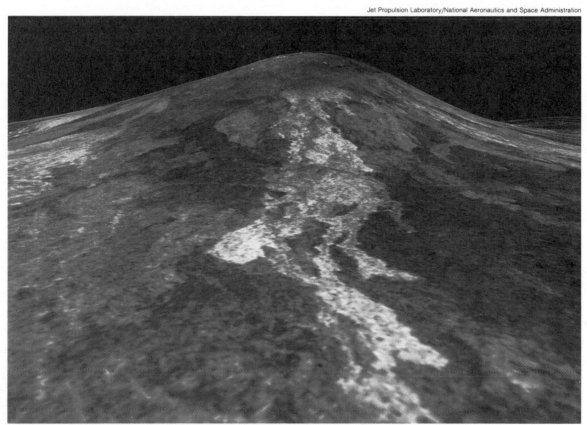

Figure 21: *View of Sif Mons.*
The perspective view of this 300-kilometre-diameter shield volcano on Venus was produced
by superimposing Magellan radar image data on altimetry data. Layers of bright and darker
lava flows are seen; the bright areas represent relatively rough flows resulting from more
recent volcanism, and the darker areas are smooth, older flows.

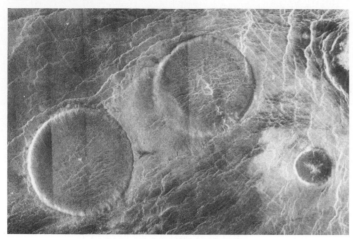

Figure 22: *Pancake-like domes on the surface of Venus.*
This image, obtained by the Magellan orbiter, shows
steep-sided, flat-topped domes that are believed to have been
produced by thick lava flows extruding from a central vent.
National Aeronautics and Space Administration

present but rare on Venus, while craters tens of kilometres in diameter and smaller are common. However, craters smaller than about three kilometres in diameter are not found. Their absence is attributable to the planet's dense atmosphere, which causes intense heating due to friction as meteorites plunge through it at high velocities. The large meteorites that form large craters are able to reach the surface, but small meteorites "burn up" (*i.e.*, vaporize) high in the atmosphere. In fact, craters several kilometres in size—*i.e.*, near the minimum size observed—tend not to be circular. Instead they have complex shapes, often with several irregular pits rather than a single central depression, suggesting that the impacting body broke up into a number of fragments as it passed through the dense atmosphere.

The large craters that are seen on Venus (Figure 23) are different in a number of respects from those observed on other planets. Most impact craters, on Venus and elsewhere, show ejecta around them; this is the material that was expelled during the impact event. Venusian crater ejecta is unusual, however, in that its outer edge commonly shows a lobed or flower-petal pattern, suggesting that much of it poured outward in a ground-hugging flow, rather than arcing high above the ground and falling back to the surface. This behaviour was probably produced in part by dense atmospheric gases that became entrained in the flow. Another peculiarity of large Venusian craters is that small sinuous flows of some sort are seen to have emerged from the crater ejecta, spreading outward from it much as lava flows would. The origin of these flows is not certain, but a likely possibility is that they are composed of rock that was melted by the high pressures and temperatures attained during the impact event.

Perhaps the strangest property of some Venusian craters is one associated with some of the youngest craters. Along with the normal ejecta, these craters are also partially

Horseshoe-shaped regions surrounded by huge, horseshoe-shaped regions of dark material, which have not been found elsewhere in the solar system. In all cases, the horseshoe opens to the west, and the crater is nestled within it, toward its eastern extremity. In radar images the dark materials tend to be smooth at small scales, and it is likely that these diffuse dark horseshoes are composed of smooth deposits of fine-grained ejecta that was thrown upward during the impact event that produced the crater. Apparently this material was lofted high enough into the atmosphere to be picked up by the high-speed, westward-blowing winds. It was then carried far downwind from the crater, eventually falling to form a horseshoe-shaped pattern.

One important property of impact craters on all planets is that they can be used to obtain information about the ages of the surfaces on which they lie. The concept is simple in principle: on a given planet older surfaces have more craters than do younger ones. Determining an absolute

age in years is difficult, however, and requires knowledge about the rate of crater formation that usually must be inferred indirectly. The absolute ages of materials on the surface of Venus are not known, but the overall density of craters on Venus is lower than that on many other bodies in the solar system. Estimates vary, but the average age of materials on Venus is almost certainly less than one billion years and may in fact be substantially less.

INTERIOR

Much less is known about the interior of Venus than is known about its surface and atmosphere. However, because the planet is much like the Earth in its overall size and density, it can be expected to have evolved to at least a crudely similar internal state. Thus, it probably has a core of metal, a mantle of dense rock, and a crust of less dense rock. The core, like that of the Earth, is most likely composed primarily of iron and nickel, although the somewhat lower density of Venus may indicate that its core also contains some other less dense material like sulfur. Because no intrinsic magnetic field has been detected for Venus, there is no direct evidence for a metallic core as there is for Earth, but as noted above this absence can probably be attributed simply to the planet's slow rotation. Calculations of the internal structure of Venus suggest that the outer boundary of the core lies a little more than 3,000 kilometres above the centre of the planet.

Above the core and below the crust lies Venus' mantle, making up the bulk of the volume of the planet. Despite the high surface temperatures of Venus, the temperatures within the Venusian mantle are likely to be similar to those in the Earth's mantle. Even though a planetary mantle is composed of solid rock, the material there can slowly creep or flow, just as glacial ice does, allowing sweeping convective motions to take place. Convection is Convection a great equalizer of the temperatures of planetary interiors. Similar to heat production within the Earth, heat is generated within Venus by the decay of natural radioactive materials. This heat is transported to the surface by convection. If temperatures deep within Venus were significantly higher than those within the Earth, the viscosity of the rocks in the mantle would drop sharply, speeding the convection and rapidly removing the heat. Therefore,

National Aeronautics and Space Administration

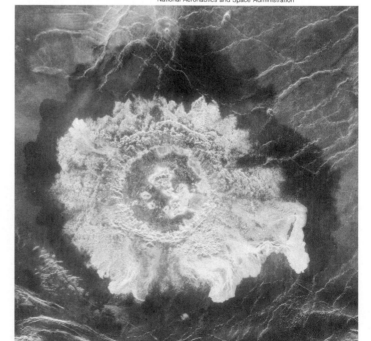

Figure 23: *An impact crater on the Venusian surface.*
This Magellan image displays characteristic features of the
large craters found on Venus. A central peak is present, and
the rim is surrounded by ejecta whose outer edge exhibits a
petallike pattern.

despite the markedly different surface temperatures, the deep interior of Venus can be expected to be rather Earth-like in character.

Convective motions in a planet's mantle can cause materials near the surface to experience stress, and motions in the Venusian mantle seem to be largely responsible for the tectonic deformation observed in radar images. Venus, unlike the Earth, displays a strong correlation of its gravitational field with topography; *i.e.,* regions with topography higher than the average on Venus also tend to be regions where the local gravitational field is higher than the average. This observation implies that much of the topography is not compensated, or supported, by lateral variations in the thickness of the low-density crust as it is on the Earth. Instead, some of the large-scale relief on Venus may owe its origin directly to present-day motions in the mantle, with raised topography, like Beta Regio, above regions of mantle upwelling and lowered topography, like Lavinia Planitia, above regions of mantle downwelling.

Despite the many overall similarities between Venus and the Earth, the surface geology of the two planets is strikingly different. Evidence suggests that the process of plate tectonics does not operate on Venus (see below *Earth: The lithosphere*). Crustal deformation on Venus seems to be driven by mantle motions, but instead of occurring primarily at the boundaries between tectonic plates, the deformation is distributed across broad zones tens to hundreds of kilometres wide. The lack of plate tectonics may be due in part to the high surface temperature, which makes the upper rigid layer of the planet—the lithosphere—more buoyant and hence less likely to subduct into the mantle. Another important difference between the two planets is the lack of water at the surface of Venus, which largely eliminates erosion as an important geologic process. Evidence of geologic events on Venus is rarely destroyed by erosion; instead, it tends to persist until it becomes obscured by subsequent tectonic activity or buried by later volcanism. Perhaps the most important geologic similarity between Venus and the Earth is simply the strong evidence that Venus, like the Earth, is presently a geologically active body.

HISTORY OF OBSERVATION

Venus was one of the five planets known in ancient times, and its motions were observed and studied for centuries prior to the invention of advanced astronomical instruments. Its appearances were recorded by the Babylonians in approximately 3,000 BC, and it also is mentioned prominently in the astronomical records of a number of other ancient civilizations, including those of China, Central America, Egypt, and Greece. The first telescopic observations were, as mentioned above, those of Galileo, which led to the discovery of the planet's phases.

Since Galileo's time, Venus has been studied in detail through Earth-based telescopes and spacecraft instruments. Telescopic observers from the 17th through the 20th centuries, including Gian Domenico Cassini of France and William Herschel of England, viewed the planet and reported a variety of faint markings on its disk. Some of these markings may have corresponded to the cloud features observed in modern times in ultraviolet light, while others may have been illusory.

Solar transits

Important early telescopic observations of Venus were conducted in the 1700s during the planet's solar transits. In a solar transit, a planet passes directly between the Sun and the Earth and is silhouetted briefly against the Sun's disk. Transits of Venus are rare events, occurring in pairs eight years apart with more than a century between pairs. They were extremely important events to 18th-century astronomy, since they provided at that time the most accurate method for determining the distance from the Earth to the Sun. (This distance, known as the astronomical unit, is one of the fundamental constants of astronomy.) Observations of the 1761 transit were only partially successful but did result in the first suggestion, by the Russian astronomer Mikhail V. Lomonosov, that Venus has an atmosphere. The second transit of the pair, in 1769, was observed with somewhat greater success.

Transits must be viewed from many points on Earth to yield accurate distances, and the transits of 1761 and, particularly, of 1769 prompted the launching of many scientific expeditions to remote parts of the globe. Among these was the first of the three voyages of exploration by Captain James Cook, who observed the 1769 transit from Tahiti. The transit observations of the 1700s provided not only an improved determination of the astronomical unit but also the impetus for many unrelated discoveries concerning the Earth's geography.

In the modern era, observations of Venus have also been made in wavelengths outside the visible spectrum. The cloud features were discovered with certainty in 1927 and 1928 in ultraviolet photographs taken by the American astronomers William H. Wright and Frank E. Ross. The first studies of the infrared spectrum of Venus, by Walter S. Adams and Theodore Dunham (also of the United States) in 1932, showed that the atmosphere of the planet is composed primarily of carbon dioxide. Subsequent infrared observations have revealed further details about the composition of both the atmosphere and the clouds. Observations in the microwave portion of the spectrum, beginning in earnest in the late 1950s and early 1960s, provided the first evidence of the extremely high surface temperatures on the planet and prompted the study of the greenhouse effect as a means of producing these temperatures.

After discovering that Venus was completely enshrouded by clouds, astronomers turned to other techniques to study the planet's surface. Foremost among these has been radar. If fitted with a transmitter, a large radio telescope can be used as a radar system, bouncing a radio signal off a planet. Because radio wavelengths can penetrate the thick Venusian atmosphere, the radar technique is an effective means of probing the planet's surface.

Earth-based radar observations

Earth-based radar observations have been conducted primarily using the Arecibo observatory in the mountains of Puerto Rico, the Goldstone observatory in the desert of southern California, and the Haystack observatory in Massachusetts. The first successful radar observations of Venus took place at Goldstone and Haystack in 1961 and revealed the planet's slow rotation. Subsequent observations determined the rotation properties more precisely and began to show some of the major features on the planet's surface. The first features to be observed were dubbed Alpha, Beta, and Maxwell, the last after the British physicist James Clerk Maxwell. These features are among the brightest on the planet in radar images, and their names have been preserved to the present as Alpha Regio, Beta Regio, and the Maxwell Montes. Gradual advances in radar technology brought improvements in Earth-based radar images, and by the mid-1980s images from Arecibo revealed surface features as small as several kilometres in size. However, radar imaging from Earth is hindered by the fact that Venus always presents the same face toward the Earth when the planets are at their closest approach, and much of the surface has gone virtually unobserved from Earth for this reason.

The greatest advances in the study of Venus have been achieved through the use of unmanned spacecraft. The era of spacecraft exploration of the planets began with the U.S. Mariner 2 mission to Venus in 1962. Since then, Venus has been the target of approximately 20 spacecraft missions.

The early Venus missions undertaken by the United States involved three spacecraft: Mariner 2 in 1962, Mariner 5 in 1967, and Mariner 10 in 1974. Each made a single close flyby of the planet, providing successively improved scientific data in accord with the advances in spacecraft and instrument technology that took place over that period. In 1978 the United States launched the Pioneer Venus mission, which placed a spacecraft in orbit around the planet and sent four entry probes deep into the Venusian atmosphere. The entry probes provided data on atmospheric structure and composition, while the orbiter observed the atmosphere from above. The orbiter also carried a radar altimeter that provided the first high-quality map of Venus' surface topography.

Venus was also the primary planetary target of the Soviet

planetary exploration program during the 1960s, '70s, and '80s, in which several spectacular successes were achieved. After a sequence of failed missions in the early 1960s, the successful Soviet exploration of Venus began with the Venera 4 mission in 1967. Venera 4 included a flyby spacecraft as well as a probe that entered the planet's atmosphere. Highlights of the ensuing sequence of missions included the first successful soft landing on another planet (Venera 7 in 1970), the first images returned from the surface of another planet (Veneras 9 and 10 in 1975), and the first spacecraft placed in orbit around Venus (Veneras 9 and 10). The most important Soviet missions in terms of the advances they provided in the global understanding of the planet were the Venera 15 and 16 missions in 1983. The Venera 15 and 16 orbiters included the first radar systems flown to another planet that were capable of producing high-quality images of the surface. They produced a map of the northern quarter of Venus with a resolution of one to two kilometres, and many of the surface features now known to exist on the planet were either first discovered or first observed in detail in the Venera 15 and 16 data.

The most ambitious mission to Venus to date has been the U.S. Magellan mission. The Magellan spacecraft was launched in May 1989 and, after interplanetary cruise, was placed into orbit around the planet in August 1990. Like Veneras 15 and 16, Magellan carries a radar-imaging system, which in this case is capable of producing radar images with a resolution that can exceed 100 metres. The orbit is nearly polar, and so the spacecraft is able to view all latitudes on the planet. On each orbit, the radar system obtains an image strip about 20 kilometres wide and typically more than 16,000 kilometres long, extending nearly from the north pole to the south pole. These image strips are assembled into mosaics, producing high-quality radar images of more than 90 percent of the planet. Magellan also carries a radar altimeter system that is capable of measuring the planet's surface topography as well as some properties of its surface materials. The Magellan spacecraft has returned more data than all previous planetary missions to Venus and the other planets combined.

(Steven W. Squyres)

Magellan mission

Trees

To many, the word trees evokes images of such ancient, powerful, and majestic structures as the redwood and the giant sequoia, among the most massive and longest-living organisms in the world. Although the majority of the Earth's biomass is represented by trees, the fundamental importance of these seemingly ubiquitous plants for the very existence and diversity of life on Earth is perhaps not fully appreciated. Our very biosphere is dependent on the metabolism, death, and recycling of plants, especially trees. Their vast trunks and root systems store carbon dioxide and water and respire oxygen into the atmosphere. The organic matter of the soil develops primarily from plant residues (that is, from decayed leaves, twigs, branches, roots, and fallen trees), which release important nutrients, such as nitrogen, carbon, and oxygen.

The tree is not an immutable biological category but rather a human concept based on visual criteria. Perhaps a general definition would describe a tree as a perennial woody plant that develops along a single main trunk to a height of at least 4.5 metres (15 feet) at maturity. This may be contrasted with a shrub, which might be loosely defined as a woody plant with multiple stems; in most cases, a shrub is less than 3 metres tall. However, a species fitting the description of either in one area of the world might not necessarily do so in other regions, since a variety of stresses shape the habit of the mature plant. Thus, a given woody species may be a tree in one set of habitats within its range and a shrub elsewhere. For example, the spruce and fir may thrive in the tree form at the base of a mountain but assume a shrub form near the mountaintop, the variation due principally to stresses exerted by such environmental conditions as altitude, temperature, and oxygen tension.

It is similarly true that the concept of tree is not a phylogenetic one, since trees are found among many plant families that also include shrubs and herbs. Further, there is no clear consensus as to whether the tree form is the advanced or primitive condition. Some paleobotanists suggest that trees are the most primitive members within these plant families. However, tree forms are found in all the vascular plants, from the club mosses and ferns to the gymnosperms and angiosperms. It is furthermore true that among the flowering plants trees are found not only among the most primitive members (Magnoliaceae) but also among the more specialized, or advanced, members, such as the rose family (Rosaceae).

Consequently, from both a taxonomic and phylogenetic perspective, the tree is an artificial category. It is on an ecological basis that the tree can be recognized as a natural construct, representing an adaptive strategy by many different taxa to exploit and dominate the habitat above the ground.

In the early stages of the development of terrestrial life, land plants were rootless and leafless; since they had their origins in aqueous environments, they did not require the specialized conducting and supporting tissues afforded by roots and stems, nor did they require localized regions of carbohydrate synthesis, since each cell was involved in metabolism, water and nutrient absorption, and respiration. Habitats farther from the water as well as aerial habitats represented available uninhabited environments.

One key to exploiting these habitats is large size. This, however, requires physiological and morphological complexity. If all the tissues of massive tree trunks were alive, for example, the physiological cost of maintaining these structures in the living state would be enormous, and probably unattainable. The elegant solution came in the form of tremendous structural adaptations: new tissues and organs permitted localization of the functions of the plant body.

The evolution of vascular tissues and localized regions of cell division (meristems) permitted the strengthening and conducting tissue, called wood, to be dead, hollow, thick-walled tubes at functional maturity. Roots provided anchorage and absorption of sufficient amounts of water and nutrients to support the huge biomass of the tree. Stems were not only strong enough to support the tree and project it into ever higher habitats but conductive enough to transport the water and nutrients to the leaves at the very top of the tree.

The shape of a tree is an ecological construct as well, since its form is dependent on the habitat and the stresses of the environment. Open-grown trees, such as those in gardens and parks, generally have foliage extending along the length of the trunk (bole) for a considerable distance. Forest trees, on the other hand, compete for growing space and generally have an expanse of foliage-free bole below a more limited tree crown. The aggregate of the tree crowns constitutes the canopy of the forest, and this may be displayed in a single layer or stratified into several layers, depending on the number and kinds of trees that make up the forest.

This article discusses the botanical and popular classifications of trees, their importance to humans, and their general structure and patterns of growth. For more information on specific plants, see FERNS AND OTHER LOWER VASCULAR PLANTS, GYMNOSPERMS, and ANGIOSPERMS. For general information on plants, see PLANTS. For coverage of related topics in both the *Micropædia* and *Macropædia*, see the *Propædia*, sections 312, 332, and 354, and the *Index*.

The article is divided into the following sections:

CLASSIFICATION OF TREES

The ancient Greeks developed a classification about 300 BC in which plants were grouped according to their general form—that is, as trees, shrubs, undershrubs, and vines. This classification was used for almost 1,000 years. Modern classifications of plants attempt to assign a plant to a particular taxon and establish relationships with other plants based on genetics, cytology, ecology, behaviour, and probable evolutionary lineages, in addition to gross morphology. Popular classifications, however, remain useful tools for studying the common stresses that the environment exerts on all plants and the general patterns of adaptation that are shown no matter how distantly plants are related.

Phylogenetic classifications.   Trees are represented in each of the major groups of the vascular plants: pteridophytes (seedless vascular plants), gymnosperms (cycads, ginkgoes, and conifers), and angiosperms (flowering plants).

Although tree ferns account for only a small percentage

of ferns, many are conspicuous members, attaining heights of 7 to 10 metres; some are 15, 18, or occasionally 24 metres tall. These graceful trees, which are natives of humid mountain forests in the tropics and subtropics and of warm temperate regions of the Southern Hemisphere, have huge lacy leaves; they are the remnants of a vastly more numerous flora that populated much of the Earth during the Carboniferous Period (360 to 286 million years ago).

Cycads compose the Cycadophyta, a division of gymnospermous plants consisting of four families and approximately 140 species. Natives of warm regions of the Eastern and Western hemispheres, they also are remnants of a much larger number of species that in past geologic ages dominated the Earth's flora.

The ginkgo is the only living representative of the division Ginkgophyta. It is a relic that has been preserved in cultivation around Buddhist temples in China and elsewhere since the mid-18th century; the tree probably no longer exists in a wild state.

Conifers (division Coniferophyta) include trees and shrubs in seven extant families and 550 species. Familiar representatives are araucarias, cedars, cypresses, Douglas firs, firs, hemlocks, junipers, larches, pines, podocarpuses, redwoods, spruces, and yews.

Angiosperms dominate the Earth's present flora; they contain more than 250,000 species, among which are the majority of the world's trees. Angiosperms are divided on the basis of a group of characteristics into two classes: the monocotyledons and the dicotyledons. The most numerous of the monocotyledonous trees are palms; others include agaves, aloes, dracaenas, screw pines, and yuccas. By far the greatest number of tree species are dicotyledons; they are represented by such familiar groups as apples, birches, elms, hollies, magnolias, maples, oaks, poplars, and willows. (G.P.B.)

Popular classifications. Trees have been grouped in various ways, some of which more or less parallel their scientific classification: softwoods are conifers and hardwoods are dicotyledons. Hardwoods are also known as broadleaf trees. The designations softwood, hardwood, and broadleaf, however, are often imprecise. The wood of some hardwoods—for example, certain willows and poplars and the softest of all woods, balsa—is softer than that of some softwoods—e.g., the longleaf pine (*Pinus palustris*). Similarly, some broadleaf trees (tree heaths, *Erica arborea*, and some kinds of *Tamarix*) have narrower leaves than do those of certain conifers (*Podocarpus*).

A popular and convenient grouping of trees is evergreen and deciduous. This is most useful at the local rather than the worldwide level: whether a particular species retains its foliage throughout the year and thus qualifies as evergreen may depend on climate. At the northern limits or, in the Southern Hemisphere, the southern limits of their occurrence and at high elevations, species that under more favourable circumstances retain their foliage may become leafless for a period. Many tropical and subtropical species that in uniformly humid climates are never without foliage are deciduous in regions in which dry and wet seasons alternate. In northern North America the term evergreen is often used as a synonym for conifer and thus excludes foliage-retaining angiosperms. But five coniferous genera— *Larix* (larch), *Metasequoia* (dawn redwood), *Pseudolarix* (golden larch), *Taxodium* (swamp cypress), and *Glyptostrobus*—are composed of or include deciduous species.

Other tree groups are popularly recognized: tree ferns, palms, and, among desert plants, the tree forms of agaves, aloes, cactuses, euphorbias, and yuccas. Sometimes the layperson includes as trees plants that botanists cannot accept as such—e.g., the banana. Such confusion arises from the fact that what appears to be the trunk of the "banana tree" is actually leafstalks rolled tightly around each other. The banana plant is entirely herbaceous, has no true trunk, and thus is not considered a tree by botanists.

THE IMPORTANCE OF TREES

Forests are of immense importance in soil stabilization and erosion control, especially in mountainous and hilly regions; they also protect and conserve water supplies and prevent floods. Small groups of trees and even single trees

Evergreen and deciduous trees

have a similar role locally in preventing washouts and in holding stream banks. As mentioned above, trees contribute significantly to nutrient recycling, carbon dioxide absorption, and oxygen generation.

Economic importance. Carbonized and fossilized wood (coal) supplies fuel for energy needs; other fossilized products of trees include amber, which is formed from the gum of pines, and kauri gum, the product of *Agathis australis*. From earliest times wood has been employed for such purposes as homes, rafts, canoes, fuel, and weapons.

Primitive peoples were dependent on trees for many materials in addition to wood. Fruits and nuts of many kinds were important foods for both humans and animals. Leaves of palms and other trees were used for thatching roofs. Tapa cloth and woven fabrics made from bark, leaves, and other tree parts were used for clothing. Utensils were fashioned from calabashes, coconuts, and other fruits. Medicines, including quinine, were obtained from trees, as were dyes, tanning materials, and spices.

Modern civilizations are no less dependent on trees. Although substitutes now are commonly used for some tree products, the demand for trees remains strong, as in the manufacture of newsprint and other papers as well as cardboard and similar packagings. The plywood industry converts immense numbers of trees into building materials.

Wood products

Many tree products other than wood and its derivatives are important. Edible fruits produced by trees include apples, cherries, peaches, pears, and others in temperate climates; avocados, figs, persimmons, and citrus fruits in warm-temperate and subtropical regions; breadfruit, coconuts, jackfruit, mangoes, and mangosteens in tropical regions; and the important fruit of desert regions—the date. The coconut (*Cocos nucifera*), the oil palm (*Elaeis guineensis*), and the olive (*Olea europaea*) are important sources of oils and fats used as food and for other purposes. From trees come such spices as cinnamon, cloves, and nutmeg; substances used in beverages, such as chocolate, coffee, and kola nuts; and chicle, the basis of chewing gum. Nonedible tree products exploited commercially include rosin, turpentine, tanbark, creosote, cork, and kapok fibre.

It is true, however, that the history of civilization also includes incidences of waste, sometimes bordering on elimination of a species from a particular region. Great forests of cedars of Lebanon (*Cedrus libani*), for example, were virtually eliminated in lumbering operations during early historic times for such purposes as the construction of King Solomon's great temple and palace. Forests that covered much of the Mediterranean region and Middle East were extravagantly exploited by the Assyrians, Babylonians, Greeks, and Romans. Today the once vast Amazonian rain forest is in imminent danger of being deforested primarily for farmland.

Trees of special interest. Mangroves actually constitute a heterogeneous group of plants with similar adaptations to a particular environment. They colonize tidal shores and brackish waters in the tropics and subtropics and in so doing not only stabilize shorelines but also create new land by trapping debris, silt, and mud among their interlacing roots. Mangroves spread out into the water by sending from their branches roots that reach into the mud and develop into sturdy supporting props. A distinctive feature of mangroves is their large fruits, the seeds of which germinate and grow into sturdy seedlings before they leave the parent plant. When the seedlings fall, they either become fixed in the mud or float away, to be washed up at some site at which the opportunity to become established may occur.

Mangroves are not the only trees that spread by dropping prop roots from their branches. The habit is well developed in several tropical figs (*Ficus*), including one popular in small sizes as a houseplant—the rubber plant (*F. elastica*). Most noteworthy of the group is the banyan tree (*F. benghalensis*) of India; its numerous prop roots develop into secondary trunks that support the widespreading head of massive, constantly extending branches. One specimen 600 metres in circumference has been estimated as being capable of sheltering 20,000 people. The wonderboom (*F. pretoriae*) of Africa grows in a similar manner; a specimen at Pretoria has a spread of 50 metres. Because of their

Strangler figs

unusual growth habits, these tropical ficuses are called strangler figs. Often they begin life high in a palm or some other tree in which a monkey, bat, or bird that has fed on the fruits deposits seeds that have passed through its alimentary tract. The seeds germinate, the roots growing into organic matter collected in crotches or crevices of the host tree. Under humid conditions the seedlings grow rapidly, sending roots down along the trunk of the host tree. Upon reaching the ground the roots branch and establish themselves. Above the ground the roots thicken until they form an interlacing cylinder around the trunk of the host.

The ombu (*Phytolacca dioica*) is a remarkable South American relative of the pokeweed (*P. americana*). A tree capable of attaining heights of 20 metres and a spread of 30 metres, it has a wide trunk; the branches contain as much as 80 percent water and very little wood tissue. From its base radiates a circle of rootlike outgrowths wide enough for a person to sit on.

The traveler's tree of Madagascar (*Ravenala madagascariensis*) has a palmlike trunk up to 9 metres tall topped by a huge, symmetrical fan of long-stalked, paddle-shaped leaves often much shredded by wind. The vernacular name alludes to the leaves having hollow bases from which, it has been reported, travelers could obtain potable water.

The talipot palm (*Corypha umbraculifera*) of tropical Asia may live as long as 75 years before it flowers and fruits just one time, then dies. The huge panicle (many-branched cluster) of creamy white blooms arises from the centre of the cluster of fan-shaped leaves topping the trunk, which may be 24 metres tall and 90 to 120 centimetres (3 to 4 feet) in diameter. Another palm of special interest is the double coconut (*Lodoicea maldivica*); a native of two tiny islands of the Seychelles group in the Indian Ocean, it has fruits that require about 10 years to mature, weigh up to 20 kilograms (50 pounds), and have the appearance of a pair of coconuts joined together. Long before their source was known, these fruits were washed up by the sea in India, and magical properties were ascribed to them.

The tallest trees are Pacific Coast redwoods (*Sequoia sempervirens*), specimens of which exceed 105 metres in height in an impressive grove along Redwood Creek valley, Calif., U.S. The species is confined to a narrow coastal belt extending from southern Oregon to California. The next tallest trees are the Australian mountain ash (*Eucalyptus regnans*), specimens of which in Victoria, Australia, exceed 90 metres, the greatest heights known for non-coniferous trees. A close relative of the redwood, the giant sequoia (*Sequoiadendron giganteum*) develops the greatest total bulk of wood, but not the biggest girth, among trees. This tree, which attains heights in excess of 90 metres and may have a trunk diameter of about 7.5 metres some distance above its flaring base, is restricted to a strip about 450 kilometres (280 miles) long and less than 32 kilometres wide in the Sierra Nevadas, in California.

Records for tree girth are held by the baobab (*Adansonia digitata*) of Africa and the Mexican swamp cypress (*Taxodium mucronatum*). The baobab attains a maximum height of about 23 metres; its barrel-shaped trunk may be more than 7.5 metres in diameter a metre or so above the ground. The most famous specimen of Mexican swamp cypress is "El Gigante," located at Tule, Oaxaca. The trunk of this massive tree is buttressed and not circular; if the bays and promontories of the buttresses are followed, the basal circumference is nearly 46 metres.

(Thomas H. Everett/Lillian M. Weber)

STRUCTURE AND FUNCTION

The early aquatic plants required few modifications for structural support or water and nutrient absorption since the surrounding water fulfilled their needs. The water, far denser than the air, buoyed the plant body; the thin integument meant a free exchange of nutrients across the entire, relatively small body surface and a passive mechanism for spreading their gametes. Once primitive plants began to invade the land, however, modifications for support, nutrient and water absorption, turgidity, and reproduction were required to compensate for the absence of a watery medium. Because organic soils were not widely developed, the earliest terrestrial plants probably first col-

onized bare rock near large water sources, such as oceans and lakes. Generations of these plants recycling nutrients (*e.g.,* nitrogen, carbon, and oxygen) and energy into the stratum contributed to the development of a rich organic soil suitable for large shrubs and herbs. With the proliferation of these low-lying plants, competition for available space, nutrients, and sunlight intensified. Aerial habitats and those farther afield from the large sources of water represented the only uninhabited environments left to be exploited. This required the physiological and morphological complexity found among the vascular plants.

General features. As vascular plants, trees are organized into three major organs: the roots, the stems, and the leaves. The leaves are the principal photosynthetic organs of most higher vascular plants. They are attached by a continuous vascular system to the rest of the plant so that free exchange of nutrients, water, and end products of photosynthesis (oxygen and carbohydrates in particular) can be carried to its various parts.

The stem is divided into nodes (points where leaves are or were attached) and internodes (the length of the stem between nodes). The leaves and stem together are called the shoot. Shoots can be separated into long shoots and short shoots on the basis of internode length. The stem provides support, water and food conduction, and storage. Roots provide structural anchorage to keep trees from

Organ systems

From (A) W.W. Robbins and T.E. Weier, *Botany: An Introduction to Plant Science,* © 1950 by John Wiley & Sons, Inc.; (B,D) *Biological Science: An Inquiry into Life,* 2nd ed. (1968); Harcourt Brace Jovanovich, Inc., New York; by permission of the Biological Sciences Curriculum Study; (C) E.W. Sinnott, *Botany: Principles and Problems,* 4th ed., copyright 1946; used with permission of McGraw-Hill Book Co.

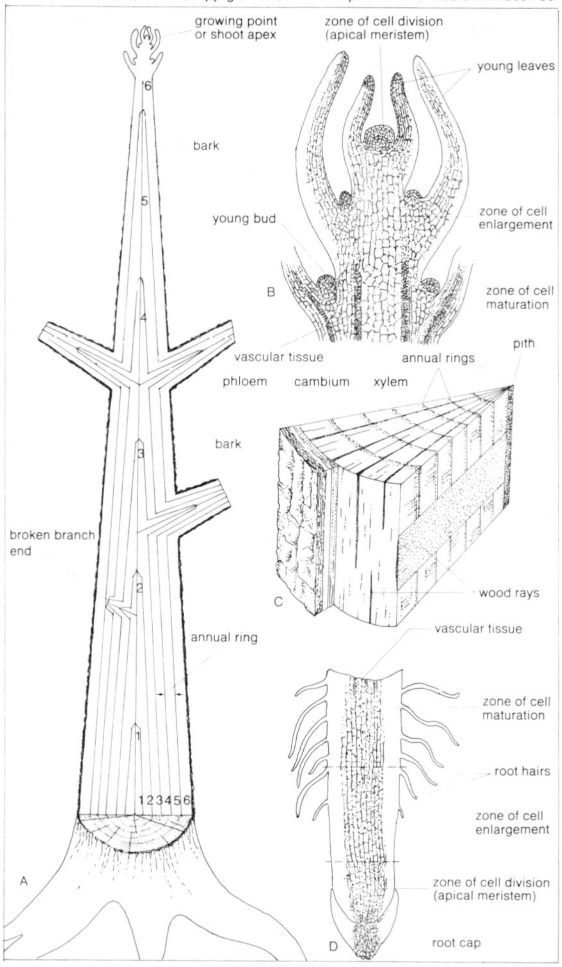

Figure 1: *Growth regions of a tree.*
(A) Longitudinal section of a young tree showing how the annual growth rings are produced in successive conical layers. (B) Shoot apex, the extreme tip of which is the apical meristem, or primary meristem, a region of new cell division that contributes to primary growth, or increase in length, and which is the ultimate source of all the cells in the above-ground parts of the tree. (C) Segment of a tree trunk showing the location of the cambium layer, a secondary meristem that contributes to secondary growth, or increase in thickness. (D) Root tip, the apex of which is also an apical meristem and the ultimate source of all the cells of the root system.

toppling over. They also have a massive system for harvesting the enormous quantities of water and the mineral resources of the soil required by trees. In some cases, roots supplement the nutrition of the tree through symbiotic associations such as with nitrogen-fixing microorganisms and fungal symbionts called mycorrhizae, which are known to increase phosphorous uptake. Tree roots also serve as storage depots, especially in seasonal climates.

As is true of other higher vascular plants, all the branches and the central stem of trees (the trunk or bole) terminate in growing points called shoot apical meristems. These are centres of continuous·growth and development, annually producing the leaves as well as a bud in the axis of most leaves that has the potential to grow out as a branch. These shoot apical growing centres form the primary plant body, and all the tissues directly formed by them are called the primary tissues. Like the stems, the growing points of the roots are at their tips (root apical meristems); however, they produce only more root tissue, not whole organs (leaves and stems). The root meristem also produces the root cap that covers the outside of the root tip.

The shoot apical meristems do not appear different between long and short shoots, but the lower part of the meristem does not produce as many cells in short shoots. In some cases, it may be totally inactive. Shoot meristems in some species may interconvert and change the type of shoot they produce. For example, in the longleaf pine, the seedlings enter a grass stage, which may last as long as 15 years. Here the terminal bud on the main axis exists as a short shoot and produces numerous needle-bearing dwarf shoots in which there is little or no internode elongation. Consequently, the seedling resembles a clump of grass. This is probably an adaptation to fire, water stress, and perhaps grazing. The root volume, however, continues to increase, increasing the chance of seedling survival once the shoot begins to grow out (*i.e.,* the internodes start to expand). This process is called flushing.

The outermost layer of cells surrounding the roots and stems of the young seedling of a vascular plant (including the leaves, flowers, fruits, and seeds) is called the epidermis. The closely knit cells afford some protection against physical shock and, when invested with cutin and covered with a cuticle, they also provide some protection from desiccation. Stomata (pores) are interspersed throughout the epidermal cells of the leaves (and to some extent on the stems) and regulate the movement of gases and water vapour into and out of the plant body.

Immediately adjacent is a cylinder of ground tissue: in the stem the outer region is called the cortex and the inner region the pith, although among many of the monocotyledons (an advanced class of angiosperms, including the palms and lilies) the ground tissue is amorphous and

no regions can be discerned. The roots of woody dicots and conifers develop only a cortex (the pith is absent), the innermost layer of which comprises thick-walled wall cells called endodermal cells.

The final structural element of the primary plant body is the vascular tissue, a continuous system of conducting and supporting tissues that extends throughout the plant body. The vascular system consists of two conducting tissues, xylem and phloem; the former conducts water and the latter food. In the stems and roots the vascular tissues are arranged concentrically, on the order of a series of cylinders. Each column, or cylinder, of primary vascular tissue develops the primary xylem toward the inner aspect of the column and the primary phloem toward the outer aspect. The multiple vascular cylinders are arranged throughout the cortex, either in an uninterrupted ring between the cortex and pith or separated from each other by ground tissues. In some monocotyledons the vascular cylinders are scattered throughout the stem. Regardless of their arrangement, however, the multiple vascular columns form strands from the leaves to the roots, moving water and nutrients where they are most needed.

Vascular tissues

In dicotyledonous and coniferous (*i.e.,* woody) trees and shrubs there is a single layer of meristematic cells, called the vascular cambium, that organizes between the primary xylem and phloem of these vascular cylinders and initiates the development of secondary xylem and secondary phloem. The cambium forms the wood and the bark of the tree and is responsible for thickening the plant, whereas the apical (primary) meristems are responsible for elongating the plant body. A cambium forms in conifers and dicotyledons and to a lesser extent in some monocotyledons and cycads. Tree ferns do not develop a cambium; hence, no secondary thickening of the trunk takes place in the usual sense.

Cells between the columns of vascular tissue connect the cambiums inside the columns of vascular tissue to form a complete cylinder around the stem. The cells formed toward the inside are called secondary xylem, or wood, and those formed toward the outside of the cambium are called secondary phloem. The bark and the wood together constitute the secondary plant body of the tree. The woody vascular tissue provides both longitudinal and transverse movement for carbohydrates and water.

The vascular cambium consists of two types of initials: fusiform initials and ray initials. The fusiform initials are long cells that give rise to the axial (longitudinal) system of vascular tissue. The cells of the axial system are arranged parallel with the long axis of the tree trunk. In conifers the cells of this system are most frequently tracheids, which are designed to form tissues for strength and water conduction; in hardwoods the axial system is composed primarily of fibres and vessel elements, an adaptation that permits specialization of the tissues. Wood grain is determined by the fibre direction and is thus a measure of the longitudinal alignment of the fibres and of their predominance. Vessel elements are much wider than fibres, facilitating water conduction.

The ray initials form the radial system of the bark and wood. These initials are more squat in shape. In the wood the radial system functions primarily in the transport of carbohydrates from the inner bark to the wood; there are some food-storage cells in this system as well. The cells lack the strength of the fibres; hence, wood is split more easily along the wood rays.

The part of the wood that carries water and nutrients throughout the plant is called sapwood. As the tree ages, the older inner portions of the sapwood are infiltrated by oils, gums, resins, tannins, and other chemical compounds. By the time the cells die, the sapwood has been converted to heartwood, a dark, dense tissue. Heartwood, although dead, persists for the life of the tree and affords structural strength unless diseased and can serve as a reservoir of water for the sapwood.

Sapwood

In normal or good growing conditions, the proportion of xylem cells formed is much greater than that of the phloem, as much as 10–20 to 1, but in extremely stressful years or situations the phloem is less affected and the ratio may drop below 1. In most cases, the phloem operates in

Graeme P. Berlyn

Figure 2: A cross section of a seedling of jack pine (*Pinus banksiana*).

Figure 3: The principal growth forms of trees are (left to right) columnar, deliquescent, and excurrent.
Drawing by M. Pahl

food transport for only a single year, while the xylem of most species may function in sap conduction for several years before it loses functionality and becomes heartwood. The tree annually produces more wood than it needs for conduction and support under most conditions; *i.e.*, there is a wide margin of safety in xylem production. In contrast, there is a much smaller margin of safety in phloem production; hence, it has higher priority of allocation of the energy resources of the tree. Under extremely stressful conditions, annual xylem production may be zero even while some phloem continues to be formed.

Branching is a significant characteristic in trees. Most conifers form a well-defined, dominant trunk with less impressive lateral branches (excurrent branching). Many angiosperms show for some part of their development a well-defined central axis, which then divides continually to form a crown of branches of similar dimensions (deliquescent branching). This can be found in many oaks, the honey locust (*Gleditsia triacanthos*), the silver linden (*Tilia tomentosa*), and the American elm (*Ulmus americana*). The palms illustrate the third major tree form, columnar, in which the central axis develops without branching until the apex of the bole.

Annual ring formation. One of the interesting features of temperate trees is the "awakening" of the cambium in the spring to form the annual ring of wood and bark. Annual ring formation probably evolved late in the Paleozoic Era (410 to 245 million years ago) in response to seasonal changes in water availability. While tree height is closely associated with the quality of the site on which the tree is growing (*i.e.*, the climate, soil, topography, and biota), radial growth is tied more to the weather conditions of the current year. For this reason, the width of annual rings has been used to provide information on past climates as well as to date events of the past. Dendroclimatology and dendrochronology are names given to these fields of study.

Growth rings

Growth rings are visible because of the differences in density between wood of the early part of the growing season and that of the later part. Where the latewood and earlywood abut, there is a visible ring. The cells of the annual ring rapidly become devoid of protoplasts because they are dead at functional maturity, at which time they serve to conduct sap (water, minerals, and dissolved substance). The hollow centre of these conducting cells (vessels, tracheids, and fibres) is called the lumen.

Deciduous trees may be divided into ring-porous or diffuse-porous trees. In ring-porous trees the vessels laid down at the beginning of the growing season are much larger than subsequent vessels laid down at the end of the season (or ring). Diffuse-porous trees form vessels of roughly the same radial diameter throughout the growing season. (Tangential diameter does not change very much in a given annual increment.) Larger vessel size permits more rapid water conduction because the rate of conduction varies with the fourth power of the radius of the vessel

lumen. Ring-porous trees are generally restricted to the north temperate zone. In a number of species the vessels become occluded by cellular ingrowths from surrounding living cells. The occlusions, called tyloses, may occur in the first year after vessel formation. The protoplast of the living cell proliferates through pores in the cell walls known as pits. Red oak (*Quercus rubra*) does not have tyloses, whereas white oak (*Q. alba*) does; this is why white oak is used to make whiskey barrels, while red oak cannot be utilized for this purpose.

As mentioned above, only the radial diameter of the cells varies appreciably within a given year and is dependent on growing conditions. In addition to soil quality, the width of the annual increment depends on the date of initiation and cessation of radial growth for the year, the rate of cell division, and the rate of cell elongation. Radial diameters of cells in the axial system are generally larger in spring because water stress is low and hormone production high.

The thickest-walled cells generally mark the end of the annual ring. There is a sharp disjunction as the next cell formed will be a large-diameter, thin-walled cell that marks initiation of the next year's earlywood. (The terms spring wood and summer wood are no longer commonly used because it is now known that in many locations most of the so-called summer wood is actually formed in the spring.) In preformer species (trees that contain all of next year's needles in their winter buds), cambial activity begins about the same time as shoot growth but generally continues for some time after shoot growth ceases for the year. In neoformers (trees that do not preform all of next year's leaves in their winter buds), leaf formation may continue for some time after diameter growth ceases.

Under adverse conditions, variations are observed: incomplete (discontinuous) rings, missing rings (no xylem formed in a given year), false rings, eccentric rings (overproduction on one side), and fluted rings (overproduction at various sites around the circumference of the ring). In

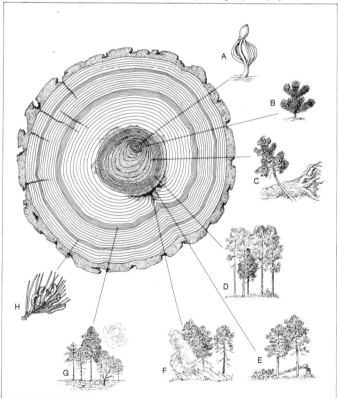

Figure 4: *Cross section of a tree trunk with events of its life indicated by growth patterns in wood.*
(A) A loblolly pine is born; (B) growth is rapid, forming relatively broad, even rings; (C) "reaction wood" is formed to help support the tree after something fell against it; (D) growth is straight but crowded by other trees; (E) competing trees are removed and growth is again rapid; (F) fire scars the tree; (G) narrow rings are caused probably by a prolonged dry spell; (H) narrow rings may have been caused by an insect.

a given tree in a given year, any combination of these variations may be seen from crown to base.

The normal condition, especially in trees of temperate regions, is the development of a single ring during each growing season. Other rings formed during the season are called false rings. The false-ring phenomenon is clearly evinced in conifers (Figure 4) when the normal growing season is interrupted by factors such as drought in the spring. As conditions worsen, the radial diameters of the secondary tissue cells decrease and the walls may thicken, and the wood may take on the appearance of latewood. Once the drought conditions have passed, the radial diameters of the cells of the secondary tissues will increase, creating the appearance of a new annual ring. This, however, is a false ring because there is a gradient of increasing cell-wall thickness and decreasing cell diameter at the start of the false ring and another gradient of decreasing cell-wall thickness and increasing cell diameter at the end of the false ring.

False rings are a challenge to dendroclimatology, but they also offer the opportunity to trace weather patterns over long periods of time. Information on past climates is encoded not only in the number of cells in an annual ring but also in the thickness and composition of the cell walls and in the lumen diameters. Complications in reading this information arise because the sheath of wood produced by a given tree in a given year may be of unequal width at different points around the bole and at different heights in the tree. Classic annual rings are found in conifers and ring-porous hardwoods, where the delineation of annual rings is clear. In diffuse-porous temperate hardwoods and ring-bearing tropical trees, variations in the cells in response to developmental, seasonal, and chronological time may obscure the limits of the tree rings.

Tree bark.   Each tree species has a bark that is unique in structure and appearance; in fact, many trees can be identified by the characteristics of their bark alone. In some species the bark looks similar throughout the life of the plant, while in others there are dramatic changes with age.

The term tree bark refers to the tissues outside the vascular cambium. The inner bark is composed of secondary phloem, which in general remains functional in transport for only one year. A second type of lateral (nonapical) meristem, called the cork cambium, develops in some of the cells of the older phloem and forms cork cells. The cork cells push the old secondary phloem cells toward the outer margins of the stem, where they are crushed, are torn, and eventually slough off. All tissues outside the cork cambium constitute the outer bark, including the nonfunctional phloem and cork cells. The cork may develop during the first year in many trees and form exfoliating bark, while in others, such as beech, dogwood, and maple, the bark may not exfoliate for several years. In cases of delayed formation, the outer covering of the stem, the periderm or the epidermis, must enlarge and grow to keep pace with the increase in stem diameter.

Bark minimizes water loss from the stems, deters insect and fungal attack, and is a very effective protector against fire damage, as is demonstrated by the high fire resistance of redwood and giant sequoia trees (which have a massive bark).

The cork cambium provides an effective barrier against many kinds of invaders; however, in being so resilient, it also cuts off the outer secondary phloem and tissues from the rest of the wood, thus effectively killing it. Thus, the outer bark is made up entirely of dead tissue.

The pattern of cork development is the main determinant of bark appearance. In some barks the cork cambium and cork tissues are laid down in a discontinuous and overlapping manner, resulting in a scaly type of bark (pines and pear trees); in other barks the pattern is continuous and in sheets (paper birch and cherry). Barks show various patterns intermediate between these extremes.

Bark varies from the smooth, copper-coloured covering of the gumbo-limbo (*Bursera simaruba*) to the thick, soft, spongy bark of the punk, or cajeput, tree (*Melaleuca leucadendron*). Other types of bark include the commerical cork of the cork oak (*Quercus suber*) and the rugged, fissured outer coat of many other oaks; the flaking, patchy-coloured barks of sycamores (*Platanus*) and the lacebark pine (*Pinus bungeana*); and the rough shinglelike outer covering of shagbark hickory (*Carya ovata*).

The cork cambium primarily produces a single cell type, the cork cells; however, the walls may be thick or thin. Birch bark peels because it has alternating layers of thick- and thin-walled cork cells. Birch bark also has numerous pores on the bark, called lenticels, and these are also associated with cork formation because they provide openings for gas exchange. In most cases, they form at the location of stomates.

Tree height growth.   The two primary determinants of height growth are the number of height growth units (the node plus its subtending internode) produced during each growing season and elongation of the internodes. This process is sensitive to environmental factors such as water availability, soil quality, and climatic variation, as well as to the time of the year when height growth units are initiated and when they elongate. This is correlated with variation in growth hormone production by expanding buds and leaves.

Most north temperate trees form their leaves during the development of the terminal buds of the previous year to some degree (preformers). In these species the number of height growth units for the year is determined to a great extent during the previous year. For example, those of the grand fir (*Abies grandis*) in the area of Vancouver, B.C., Can., are preformed in October, so that at spring bud break those height growth units elongate and develop; a new bud is then initiated in July. Thus, the environmental conditions between July and October affect the number and properties of the height growth units that grow out in the current year. Since the leaves are the source of carbohydrates required for, and used in, wood and bark formation, the climate of the previous year also affects the diameter growth of the current year. Examples of preformers are most pines, fir, hickory, spruce, Douglas fir, beech, and oak. Some trees are neoformers because they form most or all of their leaves in the current year of growth. Examples of this are birch, chestnut, poplar, willow, larch, tulip tree, and some tropical pines. Seedlings will often be neoformers and then become preformers as adults.

The monopodial form of tree growth is maintained by the dominance of the apical buds over the lateral buds. The healthy apical bud produces a sufficient hormonal influence over the lateral buds to keep them suppressed; however, some species abort the terminal bud either annually, as in the basswood (*Tilia americana*), or occasionally, as in the American birch (*Fagus grandifolia*). In these cases, the new terminal growth originates from a lateral branch, causing sympodial growth.

Besides terminal buds and axillary buds formed in the axils of leaves, buds may form outside the apical meristem. This is called adventitious growth. When a bole of a tree that has been shaded for a number of years is suddenly exposed to light, new buds, called epicormic buds, may be initiated. Epicormic buds may be adventitious in origin or formed from dormant axillary trace buds. In many cases, buds may grow out that were formed by or outside of the shoot meristem but became dormant until induced by environmental factors. Rather unique adventitious buds may develop on roots and grow out as shoots. These are called root suckers; the process is called suckering.

There is also variation in the number of bud flushes per year in temperate as well as tropical trees. Trees like the preformer eastern white pine (*Pinus strobus*) have a single flush per year followed by formation of a dormant terminal bud. Other species have several flushes per year, but each flush is followed by formation of a terminal bud.

Finally, there are species that have a terminal bud but then extend height growth unit formation throughout the growing season until setting a terminal bud with some of the following year's leaves at the end of the growing season (mixed model). Some species such as lodgepole pine (*Pinus contorta*) are polycyclic: they have several flushes from a single bud during the growing season.

Height growth is terminated at the end of the growing season by factors such as the length of day. Occasionally mild fall weather may induce buds that normally would not flush until the following spring. These are often termed lammas shoots.

Limitations on tree growth

Obviously there is a limit to the height of trees. One observation is that the tallest and most massive trees are found in moist habitats, such as the Pacific Northwest of the United States and tropical rain forests. This suggests that the process of lifting water to the tops of trees may be a major limitation to the development of tree height. The physics of the process would be necessarily complex. If, for example, a vacuum pump were attached to a tall vertical pipe, the pump can pull water up to only a height of approximately 9 metres. How then do trees, some of which may be more than 90 metres tall, get water to their tops?

The current consensus is that water is pulled up from the roots by the leaves. The Dixon cohesion theory of water ascent in trees suggests that water molecules in the trees adhere to each other along columns under tension. The stomata of the leaves, which in most plants are open during the day and closed at night, transpire water from the leaf into the air. As each water molecule leaves, the chain of water molecules is pulled up by one molecule. It therefore can be said that water is pulled up by forces acting in the leaf and is not pushed up to any extent from below.

Tree trunks often shrink in diameter during sunny summer days because of the large amount of water lost from the leaves by transpiration. The trunks will then swell during the night as water is restored to the tree from the soil. Most of the shrinking and swelling takes place in the bark, but some occurs in the wood. The ascent of the water, or sap as it is often called, is a purely physical process requiring the columns of water in the tree to cohere. Although the water columns periodically break and there is no active mechanism to restore the integrity of these water columns, as long as there is a sufficient number of water columns left, the tree will still be able to obtain sufficient water to maintain the turgidity of its leaves. As the tree grows taller, however, the problem of maintaining adequate flow of water to the top is thought to become more difficult because the frequency of column breakage increases as the columns get longer. (The term sap is used for the fluid moving up the tree because it includes not only water but also minerals and a number of dissolved substances such as sugars and amino acids.)

Another factor that is thought to limit tree height is the increased mechanical strength required as a tree becomes larger. Even the largest known trees remain well below the height/diameter ratio that would cause toppling with minimal wind sway. As trees grow taller, they must grow increasingly thicker in order to keep from toppling over. In some trees, especially in moist unstable sites, large buttressed roots spread out and stabilize the tree.

At some point, however, there is a limit to the possible adaptations that can permit increased tree height. Size makes for complexity as morphological and physiological adaptations are stressed to the limit. The phyletic lines of many animal groups, for instance, show examples of extinct ancestors that grew increasingly large until they died off. Similarly in tree heights, a single factor is seldom limiting, but rather a combination of factors interact to destabilize the tree. It is clear that large size in animal species has certain reproductive and adaptive advantages. It is not so clear what advantage large size has for trees other than insuring access to solar radiation; because large size increases the food-and-water storage capacity of a tree, it may therefore impart ability to resist stress.

Many tropical trees exhibit intermittent height growth despite ever moist and otherwise favourable growth conditions. In temperate trees there is a period of true dormancy in the fall. Chilling is required to overcome this true dormancy. After the chilling requirement is met (artificially, about one month at approximately 0° to 5° C), the buds enter winter dormancy (quiescence). This type of dormancy is simply due to low temperature, and the buds can be induced to flush merely by bringing them into a greenhouse. After bud set (*i.e.,* bud formation) in July, the buds may be considered to be in summer dormancy because they will normally not grow out until the following year. This scenario implies that hormones are the inhibiting factors. These buds may be induced to flush by defoliation or unusual weather patterns.

True dormancy is extremely difficult to break, but in some cases increasing both the length of day and temperature with or without hormonal treatments can induce some degree of flushing. As the chilling process proceeds, the window of inducing conditions enlarges. It should be noted that these buds are dormant only in the sense that no internodal elongation takes place. Other types of biological activity such as cell division and formation of primordia may take place, depending on the species. Thus, bud dormancy is a dynamic interaction between growth promoters and growth inhibitors. In some cases, active buds may be induced into dormancy by application of hormone inhibitors and then reactivated by other hormones.

Foxtailing

Some pine trees, especially in the tropics, exhibit a type of growth called foxtailing. This is primarily a plantation phenomenon wherein, after planting, the trees elongate continuously without producing any lateral branches. Several metres of branch-free bole may be produced, and then the tree may grow in a more normal pattern and may revert to foxtailing at various times. This is an ultimate expression of free growth. Species that exhibit this phenomenon include *Pinus caribaea, P. canariensis, P. insularis, P. tropicalis, P. merkusii, P. palustris, P. echinata, P. elliottii,* and *P. taeda.* The last four species constitute the southern yellow pines of the southeastern United States. The Monterey pine of California (*P. radiata*) also may foxtail in subtropical environments.

There are both genetic and environmental components involved in foxtailing; for example, a selected strain of Caribbean pine that was certified not to foxtail in Australia reportedly exhibited 80 percent foxtailing when grown in Puerto Rico. Foxtailing decreases with altitude, stand density, and soil quality. The cause is thought to be due to hormone imbalances induced by exotic environments. Some species or individuals are better able to adjust to this without foxtailing than others.

The advantages of foxtailing that have been reported are greater height growth, better stem form (*i.e.,* straight, with minimum taper), and greater dry matter production of more merchantable material. (Dry matter is the weight [mass] of plant material formed after it has been dried in an oven until it reaches constant weight.) Disadvantages have been reported to be lower stem stability resulting in greater wind damage, low seed production, lack of latewood, and more compression wood (see below *Reaction wood*). Both decreases and increases in volume production have been reported.

Flower buds.   Tree buds may be vegetative or reproductive. Vegetative buds continue to produce height growth units unless or until they are induced to form flowers. When a shoot apical meristem is induced to form a reproductive bud, its existence terminates when the pollen or seeds are shed. Exactly what induces the formation of a reproductive bud varies with species, but changes in the number of daylight hours is a common signal in many plants. Changes in the levels of hormones and carbohydrates are among the factors that signal the physiological factors that directly result in flowering.

Tree roots.   Trees have a greater variety of roots than do other vascular plants. The feeder or fine roots are similar to those of herbaceous vascular plants. Stress roots form in some species when a plant suffers from water or nutrient stress. Adventitious roots may form in external tissues while normally lateral roots form only in the pericycle tissue of the stele. Adventitious roots may form in stem tissue as well as on existing roots. Roots may grow down, sideways, or even up along tree trunks. These directions are determined by a transducing system that converts physical signals into physiological signals that control the morphological and anatomical development of the roots. The main locus of gravity perception is thought to reside in the root cap. Roots of several forms may be present in a single individual. For example, mangroves can have feeder roots for absorption, stilt roots for support, and pneumatophores for aeration.

Buttress roots

Buttress roots are aerial extensions of lateral surface roots and form only in certain species. Buttress roots stabilize the tree, especially in shallow saturated soils, thereby resisting toppling. They are common in certain tropical trees of wet lowland environments but with few exceptions, such as bald cypress swamps, are largely absent in temperate trees. A diverse number of tree families and species develop buttress roots, suggesting that they are induced by the environment and are of some adaptive advantage.

Buttress roots are characterized by thin (about 8–10 centimetres [3–4 inches] thick) planklike extensions from the tree trunk. They may be as much as 3 metres tall and extend 3 metres laterally from the base of the tree. The radial diameter of the individual vessel elements and the amount of vessel area per unit cross-sectional area of xylem are reduced in buttress roots. The amount of cell-wall area is correspondingly increased, although the individual cell walls are somewhat thinner.

Buttresses tend to be more prevalent on the windward side of the tree and thus function in tension resistance. Height growth is diminished whenever buttressing is developed, suggesting that the carbon resources of the tree are reallocated as a response to environmental conditions. There may be secondary effects of buttress roots, such as retardation of water flow around the tree base, thereby preventing nutrients and nutrient-rich litter from washing away. It is unlikely that buttresses provide aeration, as they have different anatomy from pneumatophores and as some species have both buttresses and pneumatophores—e.g., Pterocarpus officinalis and bald cypress, Taxodium distichum.

Pneumatophores are specialized root structures that grow out from the water surface and facilitate the aeration necessary for root respiration. They are found on many mangrove species (e.g., Avicennia germinans and Laguncularia raecemosa), bald cypresses, cotton (tupelo) gum (Nyssa aquatica), and other hydrophytic trees. Red mangroves (Rhizophora mangle) have stilt roots that function in both support and aeration.

Hydrophytic trees have various modifications that facilitate their survival and growth in the aqueous environment. Some species produce a high frequency of lenticels on the bark that facilitate gas exchange. Others exhibit greater permeation of oxygen through the bark and into the cambium at lower oxygen concentrations. Hydrophytic trees often have more intercellular spaces in their tissues to promote aeration of their roots. Some trees produce

adventitious water roots near the waterline after flooding conditions develop. The new roots produced have altered structure (surface sealing layers, more loosely packed cells in cortex, and poorly developed endodermis). Such roots are said to show acclimation. Hydrophytic species are often adapted to anaerobic metabolism and can endure the often toxic by-products of this process (e.g., ethyl alcohol and lactic acid). Some trees in the Amazon survive several months of total inundation each year.

Root hairs form some distance back from the root tip and mature at about the point where the first primary xylem cells mature. A type of transfer cell and supplied with many protoplasmic connections to the adjacent root cells, root hairs increase the absorbing area of the roots at minimal carbon cost and can penetrate finer pores in the soil. Phosphorus uptake is directly correlated with length and frequency of root hairs. The roots of some species form associations with certain fungi called mycorrhizae. These fungal root associations also facilitate phosphorous uptake. Root hairs are less abundant on southern pines than on associated hardwoods in the southeastern United States, and this is thought to give the hardwoods a competitive edge in some cases.

TREE LINES

As one proceeds northward or as the elevation increases, the height of the trees gradually decreases while the spacing between them increases until a point is finally reached where the trees give way to tundra. This is called the tree line.

Arctic tree lines form a ring around the Arctic Ocean and extend southward to Labrador and westward around the Bering Sea from Alaska to Siberia. In oceanic regions Arctic tree lines are characterized by birches, while in the interior Arctic larches and spruce are more common. Firs are present in some Arctic tree lines. Antarctic tree lines are more abrupt as very little tundra vegetation exists in these areas.

The shape of trees also changes with altitude. Broad-leaved trees are more common at lower altitudes, as at the base of a mountain. These tree forms gradually give way to pines and sometimes birches as the altitude increases. Spruce and fir tend to dominate forests at the highest elevations. Local conditions determine whether Alpine timberlines arise gradually or abruptly as the altitude in-

Tree forms and altitude

From W.M. Harlow and E.S. Harrar, Textbook of Dendrology, 5th ed. (1969) McGraw-Hill, Inc., New York City

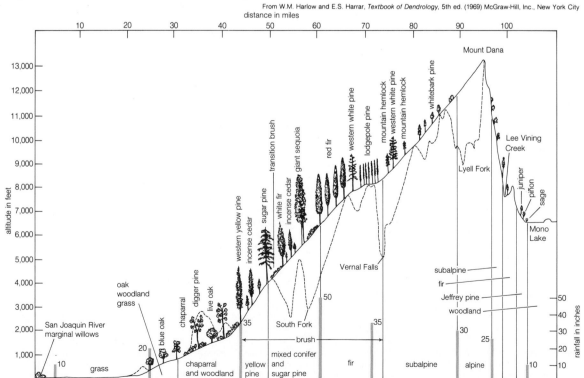

Figure 5: Profile of the Sierra Nevada showing the effects of elevation and rainfall on forest distribution.

creases. Abrupt timberlines give way to Alpine meadow and then boulder fields, followed by bare rock with life forms limited to lichens.

The transition to the treeless condition is more commonly gradual. Initially in a closed, tightly spaced forest (forest line), the spacing between trees widens rapidly as tree height decreases (the kampf zone). This zone gives way to a region of low twisted and stunted trees called the krummholz. Together, the kampf zone and the krummholz constitute the transition zone. The end of the krummholz marks the tree line.

The same woody species may continue upward in elevation as prostrate shrubs, especially in sheltered nooks and crannies. The zones are uneven because these kinds of local shelter conditions may extend the limits of each zone. Forests may extend along ridges where squirrels and other nut gatherers have stored seed, so each situation may have endemic differences from any assumed model of tree line.

The increase in spacing after forest line is correlated with a decline in the quality of the habitat, as the temperature decreases, the wind increases, and the soil becomes increasingly impoverished. As the energy content of the ecosystem decreases, the diversity of organisms in the ecosystem diminishes.

Trees that are more widely spaced have a greater chance of survival because a greater percentage of the stem is covered with foliage, and this foliage receives more light and heat. In addition, there is less competition in the roots for the available nutrients in the soil. The isolated condition, however, makes the trees more susceptible to wind damage, snow blast, and ice damage.

Tree form has a genetic component because some species are able to exist in an erect form where other species cannot. An example of this is limber pine (*Pinus flexilis*) and bristlecone pine (*P. aristata*), both of which are found in the Colorado Rocky Mountains in the United States. These species form erect trees where Engelmann spruce (*Picea engelmanni*) and Alpine fir (*Abies lasiocarpa*) can exist only as prostrate forms. One reason lies in the pines' greater resistance to winter desiccation damage at high elevation owing to the thick coating of wax and cuticle on the surface of their needles. These species differences can result in double timberlines, where one tree species or group of species forms a tree line at a different elevation from another species or group of species.

Temperature and altitude Low temperature is the main arbiter of timberlines. This is dramatically apparent in the higher timberlines that can be observed on the sunnier slopes of a mountain. Low temperature is also the reason for the increase in tree line in interior mountains with warmer summers, such as the Rocky Mountains (about 3,000–3,350 metres), as opposed to coastal mountains, such as the White Mountains of New Hampshire, U.S. (approximately 1,400 metres), where the summers are cooler and cloudier.

Another manifestation of the heat balance effect is the increase in altitudinal tree lines as latitude decreases in the Northern Hemisphere from the subarctic to the subtropical. In general, tree form is possible wherever the mean temperature for the month of July is equal to or greater than 10° C. A somewhat better fit can be obtained using the point where the daily maximum temperature is greater than or equal to 11.1° C during the growing season.

The low temperatures in the Alpine environment stem from the decrease in temperature with elevation: warm air rises; as it does so, it expands and cools. The expansion requires work (in the form of heat) to be expended in the process, and temperature drops. In general, there is a 1° C drop in temperature for every 100-metre rise in elevation. However, the temperature drop varies somewhat with conditions on individual mountains (*e.g.,* wet versus dry mountain ranges). Larger mountain massifs also show a smaller drop in temperature with increase in altitude. This is because the air mass impinging on the large massif must rise over the entire structure and the air mass does not cool as much as when only a portion of it rises over a smaller or more isolated mountain. As a consequence, timberlines are higher on a larger mountain range for a given latitude, location, and climate. Nevertheless, other factors such as radiation, moisture, cloudiness, wind, snow

and snow blast, ice, and physiography affect tree lines to various degrees.

Trees that grow at high elevations are adapted to this environment. The high-elevation environment is characterized by higher light intensity (when clear) and proportion of ultraviolet radiation, lower absolute humidity (which favours water loss) and carbon dioxide content, frequent high winds, and greater daily temperature fluctuations, radiation of heat out into space (especially at night), and precipitation (although some alpine areas are subject to drought at times). Any or all of these factors can interact to bring about unique formations. For example, cold air drainages at the crest of valleys can cause a local depression of timberline. The reason low temperatures affect timberline is that they slow biological processes, which decreases the production of dry matter, a condition that is exacerbated by the shortened growing season. As a result, fewer of the cells, tissues, and storage molecules that are needed for annual growth and reproduction are formed.

Adaptations The cell walls of the vascular tissues that carry water to the living parts of a tree are encrusted with lignin to provide mechanical strength to the walls of the vessels. This complex structure is very important in resisting wind damage. If the growing season is shortened, the optimum amount of cellulose formation and lignification may not be achieved. In fact, the amount of vascular tissue formed may itself be inadequate.

The covering layers of the tree surface also are important in resisting environmental stresses. The biotic stress and inadequate energy production and allocation that occur when temperature is sufficiently low may impair the optimum development of these superficial layers and increase the vulnerability of the tree.

Seed production requires energy reserves that may not normally be available each year. The interval between good seed years increases with elevation and latitude. It is another important aspect of survival in the cold at high elevation, although species at high elevation compensate for this somewhat by relying more heavily on asexual reproduction. Thus, the tree line may be considered to be an equilibrium space between the forces of regeneration upward and mortality downward.

Cloudiness can lower tree lines because it decreases the photosynthesis-to-respiration ratio, causing a carbon deficit. For example, tree line is lower on the warmer, cloudier western coast of Scotland than it is on the colder, clearer eastern coast because on the west the cloudy weather limits photosynthesis while the warmer temperatures promote respiration.

The factors that limit tree growth at high elevation and extreme latitude indirectly promote longevity, as in the case of the Great Basin bristlecone pine (*P. longaeva*). The factors involved are smaller tree size, slower growth rate (possibly mediated by lower night temperatures), larger allocation of carbon to roots as opposed to tops (stems and leaves), cold hardiness, efficient use of water, more reliance on asexual reproduction, and fewer pathogens in the environment.

Some long-lived trees, such as the Douglas fir (*Pseudotsuga menziesii*), have been found in lava beds, suggesting that reduced competition and the presence of fewer pathogens in this environment might be factors in the long life spans. This harsh environment probably also reduces the developmental rate, which is correlated with increased life span in some species.

The major difference between subarctic and subalpine timberline environments is that the subalpine environment has greater light intensity and more ultraviolet light, less variation in the length of the day, lower carbon dioxide, and more daily temperature variation. The subalpine also has higher precipitation, especially snow, but the soil is generally drier because of better soil drainage and the mountainous topography. The factors that are common to both are the short growing season, low temperatures, and high winds. Mountains located in arid areas may show additional complexity along elevational gradients owing to marked changes in both water availability and temperature. In the southwestern United States, small piñon pines may grow at the base of mountains, and, as elevation increases, temperature decreases along with water stress. Tree height increases as the larger ponderosa pines dominate; these in turn may give way to Douglas fir. At higher altitudes, spruce and fir predominate, and they decrease in height with altitude, forming tree lines at the upper limits.

ADAPTATIONS

The environmental factors affecting trees are climate, soils, topography, and biota. Each species of tree adapts to these factors in an integrated way—that is, by evolving specific subpopulations adapted to the constraints of their particular environments. As discussed above, the major factor is the decrease in temperature with increasing elevation or extremes in latitude. Each subpopulation adapts to this by modifying the optimum temperature at which the all-important process of photosynthesis takes place.

Many tree species that survive in unfavourable habitats actually grow better in more favourable habitats if competition is eliminated. Such trees have a low threshold for competition but are very tolerant of extremes. For example, the black spruce (*Picea mariana*) is found in bogs and mountaintops in the northeastern United States but cannot compete well with other trees, such as red spruce (*Picea rubens*), on better sites. Consequently, in the White Mountains of New Hampshire in the northeastern United States, red spruce is found at the base of the mountains and black spruce at the top, with some development of subspecies populations (hybridization) at intermediate elevations.

Competi-
tion

Competition within a species (and in some cases genus) is often most intense because the individuals compete for the same environmental resources. Since trees are unable to move in search of resources, competition for available space and resources can be important. Competition above ground centres on light, space, and symbionts (largely pollinators), while that below ground is over water, space, nutrients, and symbionts (microorganisms such as mycorrhizae and nitrogen-fixers).

The ability of a tree to coexist with other members of the species in a given habitat may depend on the diversification of the space and resources they require. In extreme environments, such as are found on mountains and the subarctic, survival depends on the physical factors of the environment, whereas in more moderate habitats biotic factors become increasingly important. Flexibility and efficiency of resource use then become more important in determining survival and reproduction.

The concept of species niche relates the species or individual to the totality of its environment. The niche for a plant species is the set of environmental conditions that permits a given species to exist based on its morphological, anatomical, cytological, and physiological capacities.

For a given species there are limiting values for each environmental factor; these define the niche. Habitats change over time, but changes in species are not as rapid or drastic as those of habitats. In addition to changes that take place within chronological time, tree species and forests change during developmental time—for example, seedlings of trees such as white pine (*Pinus strobus*) are generally more tolerant of shade than are the adult forms of the species.

Competition is actually more severe under limiting conditions than it is under toxic conditions. Under toxic pollution levels, the environment may be limited by the surplus of a single toxic element or condition and the species least susceptible will be the most successful. Plants that can most fully exploit a habitat tend to dominate it, and, since trees have evolved trunks that allow them access to the aerial environment and massive root systems that permit them to infiltrate the subterranean environment, they dominate much of the biosphere. Trees are at a disadvantage only in drier areas, in Alpine and Arctic environments, and in competition with humans.

The number of species of trees within a forest tends to increase as they approach the Equator. This is due to various environmental factors, including decreased stress in terms of light, temperature, water, and length of the growing season. The productivity and heterogeneity of the habitats also increase in these situations. Moreover, the frequency of disturbance (*e.g.,* storms, floods, landslides, and fires) is greater, as is the response to the disturbance, which also contributes to species diversity in tropical forests.

Trees may respond to their environment in a number of ways, chiefly by morphological and physiological adaptations as well as by the reallocation of available nutrients and water to those organs in most need. There are usually both genotypic and phenotypic aspects to such physiological and morphological adaptations. Moreover, there is a dynamic equilibrium between genetic stability (the capacity of individuals to produce offspring adapted to the parental environment) and genetic variability (the capacity to produce offspring with requirements that are different from those of their parents). Genetic variability produces some offspring with a greater potential to adapt to new habitats and also to changes induced by the disturbance of the original habitat.

Phenotypic
plasticity

Phenotypic plasticity is a way in which organisms can harmonize the conflict between stability and variability—that is, the way in which the morphological expression of a given genotype varies under different environmental conditions. While forest species must maintain present adaptiveness to the current environment, the future of the species may depend on sufficient variability to adapt to future environments. Further, changes in the ability of a species to utilize the available resources of the environment can have major effects on coexisting species.

The ultimate question of tree ecophysiology is why does a certain tree grow where it does. The complex answer includes the following elements: its seed or source; its adaptation to survival, growth, and reproduction in that particular habitat; and its ability to compete favourably with other inhabitants of the habitat.

The growth, structure, and composition of a forest are a function of the intensity and quality of light streaming into it. Trees partition the light resource in time and space.

The time dimensions include seasonal, successional, and developmental time. In seasonal time, the time of leafing out and leaf fall and the time of flowering, seed formation, and germination are considered. In successional time, clearings in forests initiate growth in preexisting seedlings and new germinants, which causes progressive changes in the distribution of light and results in changes in species composition over time. In developmental time, changes take place in the physiology and morphology of the tree with age.

Leaves are the primary collectors of solar energy and the organ most directly affected by the environment. They also are the most responsive to environmental signals. Leaf properties are determined by light, nutrients, moisture, and the space-time parameters.

A petiole attaches the leaf to the stem and contains vascular tissue that provides a connection from the stem to permit sap to enter the leaf and the products of photosynthesis (carbohydrates) to be transported from the leaf to the rest of the plant. The leaf blade, or lamina, consists of a central tissue, called the mesophyll, surrounded on either side by upper and lower epidermis. Patterns of the leaf veins are often characteristic of plant taxons and may include one main vein and various orders of smaller veins, the finest veinlets infiltrating the mesophyll from which they collect photosynthates. The cells of the mesophyll contain the bulk of the chlorophyll, a molecule that converts light energy into the chemical energy of carbohydrate molecules, within minute membrane-bound sacs called chloroplasts.

In most angiosperm trees only the lower epidermis contains pores, called stomates, where gas exchange with the atmosphere takes place; carbon dioxide is taken up and water vapour and oxygen are given off. The epidermis is covered with wax and a layer of polyester material called the cuticle. These tend to restrict water loss from the stomates and protect them from desiccation. Conifer leaves have less structural diversity. They contain an epidermis with wax and an underlying cuticle.

The epidermis may have one or more thick-walled layers called the hypodermis beneath it. The sunken stomates are generally located on all surfaces and the cavity is filled with wax. The vascular tissue is embedded in a layer of spongy cells called the transfusion tissue, which is thought to facilitate water distribution to the mesophyll.

Leaf adaptations The leaves of trees have a number of adaptive features, including size, number, location, and chlorophyll content of chloroplasts; size, number, and structure of stomates; thickness of epicuticular wax and cuticle; leaf stiffness and strength; and the size, number, and spacing of veins.

Trees of dry (xeric), moist (mesic), and wet (hydric) habitats have leaves that are specifically adapted structurally and functionally to these habitats. Dryness and cold induce some similar specializations because cold conditions are often desiccating conditions as well. Tree leaves of mesic environments have a set of traits intermediate between xeric and hydric leaves.

Under xeromorphic conditions, the leaf has adopted features that decrease water loss. Leaf area that is exposed to the ambient air is reduced, although the ratio of internal surface to external surface area is high (leaf volume). The cells themselves are small and the thickness of the wall is increased, as is the amount of fibrous tissue in the leaf, making the surface of the leaf rather hard. There is a larger number of veins. The epidermis is thick-walled and hairy, often with additional hypodermis and covered by a cuticle and epicuticular wax. Stomates are smaller, more closely spaced, sunken below the leaf surface, and covered with wax or hairs or both. Salt glands and water-storage cells are present in some species.

Tree leaves of supermoist environments, on the other hand, are less concerned with water loss. Large air spaces are present within the loosely packed mesophyll, and the cuticle is reduced, as is the number and frequency of veins. The stomates are larger but less closely spaced and either level with the leaf surface or elevated above it. The amount of fibrous tissue is reduced, and the hypodermis is absent. Water-secreting glands may be present. The walls of the epidermis are thinner.

Trees can reach or approach adaptation to a specific habitat by different combinations of morphological, anatomical, and physiological traits. The more closely the trees use the same subset of adaptive features, the more strongly they compete with each other for habitat resources. For this reason, trees of the same species compete more strongly with each other on a site than they do with members of other species.

Reaction wood In branches, reaction tissue forms where its inherent reaction force (pushing in the case of conifers and pulling in the case of hardwoods) will restore the intrinsic growth direction (equilibrium, or initial, position). This defines the locus of reaction tissue irrespective of the orientation of the structure with respect to gravity. Thus, reaction tissue is an adaptive morphogenetic phenomenon.

Many plant tissues show physiological and anatomical reactions due to physical displacement, but the response in wood is more permanent, more visible, and of greater economic importance since reaction wood has in-built stresses that limit its use for most building projects, such as housing and furniture.

In the lower main stem of conifers, the reaction wood, called compression wood, forms on the lower side with respect to gravity and exerts a pushing force in the upward direction. In hardwood trees the reaction wood is called tension wood and forms on the upper side of the lower trunk and exerts a contractive force that tends to pull the tree toward the upright position. In compression wood there is greater growth on the lower side of the stem where the compression wood forms; this results in an oval cross section of the tree near the ground. This type of growth is called eccentric. In hardwoods there is generally less eccentricity associated with tension wood, but the annual rings may be wider. (The names tension wood and compression wood are misleading since they were assigned when the phenomena were thought to be due to such forces in the wood. Only later was it realized that the phenomenon was morphogenetic in nature and that tension or compression wood could form in wood that was either in tension or compression.)

While reaction wood in the main stem occurs primarily in response to vertical displacement, reaction wood in branches acts against gravity to maintain the angle between the branch and the main axis. For example, the terminal shoots of pines exhibit negative geotropism throughout the growing season, and little or no compression wood is formed in the terminal shoots (although it is usually present in the laterals). In other species, like the Canadian, or eastern, hemlock (*Tsuga canadensis*), the terminal shoots droop at the beginning of the season and gradually turn upward as the growing season progresses. During the drooping phase, the terminal (leader) is extremely flexible and sways freely in the wind. As the season progresses, the leader gradually increases in rigidity and, under the influence of compression wood formation, becomes erect to a vertical position. The rigidity is enhanced by the fact that compression wood is more highly lignified than regular wood. Concomitantly, the cellulose content is reduced.

In conifers a single cell type (the tracheid) is specialized for both conduction of sap and support. In compression wood the tracheid becomes quite round in cross section, forming intercellular spaces between neighbouring tracheids. Such spaces are not present in noncompression wood except in some species of junipers. The compression wood tracheids are so heavily lignified that the wood appears visibly reddish to the naked eye. The tracheids are thicker-walled, have spiral grooves along the length of the wall, and are shorter than noncompression wood tracheids.

In hardwoods the fibres are predominantly affected, although vessel diameter and frequency are generally reduced. The fibres of hardwoods develop a specialized layer in the cell wall—the so-called gelatinous layer—that is almost completely devoid of lignin, although in the other layers the fibre wall is lignified. The gelatinous layer is primarily composed of cellulose and hemicellulose. It is rubbery in texture and does not cut cleanly. Thus, tension wood fibres may be visible to the naked eye on a sawed board as a fuzzy surface. The lumber sawed from this wood will warp, cup, and exhibit much greater longitudinal shrinkage than nontension wood.

(Graeme Pierce Berlyn)

BIBLIOGRAPHY. Information on trees is included in general botanical reference works such as LIBERTY HYDE BAILEY et al., *Hortus Third: A Concise Dictionary of the Cultivated Plants in the United States and Canada* (1976); and D.J. MABBERLEY, *The Plant-Book* (1987); and in the more specific works by BAYARD HORA (ed.), *The Oxford Encyclopedia of Trees of the World* (1981); and UNITED STATES DEPT. OF AGRICULTURE, *Trees* (1949), part of the department's *Yearbook of Agriculture* series. Tree types and distribution are presented in E. LUCY BRAUN, *Deciduous Forests of Eastern North America* (1950, reissued 1985); WILLIAM B. CRITCHFIELD and ELBERT L. LITTLE, JR., *Geographic Distribution of the Pines of the World* (1966); W. DALLIMORE and A. BRUCE JACKSON, *A Handbook of Coniferae and Ginkgoaceae*, 4th ed., rev. by S.G. HARRISON (1967); THOMAS S. ELIAS, *The Complete Trees of North America: Field Guide and Natural History* (1980); SAMUEL J. RECORD and ROBERT W. HESS, *Timbers of the New World* (1943, reissued 1972); and FREDERIC L. STEELE, *At Timberline: A Nature Guide to the Mountains of the Northeast* (1982), on identifying New England Alpine flora and fauna. Discussions of the structure and growth of trees include F. HERBERT BORMANN and GRAEME BERLYN (eds.), *Age and Growth Rate of Tropical Trees* (1981); WILLIAM M. HARLOW et al., *Textbook of Dendrology: Covering the Important Forest Trees of the United States and Canada*, 7th ed. (1991); THEODORE T. KOZLOWSKI, PAUL J. KRAMER, and STEPHEN G. PALLARDY, *The Physiological Ecology of Woody Plants* (1991); DONALD CULROSS PEATTIE, *A Natural History of Western Trees* (1953, reissued 1991), and a companion volume, *A Natural History of Trees of Eastern and Central North America* (1950, reissued 1991); W. TRANQUILLINI, *Physiological Ecology of the Alpine Timberline: Tree Existences at High Altitudes with Special Reference to the European Alps* (1979); BRAYTON F. WILSON, *The Growing Tree*, rev. ed. (1984); and MARTIN H. ZIMMERMANN, CLAUD L. BROWN, and MELVIN T. TYREE, *Trees: Structure and Function* (1971). A.J. PANSHIN and CARL DE ZEEUW, *Textbook of Wood Technology: Structure, Identification, Properties, and Uses of the Commercial Woods of the United States and Canada*, 4th ed. (1980), focuses on economic aspects.

(Thomas H. Everett/Lillian M. Weber/Graeme Pierce Berlyn)

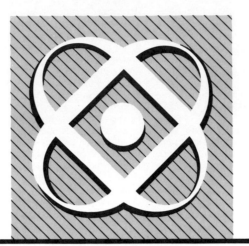

Science

Year in

Review

Contents

The Year in Science: An Overview

by Robert P. Crease

The past year's most dramatic science-related announcement took place on April 23, 1992. That morning, at the Ramada Renaissance Hotel in Washington, D.C., George Smoot, a 47-year-old physicist from Lawrence Berkeley Laboratory, Berkeley, Calif., conveyed to a packed auditorium of scientists word of the first results of the Cosmic Background Explorer (COBE) satellite. Onboard instruments, Smoot said, had detected minute temperature fluctuations in different regions of the sky. The irregularities were tiny—on the order of a few millionths of a degree—but Smoot's team had concluded that they were signature traces of the same process that had produced the present uneven structure of the universe, with its intricate networks of galaxies, supergalaxies, and clusters of supergalaxies.

"What we have found is evidence for the birth of the universe and its evolution," Smoot said. "Are we so fortunate that we live in a time when we can develop the theory of creation?" Other physicists described the discovery as the "missing link in the evolution of large structure in the universe," the "Holy Grail of cosmology," and "the most fundamental of all discoveries." In an offhand remark that was echoed by some but criticized by others who worried about encouraging misconceptions, Smoot said, "If you're religious, it's like looking at God."

Smoot was not alone during the year in appealing to the divine in connection with fundamental work, a fact that raises intriguing questions about the meaning of "fundamental" in science. What makes one discovery more fundamental than others, and why do scientists sometimes find themselves compelled to describe such discoveries with religious vocabulary?

1992: an epochal year? Certain years are remembered for epochal discoveries: 1492, for instance, sticks in the mind for Christopher Columbus' voyage to America and the dethroning, among Europeans, of an ancient view of the structure of the planet, while 1572 is another key date on the scientific timeline because it was the year a supernova exploded in the constellation Cassiopeia, overturning, again among Europeans, the Aristotelian view of the immutability of the heavens. Smoot's remark suggests that 1992 may be similarly epochal and that decades hence other scientific developments of the year will

ROBERT P. CREASE is an Assistant Professor of Philosophy at the State University of New York at Stony Brook and Historian at the Brookhaven National Laboratory, Upton, N.Y.

seem virtually insignificant in comparison. If so, an argument could be made for devoting this overview article—indeed, the entire Yearbook—to the COBE work and its implications. How could there be more fundamental work?

But a reader of "The Year in Review" soon discovers that this was a road not taken. The COBE results occupy only a part of the Astronomy article, which itself is only one of 42 articles about different fields. Moreover, many other developments of 1992 also seem fundamental: the first injection, at the University of Michigan Medical Center, of a genetically altered gene directly into a human patient; the discovery of a possible (though much more remote than initially thought) collision between a comet and the Earth; the beginning of a National Aeronautics and Space Administration (NASA)-funded search for life elsewhere in the universe (which began on October 12, the 500th anniversary of Columbus' arrival); the 53-year-old Orchard Park, N.Y., woman who gave birth to her own (implanted) grandchild (her daughter's child); the finding that infants potentially can establish close emotional ties to many caregivers rather than just two; the treaties for the protection of the environment concluded at the Rio de Janeiro "Earth Summit"; and the Pontifical Academy of Sciences' retraction of Galileo's condemnation after more than 350 years. Each of these developments, in a different way, is fundamental.

What, then, is "fundamental" science? Most scientists, it is fair to say, would prefer to do fundamental science if given the choice, and few admit to doing nonfundamental science when filling out funding applications. A scientist I know at one national laboratory has a classification scheme that runs like this: "Fundamental" discoveries are those that are made in your own field and that cost a lot of money. "Pivotal" discoveries are those that cost a lot of money in another field but that have implications for your own. "Headline-grabbing" discoveries are those that cost a lot of money and are in another field but have no implications for your own. "Bread-and-butter" discoveries are inexpensive ones inside and "tenure-getters" are inexpensive ones outside your field. Discoveries outside your field that you do not understand are "flashy" if expensive and "interesting" if not.

Drollery aside, it would be less easy than it looks to pick out the "fundamental" developments of the past year in science. *Fundamental* comes from the

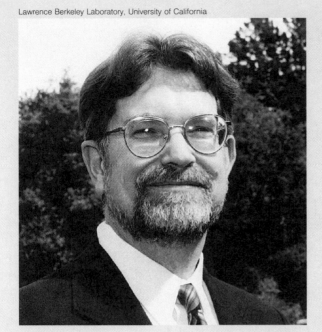

George Smoot, a physicist at Lawrence Berkeley Laboratory in Berkeley, Calif., announced in April 1992 that the Cosmic Background Explorer satellite had detected minute temperature fluctuations in different regions of the sky, "evidence for the birth of the universe and its evolution."

Latin *fundus,* or "bottom"; a fundamental discovery is one that is "first" or "bottommost." But something can be first or bottommost in many ways: logically, temporally, or epistemologically; that is, something can be fundamental because it relates to first principles, first things, or the first conditions by which something is known.

First principles. A discovery is fundamental if it has to do with the first principles of the world. Science is committed to the assumption that a small number of basic principles or phenomena underlie the seemingly infinite forms of nature, and progress in science consists of the attempt to discover these principles and phenomena, their relationships, and how subordinate principles and phenomena spring from them. This implies a hierarchy or inverted pyramid, with what is at the base or bottom determinative of the structure of what is above. In this sense of the term, the fundamental is, as it were, the blueprint of the existing universe.

In biology, for instance, fundamental work of the past year would include research on the first principles of life. Obvious examples of this include the complete mapping of two human chromosomes; the Y chromosome was mapped by scientists at the Whitehead Institute for Biomedical Research, Cambridge, Mass., while chromosome 21 was mapped by an international team of scientists from Europe, the United States, and Japan.

In astronomy, fundamental research into first principles includes investigation of the key parameters of the universe. During the past year, for instance, several different groups of astronomers in the U.K. and the U.S. began measurements of the Hubble Constant (which, like the space telescope, was named for astronomer Edwin Hubble), the difficult-to-measure but fundamental figure that specifies the rate at which the universe is expanding or contracting; their results differed widely.

In physics, a clear example of fundamental research is provided by study of the Higgs particle, thought to be responsible for particles having the mass they do. While the Higgs remains unfound (its discovery is one main aim of the Superconducting Super Collider), important theoretical work was done during recent months on the mechanism by which it may operate.

During the year *Science* magazine devoted a special section of one issue to "Large Scale Measurements," which included measurements of the Hubble Constant, gravitational waves (ripples in space-time), space geodesy (concerning measuring the separating of remote points on the Earth's surface), and changes in the Earth's atmosphere. All of these fall under this definition of fundamental research.

Is any science intrinsically more fundamental than others? This is a standard question addressed by philosophers of science. Physics, some have argued, is more basic than molecular biology because the basic units studied in the latter field are composed of units studied in the former; molecular biology is more basic than genetics for the same reason; and genetics is similarly more basic than psychology or sociology. If this were true, there would be a tyranny of a small number of sciences over all the others, fundamentally speaking. The philosophical project of reducing one field to another ultimately fails, for practical and theoretical reasons, but physicists, unsurprisingly, often assert its truth anyway. Steven Weinberg, a Nobel laureate in physics, claimed as much in an article in the *New York Times* last year, but he was merely following an old tradition among physicists. Ernest Rutherford, the British physicist and Nobel laureate who discovered the atomic nucleus, once went so far as to say, in jocular fashion, that physics is the only true or fundamental science and that all the rest are just "stamp collecting."

According to a deeply ingrained Western tradition, the basic essences of things were brought into being and are known by God. Small wonder, then, that scientists who work on first principles often describe their work, sometimes despite themselves, with divine imagery. In an amusing book published in 1992 entitled *The God Particle,* by physicist and Nobel laureate Leon Lederman with Dick Teresi, the authors remark on the frequency with which science books

279

for a general audience invoke God and then criticize and condemn the practice ("Physics is not religion. If it were, we'd have a much easier time raising money"). Nevertheless, the authors themselves succumb to the tendency not only in the book's title but also at its finale, in the form of a concluding section entitled "Obligatory God Ending." The "God particle" refers to the Higgs boson, the sought-after basic principle of mass; at one point the authors quote a passage from "The Very New Testament," describing a moment soon after Creation when the Lord's "tried and true agent," the Higgs, causes energy to grow massive and beget particles. The Higgs appears to be the single most important piece still outstanding of physicists' current blueprint of nature. If it is found, the book suggests, a view of the fundamental blueprint of the universe rivaled only by that of its Maker shall have been acquired.

Another book published in 1992 by a Nobel laureate in physics, *Dreams of a Final Theory* by Stephen Weinberg, contained a penultimate chapter entitled "What About God?" Weinberg remarked that "if there were anything we could discover in nature that would give us some special insight into the handiwork of God, it would have to be the final laws of nature"—but went on to add that he himself found no indications of godly presence. My point, however, is that when speaking of first principles and final theories, mention of the divine is almost inevitable, even for unbelievers.

What came first. A second sense in which a discovery can be fundamental is if it has to do with the most primordial form of something. What came first, after all, begat what is—the child that fathered the adult. This is a much different sense of fundamental

from the one just discussed. For instance, whereas what is fundamental to human life in the first sense described above is the basic organs and processes of life, what is fundamental to human life in this second sense is the embryo and early evolutionary stages. What is fundamental to the universe in the first sense is the basic particles and fields, and what is fundamental in this second sense is the history of the Earth, Sun, solar system, Galaxy, and (most fundamentally) the universe itself. The fundamental, in this sense, is the earliest.

As an example of this second sense, paleontologists in the Argentine badlands found during the past year a 225 million-year-old fossil of a dog-sized reptile with primitive features, named "Eoraptor." This discovery shed light on the earliest stages of the evolutionary tree of dinosaurs, appearing to confirm conjectures of a single common ancestor for all such creatures. In another case British scientists studying fossils of the wormlike conodont from Estonia, Greenland, and Britain found that the appearance of vertebrates, a crucial evolutionary benchmark, took place 40 million years earlier than had been previously believed. Also, various groups of astronomers, thanks to the Hubble Space Telescope, began to study early stages in the growth of our Galaxy, concluding that its adolescence was a troubled one marked by violent conflicts with nearby peers, conflicts that left deep marks on its matured form. Finally, and most fundamentally in this sense of the word, there was the work of Smoot's team, illuminating processes very close to the creation of the universe itself.

Cosmologists who study the early universe clearly have a lock on the bottommost part of this pyramid. Life on Earth, the Earth itself, the Sun, the solar

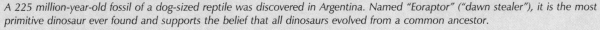

A 225 million-year-old fossil of a dog-sized reptile was discovered in Argentina. Named "Eoraptor" ("dawn stealer"), it is the most primitive dinosaur ever found and supports the belief that all dinosaurs evolved from a common ancestor.

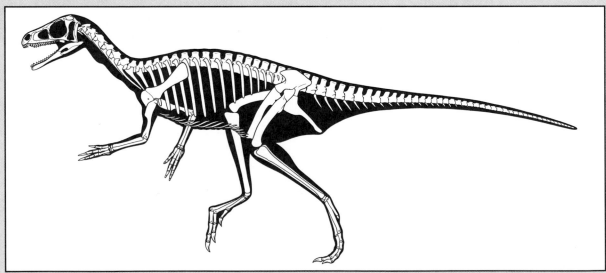

system, and even our Galaxy are late developments in the history of the universe. In this sense of fundamental, even the great Lord Rutherford himself was a stamp collector, because he occupied himself with only those johnny-come-lately (cosmologically speaking) entities that the physicists call "elementary" particles.

In this second sense of fundamental, the presence of divine imagery comes as no surprise, for the beginning of the cosmos, according to Western tradition, was God's doing. While it is unclear how many cosmologists believe in God, or even whether this is a relevant question, what is clear is that nobody has any other answer for what happened prior to the earliest segment of the history of the universe studied by cosmologists. As Lederman and Teresi wrote, "Only God knows what happened at the Very Beginning (and so far She hasn't let on)." Of four symposia at the annual meeting of the American Association for the Advancement of Science in February, devoted to "Science and Religion," one was entitled "The Religious Significance of Big Bang Cosmology."

First conditions. Something can be fundamental in yet a third sense if it serves as a basic condition of knowledge. None of the grand unified theories about first principles of nature that physicists have created, and none of the grand narratives of the history of the universe that cosmologists weave, would have existed without a vast array of instruments and techniques that, in this third sense, are "bottommost" or first with respect to the knowledge that they make possible.

Without the Cosmic Background Explorer, for instance, there would have been no millionth-of-a-degree fluctuations detected, no dramatic announcement in April at the Ramada Renaissance Hotel, no worldwide headlines. COBE itself existed prior to that. It and its instruments had been at work, circling the Earth, since 1989 and had been under development for some two decades previously. Similarly, the Hubble Space Telescope, various particle accelerators, and DNA sequencing techniques, developed years and even decades ago, made it possible to pose and answer many of the questions scientists asked during the year about first principles or first things.

Instruments and techniques worked on during the year that may make possible fundamental discoveries include the Superconducting Super Collider, under construction in Texas, and the Very Long Baseline Array, an interconnected network of radio antennas that stretches from Hawaii to the Virgin Islands. Also, a team of physicists and engineers at the University of California at Los Angeles explored a technique of accelerating particles by using plasma waves; it may revolutionize not only the construction of particle accelerators but also methods of medical therapies, condensed-matter physics, and biology. Moreover,

scientific knowledge and practice is a tightly woven fabric, with each discovery and technique dependent on numerous others and also on such technologies as information transfer, energy production and dissemination, and computing capabilities. It would be impossible, therefore, to judge any one of the developments in the following articles as not potentially contributing to future basic discoveries and thus as fundamental in this third sense.

Anomalies can also be fundamental. An anomaly is a phenomenon that appears unexceptional except that it resists attempts to fit it in with conventional theory. Scientists tend to be fascinated by anomalies because they can lead to fundamental theoretical change. "The thing that doesn't fit is the thing that's most interesting," once declared physicist Richard Feynman. Several anomalies that raised this kind of interest were discovered or examined in 1992. A conference at Washington University, St. Louis, Mo., for instance, was devoted to examining puzzling "gamma ray bursters," whose origin is unknown but whose importance to understanding the structure and history of the cosmos may be central. Another anomaly studied in 1992 was the amount of neutrinos emitted by the Sun, results about which were reported by an interdisciplinary team of scientists working at an underground laboratory in Italy; these results may lead to important changes either in the existing solar model or in existing neutrino theory. Still another of the past year's anomalies was the report by Nobel laureate Samuel C.C. Ting of the discovery of several unusual sets of fragments produced by particle collisions that did not fit in with any conventional theory.

Besides instruments, techniques, and anomalies, even ordinary concepts can also be fundamental to the knowledge of nature. In 1992 a fungus and a stand of aspens challenged the concept of "individual organism" in an odd way. The fungus, an inhabitant of a forest near Crystal Falls, Mich., consisted of an unruly but not unordinary-looking sprawl of mushrooms and molds growing over rotting logs and humus. However, scientists who performed DNA tests on it announced in April that all of it was genetically identical material that must have come from a single spore thousands of years ago. If genetic uniformity is the principal feature in the definition of individual, then this mass—weighing 91,000 kg (200,000 lb) and still growing, extending over 12 ha (30 ac), albeit with small breaks in the material—was the largest known organism, larger by far than elephants, whales, and giant sequoias. This candidate, however, was soon dethroned when scientists in Colorado announced their discovery of a stand of aspen trees in Gothic Valley, weighing 6 million kg (13.2 million lb) and covering 43 ha (106 ac), that grows together, has an interconnected root sys-

Johann N. Bruhn

Mushrooms are part of a giant fungus, Armillaria bulbosa, *growing near Crystal Falls, Mich. Covering 12 ha (30 ac) and weighing 91,000 kg (200,000 lb), it is among the world's largest known organisms.*

tem, flowers and turns colors together, and is also genetically uniform—a new titleholder for "largest organism" that challenges the existing definition of "individual."

"Nature" and "the natural" is another concept of fundamental importance to science. This concept is under perennial discussion thanks to ongoing arguments about artificial insemination, embryo implantation, environmental protection, euthanasia, risk protection, the use of animals to supply hormones and organs for human beings, life-support technology, and abortion. But the already contorted discussions of this concept took a still more bizarre turn in November when a team of physicians in Germany implanted a fetus inside the body of a brain-dead mother, attempting to save the life of the fetus. Though the attempt failed and the fetus miscarried, the action hatched a storm of controversy. A spokesman from the Roman Catholic Church attacked the procedure as "unnatural," and the German Green Society called for a public discussion of whether restrictions should be put on "the scientific mania for experimentation." On the brighter side of the bizarre, Geraldine Wesolowski of Orchard Park, N.Y., received roses when she gave birth to a baby who was at once her child and her grandchild, a baby that doctors had implanted inside her as an embryo.

Thus, a wide variety of instruments, techniques, anomalies, and general concepts can also legitimately be called "fundamental" in this third sense of the term. These are the human-created conditions for the headline-making discoveries that enthusiasts often describe by using the vocabulary of the divine.

The scientific attitude. However, there is one thing still more fundamental: the scientific attitude itself. The scientific attitude can be defined as that which views objects and events in the world not as unique and singular occurrences but as exemplars of phenomena, or things that can manifest themselves under different ways in different conditions. This attitude lies bottommost in its relation to all three of the senses of fundamental discussed above and to all of the discoveries and developments found in the ensuing articles. Though understanding the scientific attitude is a less flashy undertaking than understanding the first principles, things, and conditions of science, absence of this understanding harms the practice of science.

To understand the scientific attitude would mean a greater understanding and appreciation of the process of science itself. What would be the impact of a greater understanding of it? Almost certainly there would be less tolerance of such pseudosciences as astrology and parapsychology. People would be angered to hear, as happened last year, that the Federal Office of Research Integrity declared Robert C. Gallo, the U.S. codiscoverer of the cause of AIDS, guilty of scientific misconduct (among other things, he falsely stated his relationship to the work of French researchers), but they would not think thereby that the scientific process had broken down—any more than they would think that crooked politicians who lie about their involvements in criminal activity signify the breakdown of our political system. They would understand peculiar puzzles of the scientific process, such as when, in 1964, the detection of the uniformity of background radiation was taken as confirmation of the big bang theory, while, in 1992, detection of deviations from the uniformity of background radiation was also taken as confirmation of that same theory. They would understand the kind of appeal that basic research has and why many individuals find themselves compelled to pursue it despite the possibility of more lucrative careers elsewhere. They would understand better how the marvelous, world-transforming enterprise of science can be both one cultural practice among other cultural practices, and thus subject to economic, political, psychological, and social influences, and yet also produce a measure of objectivity or independence of such influences. Such understanding would be truly fundamental.

Anthropology

New challenges, discoveries, research, and the issue of multiculturalism combined to make the past year an interesting one for anthropologists. Multiculturalism continued its evolution into a major issue of the decade. Continuing debates on the origins of *Homo sapiens* and the migration of humans into the new world also continued to demand attention. Primatologists focused on primate evolution and raised new questions about primates and humans. Applied anthropology continued to expand into new areas and onto the international scene. Despite all this activity, the overriding concern of anthropologists during the year centered on some challenges to the discipline itself.

The myth or reality of traditional anthropology. A challenge to anthropology that erupted across the discipline in 1992 posed the greatest threat yet to the holistic perspective that had become synonymous with the field. Paradoxically, while fragmentation of anthropology loomed in the United States, at Oxford, England, the move was toward the traditional approach that integrates the subfields of physical (biological) anthropology, archaeology, linguistics, and sociocultural anthropology. The challenge to this integration grew out of discussions initially focused on training and the structure of departments. The question now being considered is whether anthropology has lost its intellectual core and is on the brink of fissioning, or whether the holistic perspective remains viable.

To support their contention that anthropology was already fragmented, some anthropologists pointed to a number of trends. These included increasing specialization, intellectual isolation of subfields from one another, and threatened department breakups. These anthropologists asserted that specialization now challenges holism, which has become stagnant and morally questionable. They further argue that communication across the subfields is difficult because of the increased amount of knowledge and the lack of a common core of theories, methods, or questions linking them.

Responses by anthropologists reaffirming the traditional approach were overwhelming in number. Most anthropologists continued to believe that holism remains the essential and coveted reality that keeps anthropology honest, represents the major claim to its uniqueness, and is the source of its intellectual vigor. They suggested that to fragment the subfields would isolate them from the ideas and models that characterize them. Supporting the retention of an integrated approach, the American Anthropological Association proposed a new governance plan that would reaffirm the centrality to anthropology of the subfields.

New challenges to anthropology were also coming from the worldwide displacement of peoples. Used to studying people in particular places, anthropologists increasingly were studying people who had moved away from their primary cultures. According to Arjun Appadurai, anthropology was becoming the study of the landscape of persons with transnational loyalties in a shifting world.

New multiculturalism. As predicted, multiculturalism became an important issue of the decade. On one side of the issue, extreme pluralists advocated teaching only the history and values of the West, while extreme particularists favored teaching the origins and histories of particular ethnic groups. Anthropology could be helpful in the current discussion, but it was largely being ignored despite a long history of explaining different cultural identities without intensifying national or partisan views. The major issues of multiculturalism (culture, cultural relativism, and the interpretations of other systems of thought) are all central to anthropology.

In considering the debate some anthropologists saw a frightening return to 19th-century concepts: a romanticism blurring the distinction between race and culture; a view of non-Western cultures as stable, tradition-bound, and timeless entities; and a tendency to see other peoples as profoundly and inherently different from oneself. According to anthropologists, the real challenge of multiculturalism is to foster multiple ways of understanding cultural differences and thereby moving beyond the ethnocentrism and fears that historically have shaped countries.

Australians Mary Kalantizis and William Cope of the University of Wollongong pointed out that multiculturalism is an international concern, not simply a U.S. issue. They further declared that the developing global economic system has made the idea of "nation" less and less useful as a cultural concept. They concluded that people throughout the world must face the reality of living with diversity.

Indigenous peoples. The Human Genome Project and numerous other studies evidenced the ongoing interest of anthropology in indigenous peoples. The Human Genome Project, aimed at identifying the chromosomal locations of all human genes, promised to be a powerful tool in the study of human diversity and evolution. A Genome Diversity Component to study genetic diversity and determine how people vary from one another was added in 1992. Anthropologists from all over the world met and identified the sample and populations to be included. Because different people wanted different things, a compromise was reached that determined that 25 individuals would be selected from 400 different populations.

Archaeologists, physical anthropologists, and linguists all became involved in the "Clovis" debate during the year. At issue was the question of who

283

first occupied the New World, the "Classic Clovis," arriving across the Bering land bridge from Siberia to Alaska about 11,200 to 10,900 years ago, or a "Preclovis" group dating from 13,000 up to 100,000 years ago. In 1991 Richard MacNeish provided evidence of human occupation from Orogrande in New Mexico, dating back some 32,000 years. His evidence included handprints, bones, tools (one embedded in bone), and fire hearths. To this he added in 1992 a human hair embedded in the clay surrounding the palm print, contending that it would provide the best evidence yet for Preclovis. The human hair is to be dated and possibly used in DNA analysis.

The problems concerning the Yanomamö and the Hopis and Navajos continued during the past year. Despite agreements establishing a 176,977-sq km (68,331-sq mi) reserve for the Yanomamö, the government of Brazil still faced pressure to rescind the agreement and allow miners to continue their invasion of the area. The Hopi-Navajo land dispute resurfaced after a pact was signed transferring 200,000 ha (500,000 ac) from the Navajos to the Hopis. Concerns about 75-year leases for Navajos on the Hopi lands and on privately owned lands in the tract only further polarized the Hopi, Navajo, and non-Indian communities.

Beyond these recurring problems, Katharine Milton's report that Amazon tribes use diet as a means of establishing cultural boundaries conflicted with the prevailing notion that food availability in different parts of the forest determined dietary habits. The quincentenary celebration of the voyage of Christopher Columbus sparked conflict between those who saw him as a discoverer or explorer and those who viewed him as a despoiler of native peoples. The

conflict proved a fertile area for anthropologists interested in how ethnicity, identity, and politics become expressed in ritual events and how the different groups see their histories and identities.

Origins of modern Homo sapiens. New discoveries and challenges surfaced during the year to intensify the debate on where and when modern *Homo sapiens* evolved. On one side of the debate were the replacement theorists, who suggested an African origin for *Homo sapiens,* and on the other were the multiregional theorists, who proposed that modern humans evolved from *Homo erectus* in a number of places. The replacement theory received its biggest boost from Allan C. Wilson. On the basis of his comparative analysis of human DNA, he supported the ideas of two migrations out of Africa and a common female ancestor for *Homo sapiens* that inhabited Africa 200,000 years ago (the "mitochondrial Eve," or "Black Eve"). Alan Templeton, who first challenged the random sample, dating, and results of Wilson's study, later questioned the methods of the original research, suggesting that the researchers misapplied computer software in their analysis.

As a result of this new challenge, many anthropologists concluded that the out-of-Africa theory had been laid to rest. However, Leslie Aiello, Alison Brooks, Christopher Stringer, Maryellen Ruvolc, and others cautioned that such a prediction might be premature.

The discovery of new fossils could significantly influence the debate. Of particular significance in this regard were the discoveries in China by Li Tianyuan (Li T'ien-yüan) of the Hubei (Hupeh) Institute of Archaeology and Dennis Etler of the University of California at Berkeley, the rediscovery of a fossil by

Archaeologist Richard MacNeish stands at the entrance to Orogrande Cave in New Mexico. Handprints, bones, tools, and fire hearths found within the cave indicate that it was first occupied by humans approximately 32,000 years ago.

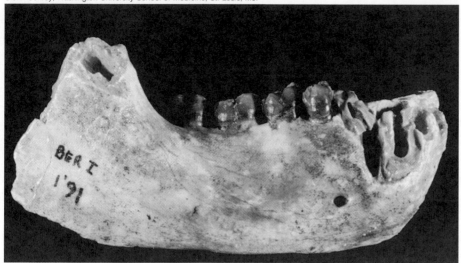

Jaw of Otavipithecus namibiensis, *a new species of hominoid, was discovered during the past year in southern Africa. Estimated to be from 12 to 14 million years old, it appeared to be the first evidence of a pre-*Australopithecus *hominoid in Africa.*

Andrew Hill and Steven Ward at the Kenya National Museum, and fossils discovered by members of a joint German-Georgian team near Tbilisi in the former Soviet republic of Georgia. If the dates for these discoveries are confirmed, they could help answer questions about the hominid exodus out of Africa.

Prehominids and primates. Primatologists reported a number of discoveries during the past year. On the basis of new fossils from China and Algeria, John G. Fleagle and K. Christopher Beard suggested that anthropoids may have come not from omomyids (extinct nocturnal primates that ate insects and fruits) or adapids (larger, diurnal eaters of plants and fruit) but from a third individual that lived in Asia as early as 50 million to 60 million years ago.

A new species of hominoid, *Otavipithecus namibiensis*, was located in southern Africa by Glenn Conroy. Dating back approximately 12 million–14 million years, the fossil could represent the first evidence of a pre-*Australopithecus* hominoid on the African continent. From Canada came reports of cranial remains discovered at Rudabanya, Hung., that could shed light on the evolutionary relationships among living hominids. The fossils tended to support the view that humans have a specific relationship with chimpanzees, an idea strongly advocated by David Begun.

Meave Leakey identified a maxilla of an apelike creature discovered in Kenya that was dated at 25 million–35 million years, the oldest hominoid found to date. From Madagascar came a report by Elwyn Simons and Laurie Godfrey on three species of hominids found in Ethiopia that could help fill in the remaining gaps in prehuman evolution. The most significant appeared to be a mandible found at Maka by Desmond Clark, Tim White, and Berhane Asfaw.

In her research during the year, Meredith Small found that primates were indiscriminate in their choice of mates. Her conclusion countered the usual belief that females prefer males of high status, fitness, or physique for fathering offspring. Reports on aspects of chimpanzee life by Jane Goodall, Irwin Bernstein, Joseph Manson, and Richard Wrangham led Frances White to propose that there may be no such thing as species-typical behavior. Muses de Waal agreed, suggesting that the ideas now being presented seemed to indicate that diversity is no longer specific to humans.

Sociocultural anthropology. A number of interesting studies were reported in the area of sociocultural anthropology. Concerning the question of height differences between males and females, Alan Rogers and Arindam Mukherjee suggested that there were many possible explanations. The researchers concluded that such a height gap could help males attract wives, could be attributed to the different roles of males and females, or could be related to nutrition. Despite the lack of agreement on the causes of the gap, most researchers agreed that the sexes were moving closer together in size.

The report of an effort to apply the natural laws of ecology to the urban environment was generating interest. To explain why different family structures exist, a team led by Jeffery Hanson looked at money as a means of converting energy in the industrial biome just as plants and animals use the Sun's energy in the Earth's biosphere. The optimal foraging theory of ecology holds that animals adopt a strategy that allows them to get the most food with as little energy as possible. Hanson suggested that people do the same in selecting the best strategy for making money. For example, people already wealthy seek to conserve their riches by having small families, while the poor have bigger families as a safety net for failure.

In another study dealing with wealth, James Ferguson reported that laws and social customs governing the exchange of different kinds of wealth in a rural Lesotho village demonstrate that degrees of wealth and poverty cannot always be objectively measured or ranked. Ferguson suggested that his study disputes such measurements because in many settings the exchange of material goods is "culturally constituted," making different kinds of wealth not comparable.

—Larry L. Naylor

Archaeology

Archaeology in the early 1990s was growing, both as a profession and as an avocation. Universities in the United States reported a substantial number of Ph.D.'s, master's, and bachelor's degrees in anthropology in 1992. The number of those degrees with archaeological specializations was high and appeared to be increasing.

Cultural resource management. A large number of archaeologists were working in "cultural resource management," which was associated with federal and state government agencies and with private or university contractors to study, preserve, and protect the Native American and historical heritage. A host of state and federal laws mandated these studies and "management" procedures before any earth-disturbing project could be undertaken on public lands. The goals of cultural resource management were to inventory and evaluate all manifestations of past human activities on public (sometimes on private) lands and to preserve in place, or through professional studies, the remains of those activities.

A remarkable amount of information about the archaeology and history of the U.S. has been gained through cultural resource management projects. In many places, such as in the Phoenix (Ariz.) Basin, most of what is now known about past cultures is based on data gathered during the archaeological study phases of large-scale development projects. Every state has many developmental projects under way at any given time, and archaeologists work with state and federal agencies to collect data on the past before dams, highways, power lines, airports, shopping malls, strip mines, pipelines, and other ground-disturbing activities are completed.

Reconstructions of the past. A survey of 1992 articles in professional journals reveals how active the field of archaeology was during the past year. Much of the work published in 1992 was directly or indirectly associated with the 500th anniversary of Columbus' voyage from Spain to the Americas. One major question that gained much popular attention was whether Columbus should be honored as a national hero or remembered as the bearer of slavery, diseases, and genocide. In this connection a thought-provoking series of essays, "Contested Pasts and the Practice of Anthropology," appeared in the December *American Anthropologist.* The general themes of the essays were calls to expand beyond the "Eurocentric viewpoint" of anthropology and archaeology in order to incorporate, listen to, contextualize, and interpret the historical perspectives and discourses of Native Americans and other "ethnic" peoples. A series of editorials, essays, articles, and book reviews dealing with similar ideas appeared throughout 1992 in *American Antiquity,* the foremost journal of U.S. archaeology.

Most archaeologists were coming to grips with these concepts, but the actual practice of archaeology had yet to formulate specific methods and techniques for putting them into practice. The next several years are expected to be exciting times as the fields of anthropology and archaeology are transformed into new, more inclusive areas of inquiry. Critics charge that this nebulous reconstruction is political, faddish, and not scientific.

Origins of agriculture. One study that attempts to examine different views of the past, especially in regard to the origins of agriculture in the American Midwest, was described in *American Anthropologist.* Douglas K. Charles of Wesleyan University, Middletown, Conn., argues that archaeologists create and interpret the past. He asks, "How do we best relate our models, as metaphors, to a presumed real past world?" Charles suggests that different models are not really in competition but, instead, may be used in conjunction with one another to provide different modes of understanding the past. For example, he reviews three current models of the origins of agricultural food production. The first, proposed by David Rindos, is strictly biological and evolutionary in approach. It proposes that evolution is predicated on three conditions: variability, differential fitness, and hereditability. This model describes the origins of agriculture as the eventual outcome of the coevolution of a mutually beneficial relationship between humans and the plants that became domesticated crops. The crux of the argument is that agriculture was not the result of an intentional set of actions by the humans that produced domesticated plants but rather the eventual outcome of a process that increased the reliance of people on certain plants at the same time that the plants became increasingly reliant on people. The model is one of a mutually beneficial feedback system, posed in terms of Darwinian evolution.

The second model Charles discusses is essentially opposite to that of Rindos. Michael Rosenberg criticizes the Rindos model for being nonintentional. He suggests that humans can direct their ability to produce innovative solutions to perceived problems. One such problem was created by population growth just prior to the advent of agriculture, which occurred about 10,000 years ago in the Middle East, about 7,000 years ago in Mesoamerica, and possibly as early as 4,000 years ago in midwestern North America. Rosenberg suggests that the perception of population stress created by increased numbers of people was addressed in a limited number of cases by food production based on plant domestication, rather than by warfare, migration, or some other behavior. He argues that it is in these limited numbers of cases that agriculture, a sedentary existence, and food storage were chosen. Such a choice was not, he believes, the gradual process of natural selection but rather a directed, relatively rapid change that reflected the intentions of the peoples involved.

The third model is that proposed by A.K. Chase, in which domestication is seen from a social rather than a biological or behavioral perspective. This emphasizes human action instead of behavior. Chase agrees with Rindos' model as it applies to the changes in plant populations in the mutually beneficial relationship. He argues, however, that the model fails to describe the ways by which humans alter their social world within the process of the developing symbiotic relationship between plants and people. Chase sees people as knowledgeable actors who determine the forms of their societies. Like language, the structures and rules of a given society are generated only by,

and exist only in, practice. Individual interactions may involve strategic changes in the rules, thereby changing the structure of society. Changes are often directed or are the results of conscious decisions on the part of some or all of the people involved. The structure of society, in this model, is defined by the systems of belief, traditions, and perceptions held by the members of that society. The processes of plant domestication cannot be solely biological phenomena because social actions include food production and distribution. Therefore, the origins of agriculture are the results of both biological and social phenomena. Chase argues that Australian Aborigines support his model in that they have chosen not to adopt European-style agriculture because the practice does not fit into their traditional forms of interaction with the landscape. Aboriginal subsistence is keyed to social relations with Europeans and not to food-producing efficiency. In this case the social action is nonevolutionary because Darwinian evolution suggests that food-gathering efficiency increases fitness and thereby imparts a greater degree of adaptedness to populations that are more fit.

Rather than evaluating all three models in regard to the origins of agriculture in the U.S. Midwest and then picking the "best" to describe the adaptation, Charles concludes that all three models have something important to relate. Evidence from the Midwest suggests that the transition from hunting and gathering mobility to sedentary agriculture occurred

Twin Mounds (foreground), Monks Mound (background), and the Central Plaza between them are among the remains of the Mississippian culture, preserved at the Cahokia Mounds State Historic Site in southern Illinois.

Cahokia Mounds State Historic Site

over several thousand years. Rindos' model seems to be correct in regard to this gradual shift, as well as in its prediction of the long period of increasing reliance on harvestable seeds seen in the archaeological record. The long transition period occurred as the mutually beneficial relationship between plants and humans gradually changed the genetic structure of certain plants and also increased the reliance of people on the seeds of these plants.

But does Rindos' biological model reveal the whole story of human-plant relations? Rosenberg's model of directed evolution may provide a better characterization of the *adoption* of plant agriculture that had been initially developed in another area. The record in the Midwest suggests that, although indigenous plants were gradually domesticated, the introduction and adoption of corn and other high-yield seed and fruit plants from Mesoamerica occurred over a short period that coincided with the beginning of the Mississippian culture. This may be a good case for the idea of a directed human response to change traditional behaviors in order to increase intentionally the quantity and quality of food production.

The evidence of Chase's structural model is less visible in the archaeological record of the U.S. Midwest. But the conscious actions of peoples in the Mississippian area who structured their interactions with other peoples may be explained by the model. The appearance, acceptance, and adoption of new traits seem to be highly dependent on the structure of beliefs and practices of a population. Intentional lack of participation in Mississippian culture by Late Woodland groups in the Illinois Valley may be an example that fits the model. Another seems to be the conscious choices to adopt a new and different material culture and a regional sociopolitical system, choices that marked the transition throughout most of the Midwest from the Woodland culture to the widespread Mississippian culture that was centered at Cahokia in what is now southern Illinois. The large mound site at Cahokia rapidly became a political force after the centralization process had begun, about AD 800. As Charles suggests, the higher yield of just-introduced corn may have underwritten the growth of Mississippian social complexity, but the spread of Mississippian culture may be better understood as having been based on the conscious choice by Woodland cultures to participate in a new social, religious, and warfare-driven social structure. Increased food production may have been a secondary benefit.

Of course, the decision to adopt the spreading and warlike Mississippian culture may have been coerced by force and oppression, on the basis of fear of what could happen if the more powerful culture was not accepted. But at least some Woodland cultures resisted the new system, possibly in ways similar to those of the Australian Aborigines' resistance to European agriculture and social structures.

Each of the three models reveals something different about the origin and adoption of agriculture, as well as the social changes associated with agriculture. The biological model may explain a large portion of the circumstances surrounding the advent of agriculture throughout the world. The directed evolutionary model may tell how people adopt new cultural traits associated with certain kinds of agriculture. And the social model may explain how social structures change in response to biological evolution and to the conscious decisions to adopt new and different ideas.

Archaeologists are coming to appreciate the fact that different pasts can be reconstructed. The focus in 1992, perhaps more than any other year, was on opening the field to alternative interpretations. As concluded by Charles: "While agreeing with the ideology-identifying aims, if not always the correctives, of these [alternative participants], I wished to address another aspect of a more relativist position. . . . Assuming not only that we construct our visions of the world, but that there is, in fact, a world out there at which we are aiming, what is the relationship between our constructions and that world? As should be apparent, . . . no one seems yet to have escaped from the various dimensions that define Western thought. We are either a Romantic, or we are Enlightened. We see structure, or we see process. We believe in progress or a steady state, internal or external causality, gradual or abrupt change. The history of archaeology consists of the reworking of these and related themes. Perhaps it is time to step back—or, rather, step down—and admit that none of us has a privileged perspective. We simply wear different shades." Thus ends one lesson from the Columbus quincentenary, a defining year in U.S. and, possibly, world archaeology.

—James D. Wilde
See also Feature Article: Dead Men's Molecules.

Architecture and civil engineering

Architectural and engineering structures represent a significant segment of a country's wealth. Prosperous times provide an atmosphere that encourages a proliferation of new projects. Taller buildings and larger factories are built in expanding economies. Bigger and better bridges, tunnels, and roads are constructed to overcome obstacles. Dams and power plants are raised to control and harness nature. During the past year, however, most of the major industrial countries experienced economic slowdowns, and many construction projects were put on hold.

The Commerzbank tower in the center foreground dominates the skyline of Frankfurt, Germany, in this photomontage. The floors of the bank will be pierced by a building-high triangular atrium that is ventilated at the top. Each of the building's three segments will contain three-story conservatory spaces that spiral around the atrium.

Almost a quarter of the architects in the United States found themselves unemployed. Olympia & York, one of the world's largest international developers, whose holdings included London's huge Canary Wharf project, went bankrupt, as did numerous other firms. It seemed to be a time for smaller, more modest projects, an opportunity for better-thought-out solutions, more careful planning, and judicious use of materials—an opportunity not universally seized. Nevertheless, significant projects were completed, and intriguing ones were evolving on the drawing boards.

Changes in the world's political structure created one of the largest architectural and city planning opportunities in decades. Some of the world's best-known architects were commissioned to design offices, hotels, and residential buildings for sites in Berlin where barbed wire and the Berlin Wall once stood. A new office tower for Moscow, projected to be the world's tallest building, was being designed by a U.S. architectural firm, Skidmore, Owings & Merrill.

Architecture. A wide range of very different approaches to the design of office buildings and work space were being explored by architects. Perched along the bank of the Seine River in Paris, Richard Meier's new headquarters for the television company Canal+ is an excellent example of a growing trend to less monumental, medium-rise office structures that respond to their occupants, articulate their function (the building contains separate massing for the television studios), and respect the scale of their surroundings. Frank Gehry's creation for Chait/Day/Mojo, an advertising agency in Venice, Calif., is an

example of whimsical use of forms for their own sake. Giant-size binoculars form the entrance, and random nonstructural beams are utilized to create an overhang and provide an arbitrary exterior texture.

The suburbs of London have been enlivened by Ralph Erskine's attention-getting building affection-

The Holocaust Museum in Washington, D.C., uses harsh, exposed steel framing to establish a historic sense of time and a deliberately skewed skylight to create an unsettling mood of tension.

The seven-story central library in Vancouver, B.C., will be encased within a pair of freestanding, overlapping, elliptical walls and topped with an amphitheater and garden. A new office tower will rise behind the library.

ately known as the "Ark." A curved, copper-covered roof rests on walls that slope outward. The building's center, carved by a nonsymmetrical atrium that funnels outward as it rises to the roof, is lighted by both a skylight and exterior glass walls. The atrium contains trees, terraces, shops, and social amenities that include a pub. Bright red ducts, columns, and elevators are all exposed in a cacophony of forms. What makes all this excitement particularly unusual is that it occurs in a structure built on speculation on a rather drab site.

Foster Associates designed a sophisticated tower for Germany's Commerzbank. To be built in Frankfurt, it will have rounded triangular floors pierced by a continuous, building-high, open triangular atrium that is ventilated at the top. Office floors will have windows facing onto both the central atrium and the exterior, permitting cross ventilation. Each of the building's three segments will contain three-story conservatory spaces alternating with stacks of six floors. These spaces, staggered vertically in relation to those in the adjoining segments, create a dramatic cohesive space as they spiral around the central atrium. The vertical service core (which contains elements such as stairs, elevators, and mechanical shafts) is divided into three parts, each located at an exterior corner. In Asia, Kuala Lumpur will have twin 85-story towers designed by Cesar Pelli and Associates massed in an attempt to reflect Islamic and Hindu architectural forms.

The Holocaust Museum opened in Washington, D.C. Designed by James Freed, of Pei Cobb Freed & Partners, it conveys a powerful emotional impact. Harsh, exposed-steel framing composed of built-up plates and angles, stylistically detailed in the manner of industrial buildings of the Holocaust era, establish a historic sense of time. A deliberately skewed skylight creates an unsettling mood of tension.

Now protected by a skylight, the light court of the Rookery office building in Chicago has been restored to its original beauty. Designed by Burnham and Root in 1888, the Rookery was renovated by McClier Architects and Engineers at a cost of more than $92 million.

Vancouver, B.C., selected an unusual design by Moshe Safdie for its central library and office complex, which will occupy an entire block. The seven-story library, topped with an amphitheater and gardens, is encased within a pair of freestanding, overlapping, elliptical walls. One wall serves as an entry concourse to the library and office tower behind. The inner wall, which contains the reading rooms, is 3.5 m (12 ft) wide and has large windows on both sides. The high, pierced, curved walls evoke the ghost of the ancient Roman Colosseum.

Plans for the Getty Center, to be located outside Los Angeles, were unveiled. Designed by Richard Meier, the complex of seven buildings will feature the Getty Museum along with various centers for art, history, and the humanities. Scheduled for completion in 1996 at an estimated cost of $500 million, it will be one of the largest groups of structures ever built for the public with private funds. Visitor parking will be located at the edge of the 50-ha (124-ac) site, and the public will ride to the museum on a tram.

A small, magnificent meditation chapel, designed by Thompson Viaivoda & Associates, was built on the edge of a cliff in a 25-ha (62-ac) wooded sanctuary outside Portland, Ore. Visitors look out to the sky through a meticulously detailed glass wall that frames a quarter circle of space. The Moyer chapel's spiritual aspects are enhanced by a sloping roof and a subtle play of reflected water cast onto its surface from pools alongside the splayed walls of the entry.

Chicago heralded the restoration of its landmark office building known as the Rookery. It was originally designed by Burnham and Root in 1888, and its lobby was remodeled in 1905 by Frank Lloyd Wright, but subsequent remodeling unfortunately obscured the building's original beauty. Carefully renovated to its former glory at a cost of more than $92 million by McClier Architects and Engineers, the 12-story historic landmark has regained its former majesty, its famous light court now protected by a skylight. Another thoughtful restoration of a national treasure was Goody, Clancy & Associates' meticulous refurbishing of Boston's Old State House, originally erected in 1713. What distinguished both of these restoration projects were the architects' sensitivity and ability to realize that some of the previous additions and changes to the original structure possessed architectural and historic significance in their own right and thus needed to be respected and restored with as much care as the original building.

The Pritzker Prize and the Praemium Imperiale awards for lifetime achievement were joined by a new biannual international award, the Carlsberg Architectural Prize, worth $225,000. It was presented to the Japanese architect Tadao Ando by the queen of Denmark. The Praemium, established by the Japan Art Association, was awarded to U.S. architect Frank

Rising from a hillside in Barcelona, Spain, Santiago Calatrava's sculptural telecommunications tower gained praise from architects but incurred considerable criticism from the general public.

Gehry. The year's Pritzker Prize went to Portuguese architect Alvaro Siza in recognition of his socially conscious projects. The American Institute of Architects selected Kevin Roche as the recipient of its 1993 Gold medal. A creator of strong forms, he is also known for his meticulous detailing and sophisticated use of material, as seen in such buildings as the Ford Foundation headquarters, the Knights of Columbus headquarters, and the Oakland (Calif.) Museum.

Civil engineering. Exploding populations require major new allocation and distribution systems for natural water resources. These types of projects tend to be gargantuan in both size and cost, and they take years (sometimes decades) to complete. China approved the start of its $11 billion Three Gorges Dam on the Chang Jiang (Yangtze River). Designed to be 175 m (574 ft) high and 2,000 m (6,600 ft) long, it will be the world's largest concrete dam and contain the largest power plant ever built. India's $6 billion Sardar Dam and canal irrigation project was proceeding amid controversy over resettlement and environmental concerns. In the U.S. the 135-m (440-ft)-high Waddell Dam Project in Arizona, initially proposed in 1947, was completed. Backing up almost 1,235,000,000 cu m (one million acre-feet) of water, it was designed to generate electricity.

The never-ending search for water was fostering cooperation across national boundaries. Recent droughts in the western U.S. generated a $4 billion scheme to dam the north fork of Canada's Thompson River and divert water from it through a 6.5-km (4-mi)-long canal to the Columbia River and on to southern California. A 30-year, multibillion-dollar project to transport 70 cu m (2,500 cu ft) of water per second to South Africa from Lesotho was under construction. The project featured a 180-m (590-ft)-high dam across the Malibamat'so River, 225 km (140 mi) of tunnels, and two power plants.

Towers have traditionally fascinated the public and at times have become national symbols, as in the case of the Eiffel Tower in Paris. Spain has acquired two outstanding new towers, both receiving professional accolades while provoking public wrath, much as Eiffel's did a century ago. Santiago Calatrava's new sculptural telecommunications tower graces a hillside in Barcelona near the site of the 1992 Olympic Games. And in Tibidabo, just outside Barcelona, Sir Norman Foster and Ove Arup's new communications tower soars. Four meters (13 ft) in diameter, its concrete tube reaches a height of 205 m (670 ft) and is topped by a television mast. The shaft, stiffened by three trusses and braced by prestressed Kevlar guys, supports 12 floors of microwave and radio transmitters and an observation platform.

In an increasingly mobile world, airport terminals continue to be an important building type. Their large spans provide opportunities for interesting structural approaches. Denver, Colo., saw the completion of a $2.7 billion, 93-gate complex to serve what is expected to be the third busiest airport

The central concourse of the new terminal at the Denver International Airport is covered by a transparent, teflon-coated, fiberglass canopy that is supported on 34 masts of varying heights (right). Below is an artist's cutaway perspective of the atrium beneath the fabric roof. On the lowest level electric trains take passengers to other concourses at the airport.

Denver International Airport

in the U.S. Its most notable feature is an intriguing transparent tent-roof structure that hovers over the central concourse. The innovative teflon-coated fiberglass canopy, designed by Horst Berger in conjunction with Severud Associates, is supported on 34 masts of varying heights. Opening in Pittsburgh, Pa., was an efficient X-shaped terminal with moving sidewalks and shuttle trains that whisk passengers underground to the 18-m (60-ft)-high central mall and to remote gates. Rafael Moneo's design for the new airport at Seville, Spain, uses masonry and Romanesque forms to create a more serene mood than commonly found in the high-tech designs of other terminals.

Work began on one of the world's largest construction projects, Chek Lap Kok airport, being built on an artificial island in Hong Kong Harbor at a projected overall cost of $17 billion. Designed to handle 35 million passengers a year, it will become the largest airport in the world. The overall project will necessitate the construction of the world's longest bridge.

While rotating restaurants atop hotels are no longer news, Sydney, Australia, will have the world's first revolving high-rise tower. Ove Arup, in conjunction with the Hassell Group architectural firm, has designed a 240-m (785-ft)-high elliptical building. The narrow end of its flat ellipse shape will track the Sun, eliminating direct radiation on the long glass walls. This will make the building very energy efficient while at the same time providing dramatic harbor views for all tenants. The tower will be divided into two similar but separate vertical segments stacked one above the other. Each will rotate at the same rate and direction around a 20-m (65-ft)-diameter circular concrete core. The rotating technology is similar to that used for locomotive turntables.

The American Society of Civil Engineers' award for the outstanding achievement went to a swing bridge (a bridge that rotates around a central pier) that experts initially said could not be built. The West Seattle (Wash.) swing bridge, designed by Andersen Bjornstad Kane Jacobs and the Seattle office of Parsons Brinkerhoff Quade and Douglas, is the only hydraulically operated double-leaf concrete bridge in the world. Each 7,500-ton leaf is rotated by two 61-cm (24-in)-diameter hydraulic cylinders.

—David Guise

Astronomy

During the past year, observations made by the Hubble Space Telescope (HST) contributed to knowledge in all branches of astronomy. Progress was made toward the positive identification of a black hole, and exciting new results concerning the cosmic background microwave radiation were announced. Some old problems were revisited, and some new ones were revealed.

Solar system. Two distant solar system objects were discovered in 1992. The first was an asteroid found in January. Designated 1992AD, it has since received the permanent name of 5145 Pholus. It was detected by David Rabinowitz of the University of Arizona on images obtained with the Spacewatch telescope at Kitt Peak (Arizona) National Observatory. Pholus is now near its closest approach to the Sun at 8.5 AU (1 AU [astronomical unit] equals 150 million km, the distance of the Earth from the Sun) and will be carried out to a distance of 32 AU in about 46 years as it moves on its eccentric orbit. (One km = 0.62 mi.)

Pholus is roughly three times brighter in near-infrared radiation than it is in visible wavelengths. Uwe Fink, Martin Hoffmann, William Grundy, Michael Hicks, and William Sears, all of the University of Arizona, measured the spectrum of the asteroid. They found a steeply sloped spectrum increasing in brightness over the range from 0.5 to 1 micrometer (millionths of a meter). They proposed that the best fit to the spectrum corresponds to the reflection spectrum of tholins, compounds that are residues left over after organic molecules are subjected to ultraviolet radiation or particle bombardment.

The second distant body was discovered in August by David Jewitt of the University of Hawaii and Jane Luu of the University of California at Berkeley with the 2.2-m telescope of the University of Hawaii on Mauna Kea. The observers obtained six images of the faint object before it was lost in bright moonlight. It has an extremely slow motion across the sky and shows no parallax, or angular shift in position. Brian Marsden of the International Astronomical Union's Central Bureau for Astronomical Telegrams gave it a preliminary designation as a minor planet and labeled it 1992QB. On the basis of its slow motion and lack of parallax, he estimated its distance to lie between 37 and 59 AU from the Earth. It is the most distant solar system object ever seen. Like Pholus, it is also very red in color and might also have a surface coating rich in organic compounds.

A much closer body, the asteroid Toutatis, at a distance of only 3.5 million km from the Earth, was imaged by a U.S. National Aeronautics and Space Administration (NASA) radar telescope. Steven Ostro of the Jet Propulsion Laboratory (JPL), Pasadena, Calif., noted that Toutatis is one of the most irregularly shaped objects in the solar system. It consists of two large pieces of rock held together by gravitational attraction. The larger piece is roughly 5 km across and the smaller 2.6 km. Both pieces are highly cratered, battered objects. Toutatis is one of the larger Earth-approaching asteroids of the several thousand believed to exist. An asteroid only two to three times bigger is believed to have struck the Earth in the vicinity of the Yucatán Peninsula of Mexico about 65 million years ago, causing the atmosphere to be blanketed with dust and causing the extinction of the dinosaurs.

George Null of JPL announced the results of the imaging of Pluto and its satellite Charon by the Wide Field and Planetary Camera of the HST. Without the disturbances in image quality encountered in ground-based observations, Pluto's position was measured to within three milliarc seconds (three one-thousandths of an arc second) and Charon's to within nine milliarc seconds relative to a star. From the precise measurement of the bodies' motion, the mass of Pluto was determined to be roughly one-fifth the mass of the Earth's Moon. Charon weighed in at one-twelfth the mass of Pluto.

Depending on the diameter of Pluto, its density lies between 1.8 and 2.1 g per cc. This implies that the interior of Pluto is rock and ice in equal proportions. Charon's density is markedly lower, between 1.2 and 1.3 g per cc. Therefore, it must be mostly ice and thus resembles the water-ice moons of Saturn more than Pluto itself. It is unlikely that Pluto and Charon formed together by accretion from a common cloud of matter.

Stars. Since its discovery in 1922, HD47129, or Plaskett's star, has generally been thought to be the most massive binary star. It has remained poorly understood, however, because the spectrum of the fainter companion star is difficult to detect in the light of the primary star. William Bagnuolo, Jr., Douglas Geis, and Michael Wiggs of Georgia State University succeeded in extracting the secondary star's spectrum by using spectra previously obtained by the International Ultraviolet Explorer. The secondary's spectrum is strongest in the ultraviolet, where that star is brightest.

The researchers found that Plaskett's star consists of two supergiant stars with a combined mass of 93.5 solar masses. The secondary star is 18% more massive than the primary and is hotter (38,400 K) than the primary (35,100 K). The primary has a larger radius, 21.5 times that of the Sun, while the secondary has a radius in the range of 14–21 solar radii. The primary star spins at its equator with a speed of 80 km per second, while the secondary has a remarkable velocity of 330 km per second. In addition, the secondary has a strong stellar wind.

The investigators proposed that originally the primary star was the more massive star. But it expanded as it evolved, losing control over its outer regions, and transferred mass to its companion. The momentum that transferred with the mass caused the secondary to spin up to its current high rate of rotation.

Many astronomers believe that, during and after the formation of a star from interstellar matter, it is surrounded by a circumstellar disk. It is from this disk that planets could subsequently form. Observational substantiation of this concept was obtained by Vilppu Piirola of the University of Helsinki, Fin., F. Scaltriti at the Astronomical Observatory of Turin, Italy, and G.V. Coyne at the Vatican Observatory. They used the Nordic 2.56-m optical telescope on La Palma in the Canary Islands to observe the stars V376 and V633 Cassiopeiae. These are young objects, less than a million years old, with masses about two to three times that of the Sun, and are believed to be emerging from the protostellar cores from which they formed. The three astronomers measured polarized light in the near-infrared region in the vicinity of the two objects. They succeeded in resolving a region of high polarization around V376, but the polarized light from the vicinity of V633 was beneath their spatial resolution limit. The polarization about V376 arises from the scattering of light by micrometer-sized dust particles lying above and below a flattened disk surrounding the star. The disk is 500 to 750 AU in size, 10 to 15 times the size of our solar system. The polarized light from V633, on the other hand, is indicative of a much more compact disk, possibly one from which planets will form.

Circumstellar matter can also arise after a star has formed. S.M. Doughtery and A.R. Taylor at the University of Calgary, Alta., used the Very Large Array radio interferometer at Socorro, N.M., to observe the star ψ Persei. It is a rapidly rotating star that throws off gas and subsequently heats the gas by radiation. The gas gives off hydrogen-line emission seen superposed on the spectrum of the star. In addition, the heated gas radiates at infrared and radio wavelengths. Dougherty and Taylor were able to resolve the circumstellar envelope around ψ Persei at a radio frequency of 15 gigaHertz. The radio-emitting region is nonspherical and has a major axis of 17 AU.

Confirmation of a mechanism for transporting energy in solar flares proposed 17 years ago was obtained by observation of the red dwarf star AU Microscopium, 30 light-years distant from the Sun. In 1967 Frank Orrall at the Institute for Astronomy in Hawaii and Frank Zirker at the U.S. National Solar Observatory suggested a way to observe proton beams, which had been proposed as that mechanism. Solar flares arise at the base of magnetic loops in the Sun's corona that extend thousands of kilometers above the Sun. A disturbance causes protons to be magnetically accelerated downward from the corona, impinging on the Sun's photosphere and helping cause it to flare in brightness. Orrall and Zirker predicted that the photons cascading into the lower solar atmosphere would capture electrons, making them momentarily capable of emitting Lyman-alpha radi-

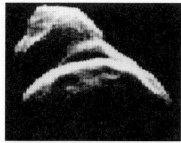

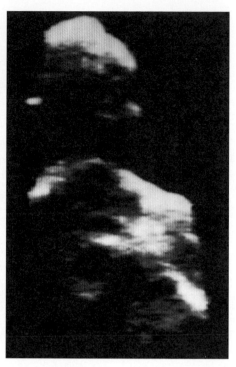

The asteroid Toutatis is revealed in a series of radar images obtained during its recent close approach— 3.5 million kilometers (2.2 million miles)—to the Earth. One of the most irregularly shaped objects in the solar system, Toutatis consists of two pieces of extensively cratered rock held together by gravitational attraction.

ation at 1216 Å (ten-billionths of a meter). (Lyman-alpha radiation is radiation emitted by hydrogen associated with the spectral line that has a wavelength of 121.5 nanometers; one nanometer = one-billionth of a meter.) Because the emitting matter is streaming at thousands of kilometers per second toward the surface, the Lyman-alpha emission would be shifted toward the red end of the spectrum.

Attempts to detect this effect in the Sun have been unsuccessful because the phenomenon is extremely transitory and is swamped by the general emission from the Sun. Bruce Woodgate, Richard Robinson, Kenneth Carpenter, Stephen Moran, and Steven Shore at the Goddard Space Flight Center, Greenbelt, Md., used the Goddard High-Resolution Spectrograph aboard the HST to monitor AU Microscopium, a star that has sudden outbursts that can double its brightness in the ultraviolet, much larger than that seen on the Sun. They recorded spectra every 0.4 second during 30-minute intervals during four orbits of the HST. Longer periods of observation were impossible because the Earth occulted the star during most of the HST's orbit. Fortunately, the star flared during the observing run. The predicted Lyman-alpha effect was detected for 3.2 seconds at the beginning of the flare. The measured redshift corresponds to particle velocities between 3,000 and 10,000 km per second. The effect was very hard to measure because the observed flare was weak. The possibility of observing the Sun directly is out of the question because the strong solar radiation would cook the sensitive instruments on the HST.

Galactic astronomy. One theory about the formation of bright stars more massive than 10 solar masses involves the collision of large clouds of interstellar matter. When the clouds collide, shock waves would be generated; these would then compress matter in the clouds into clumps that would contract gravitationally to form many stars almost simultaneously. A team of observers, including Tetsuo Hasegawa of the University of Tokyo, Fumio Sato of Tokyo Gakugei University, John Whiteoak of the Australian National Observatory, and Ryosuke Miyawaki of Fukuoka University, concluded that they had observed such a scene. They used the 45-m radio telescope at the Nobeyama Observatory to map radio signals from carbon monoxide in two massive clouds near the center of our Galaxy. Doppler shifts in the frequency of the wavelengths reveal that one cloud is moving away from the Sun at 70–80 km per second and is overtaking and colliding with a cloud moving at only 30–40 km per second. The slower cloud appears to be speeding up at the region of impact, and a cavity has formed there, caused by shock waves generated by the collision. In addition, radio maps show more than 10 concentrated radio sources near the impact region where the gas has been excited by newborn stars.

Once massive stars form, they do not last very long. Their phenomenal consumption of matter in thermonuclear reactions drives their evolution to conclusion in a matter of a few million years. These massive stars invariably end their normal stellar stages as supernovae. During the early stages of

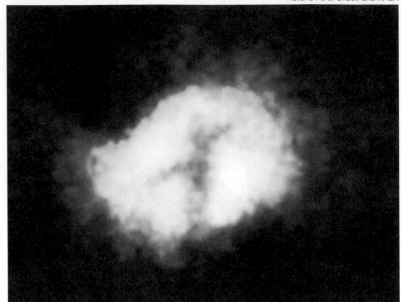

Holland Ford, STScI, and NASA

Image of the core of the M51 Whirlpool galaxy, obtained by the Hubble Space Telescope, shows a dark X silhouetted against the galaxy's nucleus. Astronomers believe that one diagonal of the X is a doughnut-shaped ring of dust and gas that is swirling around a black hole that may have a mass equivalent to one million stars like the Sun. Because the ring is seen edge on, it hides the black hole from view. The second diagonal could also be a ring seen edge on.

an association of massive stars, strong stellar winds sweep out the interstellar matter around them, encasing them in a huge evacuated bubble. As the stars terminate in supernovae, the resulting explosions heat the bubble to a temperature of 1,000,000 K or higher. The matter cast off by the explosions sweeps out the surrounding interstellar matter into a thick expanding shell. Eventually the shell expands to a size equal to the thickness of the gaseous disk of the Galaxy, and the bubble bursts into the lower pressure beyond the disk. The walls of the burst bubbles remain as structures tagged "worms" because of their tortured appearance.

Bon-Chul Koo of the Harvard-Smithsonian Center for Astrophysics and Karl Heiles and William Reach of the Goddard Space Flight Center applied a technique called median-filtering to search for low surface brightness features in published 21-cm-wavelength maps of the Galactic plane. They also created infrared maps at wavelengths of 60 and 100 micrometers from data gathered by the Infrared Astronomical Satellite as well as radio maps at 408 MHz. They found and cataloged 118 isolated structures that appear in both 21-cm and infrared radiation. This was the first significant work in this area since Heiles's pioneering efforts in 1984. Finding these structures in our Galaxy is difficult because they must be viewed through the disk of the Galaxy and appear only as slight enhancements over the general disk emission.

Extragalactic astronomy. Two images acquired by the HST appeared to be the first clear views of black holes or, at the least, the regions around black holes, since by definition black holes should not be seen. The first, announced by Holland Ford of Johns Hopkins University, Baltimore, Md., was an image of the center of M51, the Whirlpool galaxy. A dark X 100 light-years across is silhouetted against the bright galactic nucleus. One diagonal of the X is wider than the other, and it is thought to be a torus, a doughnut-shaped ring of dust and gas seen edge-on that obscures the center of the bright nucleus. A bright region shaped like an hourglass is centered on and perpendicular to this dark bar. This is believed to be light scattered by outlying interstellar matter from two beams of energy emitted in opposite directions from the center of the ring.

This picture almost perfectly fits the idea of how a black hole can power the center of an energetic galactic nucleus like that of M51. Matter from the dark torus falls inward toward a massive black hole. But, unless the matter is precisely directed, it goes into orbit and forms an accretion disk circulating about the black hole. The infall of matter into the accretion disk releases enormous amounts of energy. The energy can escape only perpendicular to the plane of the torus in two oppositely directed beams. The energy released by M51 in visible and radio wavelengths requires a black hole of at least one million solar masses, if that is the cause of the energy release. Two puzzles remain: why is the main branch of the X perpendicular to the plane of the galaxy, and just what is the thinner branch of the X?

The other Hubble image, announced by Walter Jaffe at the Leiden (Neth.) Observatory, is a picture of the active center of the galaxy NGC 4261. A torus, 300 light-years across circling about a bright knot at its center, can be seen inclined to the line of sight. The torus extends east-west in the sky, perpendicular to the north-south radio jets of NGC 4261 that

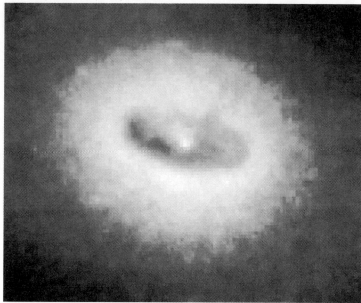

At the core of the galaxy NGC 4261 as revealed by the Hubble Space Telescope is a disk consisting of a ring of cold gas about 300 light-years across circling about a bright region. Because the disk is perpendicular to powerful radio jets emanating from the galaxy, astronomers believe that its bright hub harbors a black hole with a mass ten million times that of the Sun.

were discovered earlier by Earth-based observations. Together, the two Hubble images provide almost conclusive proof of black holes at the centers of active galaxies. The ultimate test, however, must await the installation of corrective optics into the Hubble by space shuttle astronauts. Then the image quality should be enhanced enough to enable the measurement of the orbital speed of the material at the center of NGC 4261 and to weigh the central mass to determine if there is enough mass concentrated to qualify as a black hole.

The HST also captured images of two faint galaxies that appear as mirror images of each other. The telescope was trained on AC 114, a cluster of 799 galaxies some four billion light-years distant. Richard Ellis of the University of Durham, England, announced the interpretation of the two galaxies as gravitationally lensed images of the same galaxy, six billion light-years beyond the cluster. (Gravitational lensing is caused by the bending of light rays in space warped by the presence of a large mass.) The mass required for lensing the highly detailed images separated by 10 arc seconds on the sky is 50 times greater than the visible matter in AC 114. Furthermore, the extreme separation of the images requires that the dark matter be twice as strongly concentrated as the visible matter in the lensing cluster.

Even though the acuity of its vision does not achieve the original expectations, the HST has proved a boon to astronomers studying distant galaxies. Alan Dressler of the Observatories of the Carnegie Institution of Washington, Pasadena, Augustus Oemler of Yale University, James Gunn of Princeton University, and Harvey Butcher of The Netherlands Foundation for Research in Astronomy used the Hubble

to study an ancient cluster of galaxies designated CL 0939 + 4713, located at a distance from the Earth a third of the way back to the big bang. They found galaxies of all types that are present in more modern regions of the universe. But, surprisingly, they determined that the cluster consisted of 30% spiral galaxies, compared with only 5% of such galaxies in clusters closer to the Earth. In addition, the spirals in the cluster are very blue, implying that they are in a stage of rapid star formation when bright, blue, massive stars are born. Possibly the dearth of nearby spirals results from many having used up their supply of star-forming matter so that they now exist as unrecognized relics of the past. Another possibility is suggested by the images of the member galaxies of CL 0939 + 4713. A significant fraction of the spirals in the Hubble images appear to be in the process of merging, some appearing as galactic wrecks because of interactions with other systems in the cluster. Possibly, the lack of spirals seen at closer distances occurred because of galactic collisions that transformed many spirals into featureless elliptical galaxies. In any case, the sharper views of the HST now permit better insight into galactic evolution. After Hubble's optical repair, even sharper images and tests of galactic formation and evolution should be forthcoming.

Another use of Hubble was made by Allan Sandage at the Observatories of the Carnegie Institution and Gustav Tammann at the University of Basel, Switz. They examined the galaxy IC 4182 for Cepheid variable stars, the best indicators of galactic distances because of the good relationship between their intrinsic brightnesses and the rate at which they vary in brightness. It had been all but impossible for the

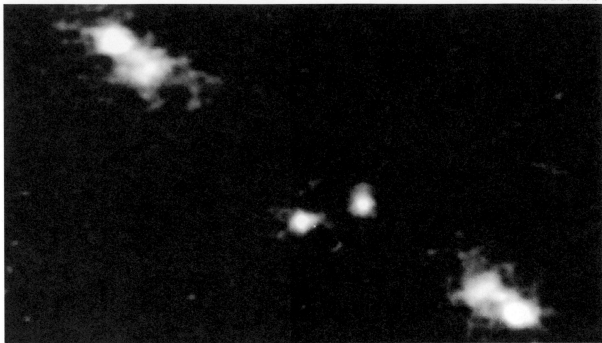

A mirror image of a galaxy (upper left and lower right) is formed by light rays bent by AC 114, a huge cluster of foreground galaxies (center). The image helped astronomers determine the proportion of dark matter in AC 114.

Cepheids in IC 4182 to be monitored by Earth-based observations, but the Hubble allowed 27 of them to be followed. The relatively small distance to IC 4182 deduced from those implies an age of the universe of 20 billion years. This is twice the popularly accepted age and, if it is supported by further observations, will have a major impact on cosmological thinking.

Not all extragalactic astronomy depended upon the HST. For example, N. Brouillet and A. Baudry, at the University of Bordeaux, France, and C. Henkel at the Max Planck Institute for Radio Astronomy, Bonn, Germany, discovered the first intergalactic molecular gas cloud ever found. They observed the M81 group of galaxies, about 10 million light-years distant, in radio waves emitted by carbon monoxide molecules. A particularly interesting feature of the M81 group is the presence of faint structures apparently linking some of its component galaxies. These bridges are believed to arise during tidal interactions between galaxies. The observers found a complex of molecular gas near M81 but not within the disk or nucleus of the galaxy. The complex does not show signs of being physically associated with M81. Since there is no bridge of carbon monoxide linking the cloud to other galaxies in the group, the investigators concluded that the cloud, which was estimated at one million to 10 million solar masses, formed in place independently of other structures. The cloud could be a small protogalaxy that might in the future become a new dwarf galaxy.

Possibly the most exciting astronomical result of the past year came from the Cosmic Background Explorer (COBE) satellite. Ever since the 2.73 K background radiation, the energy left over from a time just after the big bang, was discovered in 1964, astronomers have searched for variations in what always appeared to be a uniform brightness over the entire sky. The lack of variation seemed to say that the universe was so smooth in the beginning that the seeds needed to form the structure of the universe observed today never existed. On April 23, 1992, however, George Smoot, leader of the team responsible for the Differential Microwave Radiometer aboard COBE, announced the discovery of fluctuations in the background microwave radiation. After a full year of data had been analyzed, fluctuations were unambiguously found.

The variations were only of the order of five parts per million, and they covered huge angular sizes from 7° to 90° across the sky. They appeared to match predictions based on the inflationary model of the expansion of the universe—an extremely large expansion in the first instant after the big bang—and to be in agreement with the concept of a cold dark matter universe. COBE thus had discovered the fossil structure of the universe that existed a mere 300,000 years after its birth.

—W.M. Protheroe

See also Feature Article: THE REVOLUTION IN COSMOLOGY.

298

Chemistry

Highlights in chemistry during the past year included the determination of the structure of the key enzyme for biological nitrogen fixation and the development of a method for making the promising anticancer agent taxol that did not threaten the integrity of old-growth forests. Chemists also took a step toward devising artificial muscles and discovered a natural molecule in fresh beef gives the meat its beefy flavor.

Inorganic chemistry

Among significant accomplishments of the past year for inorganic chemistry was the determination of the structure of the enzyme nitrogenase, whose small iron- and molybdenum-containing metal clusters lie at the heart of biological nitrogen fixation. Researchers also synthesized several new cryptands, molecules that possess cavities large enough to trap atoms, ions, or small molecules inside. Proclaiming "Just say NO" and "NO news is good news," the American Association for the Advancement of Science (AAAS) picked the simple inorganic molecule nitric oxide (NO) as its 1992 Molecule of the Year.

Nitric oxide. For the second consecutive year the AAAS chose an inorganic species as its Molecule of the Year. In 1991 the honor, which is announced annually in a December issue of the AAAS journal *Science,* went to the recently discovered 60-atom, all-carbon molecule buckminsterfullerene, abbreviated C_{60}, the subject of many studies and several symposia. For 1992 the honoree was nitric oxide, a small molecule known for 400 years. Much of the inorganic and physical chemistry of NO has been in textbooks for generations. The molecule is best known to students as an atmospheric pollutant grouped with nitrogen dioxide (NO_2) as NO_x.

Nitric oxide was chosen Molecule of the Year because of numerous recently discovered biological effects. It is the first gaseous molecule known to act as a biological messenger in mammals, carrying critical signals between various cells and tissues. NO is generated in mammals, including humans, by an unusual enzyme, nitric oxide synthase. NO's physiological effects are believed to include an ability to dilate blood vessels to lower blood pressure. The molecule appears to serve as a neurotransmitter, and it may also play a role in learning and memory. The recent discoveries of significant physiological functions for this inorganic species is an example of bioinorganic chemistry, a field that explores the roles of essential (and often trace) elements and inorganic molecules in biology.

Nitrogenase. For more than a century scientists have known that some plants are able to convert, or fix, atmospheric nitrogen (N_2) into ammonia (NH_3), which subsequently nourishes the plant and enriches the soil. The process is summarized as the reaction $N_2 + 6H_2 \rightarrow 2NH_3$. Nitrogen fixation in plants, which is actually carried out by symbiotic bacteria living in the plant's roots, is an outstanding example of bioinorganic chemistry in which a biological process converts one inorganic species into another. Biological nitrogen fixation, catalyzed by proteins called nitrogenase enzymes, occurs at a pressure of 0.8 atmosphere (atm) of nitrogen (air is 80% nitrogen; hence, the pressure of nitrogen at sea level is 0.8 atm) and a temperature of about 25° C (77° F). The hydrogen (H) in the product comes from environmental water. By contrast, the Haber process (also about 100 years old) for producing ammonia industrially requires temperatures of 400°–550° C (750°–1,020° F), pressures for nitrogen and hydrogen of 100–1,000 atm, and an activated iron catalyst. Clearly, nature has a much more efficient and energy-conserving process.

Many bacterial nitrogenases have been discovered. The best known are those found in bacteria associated with the roots of legumes (*e.g.,* clover, peas, and soybeans). Research into their chemistry has shown that these nitrogen-reducing enzymes are relatively large molecules, with molecular masses of about 240,000 daltons. Nitrogenase enzymes are each made of two major components, an iron-containing protein called the Fe protein and a larger molybdenum- and iron-containing protein called the MoFe protein. The Fe protein, in turn, comprises two subunits and contains a single metal center, or cluster, made up of iron and inorganic sulfur (S, as sulfide) in approximately a 1:1 ratio. The MoFe protein comprises four subunits and contains two each of two different kinds of metal centers. One type, called the M center, is made up of iron, sulfur, and molybdenum in a 7:8:1 ratio; the other type, called the P center, is made up of iron and sulfur in a 1:1 ratio. The enzyme is inactive without molybdenum. Thus, in the nitrogenases, bioinorganic chemistry is invoked twice—once in the intervention of a biological catalyst to perform a purely inorganic transformation and again in the requirement for metal atoms at the heart of the process.

Bacterial nitrogenases are known to reduce a variety of substrates in addition to ammonia:

NH_2NH_2 (hydrazine) $+ H_2 \rightarrow 2NH_3$

CH_2CH_2 (ethylene) $+ H_2 \rightarrow CH_3CH_3$ (ethane)

HCN (hydrogen cyanide) $+ 3H_2 \rightarrow CH_4$ (methane) $+ NH_3$

$RC\equiv CH$ (terminal alkynes) $+ H_2 \rightarrow RCH\equiv CH_2$ (terminal alkenes)

CH_3NC (methyl isonitrile) $+ 3H_2 \rightarrow CH_3NH_2 + CH_4$ (and other products)

Carbon monoxide, among triple-bonded species, is not reduced by the nitrogenases. All of these processes occur under physiological conditions. All of the hydrogen added to the products comes from water. It is no small wonder that both academic and industrial scientists have been studying nitrogenases for many years.

In 1992, D.C. Rees and his associates of the California Institute of Technology reported structural models for the metal centers in the two component proteins of nitrogenase. The models were based on X-ray crystallographic studies of the Fe protein and the MoFe protein at resolutions of 290 and 270 picometers (pm, or trillionths of a meter), respectively. To appreciate the complexity of the study, consider that the MoFe protein contains 2,026 amino acids, which are linked end to end into the long peptide chain that makes up the protein. Amino acids are predominantly carbon (C), hydrogen (H), nitrogen (N), and oxygen (O). Carbon, nitrogen, and oxygen are virtually identical in their X-ray scattering power, and the X-ray scattering of hydrogen is insignificant. The only features in the structure with outstanding scattering power are the metal and sulfur atoms, but they are so few in number that their X-ray scattering is overwhelmed by that of the more numerous carbon, nitrogen, and oxygen atoms.

To sort out the X-ray diffraction data for the MoFe protein, the Caltech crystallographers compared data from three native and six chemically modified crystalline forms. The fit between experimental diffraction data and that calculated from structural models was excellent for a molecule of this size, with 64–94% of the X-ray scattering accounted for, depending on the crystal.

But the resolution distance of 270 pm is nearly double the typical C-N bond distance and somewhat longer than Fe-S and Mo-S distances of about 200 and 240 pm, respectively. How then did Rees and his colleagues deduce the structure of the proteins? They began with several additional facts. First, the overall size of an amino acid is considerably larger than 270 pm. And the structure of each of the amino acids is known with some certainty from other studies. The crystallographers also knew the sequence of amino acids in the peptide chain from experiments that selectively cleaved the long chain into segments, which were then identified by comparison with individual amino acids or short synthetic peptides made up of 2 to 10 amino acids. The researchers thus knew "what went where" on the peptide chain and the general size and shape of each link. It remained to fit this knowledge into a three-dimensional structure consistent with the observed X-ray diffraction pattern.

The challenging part of the study was the structure of the metal-containing active sites. To solve that part, Rees and co-workers drew upon two or more decades of study of small iron-sulfur clusters. (For a discussion of some of these clusters, see *1992 Yearbook of Science and the Future* Year in Review: CHEMISTRY: *Inorganic chemistry*.) The cubelike Fe_4S_4 cluster of the kind described by Richard H. Holm and his students at Stanford and Harvard universities—a structure in which iron and sulfur occupy alternate corners of the cube—approximately reproduced the X-ray diffraction pattern at the metal center of the Fe protein. The Fe_4S_4 cluster also apparently is the basis for the P center of the MoFe protein, where two such clusters are present, one belonging to each of a pair of subunits. In the P center the two Fe_4S_4 clusters are joined into an Fe_8S_8 structure by one sulfur atom from a cysteine (an amino acid) of each subunit (*see* 1).

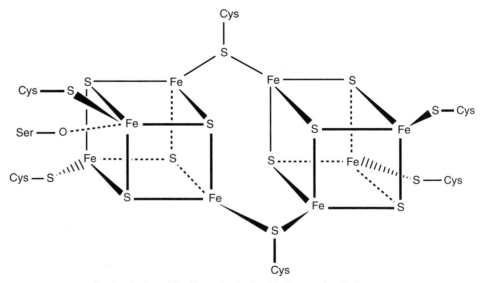

1   Fe_8S_8 cluster of the P center in the MoFe protein of nitrogenase

$^-O_2CCH_2$

Cys — S — Fe

Cys = cysteine
His = histidine

2   iron–sulfur–molybdenum cluster of the M center in the MoFe protein of nitrogenase

The basis for the second metal center of the MoFe protein, the M center, is an MFe_3S_3 cluster, in which M is either Fe or Mo. The cluster can be pictured in the following way: If one corner is removed from a cube, the three apexes nearest the missing corner lie at the corners of a triangle. In this model they are iron atoms. If the structure is placed on a horizontal surface so that it stands on these atoms, above the surface and rotated by about 45° will be a triangle of sulfur atoms. The fourth metal atom, M, will be above the center of this triangle. According to the model put forth by Rees and colleagues, the M center is made up of two MFe_3S_3 clusters, one of which is Fe_4S_3 and the other $MoFe_3S_3$ (*see* 2). The two clusters are held together by two sulfide ions and an as-yet-unidentified bridging atom (Y in the figure).

In contrast to the Fe_8S_8 structure of the P center, the three-link bridge that holds together the two clusters of the M center gives rise to a cavity some 400 pm in diameter between the clusters. The molybdenum atom is some 700 pm from the nearest iron atom of the Fe_4S_3 cluster. In addition, the molybdenum atom appears to have six atoms bonded to it, a condition that would seem to preclude direct interaction between molybdenum and nitrogen during the nitrogen fixation process. On the other hand, there is sufficient space within the cavity to bind the known substrates.

The newly described nitrogenase structure overturned the speculations of the many scientists who had expected direct interaction between molybdenum and nitrogen at the active site of nitrogenase. At the same time, knowledge of its structure will provide powerful insight into the design of small molecules as highly efficient, energy-conserving catalysts.

Cryptands. Cryptands are compounds that possess cavities of sufficient size to hold a "guest" molecule, atom, or ion that is not chemically bonded to the cryptand molecule. In effect, the guest species is trapped within the molecular "crypt" of the host cryptand. Cryptands are of interest because in many cases the trapped atom, ion, or molecule is held in a state otherwise unattainable. For example, the guest might be in a highly reactive state but unable to react because of its isolation. The lifetime of such trapped states is often extended such that they can be studied more extensively than is otherwise possible. Several new cryptand species were reported in 1992.

Song-ping Huang and Mercouri G. Klanatzidis of Michigan State University described the structure of $[NaAu_{12}Se_8]^{3-}$ as a cubic cage with selenium (Se) atoms at the corners, gold (Au) atoms at the midpoints of the edges, and one sodium (Na) ion trapped in the center of the cage (*see* 3). Attempts to prepare cages having shorter edges (*e.g.*, by replacing selenium with sulfur atoms) and smaller central ions (*e.g.*, lithium), or having longer edges (*e.g.*, by replacing selenium with tellurium) and larger central ions (*e.g.*, potassium), failed. The stability of $[NaAu_{12}Se_8]^{3-}$ appears to be a fortuitous balance of interatomic distances, promoted by the unique charge-to-radius ratio of the sodium ion.

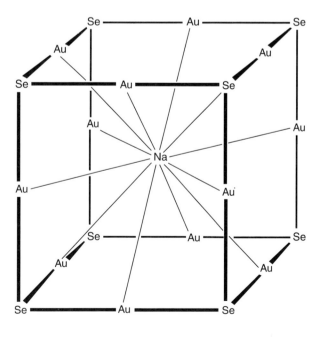

3 $[NaAu_{12}Se_8]^{3-}$ cryptand structure

301

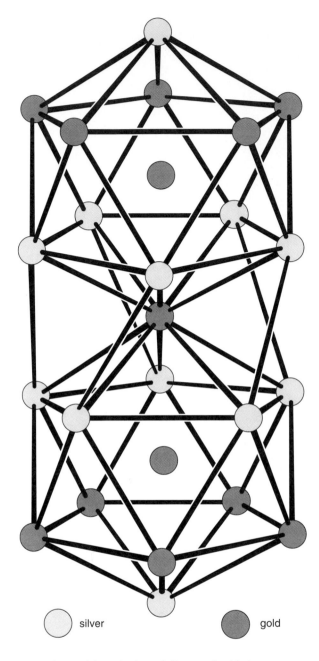

silver   gold

4   polyicosahedron of silver and gold atoms
with two trapped gold atoms

phosphorus atoms (from a phosphorus-containing molecule), and those at the silver apexes by chloride. The icosahedra are held together by silver-chloride-silver bridges. Teo and his students also found clusters comprising as many as four icosahedral units with variable modes of attachment. The high symmetry invites speculation about the electronic structures of the clusters, in which the central gold atoms are likely to participate in the overall bonding.

Karl Hagen of Emory University, Atlanta, Ga., prepared a more typical example of a cryptand complex, employing a macrobicyclic (large, double-ring-containing) diaza (two-nitrogen) hexaoxa (six-oxygen) cryptand ligand of the type pioneered by Jean-Marie Lehn in France. The product contains a manganese ion (as Mn^{2+}) encapsulated in a cubic array of nitrogen and oxygen donor atoms. In this example the ligand controls the properties of the cluster and, therefore, of the metal ion.

Self-assembly of large molecules. Again, as in the previous year (see *1993 Yearbook of Science and the Future* Year in Review: CHEMISTRY: *Inorganic chemistry*), Gerald Bernardinelli, Claude Piguet, and Alan Williams of the University of Geneva described the self-assembly of a triple-helical complex from three ligand molecules and two metal ions. In this case the rigid ligand, bis[1-methyl-2-{6'-[1"-(3,5-dimethoxybenzyl)benzimidazol-2"-yl]pyrid-2'-yl}benzimidazol-5-yl]methane (*see* 5a, designated L), was designed to accommodate ions of the lanthanide series of elements with their increased coordination number. Thus, in contrast to the previously reported cobalt complex, in which each cobalt(II) ion (a cobalt atom deficient two electrons) is six-coordinate (bonding with six ligand atoms), the europium(III) ions in the new complex, $[Eu_2L_3]^{6+}$, are nine-coordinate (*see* 5b).

Edwin Constable, Michael Hannon, and Derek Tocher of the University of Cambridge and University College, London, found that a particular polypyridyl ligand reacts with copper or nickel salts in nonaqueous solution to produce the corresponding $[M_2L_2]^{4+}$ ion (L represents the ligand, M the copper or nickel atom). The crystal structure of the nickel(II) derivative shows a double-helical arrangement for the ligands, each of which is coordinated with both metal ions. The ligands occupy four of the six nickel coordination sites, the remainder being occupied by both oxygen atoms of an acetate ion.

—George R. Brubaker

Organic chemistry

Progress in organic chemistry is made in small increments, and it is only by looking back over a period of years that the true magnitude of the progress usually becomes apparent. The past year saw in-

Boon K. Teo and Hong Zhang at the University of Illinois at Chicago constructed polyicosahedra whose basic building block is an icosahedron (*i.e.,* a polyhedron with 12 apexes and 20 triangular faces) containing 13 metal atoms. Twelve of the atoms—six gold (Au) and six silver (Ag)—are at the apexes, and one gold atom is at the center of the structure. The polyicosahedral structures share apexes (*see* 4). In the examples reported in 1992, the vacant coordination sites at the gold apexes are occupied by

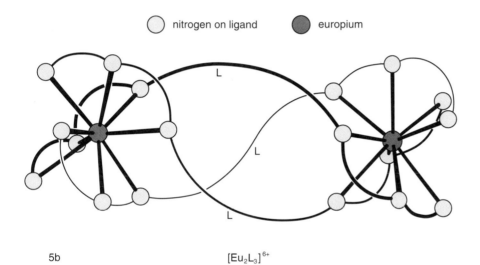

5a   ligand (L)

○ nitrogen on ligand   ● europium

5b $[Eu_2L_3]^{6+}$

cremental advances in many areas. The chemistry of buckminsterfullerene, a recently discovered elemental form of carbon with a spherical structure resembling a soccer ball, continued to provide new surprises. Chemists achieved laboratory syntheses of a variety of important molecules and prepared an extraordinary self-replicating molecule that mimics several characteristics of living systems.

Fullerene chemistry. First proposed in 1985 by Richard Smalley of Rice University, Houston, Texas, and Harold Kroto of the University of Sussex, Brighton, England, the cagelike buckminsterfullerene molecule, abbreviated C_{60}, was not characterized unambiguously until 1991 (see *1993 Yearbook of Science and the Future* Year in Review: CHEMISTRY: *Organic chemistry*). Shortly thereafter, in early 1992, came the surprising discovery by Peter Buseck and Semeon Tsipursky of Arizona State University that

the substance is not quite as new or as unusual as had been believed. Buseck and Tsipursky found small amounts of both C_{60} and its slightly larger fullerene relative C_{70} in a sample of shungite, an unusual carbon-rich rock with deposits near the Russian town of Shunga. It thus turned out that nature beat chemists to the punch in preparing these molecules by 600 million years.

Numerous chemical modifications of the fullerenes were carried out during 1992, and characterization of several more members of the fullerene family was completed. Some of the larger of the new members are the giant cage molecules C_{120} and C_{140}. Much of the chemical-modification work was directed toward formation of so-called endohedral metallofullerene complexes, substances in which one or more metal atoms are encapsulated within the fullerene cage. Among the more interesting of

1 calicheamicin

the complexes reported was a C_{82} cage containing three scandium atoms, prepared independently by Hisanori Shinohara of Mie National University, Tsu, Japan, and by Robert Johnson and Constantino Yannoni of the IBM Almaden Research Center, San Jose, Calif. Still other modifications of the basic fullerene cage included the production by Long Chiang of the Exxon Research & Engineering Co., Annandale, N.J., of water-soluble "fullerols" in which each C_{60} molecule carries 16–20 hydroxyl ($-OH$) groups attached to carbon atoms of the cage.

Synthesis of complex molecules. The enediyne family of compounds, exemplified by calicheamicin (see 1), is an important group of anticancer antibiotics with a unique ability to bind to and cleave DNA. The remarkable biological activity of the compounds provoked an enormous amount of work during the 1980s, efforts that culminated in the past year in a complete laboratory synthesis of calicheamicin, carried out by Kyriacos C. Nicolaou and a group of his students at the Scripps Research Institute, San Diego, and the University of California at San Diego. The successful synthesis both confirmed the original structural assignment and opened the way for preparation of simpler calicheamicin analogues of possible use as pharmaceutical agents.

Another important achievement in synthesis came with the announcement by Bristol-Myers Squibb Co. that it will begin commercial production of taxol (see 2), a promising new pharmaceutical agent active against ovarian cancer. Previous methods for producing taxol had relied on its extraction from the bark of the Pacific yew tree (*Taxus brevifolia*), a limited resource found in old-growth forests of the Pacific Northwest. The new method, based on chemistry developed by Robert Holton at Florida State University, begins with a compound called deacetylbaccatin III, a readily available relative of taxol that can be obtained from cultivated plants.

Other advances in synthetic organic chemistry included the report by K. Barry Sharpless and colleagues at the Scripps Research Institute of an important new method for hydroxylating (attaching hydroxyl groups to) double-bonded carbon atoms (see 3) and the synthesis by Manfred Christl and Germar Müller of the University of Würzburg, Germany, of a new relative of benzene (see 4). The hydroxylation method developed by Sharpless is noteworthy because it allows for a choice of either of two products to be made; that is, the $-OH$ groups can be added from either the top face of the double bond or from the bottom face, depending on the experimental conditions. The preparation of many important pharmaceutical agents should be simplified by the use of this method. The work by Christl and Müller, though probably of little practical value, is nevertheless of interest because it extends the limits of what is structurally possible in organic chemistry. Few chemists would have expected that a molecule

2 taxol

3   or   4   benzene

as twisted and strained as that shown in 4 could be made.

Bioorganic chemistry. The more than 100,000 naturally occurring proteins in the human body are made of just 20 different amino acid units strung together in different sequences like beads on a chain. During the past year J.D. Bain and Richard Chamberlin of the University of California at Irvine, Christopher Switzer of the University of California at Riverside, and Steven Benner of the Eidgenössische Technische Hochschule, Zürich, Switz., devised a method for incorporating nonstandard amino acids into proteins. The method takes advantage of the fact that in biological protein synthesis a group of three nucleotides (a codon) on messenger RNA recognizes and binds with a series of three complementary nucleotides (an anticodon) on transfer RNA. This complementary matching results in the specific addition of one of the 20 naturally occurring amino acids to the growing protein chain. Benner and his colleagues extended the process by preparing a new kind of artificial messenger RNA and transfer RNA that contain a codon-anticodon pair based on nonnatural nucleotides. The new codon-anticodon pairs smoothly direct the incorporation of unconventional amino acids into protein chains, making possible the preparation of new kinds of proteins having potentially greater structural diversity and different kinds of catalytic activity.

One of the hopes for biotechnology is that it will find improved methods to replace traditional chemical processes for the large-scale production of small organic molecules. A step in that direction was taken in 1992 when John Frost, Karen Draths, and Timothy Ward of Purdue University, West Lafayette, Ind., reported a bacterial method for converting glucose into quinic acid (*see* 5). Quinic acid can then be oxidized chemically to yield hydroquinone or benzoquinone, two industrially important compounds. The combined bacterial-chemical synthesis makes it possible to produce hydroquinone and benzoquinone in an environmentally safe manner through the use of a nontoxic starting material that is readily available from biomass.

Methods of biotechnology were also used by Dae-Jin Yun, Takashi Hashimoto, and Yasuyuki Yamada of Kyoto (Japan) University to boost the production of scopolamine (*see* 6, p. 306), a naturally occurring substance that is much used as a drug to combat motion sickness. After the researchers inserted a gene for scopolamine synthesis into a plant that normally produces the related substance hyoscyamine, the plant began producing scopolamine.

DNA, the so-called master molecule that encodes the genetic heritage of every living organism, acts as a template for replication by means of special enzymes, thus providing a way for exact copies of the DNA to pass from one generation to the next. Julius Rebek, Jr., Jong-In Hong, Qing Feng, and Vincent Rotello of the Massachusetts Institute of Technology designed and built synthetic molecules that not only mimic DNA's role as a replication template but also promote their own replication and even mutate into better replicators. In essence, Rebek constructed a synthetic template molecule that is able to bind and bring into close proximity two molecular building

5   D–glucose   quinic acid   hydroquinone   benzoquinone

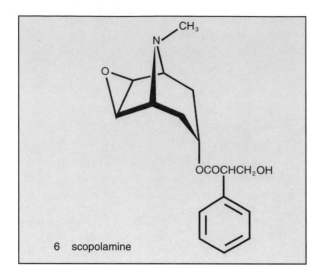

6 scopolamine

blocks. Once bound, the building blocks join to generate a new template molecule that is even more effective than the original template at promoting replication. The new mutant template rapidly takes over and makes new copies of itself. Though no one could call such molecules "alive," the work nevertheless represented an interesting and clever approach to modeling some of life's fundamental processes.

—John E. McMurry

Physical chemistry

A Canadian-American physical chemist became the 1992 Nobel laureate in chemistry for his theories of the way in which electrons transfer between and within molecules. The unusual observation that water can form bonds to benzene in a cluster showed that the chemistry of even such apparently simple and well-understood molecules still contains surprises. The increasing power of computers enabled physical chemists to calculate the shock waves of pressure and heating that are generated during the first moments of an impact of a large cluster of atoms with a surface—information that is very difficult to obtain experimentally. New scanning probe microscopy experiments yielded magnetic imaging at the atomic scale and indicated that magnetic resonance imaging of microscopic samples in three dimensions may be possible. Using an electric field to alter the interaction with a detergent-like molecule, Japanese workers made a polymer gel move with a wormlike motion, an achievement that could represent a step toward molecular machines and artificial muscles.

Nobel Prize for Marcus. The 1992 Nobel Prize for Chemistry was awarded to physical chemist Rudolph A. Marcus (*see* SCIENTISTS OF THE YEAR) of the California Institute of Technology (Caltech). The award

cited "his contributions to the theory of electron-transfer reactions in chemical systems." Such reactions involve the movement of electrons from one part of a molecule to another, or from one molecule to another during a chemical reaction. Electron-transfer reactions are extremely important, as they lie at the heart of such diverse processes as the sequence of biochemical transformations that occur in metabolism and photosynthesis and the reactions that occur in batteries and during electroplating and corrosion.

In a series of theoretical papers written between 1956 and 1965 while at the Polytechnic Institute of Brooklyn, N.Y., Marcus laid the foundations of what has come to be known as Marcus theory. That theory allows one to calculate the size of the energy barrier to the transfer of an electron from one molecule to another and to ascertain the way that the barrier is affected by changes in the structure of the molecules involved and the nature of the solvent. Once the size of the energy barrier is known, this knowledge can be used to predict how quickly electron-transfer reactions will occur. Such predictions are central to understanding processes like respiration and can be used in technological applications like battery design.

Oil and water do mix—at the molecular level. It is common knowledge that oily molecules, such as benzene (C_6H_6), do not mix with water but instead form a film on the surface of the water. Nevertheless, recent experiments by Sakae Suzuki, Peter Green,

Figure 1: The hydrogen-bonding interaction between a ring-shaped molecule of benzene (C_6H_6) and a molecule of water (H_2O) is shown in a computer graphic developed from spectroscopic studies of benzene-water clusters.

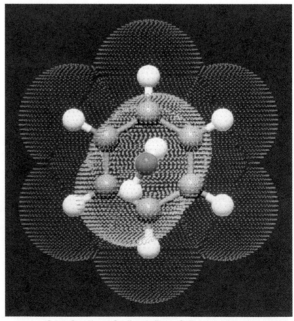

Uzi Landman, Georgia Institute of Technology

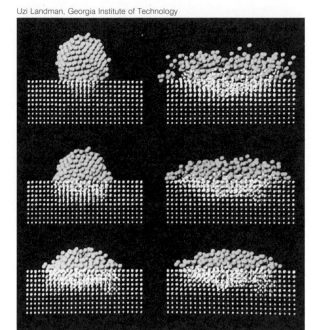

Figure 2: Sequence of computer graphics (proceeding counterclockwise from top left) represents stages in the collision of a 561-atom argon cluster with a surface of a sodium chloride crystal.

Roger Bumgarner, and Geoffrey Blake, combined with calculations by Siddharth Dasgupta and William Goddard III, all of Caltech, showed that under some circumstances water and benzene do form bonds with each other. The researchers produced a supersonic jet of benzene-water clusters by expanding a mixture of benzene and water vapor through a narrow slit into a vacuum. The experimental microwave absorption spectrum coupled with high-level calculations of the most stable orientations of the C_6H_6-H_2O complex indicated that the water molecule is positioned as shown in Figure 1, with both hydrogen atoms of the water molecule pointing toward the hexagonal ring of carbon atoms that make up the benzene molecule.

The type of bonding involved is thought to be a special type of hydrogen bond. Hydrogen bonds usually arise when a hydrogen atom that is bonded to, for instance, the oxygen atom in a water molecule becomes partially bonded to the oxygen atom in another water molecule. The source of this bonding attraction is the high density of electrons in the oxygen atom; consequently, some chemists speculated that the high density of electrons in the benzene ring might provide a site for hydrogen bonding. The results from the benzene-water cluster experiments are the first direct, unambiguous evidence for the formation of such a hydrogen bond. Although hydrogen bonds are quite weak, they may play significant roles in many important chemical systems and reactions, including the structure of biological polymers, the action of drugs, and reactions on particles suspended in the atmosphere.

Catastrophic molecular impacts. Performing imaginary experiments on a computer is becoming ever more useful as the power of modern computers continues to increase. By the early 1990s it was possible on a computer to follow the fate of large numbers of atoms undergoing extremely fast reactions much more easily and in much more detail than by means of laboratory experiments. One example of this type of experiment was reported by Charles Cleveland and Uzi Landman of the Georgia Institute of Technology. The scientists modeled the impact of a 561-atom cluster of argon atoms traveling at three kilometers (1.9 mi) per second with a crystalline sodium chloride surface. Computer graphics images of the impact resemble those seen when liquid drops are photographed colliding with a solid surface (*see* Figure 2). The cluster retains its shape for a short time, causing a severe deformation of the surface. The cluster then spreads out over the surface and partially evaporates. During the impact the shock causes the density of the argon in the cluster to increase by 50%, the pressure to increase by thousands of atmospheres, and the temperature to hit 4,000 K (6,700° F)—but only for a tiny fraction of a second. This type of calculation can form the basis for understanding new techniques of surface processing and growth that are becoming increasingly important in the microelectronics industry and in the development of new high-technology materials.

Atomic-level magnetic imaging. The family of techniques known as scanning probe microscopies that provide images of surfaces on the scale of individual atoms—scanning tunneling microscopy is perhaps the best-known example—continued to proliferate during the past year. By replacing the usual tungsten tip that is scanned across the surface with a magnetic iron tip, R. Wiesendanger, I.V. Shvets, D. Bürgler, G. Tarrach, and H.-J. Güntherodt of the University of Basel, Switz., and J. Coey of Trinity College, Dublin, were able to map for the first time the two different magnetic iron ions, Fe^{2+} and Fe^{3+}, present in a surface of the natural mineral magnetite (Fe_3O_4).

In another variation of this type of microscopy, D. Rugar and C.S. Yannoni at the IBM Almaden Research Center, San Jose, Calif., and J.A. Sidles of the University of Washington were able to detect the interaction between an applied magnetic field and the electrons in a minute quantity of the organic compound diphenylpicrylhydrazil (DPPH) through the oscillatory magnetic force induced in the DPPH. The phenomenon that was observed in the experiment is electron magnetic resonance, but the investigators hoped to increase the sensitivity of the measurements to allow the detection of nuclear

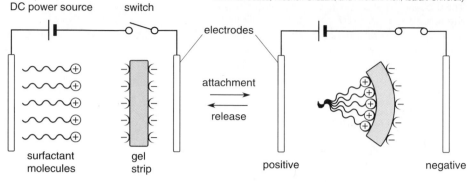

Yoshihito Osada, Hidenori Okuzaki, and Hirofumi Hori, Ibaraki University

DC power source   switch

electrodes

attachment

release

surfactant
molecules

gel
strip

positive

negative

field off

field on

Figure 3: Schematic depicts the mechanism by which a polymer gel strip in a watery medium is made to bend by the preferential attachment of surfactant molecules in an electric field.

magnetic resonance from a single proton (the positively charged nucleus of the hydrogen atom). This technique is best known in the context of magnetic resonance imaging (MRI) of human organs but at relatively low spatial resolution. If the planned experiments succeed, they may allow imaging of the three-dimensional structure of individual biological molecules with single-atom resolution.

Molecular machines: polymers that move. When living organisms use muscles or pump fluids internally, they convert chemical energy into mechanical work. Constructing chemomechanical devices, or molecular machines, that can perform this energy conversion in the laboratory has proved very difficult, with most of the progress to date coming from scientists in Japan. Yoshihito Osada, Hidenori Okuzaki, and Hirofumi Hori of Ibaraki University, Mito, Japan, demonstrated a strip of synthetic polymer gel that can be made to move with a wormlike motion through a watery medium at speeds as high as 25 cm (10 in) per minute.

The key to the movement of the polymer gel strip is the attachment and removal of surfactant (detergent-like) molecules to the surface of the strip in the presence of an electric field. The strip is positioned between two electrodes in a surfactant solution (*see* Figure 3). The polymer gel is normally negatively charged, whereas the surfactant molecules have a positively charged "head." When the electric field is turned on between the electrodes, the positively charged surfactant molecules are driven to the negatively charged polymer gel. The preferential attachment of the surfactant molecules on the side of the gel strip facing the positive electrode causes that side of the strip to shrink. As a result, the ends of the strip bend away from the negative electrode. When the electric field is reversed in sign, the surfactant molecules that are attached on the one side of the strip are released and travel to the negative electrode, while other surfactant molecules attach on the opposite side of the strip, causing it to bend in the opposite direction. When a gel strip is equipped

with hooks at its ends and suspended from a ratchet bar in a surfactant solution, repeated reversal of the electric field causes the strip to worm its way along the bar in a cycle of bending and stretching movements. A chemomechanical moving device of this type could function as a molecular machine or point the way to an artificial muscle.

—Philip R. Watson

Applied chemistry

During the past year research in applied chemistry led to developments concerning the controversial topic of cold fusion, extremely lightweight materials called aerogels, luminescent silicon, contact lenses, and food products.

Cold fusion. At a press conference in March 1989, electrochemists B. Stanley Pons of the University of Utah and Martin Fleischmann of the University of Southampton, England, announced a process for producing room-temperature, or cold, nuclear fusion. In their process an electric current is passed through a platinum wire electrode coiled around an electrode of palladium in an electrolyte solution of alkaline heavy water. (Heavy water contains atoms of deuterium [hydrogen-2], a heavy isotope of hydrogen, in place of the common hydrogen atoms present in ordinary water.) Their highly controversial "discovery" was hailed by some as the greatest scientific event of recent decades. In succeeding weeks, however, scientists around the world obtained conflicting results in their own attempts to detect the heat, neutrons, and hydrogen isotope tritium (hydrogen-3) that Pons and Fleischmann cited as evidence that fusion was actually occurring.

No unanimity on the reality of cold fusion had been reached by the end of 1991 (see *1993 Yearbook of Science and the Future* Year in Review: CHEMISTRY: *Applied chemistry*). Despite dismissive articles in mainstream science journals, the issue remained unsettled throughout 1992, although with less coverage as the media and many scientists lost interest.

308

Yet the quest for cold fusion failed to fade away, and the scientific community remained sharply polarized between the skeptical majority and a minority of cold fusion supporters.

On Jan. 2, 1992, at the Stanford Research Institute (SRI), Menlo Park, Calif., a gas outlet valve on an electrolytic cell similar to Pons and Fleischmann's cold fusion apparatus became accidentally blocked, and the pressurized oxygen-deuterium mixture ignited. The resulting explosion killed one research worker and injured three others, including electrochemist Michael McKubre, director of the SRI project, which had been funded since 1989 by the Electric Power Research Institute (EPRI), the research-and-development arm of the U.S. electric utility industry. In 1991 at the second annual Cold Fusion Conference at Como, Italy, McKubre had reported measuring reproducible and slow but steady "excess" heat in a deuterium-palladium electrolytic cell. A five-month investigation of the 1992 explosion concluded, however, that the accident was not related to excess heat caused by a runaway cold fusion reaction or by any kind of nuclear reaction.

The year 1992 saw the publication of several articles and at least one book devoted to cold fusion and an attempt to place it in a scientific context. In an article in the January–February issue of *American Scientist*, Denis L. Rousseau, a physical chemist at AT&T Bell Laboratories, characterized the controversy as a case study in "pathological science," a term devised by Nobel chemistry laureate Irving Langmuir to characterize "the science of things that aren't so." Rousseau condensed Langmuir's six "symptoms" of this "disease" to three and applied them to cold fusion and two other cases. In Rousseau's version of the symptoms, (1) "the effect being studied is often at the limits of detectability or has a very low statistical significance," (2) the investigator involved demonstrates "a readiness to disregard prevailing ideas and theories," and (3) "the investigator finds it nearly impossible to [carry out] . . . a critical series of experiments [to] . . . give a definitive answer—either the effect is real or it is not."

In a letter to the editor of *American Scientist*, Steven E. Jones, a physicist from Brigham Young University, Provo, Utah, and co-workers, whose claims for cold fusion have been much less flamboyant than those of Pons and Fleischmann, stated that "we have repeatedly explained the enormous differences in methods and results between [our group and Pons and Fleischmann's group]; . . . we have consistently adhered to standard peer-reviewed channels." They pointed out that "it is possible for there to exist a tiny nuclear effect in deuterium-charged solids without there being measurable 'excess heat' produced by 'cold fusion' in electrochemical cells." They cited their ongoing "collaborative experiments with physicists at Los Alamos National Laboratory, the University of Bologna [Italy], the University of Tokyo and elsewhere," which were "not mentioned in Dr. Rousseau's article even though results have been published and presented at scientific meetings. . . . Numerous investigations of low-level nuclear reactions in deuterided solids are proceeding worldwide with both positive and null effects reported. We and others have reported signals suggestive of neutrons of fusion origin whose source we wish to understand." They asked for the "protection for small or nascent areas of physics against the 'tyranny of the majority' " and "appeal[ed] for tolerance as we try to sort out our findings."

In reply Rousseau stated, "I do not wish to stifle continued and future work by Dr. Jones and his collaborators in the nascent area of the study of possible low-level nuclear reactions in condensed matter." He concluded that "once their findings are sorted out, they could uncover some interesting new physics."

In March, at a press briefing in Washington, D.C., held to mark the third anniversary of Pons and Fleischmann's announcement, Eugene F. Mallove, author of the pro-cold fusion book *Fire from Ice: Searching for the Truth Behind the Cold Fusion Furor*, attacked the "arrogance" of the scientific establishment and "vested interests," which have ignored evidence for "massive amounts" of excess heat not explicable by any known chemical reaction and "weak traces" of tritium, neutrons, and charged particles. According to chemist John R. Huizenga, cochairman of the 1989 U.S. Department of Energy (DOE) panel of 22 scientific authorities who investigated the claims of cold fusion, such results violate the "well-founded results and principles of nuclear physics." At the briefing theoretical physicist Giu-

"Well, if you burned yourself, it can't be cold fusion."

liano Preparata of the University of Milan, who had proposed a theory to explain cold fusion, claimed that the scientific establishment is hostile because it "cannot tolerate an abrupt change in the paradigm." He also reported that Pons expected a demonstration device to be ready before the end of 1992, a promise that apparently was not fulfilled.

In early 1992 Huizenga's own book, *Cold Fusion: The Scientific Fiasco of the Century,* appeared. The author concluded that the affair shows that "the scientific process works by exposing and correcting its own errors," and he discussed the general lessons and caveats to be learned; for example, "Whenever the inability of qualified scientists to repeat an experiment is met by an onslaught of ad hoc excuses: Beware."

Although EPRI was funding some exploratory cold fusion research, no significant federal or state funds were allocated for the purpose in the U.S. Meanwhile, the focus of such research shifted to Japan, where more than 100 scientists at about 40 academic and industrial laboratories were investigating the phenomenon. Technova, Inc., a think tank based in Tokyo, was funding Pons and Fleischmann's latest research being carried out in France, and engineering professor Akito Takahashi of Osaka (Japan) University reported, but did not publish, findings of excess heat and neutrons from an electrolytic cell similar to that of Pons and Fleischmann. In July Japan's Ministry of International Trade and Industry (MITI) confirmed that in 1993 it would begin funding, to the extent of $1 million–$3 million annually, a five-year project to explore possible applications of "hydrogen energy" (MITI avoided the term *cold fusion*). This first significant government funding of such research in Japan was to involve researchers from universities and about 10 utility, electronics, and metallurgical firms and was to begin with small-scale projects and collection of data worldwide.

In late September, at the Massachusetts Institute of Technology, McKubre reported details of his group's consistent and reproducible production of excess heat from Pons-Fleischmann-type cells. Although the amount of heat was small, it was more than that expected from any known chemical reactions. For the first time, McKubre revealed the specific conditions required: (1) the palladium electrodes must be "loaded" with deuterium atoms from heavy water, (2) "loading" must be maintained for about 300 hours, a process facilitated by having the palladium rods coated with silicon or aluminum, and (3) the current run through the cell must exceed 200 milliamperes (thousandths of an ampere). Because neutrons or other products of nuclear reactions were not observed, McKubre, who admitted that "the effect is either real or some obscure artifact," could not explain the source of the heat.

As 1992 ended, a group of small but vocal advocates still believed in the reality of a process that could be an unlimited source of energy, while most scientists remained skeptical pending a definitive demonstration. In the words of astronomer and science popularizer Carl Sagan, "Extraordinary claims require extraordinary evidence." Such evidence apparently has yet to emerge.

Organic aerogels. Aerogels are strong, light, airy gels from which all the liquid has been removed, leaving a porous framework having interstices filled with air. These materials have been known since the 1930s, but recently the number of articles about them and their possible applications has increased tremendously (see *1992 Yearbook of Science and the Future* Year in Review: CHEMISTRY: *Applied chemistry*). Inorganic aerogels based on silica make good thermal insulators with possible applications in freezers and refrigerators and heat-storage-and-transport systems. Because nonporous organic materials generally have smaller thermal conductivities as solids than similar inorganic materials, X. Lu, M.C. Arduni-Schuster, J. Kuhn, O. Nilsson, and J. Fricke of the University of Würzburg, Germany, prepared and measured the conductivities of organic aerogels previously fabricated by R.W. Pekala of Lawrence Livermore National Laboratory, Livermore, Calif. Resorcinol-formaldehyde (RF) aerogels were synthesized by the base-catalyzed aqueous polycondensation of resorcinol (1,3-dihydroxybenzene) with formaldehyde, followed by substitution of the water in the gel pores, first by an organic solvent like acetone and then by carbon dioxide. Not only did the gels possess a record-low thermal conductivity, but they also exhibited considerable mechanical flexibility, compared with the more brittle inorganic silica aerogels. Organic aerogels may find application as substitutes for the insulating foams made with environmentally harmful chlorofluorocarbons (CFCs).

Luminescent silicon. Silicon, the second most abundant element in the Earth's crust and the basis for semiconductor and computer technology, had been considered "optically dead" until 1990, when porous silicon was found to glow intensely on stimulation with light or electricity. Previously, scientists seeking to couple optics to electronics to create a new hybrid field of optoelectronics had concentrated on light-emitting semiconductors like gallium arsenide or gallium phosphide and had neglected silicon.

Small colloidal suspensions of semiconductor particles in the 10-nanometer (nm) range (a nanometer is a billionth of a meter) are known to deviate in properties from those in the bulk condition. In 1992 chemists Michael J. Sailor, Julie L. Heinrich, Corrine L. Curtis, and Grace M. Credo and electrical and computer engineer Karen L. Kavanagh, all of the University of California at San Diego, used a

310

"convenient" procedure to prepare porous silicon by electrochemically etching a wafer of the pure, crystalline element. After exposure to ultraviolet light, the etched wafer was luminescent, emitting red-orange and orange-yellow light. The fragile wafer was then ultrasonically dispersed into organic solvents (toluene, methylene chloride, acetonitrile, or methanol) or water. The resulting colloidal suspension of fine silicon particles still luminesced after exposure to ultraviolet light. Analyses by transmission electron microscopy showed the particles to be irregular in shape with diameters in the nanometer-to-micrometer range (about 40 billionths to 40 millionths of an inch). The researchers prepared luminescent, composite plastic silicon films by adding polystyrene to a toluene suspension of the silicon particles and allowing the resulting solution to harden on a glass slide. The films glowed less intensely than the suspensions and luminesced at shorter wavelengths, but the light remained visible to the eye. According to the San Diego scientists, "In contrast to the gas-phase preparations of colloidal Si [silicon], this technique produces Si particles from high-purity semiconductor-grade substrates, resulting in a more convenient synthesis that avoids contamination by SiO_2 [silica] and other impurities." It also permits easier processing of the luminescent silicon into other forms.

Because different solvents change the reddish luminescence of porous silicon, Sailor and his coworkers also were able to use silicon to distinguish benzene (C_6H_6) from toluene (C_7H_8), similar substances that differ by only one carbon and two hydrogen atoms. Together with graduate student Vincent V. Doan, Sailor formed patterns of luminescence on a porous silicon wafer by projecting light onto it, which created small electrical currents in the wafer. Varying the current while etching the wafer was found to change the color of the luminescence, and Doan and Sailor were able to project a picture of a face onto the silicon during etching so as to make the wafer glow with the image. Although the 20-micrometer (about 0.8 thousandths of an inch) resolution that they obtained does not compare with the one-micrometer resolution possible in integrated circuits, their technique could be useful for connecting adjacent computer chips with optical fibers, rather than with copper fibers, for faster computing.

In a later development Doan and Sailor used their etching process to imprint a complex pattern on the silicon chip's surface. They projected a reduced black-and-white image of George Washington from a U.S. $1 bill onto a 0.5-sq cm (0.0775-sq in) wafer electrode immersed in an etching bath of a 50:50 (by volume) solution of 49% aqueous hydrofluoric acid and 95% ethanol contained in an electrochemical cell. Photoelectrochemical etching for 30 minutes at

a current density of 100 microamperes (millionths of an ampere) per square centimeter transferred the image to the wafer. Although such patterning had been previously produced by photoresist and other techniques limited to black-and-white images, this was the first time gray-scale images had been imprinted on luminescent silicon photoelectrochemically.

Doan and Sailor's technique has led to three separate and simultaneous ways of storing information on porous silicon. First, viewed under visible light, the etched image appears iridescent because of thin-film optical interference, an effect that may be useful for designing optical waveguides of porous silicon. Second, after irradiation with ultraviolet light, the image photoluminesces red-orange with intensities proportional to the light and dark areas of the original image, a property that may prove useful for optical data storage or for future optoelectronic circuits requiring a variety of emission wavelengths. This property may also help make possible an optical computer, which, because light travels faster than electrons, would work faster than electronic computers. Third, photoetching a grid or multiline pattern produces a three-dimensional diffraction grating, a procedure with possible applications in optical or holographic display, waveguide, and data-storage technologies. (For further information on luminescent silicon, *see* Year in Review: PHYSICS: *Condensed-matter physics*.)

Contact lenses. A silicon-oxygen compound, siloxane, was being used in the preparation of strong, flexible, extended-wear soft contact lenses. Chemist Jay Künzler and co-workers of Bausch & Lomb, Inc., Rochester, N.Y., produced a lens material 25 times more permeable to oxygen than previously marketed lenses. Because a lack of oxygen irritates the tissue in the eyes, the new polymer blends may lead to carefree lenses that can be worn for weeks without being removed.

Because unmodified siloxanes do not wet easily, lenses made from them are uncomfortable, and because they attract lipids (fatty secretions from the eye and body), they become cloudy and distorted. Therefore, Künzler's group attached fluorine atoms to siloxane molecules and copolymerized these polymers with other fluorinated compounds, resulting in a material less likely to attract lipids. They also attached a wetting agent to the polymers that, on boiling in the saline solutions with which lens wearers treat their lenses, opens its ring structure to expose its hydrophilic (water-loving) groups so that the lens is easily wet by tears. The researchers were also improving the material so that the lens does not adhere to the eye. Their goal is to produce "the ultimate extended-wear lens" such that "the eye doesn't even know it has a lens on."

Food products. In countries like the U.S., where a large proportion of the population is overweight and

A new extended-wear contact lens, made from fluorinated, copolymerized siloxane, is 25 times more permeable to oxygen than previously marketed lenses and thus less likely to irritate eye tissue from prolonged contact.

the average citizen consumes close to 40 kg (90 lb) of sugar annually, low-calorie sweeteners and sugar substitutes are important products and the continuing goal of researchers. In 1992 a new, markedly different low-calorie sweetener named Splenda that looks, feels, and tastes like sugar began to be marketed in Canada after approval for sale in supermarkets and pharmacies by the Canadian Department of National Health and Welfare. According to Les Klainseck, product director for McNeil Consumer Products Co., Guelph, Ont., Splenda is not a synthetic product but is based on natural cane sugar; it is marketed in granular form like ordinary sugar rather than in tablets or drops, and unlike some other artificial sweeteners, it will not decompose when used in cooking and baking. It is produced from cane sugar (sucrose) modified in ways that make it 600 times sweeter and much harder to digest. Consequently, the human body absorbs only 2 calories per teaspoon, compared with 16 calories for sucrose. In early 1993 the sweetener was awaiting approval in the U.S. and other countries.

At the spring 1992 American Chemical Society (ACS) national meeting in San Francisco, Calif., Arthur M. Spanier reported that he, James A. Miller, and co-workers at the U.S. Department of Agriculture's Southern Regional Research Center, New Orleans, La., had isolated a molecule from fresh beef that gives meat its natural beefy flavor. Called beefy meaty peptide (BMP), it consists of eight amino acids (the building blocks of protein) bonded together in a chain and is produced, probably by enzymes, from a bigger, still unknown protein during the aging of beef, a fact that may account for the preferred taste of aged beef over fresh. BMP is also produced when meat proteins are broken down by tenderizers or marinades, which also improve the flavor of cheaper cuts of meat. In a similar way, BMP could improve flavor if it were added to less expensive meat such as the precooked beef used in convenience and institutional foods, which constitutes 35% of U.S. beef. According to Spanier, "It could make a chuck steak taste like a T-bone."

Although other flavoring agents are made of amino acids and sugars, BMP is the first significant naturally occurring flavor peptide to be discovered. Unlike monosodium glutamate (MSG), another flavor-enhancing amino acid derivative, to which some persons are allergic, Spanier speculated that BMP is "probably hypoallergenic, or people would be allergic to beef." He expected little difficulty in obtaining the approval of the Food and Drug Administration needed to market BMP in the U.S. because it already occurs naturally in food. Spanier and his co-workers were seeking compounds similar to BMP in poultry and pork and were attempting to identify the enzymes and proteins involved in the formation of BMP.

Anniversaries. The year 1992 marked a number of anniversaries related to applied chemistry. In 1792, 200 years ago, the Chemical Society of Philadelphia, one of the world's earliest societies of chemists (sometimes mistakenly considered the earliest), was founded. In 1842, 150 years ago, John Bennet Lawes, an English agricultural scientist, patented a method for manufacturing the first artificial chemical fertilizer, still used today, which he called superphosphate. In 1892, 100 years ago, British chemists Charles Frederick Cross and Edward J. Bevan developed viscose or xanthate rayon, an improvement over earlier types of rayon. Also in 1892 Scottish chemist and physicist James Dewar constructed a double-walled flask (Dewar flask) with a vacuum between the walls; now known as the thermos bottle, it is used to keep food and beverages hot or cold.

Fifty years ago, on Dec. 2, 1942, the atomic age began when the last control rod of cadmium (a metal that efficiently absorbs neutrons) was partly extracted from the first atomic reactor, or atomic pile, built of 40,000 graphite bricks containing spheres of uranium and uranium oxide, resulting in a self-sustaining nuclear chain reaction. This event, which led to the production of plutonium and the atomic bomb and which ushered in the nuclear power industry, took place under conditions of strict wartime secrecy in a former squash court under the west stands of Stagg Field, a stadium at the University of Chicago, which had terminated its football program several years earlier. American physicist Arthur H. Compton notified James B. Conant, the chemist who was president of Harvard University, of the success of the project by a long-distance code message: "The Italian navigator has landed in the New World." The Italian-born physicist Enrico Fermi, who had immigrated with his Jewish wife to the U.S. after accepting the Nobel Prize for Physics in Stockholm in December 1938, was in charge of the project.

—George B. Kauffman

See also Feature Articles: THE CHEMISTRY OF ULTRASOUND; COMPUTER-AIDED MOLECULAR DESIGN.

Defense research

Defense research underwent a significant shift during the past year with the election of a new administration in the United States, one that promised to accelerate the transfer of military technologies to consumer and industrial markets. Throughout the cold war the foundation of U.S. science policy had been a reliance on military support of the basic sciences in order to stimulate critical technologies, initially to meet the nation's defense commitments and later to be made available for nonmilitary purposes. That strategy was spelled out by Pres. Harry Truman's science adviser, Vannevar Bush, in his post-World War II report *Science: The Endless Frontier*. It enabled the U.S. to check Communist aggression, but it assigned a lower priority (and fewer government resources) to the commercialization of military technology. Although many technological spin-offs did occur during the early years of the cold war, such as advanced electronics for commercial aviation, space exploration, personal computers, and other consumer products, the process was cumbersome. As a result, other countries seized leadership in developing such products as videocassette recorders (VCRs) and the new liquid crystal displays (LCDs). When the administration of U.S. Pres. Bill Clinton took office in January 1993, it set out to reverse this process. Civilian research was given top priority in an effort to rebuild the nation's technology base and make U.S. products more competitive in international markets.

In response to Vannevar Bush's report, the Clinton team issued a report of its own, *Technology: The Engine of Economic Growth,* in which it announced the change in policy. "America cannot continue to rely on trickle-down technology from the military to maintain competitiveness of its high-tech and manufacturing industries," the report stated. "Civilian industry, not the military, is the driving force behind advanced technology today. Only by strengthening our civilian technology base can we solve the twin problems of national security and economic competitiveness."

The report also spelled out the distinction between science and technology policies: "Technology policy picks up where science policy leaves off. It is not limited to just research and development. It also focuses on the rapid application of new ideas."

During the 1950s and '60s the military services, with their large research and development budgets and their large purchases of advanced electronic devices, virtually created the modern solid-state electronics industry (so named because it replaced the less reliable vacuum tubes of the past with devices made of solid crystalline materials, initially in transistors and later in integrated circuits). The large missile programs, in particular, created the economies of scale that stimulated explosive growth in the electronics industry.

By the 1980s this technology flow had begun to reverse itself. The Clinton team's report cited an early microprocessor chip, the Intel 8088, which was credited with the success of the Patriot air defense system during the war in the Persian Gulf. Yet in 1993 that chip was considered so outdated by the electronics industry that it was no longer used in personal computers. Also, because the fiercely competitive consumer electronics business forces companies to rush their products to market or lose sales to their competitors, the companies have often found themselves hampered by the stringent procurement regulations and specifications of the military in developing what have come to be known as "dual-use technologies."

To support its new policy, the Clinton administration proposed in January 1993 to shift $7.6 billion— 10% of the $76 billion that the federal government spends each year on research and development— from the Department of Defense to civilian agencies. This would amount to more than $30 billion during the next four years and reduce the Pentagon's share of total federally sponsored research from 60 to 50%. Among the technologies targeted for these funds were ceramics, computer software, sensors, photonics, robotics, computer-aided manufacturing, biotechnology, composite materials, artificial intelligence, superconductivity, and fiber-optic communications.

The shift in funds would also change the role of the nation's 726 federal laboratories, most of which were working for the Departments of Defense and Energy. They had an annual budget of $23 billion and devoted about half of that to military research and development. The administration plan called for those laboratories that could contribute to U.S. competitiveness to assign 10–20% of their budgets to establishing joint ventures with industry.

In the past the focal point for federal support of critical technologies had been the Pentagon's Defense Advanced Research Projects Agency (DARPA), but the new administration began looking for an alternative among civilian agencies. The principal beneficiary of this search was a smaller counterpart of DARPA within the U.S. Department of Commerce known as the National Institute of Standards and Technology (NIST, formerly the National Bureau of Standards). Under the administration of Pres. George Bush, NIST had a budget of $68 million for its Advanced Technology Program (ATP), which was established to assist industries in developing innovative technologies and had planned to fund about 40 projects in 1993 in such areas as neural networks, thermal insulators, and plastic-recycling methods.

313

Defense research

The Clinton administration called for an immediate doubling of NIST's budget, and ATP was expected to grow to a $500 million effort.

One of the key areas of defense research with both military and commercial applications in which DARPA continued to play a role in 1993 was a program to regain U.S. leadership in the active-matrix LCD business. Active-matrix LCDs are advanced versions of the passive-matrix LCDs used in digital watches. But, instead of displaying only pre-programmed letters and numbers in black and white, active-matrix LCDs can display any information in the full range of color. They were expected to be the critical enabling technology for such new products as high-definition television (HDTV) sets, advanced laptop computers, videophones, and future weapons systems. Although the U.S. pioneered this technology more than 30 years ago, its share of a worldwide market estimated at $3.5 billion in 1992 had shrunk to 5%. This lack of a domestic source of supply was considered a potential national security problem because these high-performance flat screens are used in navy ships, armored vehicles, cockpits of fighter aircraft, military simulators, and command and control centers. Advanced LCDs were also expected to be essential for the next-generation HDTV sets that electronics industry observers hoped would sweep the consumer marketplace in the mid-1990s.

The DARPA program, launched in late 1992, was aimed at creating a joint venture between industry and government known as the U.S. Display Consortium (USDC). This new organization would resemble Sematech, an earlier industry consortium established by the U.S. government in Austin, Texas, to regain American leadership in semiconductor production equipment. In each case the participating companies would share information during the basic research phase but would be free to compete with one another when the technology evolved to the point of production and consumer sales. The significance of this cooperative effort, according to the observers, was that advanced displays were expected to be as important to the electronics industry in the 1990s as computer chips and other semiconductor products were during the 1970s and 1980s.

These new partnerships, which had been opposed by the preceding Reagan and Bush administrations on the grounds that they represented a wasteful and innovation-inhibiting "industrial policy" of government toward industry, drew generally favorable comments from leading observers. Kent Hughes, president of the Council on Competitiveness, a private group based in Washington, D.C., told the *New York Times* that the changed atmosphere was "a watershed" in government-industry relations. Erich Bloch, also a member of the council and a former director of the National Science Foundation, called

Les Aspin (foreground), formerly a Democratic congressman from Wisconsin, was appointed U.S. secretary of defense in 1993. In Congress he had served as chairman of the House Armed Services Committee.

it "a paradigm shift" in the federal role in technology. Dissenters, such as conservative economist Murray Weidenbaum of Washington University, St. Louis, Mo., warned that Congress would be tempted to vote money for marginal projects in an attempt to please constituents. Other critics complained that any industrial policy meant "putting the government into the business of picking (technological) winners and losers," although they conceded that this had been a common practice among other industrialized nations.

The new administration also moved to coordinate military and civilian research under Vice Pres. Al Gore, who had been active in science policy issues when he was a member of the U.S. Senate. There he championed a national broadband communications network using fiber optics and other technologies developed under military sponsorship. "Such a network could do for the productivity of individuals at their places of work and learning what the interstate highway of the 1950s did for the productivity of the nation's travel and distribution system," the Clinton team's report noted.

Even more significant than the change in leadership in the White House, from the standpoint of defense research, may have been the change in leadership at the Department of Defense. The new secretary of defense, Les Aspin, a former Democratic congressman from Wisconsin, had accumulated considerable expertise in military issues while serving as chairman of the House Armed Services Committee. He supported efforts to maintain U.S. superiority in military technologies but generally opposed large new programs such as the Strategic Defense Initiative, the so-called Star Wars space-based antimissile system. Instead, he favored testing new technologies in prototype systems to the point where the technologies would be available for operational systems but then deferring the decision on production until international conditions required it, a policy called "fly but not buy."

Aspin's philosophy, which was expected to be influential in the new administration, was to upgrade existing weapons systems with new technologies as much as possible. New avionics (aviation electronics) equipment would extend the operational lives of existing aircraft, for example, and would be much less expensive than developing new aircraft. One example was the air force's proposed next-generation fighter, the F-22, which had experienced weight and cost increases. Critics of the program contended that the performance of any fighter aircraft depended more on advanced avionics than on the airframe and that it would, therefore, be more efficient to upgrade the existing F-15 and F-16 fighters than to proceed with a new aircraft.

This approach was expected to shift defense funds away from procurement and toward technology-development programs and system modifications. However, this strategy posed a problem to the defense industry: maintaining a sufficient production capability to meet the requirements of a larger conflict than the one in the Persian Gulf. Also, when only a few advanced weapons systems are produced, the cost for each one is greater than if research and the other start-up costs could be amortized over a larger production run.

The issue of maintaining a production base had also troubled the Bush administration since the end of the cold war, and one of Aspin's proposed solutions was what became known as selective low-rate procurements. "For some systems, a strategy of upgrading will not be sufficient to maintain a viable production base," Aspin said. "In such cases, we should consider maintaining a low volume procurement rate to sustain critical suppliers." Another approach was what Aspin called "silver bullet procurements . . . highly capable systems procured in limited quantities and reserved for operations where a high-tech advantage could maximize U.S. leverage."

The impact of this new strategy on the defense industry was expected to be severe. In a year-end analysis of the aerospace portion of the industry, Don Fuqua, president of the Aerospace Industries Association, reported that U.S. aerospace sales fell from $139 billion in 1991 to $134 billion in 1992. He predicted a further decline to $126.5 billion in 1993. Almost all of this decline could be attributed to falling military sales of aerospace products—from

Boeing Helicopters

The Boeing Sikorsky RAH-66 Comanche armed reconnaissance helicopter, under development for the U.S. Army, is designed to provide tactical data from large areas during rapidly changing combat situations.

$56 billion in 1991 to $52 billion in 1992 to a projected $46 billion in 1993, according to Fuqua. Modest increases in sales of commercial aircraft partially offset the industry's downward trend, but Fuqua reported that industry employment fell by 117,000 jobs in 1992; projected for 1993 was another decline of 47,000 to a total employment level of about one million.

Another industry observer, Peter F. McCloskey, president of the Electronic Industries Association, warned of the difficulties of converting a defense industrial base to commercial production and then reconstituting it in times of emergency. In testimony before Congress, McCloskey said that once a defense company has shifted to commercial production, the job skills unique to defense production "may not be reconstituted in a timely way to meet national security surge requirements."

Among the specific defense research projects that faced the new administration were the air force's C-17 transport aircraft and the experimental V-22 tilt-rotor Osprey (an aircraft that combined features of helicopters and fixed-wing aircraft in order to achieve greater speed while operating from small landing areas) for the Marine Corps. On the basis of the important contributions of airlift and mobility to the allied victory in the Gulf war, the new administration at least tentatively endorsed both programs. However, the Pentagon also continued to study extending the life of the air force's existing transport aircraft, the C-141. An army program to develop a new helicopter, the RAH-66 Comanche, continued, but at a slower pace, during the past year. A joint venture between the air force and navy to develop an even more futuristic aircraft, the A-X multimission combat plane, was limited to studies on paper.

The new administration also faced decisions on whether to proceed with two other research projects with defense implications: the $8 billion Supercon-

A U.S. Air Force C-141 cargo plane lands at Mogadishu, Somalia, on Dec. 9, 1992, as U.S. marines in armored vehicles hold back the crowd. The plane was the first U.S. military aircraft to land in Somalia as part of the effort to provide food for thousands of starving Somalis.

ducting Super Collider being developed for the Department of Energy to study subatomic particles and the $40 billion manned space station *Freedom* of the National Aeronautics and Space Administration. As a candidate, Clinton had voiced support for both programs during the 1992 election campaign.

—John Rhea

Earth sciences

During a year marked by unusual weather, an El Niño, and several destructive earthquakes, Earth scientists continued their efforts to increase understanding of these phenomena. They also devoted considerable research to such subjects as mass extinctions, plate tectonics, paleontology, groundwater flow, and ozone depletion.

Atmospheric sciences

During the past year the atmospheric sciences continued to be in the forefront of public attention as new technological achievements were made. Also, the weather itself was particularly noteworthy.

Notable weather events. In August 1992 Hurricane Andrew caused up to $30 billion worth of damage across extreme southern Florida and the southwestern coast of Louisiana. Typhoon Omar devastated the island of Guam during the same month, and on September 11 Hurricane Iniki struck the island of Kauai, Hawaii. Coincidentally, each of these storms directly affected tropical cyclone forecasting centers in Miami, Fla., Honolulu, and Guam.

Extreme weather conditions also occurred elsewhere. August 1992 was the second coldest in 98 years across the eastern two-thirds of the United States, while the Middle East and northeastern Africa had one of the coldest winters on record. Ontario had the coldest July in 100 years. Crop damage associated with the cool weather occurred in western Canada, a result of early fall snows and freezes. In October 1992 areas of northwestern Siberia reached $-50°$ C ($-58°$ F), while in early October some 1,000 caribou migrated to Fairbanks, Alaska, from the Alaskan Range for the first time in 50 years. In contrast, from December 1991 to February 1992 large portions of the United States and southwestern Canada, northwestern Europe, and central Asia had one of the warmest winters on record.

An El Niño that occurred in late 1991 and 1992 apparently contributed to unusual weather in many locations throughout the world, including the warm winter in much of North America and the abnormally cold winter in the Middle East. An El Niño occurs when exceptionally warm waters develop west of the tropical South American coast, resulting in major changes in the flow of heat and moisture to higher latitudes.

The eruption of Mt. Pinatubo in the Philippines in June 1991 also exerted a major effect on the weather. The eruption apparently resulted in a global temperature decrease of more than $0.5°$ C ($0.9°$ F) by May 1992, with a Northern Hemisphere decrease of almost $1°$ C ($1.8°$ F), according to Ellsworth Dutton of the Climate Monitoring and Diagnostics Laboratory, Boulder, Colo. Thus, the extreme cool weather observed during the past year could be attributed, at least in part, to the reduction in solar radiation reaching the Earth's surface as a result of the volcanic sulfates in the stratosphere. The sulfates also caused a reduction in the ozone layer over the tropics by as much as 6%, according to Guy Brasseur and Claire Granier of the U.S. National Center for Atmospheric Research (NCAR), Boulder, Colo.

Aerosols injected into the atmosphere as a result of human activities during the 1991 Gulf war apparently had less of an impact on the weather than many had expected. The World Meteorological Organization (WMO) concluded that there were no global effects from the Kuwaiti oil fires that burned long after the war. The WMO scientists noted that the smoke from the fires never rose above 6 km (3.7 mi).

Trace gases. Atmospheric trace gas concentrations continued to be intensively observed. Among recent conclusions was the consensus that global methane accumulation in the atmosphere had been slowing, a conclusion based on 10,000 air samples collected at 45 sites around the world. In 1983 the concentration increase was 13.3 parts per billion by volume per year, while in 1990 the rate had decreased to 9.5 parts per billion. While the reason for the reduced rate of methane input was not known, global concentrations would begin declining in about 15 years if the trend continued, according to scientists from the U.S. National Oceanic and Atmospheric Administration (NOAA) and the University of Colorado.

The Mauna Loa (Hawaii) carbon dioxide record revealed a 12% increase in the mean annual concentration in 32 years, with the 1990 level at 354 parts per million by volume, on the basis of data summarized by the Carbon Dioxide Information Analysis Center. Chlorofluorocarbons (CFCs) had also been increasing, with concentrations through 1985 of nearly 400 parts per trillion by volume of CFC-12 and 300 parts per trillion of CFC-11. These

Mobile home park in southern Dade county, Florida, lies in ruins after being struck by Hurricane Andrew in August 1992. The storm caused up to $30 billion in damage in Florida and Louisiana.

© John Lopinot/Palm Beach Post—Sygma

two forms of CFCs act as greenhouse gases and also rise to the mid-stratosphere, where they decompose, releasing halogen atoms that cause a chain-reaction destruction of the ozone. Levels of nitrous oxide, another greenhouse gas, have been increasing as well.

Air pollution. The amount of solar ultraviolet radiation reaching the Earth's surface in rural areas had decreased by 5 to 18% since the beginning of the Industrial Revolution, a result of the scattering of electromagnetic radiation by pollutant sulfate aerosols in the troposphere, according to S.C. Liu of NOAA, S.A. McKeen of the University of Colorado, and Sasha Madronich of NCAR. L.A. Barrie of the Atmospheric Environment Service, Ontario, reported on Arctic haze, which is a result of pollutant aerosols—mostly acidic sulfur compounds—that reduce visibility. These pollutants were transported into the Arctic mainly from sources in Europe and the former Soviet Union. The haze was 10 to 20 times more intense during the winter. Acid deposition onto the Agassiz Glacier of northern Ellesmere Island in the Arctic has been noted since the mid-1950s.

The WMO/UN Environment Program's Intergovernmental Panel on Climate Change published a report in 1992 updating general-circulation model estimates of global warming due to the addition of carbon dioxide, methane, and other trace gases to the atmosphere. Higher concentrations of these gases reduce the heat loss from the Earth by long-wave electromagnetic radiation (the absorption and partial downward emittance of this radiation by the trace gases is referred to as the greenhouse effect). Their estimate, made originally in 1990, of a warming effect of about 0.3° C (0.5° F) per decade remained in force, although their models did not include the possible cooling effects of sulfate aerosols, stratospheric ozone depletion, or landscape changes.

Climate change. Observations of climate change also continued. In its 1991 summary, the World Glacier Monitoring Service reported that there was considerable variability in the status of mountain glaciers, with gains in mass occurring in some humid coastal regions such as Norway. Such variability was characteristic of the current time period from about 1950, replacing the almost uniform shrinking tendency of earlier decades.

G.J. Kukla and T.R. Karl, reporting for the U.S. Department of Energy's Carbon Dioxide Research Division, found that the surface warming trend indicated in the U.S., China, and the former Soviet Union since 1951 had occurred primarily at night. They suggested that the warming was a result of increased cloud cover.

The U.S. Greenland Ice Sheet Project Two and the European Greenland Icecore Project continued to collect and analyze ice cores from central Green-

Earth sciences

land, looking for changes in the cores' composition of such gases as carbon dioxide, methane, and dust over as much as 200,000 years with an accuracy (resolution) of ± one century. Yearly resolution to at least 20,000 years ago was expected to be attainable. A similar coring project was proposed by the U.S. Ice Core Working Group for an area in West Antarctica in order to correlate ice sheet changes in the Northern and Southern hemispheres. Among the critical questions to be asked was whether continental glaciation is a gradual process described by the precession, obliquity, and ellipticity of the Earth's orbit (the Milankovitch hypothesis) or a sudden onset, occurring within a few years or decades, as proposed by W.S. Broecker and G.H. Denton in a 1989 article in the journal *Geochimica et Cosmochimica Acta*. (For additional information on the Greenland Ice Sheet Project Two, *see* Feature Article: CLIMATE IN THE ICE.)

In June 1992 representatives of 178 nations signed accords at the "Earth Summit" in Rio de Janeiro, Brazil, agreeing that the world's industrial nations would seek to cap emissions of carbon dioxide and methane at 1990 levels. This represented an attempt to reduce the human impact on the atmosphere, even though the magnitude and even the sign of a global climate change remained uncertain.

The World Climate Research Program, the International Geosphere-Biosphere Program, and the Human Dimensions of Global Environmental Change Program—established by such international agencies as the WMO, the International Council of Scientific Unions, the Intergovernmental Oceanographic Commission, and the International Social Science Council—represented global efforts to investigate the interdisciplinary questions regarding potential climate change. The U.S. government funded climate-change research at a level of $1,110,000,000 in 1992 and $1,372,000,000 in 1993.

Ozone depletion. Concern regarding the hole in the ozone layer continued during the year as a large reduction in ozone concentrations over Antarctica occurred during the Southern Hemisphere spring. The loss of ozone is attributed to chemical reactions in polar stratospheric clouds that are caused by such gases as human-generated CFCs and by the isolation of the Antarctic stratosphere from the remainder of the atmosphere during the Antarctic spring. A reduction of ozone in the stratosphere increases the levels of solar ultraviolet radiation transmitted down to the troposphere. High levels of this electromagnetic radiation have been associated with skin cancer. Ozone decreased in the stratosphere between 1979 and 1991 by about 5.3% per decade at latitude 45° S and by 3.4% per decade at latitude 45° N, according to a March 1992 report of the U.S. Office of Environment and Energy. By contrast, at the equator there was no discernible trend in ozone during this time period. The Upper Atmosphere Research Satellite, launched on Sept. 12, 1991, was providing data on chlorine monoxide, ozone, sulfur dioxide, and water vapor in the Earth's stratosphere and mesosphere. This information was critical for understanding stratospheric chemistry. U.S. National Aeronautics and Space Administration scientists found that the reduction of stratospheric ozone in the Arctic at the end of the 1991–92 Northern Hemisphere winter was less than expected, despite record levels of ozone-depleting chemicals such as chlorine monoxide. A rise in stratospheric temperatures in late January 1992 apparently prevented the formation of polar stratospheric clouds. These clouds are necessary for large-scale rapid ozone depletion, such as that found each year in the Antarctic late winter.

As required by the Clean Air Act Amendments of 1990, the U.S. Environmental Protection Agency banned the sale and distribution of certain chemical products believed to contribute to stratospheric ozone depletion. These included noncommercial cleaning fluids containing CFCs. U.S. Pres. George Bush announced that he was moving the closeout of CFCs in the U.S. from the year 2000 to 1995.

Measurement systems. New observational technologies were introduced during the past year. A network of 29 wind profilers became operational in 15 central states in the U.S. They would provide weather forecasters with hourly profiles of winds throughout the troposphere at those sites, in contrast to the routine 12-hour-interval data available at radiosonde balloon soundings elsewhere.

The introduction of next-generation Doppler radars (WSR-88s) to operational forecasting continued with the acceptance of the first two in Houston, Texas, and Sterling, Va., in June 1992. Using this new technology, forecasters increased the amount of warning time from the previous 0–4 minutes to 20 minutes. Unlike prior weather service radars, Doppler radars can measure wind speed and direction inside thunderstorms and in the prestorm environment. Eventually, 141 WSR-88 systems were to be installed in the continental U.S.

These efforts were part of the $4.4 billion modernization of the U.S. National Weather Service. Other components of this program included the planned launch of the first next-generation geostationary meteorological satellite in early 1994, the replacement of human observers at airports, and the installation of automated surface weather observing systems at currently unmonitored sites.

Field programs. The four-month field phase of the Tropical Ocean Global Atmosphere program's Coupled Ocean-Atmosphere Response Experiments began on Nov. 1, 1992. The program was located in the equatorial Pacific Ocean, including Papua

318

The WSR-88D, a new Doppler weather surveillance radar, increases the warning time for severe storms from the previous 0– 4 minutes to 20 minutes. Unlike previous weather service radars, Doppler radars can measure wind speed and direction inside thunderstorms and in the prestorm environment.

New Guinea and the Solomon Islands, and involved approximately 700 scientists and support personnel from around the world. With the warmest ocean water on the planet, this region receives nearly 5 m (16.4 ft) of rain each year and contributes significantly to the Earth's energy and water budget. An understanding of weather in this region is essential for improved weather forecasts and climate studies. (For additional information, *see* Oceanography, below.)

The introduction of sulfate aerosols to the oceanic atmosphere by certain forms of phytoplankton around the Azores in the eastern Atlantic Ocean was investigated during the Atlantic Stratocumulus Transition Experiment in June 1992. The phytoplankton release dimethyl sulfide gas, which is oxidized to form sulfate particles that have the potential for significantly influencing the radiative properties of stratocumulus clouds. Such clouds are an important influence on the amount of radiation received and emitted by the Earth.

—Roger A. Pielke

Geologic sciences

Mass extinctions and plate tectonics were among the subjects that occupied the attention of many geologists during the past year. Important discoveries were made by paleontologists.

Geology and geochemistry. *Mass extinctions.* The search for the site of the cataclysmic event believed to have initiated the mass extinction at the end of the Cretaceous Period about 65 million years ago contin-

ued unabated during the past year. Scientists came to general agreement that the Chicxulub structure, which lies buried beneath the thick limestones of the Yucatán Peninsula and the adjacent Caribbean Sea, was caused by the impact of an asteroid or comet. Drill cores from the site that were thought to have been lost were recovered, and they contained additional evidence of a high-velocity impact in the form of pronounced fragmentation of surrounding rocks and the presence of minerals whose structure revealed that they had been subjected to extremely high shock pressures. The exact time of the impact was not yet fixed, but stratigraphic evidence was consistent with a date corresponding to the end of the Cretaceous Period. The impact consequently became a leading candidate for the cause of the mass extinction that occurred at that time.

A major impact such as this must have resulted in the ejection of a huge quantity of particulate material into the atmosphere, even the finest fraction of which must have settled within a few years. Longer lasting would have been the effect of chemical alterations to the atmosphere, which would depend to a significant degree on the character of the rocks at the impact site. The Chicxulub impact penetrated thousands of meters of carbonate sediments that had accumulated at the site by the end of the Cretaceous. This would have resulted in the sudden release of carbon dioxide and a consequent heating of the atmosphere by means of the greenhouse effect. Paleobotanical and oxygen-isotope studies revealed, however, that at the beginning of the Tertiary there was a period of cooling, followed by the expected warming lasting thousands of years. William McKinnon of Washington University, St. Louis, Mo., suggested that this initial cooling can be explained by the vaporization of massive deposits of anhydrite present at the Chicxulub impact site; this vaporization would have released sulfur dioxide into the stratosphere, where it would have combined with water vapor derived from the vaporized ocean. The resulting sulfuric-acid aerosol would have scattered visible solar radiation, causing a cooling of the stratosphere and troposphere and an interruption of photosynthesis because of a darkening of the Earth's surface. This period of cold darkness would have lasted longer than any caused by dust in the atmosphere, coming to an end eventually as the sulfuric acid, being in aerosol form, settled to the surface of the Earth to make its own, more direct, contribution to the extinction of plants and animals.

Amid the recent preoccupation with the destructive effects of meteorite impacts, it is important to remember that obviously not all kinds of organisms suffered extinction. What characteristics distinguished those organisms that survived from those that perished? Studies of marine organisms have shown that those forms in food chains that depended directly on the primary productivity of living photosynthetic organisms were more likely to become extinct than those in food chains that depended primarily on organic remains. This finding was consistent with the conclusion that an interruption of photosynthesis during the period of darkness following the impact would have been a principal factor in extinction.

A similar cause of differential survival might have operated among terrestrial organisms. Peter Sheehan of the Milwaukee (Wis.) Public Museum and David Fastovsky of the University of Rhode Island studied fossil faunas from the Cretaceous Hell Creek formation, which lies just below the boundary between the Cretaceous and Tertiary periods, and the Tertiary Tullock formation, which lies just above. They concluded that 90% of the species in freshwater assemblages and only 12% of land-dwelling species survived into the Tertiary. The authors suggested that the difference in survival rate may reflect the fact that the terrestrial food chain—which included such forms as dinosaurs, lizards, and mammals—tended to be dependent on the primary productivity of living photosynthetic organisms. The freshwater food chain—which included species of fish, aquatic amphibians, and crocodiles—would, on the other hand, have been largely dependent on plant and animal remains as a source of organic carbon. These remains would have persisted after the impact. Sheehan and Fastovsky cautioned that the pattern of extinction inferred from the Hell Creek and Tullock faunas could not, without further studies, be regarded as typical of those across the entire Cretaceous-Tertiary boundary.

The attention of geologists focused on the sites of impacts believed to have been the cause of mass extinctions. A growing conviction that these catastrophic events had occurred frequently throughout the history of the Earth, however, led increasingly to their invocation in geologic explanations of all kinds. C. Wylie Poag of the U.S. Geological Survey and his colleagues attributed the origin of a marine boulder bed—covering more than 15,000 sq km (5,800 sq mi) beneath the Chesapeake Bay and the adjacent Atlantic coastal plain—to an impact-generated wave train that scoured the ancient continental shelf in late Eocene time, about 35 million–40 million years ago. The bed consists of chaotically mixed boulders, cobbles, and finer materials, including impact ejecta, derived from sediments ranging from the Cretaceous to the Eocene in age (135 million—35 million years ago). The bed is similar in age and character to a layer of impact ejecta discovered during drilling on the continental shelf off New Jersey. The profiles of reflected seismic waves reveal the presence of a possible impact crater in the same area.

Plate tectonics. During the first half of the 20th century, geologic knowledge accumulated against the background of the 19th-century view that, although great changes might occur locally, the Earth remains overall in a steady state. Beginning with the growing evidence for continental drift in the 1950s and the introduction of the theory of plate tectonics in the 1960s, geologists were increasingly regarding the Earth's history as a succession of irreversible changes; that is, as evolutionary. Just as plate tectonics began to be widely accepted, Luis Alvarez' 1980 hypothesis that an asteroid struck the Earth with devastating effect at the end of the Cretaceous Period some 65 million years ago introduced another major factor to be taken into account in the history of the planet. So dramatic was this hypothesis, entailing as it does a catastrophic event resulting in the extinction of hundreds of species of plants and animals, that it tended to distract the attention of the general public from the continuing role of plate tectonics as the major organizing principle of late 20th-century geology. Recent events, however, served as a reminder of the ability of tectonics to generate exciting and productive research programs.

The apparent "fit" of the western coast of Africa and the eastern coast of South America figured significantly in the development of the hypothesis that the two continents had at one time been joined and had subsequently drifted apart. The margins of other continents do not form such evident patterns, and more indirect means of inferring them have had to be employed. Linear belts of deformed crust, or orogens, although now discontinuous and widely separated, might suggest continuity at some time in the past if the belts are similar in structure and composition and were formed at the same time. E.M. Moores of the University of California at Davis concluded that the western margin of North America formed as a result of rifting from the Australia-Antarctic shield that began in Precambrian time, perhaps as early as 1.2 billion years ago. He based his belief partly on the grounds that the Wopmay-Taltson orogen of northwestern Canada might originally have continued into southeastern Australia. Grant Young of the University of Western Ontario pointed out that the striking similarities between the succession of late Precambrian rocks in southeastern Australia and in northwestern Canada support Moores's hypothesis that the two regions were juxtaposed prior to the rifting that formed the Pacific Ocean basin. Young's investigations opened the possibility that meteorite impact studies might have a significant role to play in the study of stratigraphy. Impact debris had been discovered in the late Precambrian sediments of southeastern Australia. If similar debris were to be found in the late Precambrian sediments of northwestern Canada, it would support the hypothesis that

Skull of a Herrerasaurus ischigualastensis *was found in South America in Triassic Period rock deposited about 200 million years ago. One of the earliest of the dinosaurs,* Herrerasaurus *was a small and primitive version of such later carnivores as* Allosaurus *and* Tyrannosaurus rex.

the Pacific Ocean basin originated in the separation of the two continents.

New space geodetic measuring techniques such as very long-baseline radio interferometry, laser ranging, and the global-positioning system made it possible to obtain the accurate long-distance measurements needed to estimate the rates at which the tectonic plates are now moving. These measurements supported two hypotheses that served as the foundation of tectonic studies. The first was that the plates are rigid. Richard Gordon and Seth Stein of Northwestern University, Evanston, Ill., reported that plate interiors appear to be rigid to within a few millimeters per year. The second hypothesis was that the plates have moved at steady average rates since their origin, perhaps as long as 3.5 billion years ago. According to Gordon and Stein, the average rate of motion measured over decades by space geodetic methods compares closely with the average rate of motion over millions of years. Analyses of magnetic anomalies associated with seafloor spreading from oceanic ridges yield estimates of plate divergence averaging about 40 mm (1.6 in) per year over the last few million years. Geoffrey Davies of the Australian National University, Canberra, and Mark Richards of the University of California at Berkeley concluded that thermal convection in the Earth's mantle, which was widely regarded as the source of plate motion, could yield velocities comparable to those observed among the plates.

Plate tectonics was making a contribution to economic geology by enhancing the understanding of the genesis of ores. Don Elder and Susan Cashman of Humboldt State University, Arcata, Calif., concluded that gold-bearing veins found in the Klamath Mountains of northern California were formed by mineralization from hydrothermal fluids produced as a result of intense pressures and temperatures generated as the Farallon plate passed under the margin of the North American plate. Sutures and fault zones that developed during the subduction served as conduits for the rising fluids.

Paleontology. Richard Fox and Gordon Youzwyshyn of the University of Alberta and David Krause of the State University of New York at Stony Brook reported the recovery of a tiny jaw fragment less than 10 mm (0.39 in) in length from the late Paleocene Paskapoo formation in Alberta, which greatly extended the range of the order Therapsida in the fossil record. Within this order, paleontologists were able to trace a transition from skeletal characteristics that are distinctly reptilian to those that are so nearly mammalian that it was generally agreed the mammals originated from a therapsid ancestor. The remains of therapsids had been found in sedimentary rocks ranging in age from early Permian, about 285 million years ago, to middle Jurassic, about 160 million years ago, not long after the origin of mammals.

The Alberta discovery in rocks of late Paleocene age indicated that some members of the order survived for another 100 million years. An important distinguishing characteristic of mammals is that the lower jaw consists of a single bone element, the dentary. The extra reptilian elements of the lower jaw were not preserved in the Paleocene specimen, but the location of articular surfaces on the posterior surface of the dentary suggested that they were present in the living animal. Furthermore, the fact that the three preserved postcanine teeth are single rooted is suggestive of reptilian rather than primitive mammalian affinities. The authors suggested that the failure to find therapsid remains in sediments deposited in the 100 million-year interval between the late Jurassic and the mid-Paleocene might be explained by the restricted geographic range and the extremely small size of the living animals.

It had been known for more than 30 years that fragmentary remains of the most primitive dinosaurs occur in the Triassic rocks of South America. Recently, a complete skeleton of *Herrerasaurus ischigualastensis* from the Upper Triassic Ischigualasto formation of Argentina, which was deposited about 200 million years ago, was found. Paul Sereno of the University of Chicago and Fernando Novas of the Museo Argentino de Ciencias Naturales, Buenos Aires, determined that, although the skeleton has many of the features to be expected in the ancestor of all the later dinosaurs, it displays characteristics of the skull, neck, and forelimb found only in saurischian dinosaurs, such as the brontosaurus. Thus, it appeared that the major division between the saurischian and ornithischian dinosaurs (such as the stegosaurus) had already occurred in late Triassic time. The fossil remains recovered from the Ischigualasto formation suggested that, although several kinds of dinosaurs had already evolved by late Triassic time, dinosaur species had not yet come to dominate vertebrate faunas as they did during the Jurassic and Cretaceous periods, from 195 million to 65 million years ago.

Although it was clear that the bone structures of fossil vertebrates would remain the principal source of evidence of their evolution, biochemical properties might also soon begin to make a contribution. Most biochemically significant compounds were found in the soft tissues of plants and animals, but geobiochemists had, nevertheless, had increasing success in recovering these compounds from fossil remains. Not surprisingly, the most dramatic successes had been achieved with organic remains of recent origin, but if the burial of an animal was rapid and was not later affected by groundwater leaching and exposure to high temperatures and pressures resulting from crustal deformation, complex organic compounds might be preserved for a very long time. For example, Gerard Muyzer of the University of Leiden, Neth., and his colleagues recovered osteocalcin, a bone-matrix protein, from several fossil bones, including those of dinosaurs of late Cretaceous age (about 70 million years ago). They accomplished this by raising antibodies against osteocalcin in modern vertebrates and testing them for cross reactivity against osteocalcin recovered from the fossil remains. They found that the reaction was strong against the younger fossil material and significant against that obtained from the dinosaur remains. They hoped that such geobiochemical investigations would eventually contribute to the understanding of the relationships between fossil vertebrates.

—David B. Kitts

Geophysics. Attention during the past year was focused on California, where destructive earthquakes occurred at two complex tectonic junctions near the north and south ends of the San Andreas Fault system. The largest ground shaking ever measured in California was recorded near Cape Mendocino, and an unexpected sequence of strong earthquakes and aftershocks tore through the Mojave Desert east of Los Angeles, providing a research bonanza for seismologists and geologists. As the year ended, an anticipated magnitude-6 earthquake on the Parkfield

segment of the San Andreas Fault, midway between San Francisco and Los Angeles, failed to occur as the official 10-year earthquake-prediction window closed.

International earthquakes and volcanoes. Destructive earthquakes occurred in Turkey, Nicaragua, Egypt, and Indonesia in 1992. A magnitude-6.8 earthquake on the North Anatolian Fault near Erzincan, Turkey, on March 13 killed more than 500 people and destroyed more than 200 multistory structures. The strongest ground shaking lasted 5–6 seconds and was probably amplified in the alluvial basin under the city. A magnitude-7 earthquake on September 1 off the west coast of Nicaragua generated a destructive tsunami (long wave) that locally swept inland as far as one kilometer (0.62 mi), leaving more than 100 people dead or missing. The 9-m (29.5-ft) tsunami was much larger than was expected for that earthquake. A magnitude-5.9 earthquake on October 12 near Cairo killed more than 500, injured more than 6,500, and caused more than $300 million in damage, primarily from ground shaking. Most of the damage to engineered structures was due to poor design, materials, and construction. The unusually large number of casualties for a moderate earthquake was caused by the widespread use of adobe, a material known to be very vulnerable to shaking. Earthquake engineers have tried to discourage the use of adobe and encourage the use of good-quality masonry and mortar for houses in areas like Egypt. The deadliest earthquake of 1992 occurred on December 12 near the island of Flores, Indonesia. The magnitude-7.5 tremor generated a 25-m (82-ft) tsunami that swept inland more than one kilometer, causing extensive damage and killing more than 2,200 people.

The past year was a relatively quiet one for volcanoes. Geophysicists studied data from the well-documented eruptions at Alaska's Redoubt Volcano in 1990 and Mt. Pinatubo in the Philippines in 1991. Active fields of research included the recognition of geophysical precursors to eruptions and the effects of the Pinatubo eruptions on worldwide atmospheric chemistry. The Mayon volcano in the Philippines erupted without warning on Feb. 2, 1993. The eruption created a 5-km (3-mi)-high ash plume and showered boulders on nearby fields and villages, killing more than 10 people.

The Petrolia earthquakes. The Petrolia earthquake sequence occurred near the Mendocino triple junction in northern California, an area of rapid tectonic uplift and ongoing seismicity, where the Pacific, North America, and Gorda tectonic plates meet, and the San Andreas Fault turns westward and merges offshore with the Mendocino fracture zone. The magnitude-6.9 Petrolia main shock occurred on April 25, 1992. It had a shallow thrust mechanism and was apparently associated with subduction between

Workers in Cairo clear away debris produced by a magnitude-5.9 earthquake that struck the area on October 12. Centered just southwest of the Egyptian capital, the quake killed more than 500 and caused more than $300 million in damage.

the Gorda and North America plates. (Subduction is the process whereby the edge of one crustal plate descends below the edge of another.) Magnitude-6.5 and magnitude-6.6 aftershocks occurred 30 km (19 mi) west of the main shock on April 26. Both were confined to the Gorda plate.

The main shock and large aftershocks were recorded by networks of strong-motion accelerographs operated by the U.S. Geological Survey (USGS) and the California Strong-Motion Instrumentation Program (CSMIP). Strong-motion accelerographs are rugged, low-sensitivity instruments that can record large ground accelerations near the epicenter of a damaging earthquake, shaking that saturates or even disables other seismographs. Acceleration (usually measured in units of the acceleration of gravity, or g) is the measure of motion preferred by earthquake engineers and strong-motion seismologists because it can be directly related to shaking-induced forces in man-made structures. Engineers often prefer to install strong-motion recorders within structures—buildings, dams, and freeway overpasses, for example. With suitable computer models, structural forces and deformation can be analyzed in great detail. Seismologists, who study such problems as the decrease of shaking with distance from the earthquake and the effect of geology and topography on shaking, prefer to install recorders away from the influence of structures at so-called free-field sites.

The USGS and CSMIP networks in northern California consist primarily of accelerographs that record three components of ground acceleration (Up, North, and East, for example) on photographic film that is exposed by light beams deflected by shaking mirrors. It is a tried-and-true, low-maintenance design, intended to trigger and operate reliably during severe shaking after long periods of dormancy.

The Petrolia main shock was recorded by 9 USGS and 14 CSMIP strong-motion accelerographs at dis-

tances from the epicenter up to 110 km (68 mi). The most interesting recording was made at the CSMIP free-field site near Cape Mendocino. About three seconds after the instrument was triggered by first-arriving energy, a short pulse (approximately 0.1 second) of very large ground acceleration apparently occurred at that site. Motions of the three light beams were so rapid that the traces exposed on the film became very faint and braided together. Shaking briefly exceeded the specified range of the instrument; the accelerator mass hit a stop on the Up component, and the light beam missed a mirror on the North component. The record, therefore, was exceedingly complicated and difficult to interpret. After reconstructing the traces, CSMIP technicians concluded that acceleration peaks reached 2.2 g Up and 1.8 g North, the largest values ever measured in more than 60 years of strong-motion recording in California. These huge accelerations caused immediate consternation among strong-motion seismologists and engineers. This was tempered, however, by growing evidence that peak acceleration has historically been overrated as a concern for engineers. Other research had shown that spectral measurements, which use all the information in a record, correlate better with earthquake damage than does peak acceleration, especially from isolated, short-duration peaks. The cause of the peak motions was not known, and complete analysis of the records awaited their digitalization and processing.

Even though the two large aftershocks were located offshore, farther from the strong-motion network stations, and were smaller than the main shock, the maximum accelerations recorded during the aftershocks were comparable to or larger than the main-shock motions at several stations. Modeling experiments had shown that shaking may be relatively amplified ahead of and reduced behind a propagating rupture. If the Petrolia main shock propagated

Damage to buildings in northern California resulted from the Petrolia sequence of earthquakes in April 1992. The main shock, with a magnitude of 6.9 on the Richter scale, occurred on April 25 near the town of Ferndale. Because the area was sparsely populated, there were few injuries and little destruction of property.

offshore (consistent with the spatial distribution of the aftershocks), this might explain the unusual relationship between main-shock and aftershock ground motions. A comparison with the historical data in California, however, revealed that the Petrolia main-shock motions were actually somewhat larger than those from other earthquakes of comparable size, suggesting that there was something peculiar either about the mechanisms of the Petrolia earthquakes or about wave propagation in that part of the California crust.

Several groups deployed portable digital seismographs in the Petrolia area beginning on April 26 to record aftershocks. For aftershock work these recorders were configured to be triggered by small earthquakes that are ignored by the strong-motion recorders. Seismic-hazard work naturally emphasizes large earthquakes, and so, even though small aftershocks are relatively plentiful and easy to record, the wisdom of collecting data about them might not be obvious. Aftershock recordings are valuable, however, because, in theory, they contain some of the same wave-propagation information as large-earthquake recordings. For example, if the exceptionally large ground acceleration at the Cape Mendocino site was due to a peculiar wave-propagation effect (steep topography near the site, for example), the effect would also be evident in aftershock recordings. Small-earthquake records can also be combined to simulate shaking in larger earthquakes. Such a summation might be used to predict ground motion from a hypothetical main shock, an important seismic-hazard tool. These arguments assume that aftershocks were recorded at the same sites that recorded the main shock. A common strategy that was used at Petrolia was to deploy the aftershock recorders as close to the strong-motion accelerographs as possible.

The Joshua Tree-Landers-Big Bear earthquakes. The Joshua Tree-Landers-Big Bear earthquake sequence was the largest in California in 40 years, since the

Kern county earthquake in 1952. It began with the magnitude-6.1 Joshua Tree earthquake on April 22, 1992, near Indio and peaked with the magnitude-7.4 Landers and magnitude-6.6 Big Bear earthquakes on June 28. Owing to its proximity to the Coachella Valley segment of the San Andreas Fault and its relationship to background seismicity, the Joshua Tree earthquake was originally given a chance of being a foreshock to a larger earthquake on the San Andreas Fault. Instead, the subsequent Landers earthquake took geophysicists by surprise. Principal faulting extended 60-70 km (37-43 mi) north-northwestward, away from the San Andreas Fault, through a sparsely populated region of the Mojave Desert. The Big Bear aftershock occurred several hours later, 30 km (19 mi) to the west. The entire sequence was accompanied by tens of thousands of smaller aftershocks spread over a zone 180 km (112 mi) long by 100 km (62 mi) wide.

The remote desert location minimized injuries and damage but maximized superb exposures of surface faulting. Furthermore, the earthquakes occurred within permanent seismograph and geodetic networks, and dozens of portable seismograph units were deployed during the aftershock sequence. Thus, the sequence yielded rich new data sets for Earth scientists, and research related to it dominated the December 1992 American Geophysical Union meeting in San Francisco. The following discussion concentrates on the Landers event, the primary earthquake in the sequence.

Geologists arrived in the epicentral zone within hours of the Landers earthquake and began to document a remarkable pattern of faulting. Surface rupture extended 85 km (53 mi), locally following and crossing between five previously mapped faults that trended north to northwest (none of which was large enough to support a magnitude-7.4 earthquake by itself). Faulting was complex and discontinuous. Typical horizontal offsets were 2–3 m (6.5–9.75 ft)

324

in a right-lateral direction (the same type of slip as the San Andreas) but ranged between zero in a 5-km (3-mi) gap and a maximum 5–6m (11–19.5 ft) near the north end of the zone. Vertical offsets were smaller, averaging 0.3 m (one foot).

Seismologists computed slip histories on idealized Landers Fault models based on digital ground-motion data. They found that rupture propagated from south to north and confirmed that most of the slip occurred near the northern end of the zone, consistent with the geologic observations. Landers was one of the first large earthquakes to fall within a large, closely monitored Global Positioning System (GPS) network. Crustal displacements inferred from pre- and post-Landers measurements were in close agreement with the geologic and seismological results.

The Landers earthquake was large enough to have potentially altered static stresses on nearby faults, bringing some faults closer to failure and relaxing others. Although results were somewhat sensitive to assumptions about fault geometry and Earth-material parameters, several researchers computed stress changes for idealized models. Stress was found to have increased at the sites of several large aftershocks, including Big Bear. Regarding future seismic hazards in the region, stress probably increased on the San Bernardino Valley and Coachella Valley segments of the San Andreas Fault and the San Bernardino Valley and San Jacinto Valley segments of the San Jacinto Fault.

Another remarkable aspect of the Landers earthquake was a sudden increase in seismicity observed minutes after the main shock at remote sites throughout the western U.S. Triggered seismicity occurred at distances up to 1,250 km (775 mi) and was most prominent at sites marked by volcanic or geothermal activity. The largest triggered event was the magnitude-5.6 Little Skull Mountain earthquake in Nevada 280 km (174 mi) from Landers. The triggering mechanism was poorly understood, but somehow stresses carried by passing seismic wave fields must have interacted with fault-zone materials, pore fluids, or magma. Seismologists were even reviewing data from the great 1906 San Francisco earthquake to see if that event might have triggered others, including a magnitude-6.2 earthquake 700 km (434 mi) away in the Imperial Valley.

Given long-term strain rates across the central Mojave region based on several decades of geodetic measurements, a large Landers-type earthquake must be a rare event (perhaps occurring every 700 years or so). The Joshua Tree-Landers-Big Bear sequence showed how a significant part of the relative motion between the Pacific and North American tectonic plates is accommodated inland from the main plate boundary to the west; in some sense this newly recognized shear zone is in competition with the San Andreas Fault. It must also play a role in linking deformation in the western Great Basin with the southern San Andreas / Gulf of California system to the south.

—Charles S. Mueller

Hydrologic sciences

The value of basic research in hydrologic science was evident during the past year, in supporting programs in environmental protection, planning for management of water resources, and understanding the world's oceans and their interactions with the overall environment.

Hydrology. The U.S. government has been investigating the possibility of constructing an underground disposal facility for high-level radioactive waste generated at commercial nuclear-power plants. The site under consideration was at Yucca Mountain in southwestern Nevada. Because the transport of dissolved radionuclides by groundwater flow in the host rocks was the most likely means by which radioactivity would reach the biosphere, there were a number of fundamental scientific issues related to the hydrology of the site that had to be resolved in order for the suitability of Yucca Mountain as the site of the repository to be evaluated properly. The U.S. program was unique among international projects investigating geologic disposal of radioactive waste because of its reliance on the partially saturated zone above the water table as a candidate site for a repository.

The proposed design for the geologic repository involved emplacement of the wastes in volcanic rocks, some 300 m (1,000 ft) above the water table. The deep water table at Yucca Mountain was thought to be evidence that, historically, rates of downward groundwater flow had to have been exceedingly low at this site, owing to the limited infiltration of rainfall at the ground surface. It was argued that above the water table any radionuclides escaping the engineered barriers encasing the nuclear waste would move at very low rates through the partially saturated rocks. The possibility that hydrologic conditions could change at Yucca Mountain, causing a significant rise in the water table, was a critical issue that had to be addressed. Two methods were available to deal with the issue. Paleohydrologic reconstructions attempted to analyze field evidence for indications that the water table might have been higher in the past, while mathematical models were used to assess the conditions that could lead to a significant water-table rise at some time in the future.

In April 1992 the U.S. National Research Council (NRC) released a report entitled "Ground Water at Yucca Mountain: How High Can It Rise?" This report presented the views of a panel of experts brought together to consider whether there were any plausible mechanisms by which the water table at Yucca Mountain could rise to the level of the proposed repository. If this were to occur, the potential would exist for much higher rates of radionuclide transport by subsurface fluid flow, making it likely that Yucca Mountain would be deemed unsuitable as a site for the nuclear-waste repository.

At the request of the U.S. Department of Energy (DOE), the NRC panel had been formed to determine if the water table had risen during the recent geologic past to the level of the proposed repository. A staff member of the DOE proposed the controversial idea that field observations at and near Yucca Mountain provided clear evidence that the water table had risen to the ground surface numerous times in the geologic past and that it could be expected to do so again in the future. Deposits of carbonate and silica at the surface, both in veins and as surface-parallel deposits, were cited as evidence of the recurrent surface discharge of groundwater originating at depth beneath Yucca Mountain. Earthquake or thermal processes that pressurized the groundwater system were proposed as causes of the upwelling of groundwater along the many faults in the area.

The NRC panel concluded that none of the field evidence cited by the DOE staff member as proof that there had been repeated upwelling of groundwater at Yucca Mountain could be attributed to a model whereby tectonic processes would have caused the water table to rise to the ground surface. Instead, the surface-parallel carbonates observed in the field and geochemical data from those deposits were consistent with soil-forming processes common in arid environments.

The NRC panel also considered whether any other mechanism could cause a significant water-table rise at some time in the future. The three mechanisms discussed were: (1) an increase in rainfall associated with a long-term climate change; (2) an intrusion of volcanic rock in the vicinity of the design repository; and (3) stress/strain changes in the subsurface that occur during an earthquake. The panel concluded that, because techniques for relating changes in precipitation to consequent changes in rates of groundwater recharge were uncertain, the possibility of a water-table rise due to a climate change could not be ruled out. Further data collection and research were needed to examine this process. The possibility of a water-table rise due to a volcanic intrusion was not considered to be a threat to site suitability. Significant water-table changes due to seismic rupture on nearby faults were thought to be unlikely. Calculations carried out by the panel suggested that a water-table rise of more than 30.5 m (100 ft) was unlikely. Because of considerable uncertainty

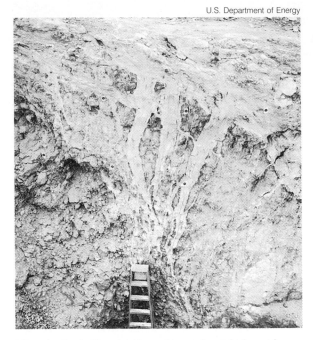

Mineral veins in Nevada's Yucca Mountain might be evidence of past upwellings of groundwater. The mountain has been proposed as the site of a nuclear waste repository, and future upwelling would threaten the stability of stored wastes.

in evaluating such a hypothesis, however, the panel recommended that efforts be continued in order to obtain the data necessary for better definition of the potential for seismic events to cause a change in the elevation of the water table.

Iowa study. It is often difficult to assess the frequency of severe drought conditions in a particular geographic region because precipitation measurements are usually available on time scales of decades rather than hundreds of years. Tree-ring data were used effectively to extend existing records of precipitation in an attempt to better estimate frequencies and durations of droughts and periods of extreme wetness. M.K. Cleaveland of the University of Arkansas and D.N. Duvick of Iowa State University published the results of a reconstruction of the climate of Iowa for the period from 1640 to 1982 (*Water Resources Research,* 1992). Precipitation measurements providing good coverage of the state did not begin until the 1870s. Tree-ring analysis related tree-ring width to climate variability, given a correlation between soil moisture and tree growth during the growing season. In the Iowa study, the authors analyzed data from 17 moisture-sensitive white-oak sites across the eastern and central regions of the state. Before interpreting the data, researchers had to complete a detailed statistical analysis in order to remove trends not related to climate and to detect those biological effects of advanced age in oaks that reduce the growth response to climatic variability.

The authors concluded that overall drought frequencies in Iowa had changed little since 1640. Extreme drought conditions occurred, on average, during one year in 12. Multiyear episodes of severe drought had occurred several times per century. Some droughts were more severe than any that had been recorded since precipitation data were collected on a routine basis. These periods were considerably worse than that experienced in the 1930s. If the extreme droughts seen in the tree-ring record were to occur today, the authors warned, the effects on water supplies and agriculture would be devastating to the state.

Decade-scale wetness anomalies showed no clear change in frequency within the period of climate reconstruction. While the 14 wettest years all occurred before 1852, the authors suggested that this observation could be caused by a changing response of the oak trees to moisture conditions as the trees aged, rather than indicating a trend to generally drier conditions. An understanding of the variability in past climate on time scales of hundreds of years is essential in examining the data record for indications of present-day climate change that might be linked to greenhouse warming.

Other developments. Danny Marks and Jeff Dozier, working at the University of California at Santa Barbara, published the results of an important study on climate and energy exchange at the snow surface in an alpine watershed. Their study site was in the southern Sierra Nevada of California. Using a variety of meteorologic measurements and model parameters, they calculated the net energy transfer to the snow cover by solar and thermal radiation, sensible and latent heat exchange with the atmosphere, conduction from the underlying soil, and heat transfer to the snowpack by precipitation. They found that during their period of observation net radiation contributed the largest amount of energy for snowmelt, followed by sensible and latent heat exchange. Soil conduction generated significant melting at the base of the snowpack during midwinter. During the snowmelt season net radiation contributed 5–10 times the energy input for snowmelt in comparison with all other forms of heat transfer. The authors noted that this finding was valuable because radiation was one of the easier variables to measure, and its distribution over the topographic surface of a watershed could be modeled in a straightforward manner. These results were encouraging for efforts to predict snowmelt and snowmelt runoff for much larger geographic areas that could not be instrumented in detail.

Mathematical models were in common use for making predictions of the response of a groundwater system to new stresses, such as the development of a well field in an aquifer system. A key step in the development of these prediction models is the representation of the hydrogeologic properties of the subsurface aquifers. Because it is expensive to obtain measurements in boreholes, it was often the case that there were only a small number of data points on which to base the description of aquifer properties. Because geologic media are heterogeneous, the availability of only limited data to characterize that spatial variability led to considerable uncertainty in the model predictions.

A promising new method for obtaining an improved representation of the hydrogeologic properties of a shallow aquifer was described during the year. Yorum Rubin at the University of California at Berkeley and his co-workers, writing in the journal *Water Resources Research,* described a methodology for combining conventional hydrologic measurements with data obtained from a seismic-reflection survey. In a seismic-reflection program, elastic waves were generated, and their propagation through the subsurface was monitored by receivers at the ground surface. The recorded signals were interpreted as reflections from the boundaries between units with contrasts in material properties, such as sediment density. Geophysical surveys provided excellent areal coverage at relatively low cost. A key issue that needed to be resolved involved the difficulty of relating seismic properties of a saturated porous medium (velocity and attenuation) to its hydrologic properties (porosity and permeability). The authors presented a semiempirical relationship to describe this dependence and then incorporated this procedure into a numerical algorithm (step-by-step procedure) for mapping the spatial variability of aquifer properties. They demonstrated that there could be considerable improvement in the estimates of the model parameters when both hydrologic and seismic data were used, in comparison with a model constructed solely with hydrologic data. This work pointed to the considerable potential of a broad range of geophysical methods for improved mapping of the spatial variability of aquifer materials.

—Leslie Smith

Oceanography. Research efforts during the past year focused on such phenomena as El Niño, the global water cycle, and drilling in the ocean floor.

El Niño/Southern Oscillation. The 1991–92 El Niño/Southern Oscillation (ENSO) was a major event. The first signs occurred in mid-1991 with unusually warm surface waters in the central and eastern equatorial Pacific. The water warmed further during the latter half of 1991, while at the same time the Pacific trade winds weakened. The ENSO event peaked in the winter of 1991–92 and contributed to worldwide weather disturbances, including drought in the Philippines, eastern Australia, Indonesia, eastern Africa, and South Africa; excessive rainfall in

Texas and the Gulf Coast states and in Peru and Ecuador; and an unusually warm winter in the Pacific Northwest. The changing climatic conditions reduced upwelling of cold nutrient-rich waters along the west coasts of North and South America, resulting in disruptions of coastal ecosystems and fisheries.

Cold sea-surface temperatures returned to the eastern equatorial Pacific in the summer of 1992. As of early 1993 the trade winds had not yet returned to full strength in the western Pacific, and it was possible that this could result in a return to ENSO conditions in the winter of 1992–93. Like the previous ENSO of 1986–87, this event was predicted about one year in advance by researchers working with a coupled ocean-atmosphere model. The event's evolution was also monitored daily by a tropical ocean observing system and satellites, making it oceanographically the best documented event on record.

In order to better understand the climatic system that leads to the El Niño/Southern Oscillation and to make better long-term climate predictions, the Tropical Ocean Global Atmosphere (TOGA) Coupled Ocean-Atmosphere Response Experiment (COARE) began operations in 1992. TOGA COARE was specifically designed to study the significance of the warm pool of water in the tropical ocean-atmosphere system in a region along the equator just northeast of Papua New Guinea. TOGA COARE involved more than 700 scientists from 19 nations. Ships, aircraft, satellites, and other observing tools would measure ocean-atmosphere energy exchange over the western Pacific. The joint U.S.-French scientific satellite Topex/Poseidon orbited over the area twice per day and measured ocean-surface topography, wave height, water vapor, and wind speed. In addition, the U.S. National Oceanic and Atmospheric Administration planned to shift the position of its GOES-2 satellite so that it would relay data from the COARE instruments on ships and remote Pacific islands back to the U.S.

In order to study the effect of El Niño on chemical and biological distributions, the first cruises of the U.S. Joint Global Ocean Flux Study on the equatorial Pacific were conducted from January to May 1992. There were no previous data of this type for the central equatorial Pacific, and the results were not as expected. In particular, the data revealed upwelling of warm, nutrient-rich water at the equator, the origin of which was not understood.

Also during the year, a team of French and Brazilian scientists reported evidence for El Niño-like climatic conditions occurring over the past 7,000 years. They presented paleoclimatic data that showed the occurrence of climatic oscillations of winds and waves over periods of 10 to 100 years. This new information would help researchers develop a better understanding of the climatic system.

Global water cycle. The role of the ocean in the global water cycle began to receive more attention during the past year. Long neglected because of the lack of rainfall estimates over the sea, the global water cycle was increasingly being recognized as of key importance to the circulation of the ocean. There was paleoclimatic evidence that the discharge of glacial meltwater at the end of the last ice age caused a temporary shutdown of the ocean-circulation system that maintains the moderate climate of Europe. Models suggested that the transition between ocean-circulation states can be abrupt, possibly explaining the rapid climate changes seen in ice cores and in some sediment cores.

Work published during the year showed that rapid changes in air and sea temperatures of as much as 7° C (12.6° F) in 50 years around the North Atlantic Ocean indicated that greenhouse warming and the melting of ice and snow at the poles might have far more rapid effects on ocean and climate conditions than previously thought. The temperature changes, caused by sudden shifts in the ocean-circulation system that transports heat from the equator toward the poles, were found in data from cores in the seafloor in deep parts of the ocean. It now appeared that the heat balance of much or all of the Southern Hemisphere underwent dramatic changes in response to the oscillations in the formation of bottom water in the North Atlantic.

Ice Station Weddell. The southern ocean is an area not very well studied, and, in particular, the areas covered with ice have remained largely unexplored. The year-round sea ice cover of the western Weddell Sea, south of South America, contrasts with the seasonal sea ice of most of the ocean surrounding Antarctica. It is an area of importance for bottom water formation, but until recent months little data had been collected because of the ice cover. The Weddell Gyre is the largest of the cyclonic flowing gyres (giant circular surface currents) occupying the region south of the Antarctic circumpolar current. It is nearly completely covered by sea ice in the winter, marking the largest latitudinal range of seasonal sea ice around Antarctica.

After four years of planning, U.S. and Russian scientists, led by the Lamont-Doherty Geological Observatory, deployed a scientific station on the ice in 1992. This marked the first (intentional) Antarctic drifting station since Sir Ernest Shackleton's ship *Endurance* was frozen into the ice in 1915. Ice Station Weddell began operations on Feb. 11, 1992, with support from the Russian research ship *R/V Academik Federov*. The ice floe carried scientists on a 117-day, 650-km (400-mi) journey through the ice-packed sea. A total of 60 researchers spent time aboard the floe, conducting experiments on the formation and movement of sea ice, ocean currents, at-

(Right) Scientist at a research station on the ice-covered western Weddell Sea, south of South America, deploys an instrument over the edge of the ice floe. (Left) Russian (in background) and U.S. icebreakers dock alongside the floe to recover the scientists after 117 days on the ice.

mospheric conditions, and the rich marine plant and animal life. They gathered the first extensive data on the rates of heat exchange between the atmosphere and ocean, the intervening role of the sea ice cover, and the circulation of the ocean below the ice in the Weddell Sea. In March and April 1992 part of the U.S. team was replaced by means of aircraft and the new U.S. icebreaker *R/V Nathaniel B. Palmer*.

Ocean Drilling Program. Results from the 45th expedition of the international Ocean Drilling Program in the North Pacific Ocean gave scientists new evidence concerning the initiation of a massive ice buildup almost three million years ago. The cores extended to 400 m (1,300 ft) in depth and included the longest sections of undisturbed core ever obtained. Although scientists knew that glaciation had occurred worldwide during that time, they did not know how the North Pacific had responded to a colder climate. The drilling samples showed evidence of massive glaciation, including sediment deposition, stones dropped by floating ice, continental debris, dust, and volcanic ash.

The drilling results indicated that volcanic activity beginning 2.6 million years ago dwarfed earlier events in the region's geologic history. The abundance of volcanic ash in the cores at that geologic time could cause scientists to reconsider the effects of volcanic eruptions on Northern Hemisphere temperatures. By drilling into a sediment deposit called the Meiji drift, they discovered that bottom water flowing south from the Bering Sea has been churning the ocean for at least 35 million years.

Arctic plumes. For several years researchers had speculated that the sporadic plumes seen by satellites over Bennett Island in the eastern Siberian Sea were caused by methane gas bursting from beneath the seafloor. Presumably the gas came from methane that was trapped in permafrost flooded by a rising sea level.

Until recently, Western scientists had been prohibited from visiting the area, but in March U.S. scientists were able to sample a recently formed plume with aircraft measurements. No elevated concentration of methane was found, thus proving that the Bennett Island plume is a meteorological phenomenon, not related to methane release.

Biofouling. Biofouling on ship hulls has plagued seafarers at least since the time of the Phoenicians and the ancient Greeks. Biofouling increases drag and acoustic noise and can cause ship failures, but it is costly to keep hulls clean. The traditional approach had been to use coatings containing heavy metal toxins (tin or copper), which kill barnacles, mussels, and slime-forming bacteria as well as wood-boring organisms such as molluscan shipworms. These toxins, however, polluted the environment and persisted for long periods of time.

New nontoxic antifouling agents were developed by the U.S. Navy. Based on the use of biopesticides and natural repellents found in other marine organisms, these naturally occurring substances would not contribute to marine pollution.

Aggregates. Biological oceanographers have long been puzzled by the fact that they see a high abundance of aggregates of particles in the ocean, while theory would predict low aggregation rates. During the year experiments by scientists at the University of California at Santa Barbara and the University of

Arizona showed that marine aggregates are generated by collisions of large particles formed by exudates from phytoplankton and bacteria. These large particles may be significant to many marine processes, including transformations of material between the pools of dissolved and particulate matter, microbial activity, food webs, and marine chemistry.

Shrimp and sole. A new species of shrimplike creatures was found near seafloor spreading centers along the East Pacific Rise, at latitude 9° N off the coast of Mexico. Scientists diving in the Woods Hole (Mass.) Oceanographic Institution submersible *Alvin* found swarms of these creatures, estimated to contain between 5,000 and 50,000 individuals, at a depth of 2,500 m (8,250 ft). It was not yet known what the tiny amphipod eats or how it swims so fast, estimated at up to 2 km (1.2 mi) per day. This was the 2,500th dive for *Alvin,* a new diving record by the United States' first and most active deep-diving submersible.

From September through November 1992, a team of fisheries biologists and other scientists from the French agency IFREMER (Institut Français de Recherche pour l'Exploitation de la Mer) launched a major operation to better understand the migration of sole in the Gulf of Gascony, one of the primary small-craft fishing sites along the French coast. The patterns of movement between younger and older fish were expected to provide valuable information about reproductive patterns. Researchers were hoping to distinguish between the influences of climatic conditions, biological productivity, diseases, and overfishing.

Parting the Red Sea. During the year oceanographers from Florida State University and the Hebrew University of Jerusalem proposed an explanation of the biblical description of the "parting" of the Red Sea during the Israelites' exodus from Egypt. The Bible describes a strong wind prior to the event, receding water, and then the crossing in the midst of the sea.

The researchers showed that a strong wind will slowly cause the water at the edge of the sea to recede. Owing to the sea's unique geometry, even a moderate storm can cause the sea level to recede more than one kilometer (0.62 mi) and to drop more than 2.5 m (8.2 ft). When the storm stops, the water returns to its prewind conditions with a wave that floods the entire zone within minutes. For the event to have occurred as proposed, the wind would have to have been about 72 km/h (45 mph) and blown for 10 hours—not an impossibility. The Israelites may have crossed while the water receded, and the drowning of the Egyptians could have been a result of the rapidly returning wave. The event would not be a common one but was certainly plausible from a scientific point of view.

Swarms of tiny shrimplike amphipods, never before seen, were discovered by scientists aboard the submersible Alvin *at depths of about 2,500 meters (8,250 feet) near seafloor spreading centers off the Pacific coast of Mexico.*

Tsunamis. The year 1992 was also unusual for tsunamis, the long waves that are caused by underwater earthquakes. Two tsunamis were generated in places that were historically quiet. On April 25 an earthquake measuring 7.1 on the Richter scale generated a tsunami that had a major impact on the beaches of Eureka, Calif. On September 1 an earthquake of magnitude 7.3 about 100 km (60 mi) offshore of central Nicaragua generated a 9-m (29.5-ft)-high tsunami that killed more than 100 people, destroyed over 700 homes, and left more than 10,000 homeless along 230 km (120 mi) of coastline. The earthquake was barely felt by the coastal residents. This represented the worst situation for trying to warn against tsunamis—a small earthquake accompanied by a large tsunami. A tsunami warning was not issued for either event, indicating the current inability to estimate tsunami potential from seismic information alone.

Satellites and ships. After 10 years of planning, the joint National Aeronautics and Space Administration/French Space Agency precision altimeter mission Topex/Poseidon was launched in August on an Ariane rocket from Kourou, French Guiana. This was the first altimeter mission planned from the very beginning as a scientific experiment; the mission was designed to measure the ocean surface topography with an accuracy of a few centimeters for three to five years. With this accuracy all of the major features of the ocean circulation could be described and monitored. Almost 200 U.S. and French scientists were involved in the program.

The lengthened, modernized, and refurbished research vessels *Knorr* and *Melville* reentered the academic oceanographic research fleet during the past year. Originally built in 1968–69, these ships, operated by the Woods Hole Oceanographic Institution and Scripps Institution of Oceanography, respectively, almost doubled the U.S. capability for worldwide deep-water research compared with 1991.

—D. James Baker

Electronics and information sciences

Desktop workstations with increased computing power, microprocessor chips designed to perform specialized tasks, new advances in wireless communication, and a new generation of communications satellites were among the important developments in electronics and information sciences during the past year. Employment in the electronics industry in the United States continued to decline.

Communications systems

Technological advances in dozens of areas dealing with communications systems were made during the past year. They ranged from "800" numbers to global positioning systems.

The "800" numbers. The "800" numbers are those telephone numbers in which the called party, rather than the calling party, pays. The concept was developed in 1967, and in that first year some 7.8 million calls were placed. By early 1993 there were more than twice that many calls every day. In fact, on many days of the year the number of "800" calls approached the number of conventional long-distance calls.

These calls and, in fact, all calls are often answered automatically, and the caller is offered the option of personally routing the call by pressing appropriate buttons on the telephone ("push '1' for new accounts, '2' for account status, or stay on the line and an operator will assist you"). Some systems allow the caller to say a word, after which a voice-recognition system with a surprisingly large vocabulary will properly route the calls. And yet another newly released feature will, in the event that "all agents are busy," offer to return the call automatically when an agent is free.

The demand for "800" numbers was driving technology in yet another way. One of the problems with the service in past years was that particular blocks of numbers were assigned to particular long-distance carriers; for example, Sprint would own a block of numbers with one three-digit exchange code, and AT&T would own a different block with a different three-digit exchange code. But that meant that a subscriber who chose to change carriers would also have to change telephone numbers. Many people were not willing to do this. Consequently, technology was developed to facilitate the portability of "800" numbers. It was expected to be fully operational in mid-1993. This was being done with a massive new network and data base that would keep track of every assigned number; each time an "800" number was dialed, this data base would be queried in

regard to the assigned carrier and the appropriate routing. This new capability would allow even more features; for instance, a call to a particular "800" number might be routed to a local call center during the daytime hours but to a single national call center at night.

Wireless communications. A technology area that experienced an astounding change during the past year was wireless communications. Until recently this area was called "cellular radio," "cellular telephone," or simply "cellular." But as the value of the concept grew, so did the concept itself.

Cellular, in fact, grew rapidly. First introduced commercially in 1983, it grew by at least 10% each year after that, and in late 1992 the 10 millionth customer was added. The importance of this field and that of the broader "portable communications devices" did not go unnoticed. Motorola Inc. expected that by the year 2000 half of all semiconductors produced would be used in portable devices.

AT&T, blocked from repurchasing any of the Bell operating companies spun off in the 1984 divestiture action, was negotiating the purchase of a 33% share of McGaw Cellular Communications, the nation's largest cellular operator. AT&T would also acquire an option for voting control of the McGaw properties. This would, some said, place AT&T squarely back in the local telephone business.

It was not only for the cellular operations that AT&T was vying; it was also for the opportunity to participate fully in what had come to be known as Personal Communications Services (PCS). PCS differed from cellular in one major aspect: size. First, the cell was smaller. In a cellular system the area of coverage of a particular transmitter was, perhaps, several kilometers in diameter. As a particular mobile subscriber moved from one cell to another, the electronic equipment "handed off" the call to the next cell, without interruption of the conversation. The cell in a PCS network would be only hundreds of meters, and in some cases only hundreds of centimeters, in diameter. Moving from one cell to another was still possible—but not at 90 km/h (55 mph). Because the cell was smaller, the telephone itself needed to transmit for only a short distance and required less battery power. Thus, it too was smaller and could fit in a shirt pocket.

The technology of PCS was an evolving one. By 1993 hundreds of trials were taking place around the world. Each trial was attempting to determine just what services and features were important and what transmission scheme was best. In early 1993 three transmission schemes were in contention: frequency division multiple access (FDMA)—essentially an analog scheme; time division multiple access (TDMA)—essentially a digital scheme; and code division multiple access (CDMA)—a unique digital

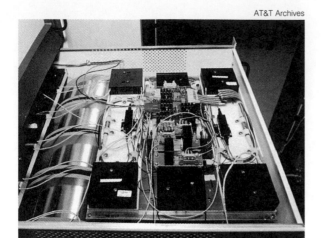

Optical amplifier consists of an assembly of electronic and fiber-optic components. A weak signal introduced into one side of the amplifier grows in strength along the length of the optical fiber, resulting in increased power.

scheme frequently used by the military for handling secure communications.

The transmitting-scheme debate applied to cellular as well as to PCS. In the U.S. the analog scheme (FDMA) was being used everywhere, but a decision was made to move to TDMA. The question as to the value of moving to CDMA remained. (It was claimed that a TDMA system had at least three times the subscriber capacity of an FDMA system and that a CDMA system had three times the capacity of a TDMA system.)

Europe was spending less time debating the issue; its GSM (Groupe Spécial Mobile, or Global Standard for Mobile Communications) system was digital, and significant progress was being made to finalize the standards and deploy the system. The GSM standard was also adopted in Hong Kong, Singapore, Australia, New Zealand, India, South America, and some nations in the Middle East.

Another wireless communications system was also being developed; it would rely on satellites in low Earth orbit. Iridium, being developed by Motorola and others, was an example. Some 77 satellites (later reduced to 66) were to be deployed at an altitude of between 740 and 840 km (460 and 520 mi), and the orbits would be designed so that every point on the Earth was always within sight of one of the satellites. A person on the Earth could communicate directly with the satellites by means of small handheld units, and the satellites would be equipped to communicate with one another. Thus, a call could always be placed—anytime, anyplace—on Earth. As a particular satellite moved out of range of a subscriber, a hand-off, as with cellular, would take place, and the subscriber would then be in touch with the new satellite.

Iridium was not being designed to be a high-capacity system—it would be able to handle only two million to three million customers throughout the world. Its chief market was expected to be people making overseas calls. In less developed countries, however, solar-powered Iridium phones might be commonly used for local calls.

Global Positioning System. The ability to transmit information to and from satellites with relative ease led to yet another new service, Global Positioning System (GPS). Developed by the U.S. Department of Defense at a cost of $3 billion during the past 15 years, GPS proved itself in the Gulf war when soldiers were able to accurately pinpoint their positions in the trackless desert. Trucking companies began using it to keep track of their trucks automatically, instantly, and accurately (location on the Earth's surface could be determined to within about 15 m [50 ft]).

GPS was operated by a string of satellites orbiting the Earth. On board each were several atomic clocks that each satellite used to broadcast time data along with other information identifying itself and describing its path. Receivers on a vehicle on the Earth compared these signals with their own clocks and then determined their location by calculating the distance between them and the satellite. Signals from one satellite would locate a vehicle somewhere on the perimeter of a circle on the Earth's surface. Two satellites would cut the possibilities to two points. Four satellites were actually used, and the resulting locating process was very accurate.

Fiber optics. For several years people had been hearing of the wonders of fiber optics, thin strands of ultrapure glass carrying short bursts of light. These light pulses were triggered on and off at rates as high as a billion times a second, and this on-off sequence provided the coding for high-speed data. This, of course, was significantly faster than was possible with electricity on a long copper wire. Consequently, a single strand of glass could substitute for a hundred or even a thousand wires. Fiber and the electronics associated with it were being improved rapidly. In fact, the transmission capacity of a strand of fiber was doubling each 18 months owing to technological advances.

Single-mode fiber, the type used for all long-distance transmission, had an inner strand of ultrapure glass that carried the transmitted signal. The diameter of this inner strand was about eight micrometers (millionths of a meter) in diameter. This strand was covered with a protective glass coating so that the overall diameter was about 125 micrometers.

Recent advances in the chemistry of the inner strand doubled the distance that a signal could be transmitted; therefore, "regenerative repeaters," the devices that break down and reform those bursts of light, could be used more sparingly. This was advantageous because a regenerative repeater utilized electronics and had to have a source of power. Also, it was code-specific; that is, it was designed to handle only one particular coding protocol.

A second technological advance was the optical amplifier, a short length of fiber containing glass doped with the rare earth element erbium. Associated with it was electronic circuitry. A weak signal introduced into one side of the amplifier would grow along the length of the fiber, resulting in increased power, or gain. The principle behind the device was the same as that in a laser itself; light is amplified by the stimulated emission of radiation. In a 1992 demonstration AT&T and Kotusai Denshin Denwa of Japan transmitted data through such an amplifier at 5 Gbps (5 gigabits, or 5 billion bits, per second) for more than 9,000 km (5,580 mi). Instead of being regenerated every 65 km (40 mi) or so, the signal was simply amplified.

Another new fiber-optic product was the "splitter." It was a passive device (that is, it did not require electricity) that had one fiber input and a plurality of fiber outputs. A 1 × 4 splitter, for example, divided the incoming light four times, providing on each of the four output ports a light beam identical with the one that was input though at one-fourth the brightness. This device was becoming most valuable in fiber-to-the-home systems, where signals were carried to a neighborhood via fiber rather than by copper.

The continued advances in technology had made fiber the medium of choice for transmitting both voice and data. This was true not only for terrestrial networks but also for those undersea. Dozens of fiber cables covered the ocean floor, and from a transmission standpoint San Francisco and Singapore were no farther apart than San Francisco and Seattle, Wash. The record for the longest fiber-optic system was SEA-ME-WE2, which connected Singapore with France. When completed in 1994, it would be 17,965 km (11,160 mi) long. However, late in 1992 an even longer system was announced. FLAG would extend from the U.K. through the Mediterranean Sea, down the Red Sea, to India, Indonesia, Singapore, Malaysia, North and South Korea, and Japan. When completed it would be 24,150 km (15,000 mi) long and support 600,000 conversations simultaneously.

Networks. An event that took place in November 1992 and could prove of great significance was called the "Golden Splice." It marked a symbolic first national Integrated Services Digital Network call from the west coast to the east coast of the U.S. and demonstrated the capability of ISDN. Designed to be a worldwide service, it provided a transmission capability that observed a single standard.

As fiber was introduced in more and more places and as transmission speeds increased dramatically, no worldwide standards were established. Companies had been developing high-speed systems (called proprietary systems) that operated at whatever speeds were convenient, and they used whatever interface criteria seemed best. Thus, there were no standardized speeds, and there was no possibility for end-to-end compatibility between equipment made by different manufacturers. SONET (Synchronous Optical Network) was being designed to correct that situation. An immense amount of effort was being expended to achieve single standards on speed and equipment; as a result, manufacturers were rapidly building equipment that was "SONET compatible."

—Robert E. Stoffels

Computers and computer science

Computer manufacturers struggle to produce machines that are both computationally fast and inexpensive. As a result, the computer industry often vacillates between producing new technologies that allow computers to run faster and finding ways to make their current computers less expensive. During the past year manufacturers emphasized ways that their new computers could be cost-effective. Some manufacturers produced machines that could be upgraded in steps, while others tried to lower the cost of producing software for new models.

Computer communications became more important during the year as many companies interconnected their machines by using computer networks. New computer communication technologies that provided communication at increased speeds over long distances became available. Telephone companies began using the new technologies to offer computer communication services. The U.S. National Science Foundation used some of the new networking technology to upgrade its Internet backbone.

Finally, a shift in the computer market from large mainframe computers to smaller desktop workstations deeply affected the largest computer company, IBM Corp. Although IBM at one time had dominated much of the worldwide computer market, it suffered severe losses during the past year.

New computer models. Desktop workstations, used heavily by scientists and engineers, allow an individual to control the workstation completely in much the same way that one controls a personal computer. The scientist can decide which problem to solve at a given time. One of the main differences between a scientific workstation and many personal computers lies in the workstation's ability to perform multiple computational tasks at the same time, whereas a personal computer is usually restricted to a single task. The scientist can devote all of the workstation's

SPARCstation 10, a desktop workstation introduced by Sun Microsystems Inc., can be configured to contain additional central processing units, thereby increasing its speed and processing power.

processing power to a single program so that it completes the task quickly or can run several programs and allow each to proceed more slowly.

Sun Microsystems Inc. was the leading manufacturer of desktop workstations. During the year Sun announced a new model called the SPARCstation 10. In its simplest form the new machine had slightly more computational power than Sun's existing SPARCstation 2 model, and was approximately the same price. However, the new machine differed in an important way; it could be configured to have additional central processing units (CPUs).

Technically, a computer with multiple CPUs is called a multiprocessor. The advantage of multiprocessor workstations is their speed. If the scientist or engineer using the workstation has many problems to solve, a multiprocessor can solve them simultaneously. Furthermore, most workstations have computational tasks to perform in addition to the applications that they run. Workstations usually connect to a network, and so they must accept and process information that arrives over the network. Workstations also have complex monitor screens that can display graphics as well as text, and so they must manage the monitor and process commands that instruct the system to display and move complex graphic images. Finally, workstations usually allow the user to execute an application in background while interacting with another application. For example, a user can instruct the workstation to print one document while the user interacts with a text-processing application to edit another document. A workstation with multiple processors allows computation to be much faster because it can devote one processor to each computational task. For example, one processor can handle display management and another can handle background printing, while a third operates a text-processing application.

In addition to speed, Sun stressed that a multiprocessor design would provide customers with a method to increase processing power without buying an entirely new computer. A customer could begin with a base model that had one processor. If he or she then needed a more powerful workstation, the customer could add another processor. The SPARCstation 10 allows a customer to configure up to four processors; multiprocessor systems from other vendors allowed even more.

Digital Equipment Corp. revealed its plans for a new workstation that would use a processor chip that Digital developed, called Alpha. Although the workstation would have only one processor, it would perform much faster than existing workstations in its price range. Digital announced that the first commercial version of the Alpha chip would operate at 150 million instructions per second, making it one of the fastest processors available. Surprisingly, the workstation was expected to cost about the same as those from competitors that offered much less speed.

To make their new processor more appealing, Digital announced that it designed the Alpha chip so that it could emulate existing processors. In essence, the new chip could be programmed either to run the instructions that had been designed into it or to read new instructions from a software library of old programs. Alpha operated more slowly on the old programs than when executing its native instructions. However, the Alpha chip was so fast that it outperformed the machines originally designed to run the old programs. The advantage was that customers could use the new computer to upgrade their existing equipment without changing all of their software. Then, as customers rewrote their programs to use the Alpha processor's native instructions, the programs would be executed even faster.

Computer networks. During the year many corporations used computer networks to link their computers together. The idea behind such "distributed computing" is simple: computer networks allow users in separate physical locations to share resources. For example, if a company attaches a printer to a computer network, any computer attached to that network can use it to print documents. Computers can also use the network to access other shared devices. For example, a company can attach to the network a computer that has a large hard disk and allow other computers to share the increased storage provided by that disk. Using a network to share resources makes it easier to manage them and to perform routine maintenance tasks. As long as it costs less to connect a computer to the network than to purchase copies of the resources being shared, the company saves money by using a network.

To keep costs low, computer communication networks use packet switching, a technique in which a computer sends data in small packets. Using packets instead of permanent connections results in low costs because it permits many computers to share a single network. After a computer sends a packet, it waits for other computers to send a packet before it sends its next one. If a computer has nothing to send, it does not participate and does not use network resources. When a packet-switching system works well, it provides each computer with a fair share of the network time. If only one computer has data to send, it can use the network freely. If N computers have data to send, each receives approximately $1/N$ of the available network bandwidth.

Packet-switching technologies are grouped into broad categories, depending on how they can be used. In addition to local area networks that operate across a small geographic area, such as a single building, new network technologies are emerging that permit companies to interconnect computers across long distances. The new technologies are called wide-area networks to distinguish them from local-area networks. Wide-area networks, which can span distances in excess of 1,500 km (1,000 mi), cost much more to install and operate than local-area networks.

During the past year common carriers began offering several new wide-area network services. For example, the International Telegraph and Telephone Consultative Committee (CCITT), an international organization that sets standards for telephone companies, published a standard referred to as frame-mode bearer service or, more popularly, frame relay. A corporation can use frame-relay service to interconnect computers at multiple sites, even if the sites are located in separate cities or separate states. Each site leases a frame-relay connection from its local telephone company. A computer uses the service to communicate with another computer in much the same way that computers use a local-area network to exchange packets. Companies that can afford the cost can establish a permanent frame-relay connection between sites.

Computers can use frame-relay services to exchange data. For example, a company can use the service to send customer orders from an office in New York City to an office in Los Angeles. The chief difference between a frame-relay connection and the connection provided by a local-area network arises from delay; it takes more time to send a packet by frame relay across the U.S. (hundredths or even tenths of a second) than it does to send a packet by local-area network down a hall inside a building (thousandths of a second). While this additional delay for a single packet may not seem large to humans, it may increase the time to transfer data between computers by a factor of between 10 and 100. Companies that use frame relay understand that they cannot ship data as quickly and thus use techniques like data compression to reduce the size of files before sending them.

Telephone companies have provided wide-area computer communication services for many years; the idea is not new. In the past, however, the services the phone companies provided had limited speed. For example, the service that phone companies supplied most commonly in the past was known as X.25, the name being derived from the name that CCITT used for the published standard. The difference between frame relay and the older X.25 service is that while frame relay can support communication speeds of up to two million bits per second, the older X.25 service could support communication speeds of only up to 64,000 bits per second.

During the year telephone companies began experimenting with another new wide-area network service known as Switched Multimegabit Data Service (SMDS). As its name implies, SMDS was designed to interconnect computers at high speeds. Although it could operate at speeds as low as 1,540,000 bits per second, vendors expected, after the service had been tested, to offer SMDS services with speeds of up to 155 million bits per second. Both AT&T and MCI, Inc., conducted trials of SMDS services during the past year.

Internet. One of the largest computer communication systems in existence, Internet connects more than 12,000 computer networks in 45 countries. Many individual computers are attached to each network that is part of the connected Internet, making it possible for more than 1.1 million computers to communicate.

The U.S. government funded the research and engineering that originally produced Internet and continued to finance research and engineering projects needed to keep expanding it. In addition, the U.S. government paid most of the cost for a central interconnection known as the Internet backbone.

The Internet backbone consists of a wide-area network composed of packet switches and leased communication lines. It spans the continental U.S. and is connected to regional networks that cover each area of the country. For several years government agencies funded both the development and the operation of the Internet backbone. Recently the U.S. National Science Foundation (NSF) has had the major responsibility for funding networking research. When the U.S. Congress charged the NSF with funding networking research, it included responsibility for Internet. Initially the NSF funded research to provide Internet connectivity between computer scientists. Later the agency realized that computer networks would become fundamental to science and engineering research, both academic and industrial. Thus, by 1993 the NSF was using its funding to encourage industrial research laboratories as well as colleges and universities to connect their computers to Internet.

When the NSF first began to fund Internet activities approximately six years ago, it created a backbone, called NSFNET, in which the connections between sites operated at 56,000 bits per second. However, Internet grew at phenomenal rates, more than doubling in size each year. As more computers were added to Internet, the packet traffic grew. Several years ago computer scientists working on Internet realized that traffic would quickly exceed the backbone capacity. To accommodate the increases in traffic, the NSF redesigned the backbone and increased the speed of circuits from 56,000 bits per second to 1,540,000 bits per second (known as T1 speed).

When the NSF first installed the T1 backbone, some computer scientists assumed that the vast increase in capacity would satisfy needs for a decade. At first the T1 backbone was mostly idle because existing traffic used only a small portion of the capacity. Internet, however, continued to grow rapidly. As new sites connected their computers to the network, the new computers contributed additional packets to the load on the backbone. A few years after it was installed, it became apparent that the T1 network would also become inadequate. The NSF then contracted with a private company, Advanced Networks and Services (ANS), to construct a new backbone network with much more capacity. ANS constructed a T3 backbone that operated at 45 million bits per second, producing almost 30 times more capacity than the T1 backbone.

During the past year the NSF completed moving all Internet traffic to the new T3 backbone and then decommissioned the T1. During its last month of service, the T1 backbone carried more than one billion packets in one day, which confirmed that a backbone with greater capacity was needed.

Because all networks attached to Internet were switched to the new T3 backbone, hundreds of thousands of individual scientists and engineers that use the network daily did not even know the change had occurred. However, computer scientists involved in networking research expected the T3 backbone to accommodate growth for the next few years and make possible research on new applications that use the network.

IBM. During the past year the world's largest computer manufacturer, which once had been one of the most profitable companies in the U.S., encountered economic difficulty that stemmed from technical de-

cisions. IBM's leadership role in the industry had been unchallenged for years. Although it began as a company that sold typewriters and tabulating equipment, IBM recognized early that computers had an important place in the business world. By concentrating on business applications, IBM grew quickly and dominated the computer market. Instead of selling computers to the small set of scientists and engineers in industrial laboratories and universities, it sold many machines each year to businesses for such applications as accounting and payroll. For many years it practically controlled the computer market throughout the world.

IBM concentrated on selling large mainframe computers that cost millions of dollars to install and maintain. The computer market, however, was shifting to distributed computing, in which computer networks connect many inexpensive desktop computer systems. More important, by 1993 the fastest desktop workstations had much more computational power than large mainframes did several years ago. Although IBM continued to have impressive technical capability, for many years the company chose to ignore the workstation market and instead clung to its mainframe business. As the mainframe market shrank, IBM faced a severe loss of revenue. During the past year the financial losses caused a sharp drop in IBM stock prices and forced the firm to lay off thousands of its workers.

—Douglas E. Comer

Electronics

During the first three months of 1992, the number of jobs in the U.S. electronics industry declined by 400,000 from a total of 2,390,000. This compared unfavorably with the peak employment of the industry in August 1989, which stood at 2.6 million. During the same period, employment in the computer industry fell by 1.3% to 403,000 jobs, while at 133,400 the software sector remained flat in terms of the numbers employed.

The demise of the communist system in East Germany provided the newly united Germany with an opportunity to serve its eastern regions with a fiber-optic communications network. The poor state of the existing telecommunication facilities in the former East Germany and the superiority of fiber-optic systems over those based on copper were behind the drive by the Germans to install a fiber-optic system, with a cost to reach about $37 billion by 1997.

Deutsche Bundespost Telekom, Germany's government-owned telephone network, started a pilot project in the city of Leipzig connecting a total of 800 homes and businesses to a newly installed fiber-optic cable system. In 1993 the network was to be expanded to about 200,000 customers, who would be able to do telephoning and faxing and to receive about 46 radio stations and more than 30 TV channels.

The firms of Motorola Inc. and Nokia were competing to build a cellular phone system in Turkey that would be privately owned and operated. Though Turkey already had a state-owned analog cellular system, it was seeking to deregulate its telecommunications sector.

The Olympic Games in 1992 provided the dress rehearsal for the commercial appearance of high-definition television (HDTV) in Europe by 1994. The Games provided the first large-scale opportunity to broadcast programs in the HDTV standard that the industry had been developing since 1986. That standard produces on a wide screen pictures with the clarity of a 35-mm film. Not satisfied with their present electronic laurels, the Europeans were looking ahead to digitally transmitted HDTV. They were aware of the development of that technology in the U.S. and were forming national groups and consortia to work out the techniques needed to implement it.

Americans were, indeed, working on a digital HDTV system. The Zenith Corp. and AT&T sent clear and crisp HDTV images for a distance of 120 km (75 mi) between Milwaukee, Wis., and Glenview, Ill., on May 28, 1992. It proved, in the opinion of those companies, that HDTV had overcome a major hurdle and could now span the distance required for conventional TV. The images, transmitted in digital format, were as sharp as those from a movie, and the sound quality compared favorably with that from a compact disc. In the test the total power used to transmit both picture and sound was only one-tenth of that required by conventional television stations. The signal suffered no "snow" in its transmission, nor did it suffer from interference with a conventional television station located near the transmission path.

A new gold rush was under way during the past year. Some of the world's largest electronics manufacturers, such as the Electronics Devices Ltd. of Hong Kong and the Philips NV of The Netherlands were moving to China in search of the gold of cheap labor to be found there. Koreans were arriving in large numbers at Weihai (Wei-hai) in Shandong (Shantung) province, making that province the third most populous one and causing it to become a base for manufacturing TV tubes, calculators, automobile stereos, and digital clocks. The magnitude of the influx was staggering. On any given day during recent months, some 80,000 people and about 15,-000 trucks crossed into China to set up production there. The Philips company by 1993 had a $130 million investment in China and was making radio cassette recorders, fluorescent lamps, color cathode-ray tubes, optical fiber equipment, and many other electronic consumer products.

Motorola

Cellular telephone introduced by Motorola Inc. weighs less than one quarter of a kilogram (half a pound) and can fit into a shirt pocket. Sales of such phones totaled more than one million in 1992, compared with 87,000 in 1991.

Chips. After having first dominated the world's chip market, U.S. chip manufacturers were devastated by foreign competition during the last decade. The industry lost more than $4 billion in income and 25,000 jobs between 1983 and 1989. These losses were caused in part by low-cost Asian copies of U.S. chips that were dumped on the U.S. market at low prices. However, the shoddy workmanship and high defect rates of U.S. chips also contributed to the downfall of the industry. For instance, while the failure rate of Japanese-produced chips was less than 10%, that of the U.S. chips was about 40%.

In the face of this decline, the U.S. chip industry began to mount an impressive comeback. Innovative product lines, protectionist trade policies, and streamlined manufacturing facilities and processes combined to turn the industry around. While the Japanese firms of NEC and Toshiba remained the largest producers of chips, U.S. market share increased from 37 to 42% during 1992.

Underlying the impressive comeback of the U.S. chip industry was the manufacturing of specialized chips. While the Asian firms were strong in the mass manufacture of basic memory chips, the U.S. industry concentrated on the making of highly specialized chips with many functions and, consequently, higher profits. By way of example, U.S. manufacturers had always dominated in the production of microprocessors, the electronic traffic cops that direct the flow of electrons along the electronic highways to perform various functions within the computers. During the early part of November 1992, the Digital Equipment Corp. introduced its Alpha chip, which, it was alleged, was the fastest chip on the market

337

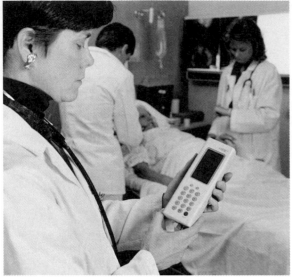

Blood analyzer developed by the i-STAT Corp. contains biosensors that create electrical impulses when testing the blood and a computer that converts the impulses to data that can be read on a screen.

and should further promote the dominance of the U.S. chip industry (see *Computers and Computer Science,* above). Furthermore, the effective cooperation between the Sematech consortium and industry was proving highly effective. For instance, Sematech cajoled U.S. semiconductor industries to buy more chip-making machinery from U.S. manufacturers. As a result, market share for such machinery increased during the last two years from 44 to 47%.

Microprocessors continued to increase in their operating speed, owing in part to the introduction of reduced instruction set computing (RISC). However, memory chips, while able to store increasing amounts of information, had not progressed sufficiently in their ability to transfer that information quickly enough to microprocessors. To eliminate this bottleneck, Rambus, Inc., announced in March 1992 the introduction of a new memory chip that would provide a 10-fold increase in the speed at which the memory chips would supply the microprocessor chips with the needed electronic data. To ensure the proliferation of these chips, Rambus licensed this particular technology to three of Japan's largest chip makers, Fujitsu, NEC, and Toshiba.

The Rambus technology employed the structure of a new electronic highway by which the electronic traffic could flow more quickly to its appointed destinations. In this approach both the microprocessor and the memory chips had to be modified. While many experts agreed that the Rambus approach was clever, they also foresaw another new technology called synchronization, in which the operation of the microprocessor and the memory chip would be in electronic lockstep. In this technology, while the memory chip might not necessarily operate faster, the microprocessor would demand electronic information only when the memory chip was ready to release it. In the meantime, the microprocessor would be kept busy with other tasks.

Automotive. The Dual Tech Co. of Clearwater, Fla., during the year introduced a dual-function headlamp, which, by the flip of a dashboard-mounted switch, could change its light either to the traditional white or to amber fog lights. An effort to use short-range radar in the detection of cars ahead of one's own came to fruition with the emergence of a system called Traffic Eye by the Nissan Diesel Motor Co., affiliate of Nissan Motor Co. The system incorporated a laser emitter-sensor mounted at the front of the vehicle, a speed sensor connected to the transmission, and a display unit positioned in the cab of the vehicle. All three components were connected by fiber-optic cables to ensure a quick response. The system worked by bouncing pulses of an infrared laser beam off the taillight reflectors of a vehicle ahead. The display unit in response calculated the relative speed of the two vehicles and the distance between them. If the trailing vehicle was moving more than 3.62 km/h (2.25 mph) faster than the leading vehicle and was within a "safe range" distance of that vehicle, an alarm would sound.

Low-cost fiber-optic cables were finding ever more extensive use in automobiles. By 1993 they were being used to conduct light to fiber-optic headlamps from a single light source and as a high-speed communication link between components of onboard computer systems. The high cost of the fiber cables, however, prevented their more extensive use. In response, the Hoechst Celanese Co. introduced a polymer optical cable that it claimed was less expensive and more durable than existing fiber cables.

The glass division of Libbey-Owens-Ford developed a sensor to detect rain on the windshield of a car and automatically turn on the windshield wipers. The control unit consisted of a small infrared transmitter and a sensor fixed to the windshield. Rain on the outer surface of the windshield altered its reflection characteristics and, consequently, the amount of infrared light that reached the sensor. After sensing this change, a microprocessor activated the wiper motor in response. Even after the system was deactivated, it added a few extra wipes so that no streaks would be left on the windshield.

New products. When Bill Clinton appeared on the podium of the Democratic national convention as the nominee for president, that image was sent within 11 minutes to the desks of newspaper editors across the U.S. This speed was made possible by a process that employed a digital camera, the Kodak DCS 100. The camera was connected to a modem, which, in turn, was connected to a computer. By 1993, however, the DCS 100 was being superseded by the DCS 200, a second generation of digital still-imaging cameras. The new models, which at $8,000 cost about half that of the DCS 100 models, produced still images without film or the need for chemical processing. As of 1993 the Kodak cameras did not directly plug into the home television set but were connected via modem to a computer such as the Macintosh IIfx. Standard 35-mm film currently had better imaging qualities than the Kodak cameras, but the latter were improving. The use of the cameras was no more complicated than that of a standard 35-mm camera. When the camera was linked to a computer screen, editing became easy. For instance, details in shadow areas that would have been lost could easily be enhanced. For field use the new DCS 200 camera used a laptop computer and a modem.

Two electronic fairs held in 1992, one during January in Las Vegas, Nev., and the other one in Chicago during May, both showed in the products exhibited that evolution took precedence over revolution in product development. Consistently, existing technology was applied in innovative fashion to consumer electronics products. Specifically prominent at these shows were multimedia systems. While the components of such systems: computers, a high-density data source such as a CD-ROM (compact disc—read-only memory) disc, and a good sound source were not fundamentally new, their application and integration into more and more areas of consumer use was. Similarly, while not new, electronic games were increasing their presence. Popular among the systems exhibited were electronic home theaters. These had television screens considerably larger than those of conventional TV sets and also high-quality stereo sound.

The Bell South Co., one of the largest suppliers of paging services, and the Swatch company, maker of electronic watches, conspired to make sure that people could be contacted at any time and place. This was done by a device that was a watch with a built-in pager. Christened the Piepser, it could receive signals from as many as four callers simultaneously. It used four tones to alert the wearer to incoming calls. Each of those tones was activated by a particular telephone number that the user had assigned to different callers. The wearer could identify the caller by tone. The call went to a central paging computer and from there via a radio tower to the wrist of the Piepser wearer. Should the latter not want to be contacted, Piepser could be put into a silent mode during which incoming calls were stored for later response.

Never a company caught with a dull product name, the Apple Co. introduced a new portable computer christened the BOB W. No, it was not named

for its inventor but for the fact that the new product was the "best of both worlds." The both worlds represented those of the desktop and the portable computers. The BOB W eliminated, so the company claimed, the need to have both a desktop and a portable machine.

During the spring of 1992 a hand-held blood analyzer was introduced by the i-STAT Corp. of Princeton, N.J. It allowed physicians to make decisions about a patient's blood more quickly and at a greatly reduced cost to the patient. The machine used whole blood, could be operated by either a doctor or a nurse, and provided the results of a blood analysis in about 90 seconds. The unit, about the size of a cellular phone, contained a computer and a disposable cartridge with biosensors that reacted electrically by creating electrical impulses to the blood under test. The computer converted these impulses into data that could be read on its screen.

—Franz J. Monssen

Information systems and services

More information was available by 1993 than anyone had time enough to read or use. The problem faced by information services was not to supply more information but to deliver the information it did supply in a convenient and accessible manner. Computers and telecommunications improved access to information and also provided new ways of processing and distributing information. These capabilities were recognized by the information industry almost as soon as the new technologies became available, and publishers began to produce information in electronic digital formats as well as the traditional printed form. The change caused a problem for many libraries, especially those in less developed countries that were unable to pay for the new technology.

By 1993 there were more than 75,000 libraries of varying types and sizes in Europe and even more in the U.S. and the rest of the world. These libraries stocked billions of books and other materials such as periodicals, maps, and manuscripts. Libraries also stocked films, audio tapes, compact discs, and video recordings. Modernization was expensive for libraries, and because of tight budgets they could not achieve it overnight. However, the need was recognized, as was the value of library services, and information industries were determined to supply the library market with new technologies such as the CD-ROM (compact disc—read-only memory), microcomputers, and library-management systems.

U.S. information systems. CD-ROM data bases are high-density, cost-efficient information storage and retrieval devices, for the information they contain can be accessed again and again free of search and telephone-connection charges. Having recognized these advantages, manufacturers produced increasing numbers of compact disc data bases.

Chemical PatentImages, published by MicroPatent, consisted of 17 years of U.S. chemical patents on 300 CD-ROMs. Included in each record was the full text of the patent application with all structures, formulas, and diagrams. Although expensive, this library of chemical patents dramatically simplified the patent research process. Patent attorneys or others could search the PatentImages file by patent number, class, inventor, or a key word. The selected patent records could be previewed on a computer monitor and the images rotated, enlarged, moved forward or backward, and printed, thus eliminating considerable waiting time.

The PAIS (Public Affairs Information Service, Inc.) data base indexed relevant articles and reports published in more than 1,400 periodicals, specialized journals, books, agency reports, and statistical publications. The data base contained reports on public policy aspects of business, economics, government, public administration, international relations, and other social sciences. The more than 340,-000 records included documents in six languages—English, French, German, Italian, Portuguese, and Spanish. All non-English documents were indexed with English-language terms and were provided with short abstracts in English.

Anatomist, a human anatomy data base on CD-ROM for Macintosh computers, used the computer's hypermedia program capabilities to prepare a complete anatomy textbook with text and color illustrations. Unusual features of this electronic textbook made possible by the hypermedia program included the ability to add personal annotations and lecture notes to the supplied text, to hear the correct pronunciation of anatomic and other medical terms,

and to rotate or magnify portions of the illustrations. This software book was available from Folkstone Design, Inc., in British Columbia.

The Environmental Resources Technology data base (ERTH) focused on petroleum-related environmental issues. The more than 22,000 records, published from 1963 to the present, provided worldwide coverage of pertinent periodicals, patents, and conference proceedings. Subjects covered included oil spills, waste disposal, petroleum toxicity, wildlife hazards, and other ecological and safety issues. Included in each record were the title, author(s), source, date of publication, index terms, and, in most cases, an abstract.

The *First Electronic Jewish Bookshelf* was published on a CD-ROM and released by ScanRom Publications in Cedarhurst, N.Y. Featured were two volumes of *The Jewish Book of Why,* a compendium of questions and answers about Judaism on a variety of topics. Also included on the disk were an encyclopedia of Jewish knowledge, a book of Jewish humor, several other general-interest Jewish titles, and hundreds of photographs and drawings of famous Jewish figures in all walks of life. In addition to the *First Electronic Jewish Bookshelf,* other titles in the series were expected to be published periodically.

A unique art history digital data base of text and video images was produced by the combined efforts of the Getty Art History Information Program in Los Angeles, the Bibliotheca Hertziana in Rome, and the Warburg Institute in London. It was called Census, the full name being the Census of Antique Art and Architecture Known to the Renaissance. The data base included antique monuments, sculpture, and other art objects together with Renaissance sketchbooks, manuscripts, and documents related to them. In addition, the data base provided up-to-date in-

A digital data base of text and video images, the Census of Antique Art and Architecture Known to the Renaissance, was produced by the Getty Art History Information Program in Los Angeles, the Bibliotheca Hertziana in Rome, and the Warburg Institute in London.

formation on these same objects taken from travel guides, photographs, and scholarly monographs. The approximately 45,000 records and 25,000 associated images that made up the Census data base were stored on videodisc. The two video screens of the computer monitor allowed the user to call up various combinations of images and related texts, making it possible to compare a modern photograph of an ancient monument with its depiction in a Renaissance drawing. Census was installed in the buildings of the three sponsoring organizations.

Research Libraries Group, Inc. (RLG), a not-for-profit corporation including universities, archives, museums, and historical societies, signed an agreement with the Institute of Scientific Information in the Social Sciences (INION). The agreement specified that all INION data bases would be made available through RLG's on-line and document-delivery services for a period of three years and INION would have unlimited free searching for this same period. All periodicals in the humanities and social sciences that published in what was now the Commonwealth of Independent States and in other eastern European nations were abstracted and indexed by INION and produced as printed bibliographies. Having these data bases on-line should directly benefit international scholarship.

International information systems. European information services existed in a market where linguistic, regulatory, and technical barriers obstructed the free movement of information and the growth of information industries. Recognizing this situation, the Commission of the European Communities (CEC) supported the development of a single European market for its information technologies and services. Such development required the rapid removal of existing legal and structural obstacles between the member countries of the European Communities (EC) and other nations.

The CEC also encouraged the creation of a coherent European system of standards and certifications and the establishment of rules for fair competition on a worldwide level. Although the tasks were formidable, significant progress was made toward achieving an integrated European information service marked with improved accessibility of information and economic recoverability.

The TIDE program (Technical Initiative for Disabled and Elderly People) was sponsored by the EC and designed to aid the approximately 30 million disabled people living in Europe. This research and development program centered on the manufacture of home systems and equipment for people with reduced mobility and those with visual or hearing impairment.

An EC Spirit project supported the application of advanced information technology procedures to

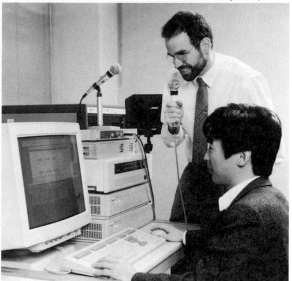

Advanced Telecommunications Research Institute International, Kyoto, Japan

Experimenters at the Advanced Telecommunications Research Institute in Kyoto, Japan, work to develop a system of automatic translation of spoken Japanese into synthesized sounds of spoken English.

art conservation. Specifically, the project supported the application of state-of-the-art aerospace measuring devices to detect hairline cracks in the surface texture of paintings and to measure the impact of different environmental conditions on color deterioration. Also investigated was whether vibrations that occur during the transportation of paintings cause the widening or lengthening of existing cracks or the creation of new ones.

Unesco and other international organizations established the International Network for the Availability of Scientific Publications (INASP). The organization's objective was to create an effectively functioning computer network of donors and to expand programs that distribute scientific books and journals to institutions, mainly in less developed countries and then in central and eastern Europe. The secretariat, located at the African Institute in London, published a directory of major book-donation programs and established an E-mail network for book donors and recipients.

The UN Intergovernmental System of Information in Science and Technology launched the Memory of the World project to preserve and restore rare library and archival materials that might otherwise be lost forever through natural or man-made calamities. The first objective was to safeguard endangered printed material photographically, and the second priority was to preserve the original documents in the safest possible conditions. An initial pilot project was implemented in Yemen, and future expansion could take place in eastern Europe.

Research. The British Library Research and Development Department awarded a special grant to the Pilkington Library of the Loughborough (England) University of Technology to conduct an intensive evaluation of the document-delivery service provided by the EI Reference Desk, a product of Engineering Information, Inc. Prototypes of the EI Reference Desk, a software and data base workstation, were tested in different environments throughout the U.S. and Europe, including government, academic, and industrial organizations. Researchers at Loughborough customized software to link the EI workstation to the British Library Document Supply Centre, a leading supply and document-delivery institution, located at Boston Spa, Yorkshire. The linkage enabled a person who had located needed reference citations to order those documents electronically from Boston Spa with a minimum of delay. During the year Loughborough began to evaluate the ease of operation and the cost-effectiveness of the total retrieval and document-delivery system.

Japanese information scientists developed a prototype speech-recognition system for dealing with their language. Written Japanese requires the use of more than 7,000 characters, making the kanji typewriter keyboard a bulky and difficult machine to use. Consequently, an automatic speech-recognition system that would bypass the use of a keyboard when preparing printed documents would be a particularly useful technology. In the prototype system Japanese words spoken into a microphone were analyzed into frequency bands to identify different sound segments. Phrases were then parsed by a computer program that identified and labeled the parts of speech for each word—noun, verb, adjective, etc. The spoken phrase, properly identified, was placed in a meaningful context and the printed record prepared.

The Office of Educational Research and Improvement of the U.S. Department of Education awarded the Library Science Program at Wayne State University, Detroit, Mich., a Library Career Training Grant for the education of urban library youth specialists. The grant funded fellowships for eight full-time library science students who planned to work in urban areas and serve the information needs of multiracial, multiethnic populations.

The Public Health Service awarded a grant to Knowledge Access International, Inc., to develop a data base of health-promotion programs and products for cancer prevention. William Paisley, the organization's vice president, explained that "the grant provides funds for both data base development and a delivery system for disseminating information about cancer prevention and early treatment communication programs." When completed, the data base would be released first on magnetic media and then, when the size increased, on a CD-ROM.

RLG in the U.S. received a three-year grant from the Hewlett Foundation to support cooperative solutions between research libraries, archives, and museums concerned with the preservation of brittle paper materials, photographs, and electronic media devices. RLG used the grant money to mount pilot projects dealing with cooperative preservation of materials, to improve access to scholarly resources, and to investigate new opportunities as they arose.

—Harold Borko

Satellite systems

Earth application satellites consist of three general classes: communications, Earth observation, and navigation. These automated civil and military spacecraft are designed, built, launched, and operated by nations, groups of nations, and commercial firms. During recent years they have profoundly affected economic, political, social, and religious systems throughout the world. Serving as prepositioned military assets available to coalition forces, they dramatically altered the conduct of warfare in Operation Desert Storm.

During the past year, prevailing economic and political conditions slowed plans for many new astronautical endeavors. Where instrumented Earth-orbiting spacecraft met widely recognized public service applications, however, they received government support. The distinction between civil and military satellite programs, meanwhile, continued to blur. Civil organizations increasingly benefited from using military space systems, and civil space systems supported national and international security efforts.

In the former Soviet Union, Russian Pres. Boris Yeltsin established a Russian Space Agency (RSA) in February 1992 patterned after the U.S. National Aeronautics and Space Administration (NASA). Rocket and spacecraft design bureaus and manufacturing firms affiliated with the RSA, now operating as commercial entities, also moved quickly to establish themselves in Western markets. In November representatives of the 13-nation European Space Agency (ESA) convened in Granada, Spain, and redirected the agency's spaceflight objectives for the remainder of the century. Most notably, ESA approved automated space systems that directly met social needs, such as a data-relay satellite, and it authorized $2.2 billion to design, build, and launch two large polar-orbiting satellites that would furnish data on the Earth's environment.

Communications satellites. This largest class of commercial satellites continued to grow in size, complexity, and performance. By the end of 1992, indicative of the increasing role of direct satellite-to-home broadcasting, some five million small satellite receiver dishes were in use.

The Russian satellite communications program, which suffered setbacks in 1991 because of deteriorating economic and political conditions, demonstrated a resurgence. New developments included the completion of two new satellite designs known as MAYAK and Express, to replace the aging Gorizont and Molniya satellite systems, and the creation of two low-orbit satellite system designs for mobile services, known as GONETS and Courier.

The commercial cooperative International Telecommunications Satellite Organization (Intelsat) continued to be the major provider of global transoceanic telephone and television services. Its 19 satellites, which were positioned in geostationary orbits, provided international communications for 180 countries, territories, and dependencies. (A satellite in geostationary orbit travels at the same speed as the Earth rotates; thus, it seems to remain in the same place.) In 1992 Intelsat provided 122,-000 two-way telephone circuits and two dozen full-time TV channels through some 1,000 international Earth stations.

In May the crew of the U.S. space shuttle *Endeavour* conducted a dramatic capture of the Intelsat 6 satellite, which had been launched in March 1990 into a useless low Earth orbit. Three space-walking astronauts retrieved the 4.5-ton satellite, attached a new rocket booster stage, and subsequently deployed it into proper orbit. This was the last of the Intelsat 6 series. The first of 10 new Intelsat 7 satellites was launched in October. During the summer Intelsat broadcast global television coverage of the Olympic Games from Barcelona, Spain, to approximately 150 countries. In December, when Operation Restore Hope began in Somalia, Intelsat rotated the antenna on one satellite, aiming a spot beam at the country. This made reliable, 24-hour television news coverage possible for world news networks.

London-based Inmarsat, the International Maritime Satellite Organization (67 member countries), provided increased mobile satellite communications throughout the world. Four Inmarsat 2 satellites in geostationary orbits offered a variety of communications services to ships, drilling platforms, and, increasingly, crews and passengers on commercial aircraft. Some 23,000 user terminals currently were in use. Inmarsat introduced a number of services during the year, such as digital communication technologies and low-cost, briefcase-size Inmarsat M terminals for portable satellite telephone service. In November Inmarsat announced that one of four follow-on Inmarsat 3 satellites would be launched by the Russian Proton rocket—the first Western-based organization to contract use of a Russian launcher. Three other Inmarsat 3 satellites were scheduled to use U.S. (Atlas-Centaur) and ESA (Ariane) launch vehicles.

Experimental communications satellite activity made significant progress during the year. The U.S. Advanced Communications Technology Satellite completed integration tests. Launch was planned in 1993. In Japan the Experimental Test Satellite ETS-VI underwent systems checkout of new features. These included optical laser communication links, flexible solar power arrays that unroll, and onboard data processing. It was scheduled for launch in 1994.

In Europe several experimental communications satellite projects were active. These included SILEX (Semiconductor . Laser Intersatellite Link Experiment); the Artemis test project to examine onboard data processing; Archimedes, an experimental system for European land mobile services; and Italsat, an Italian experimental satellite to test use of millimeter-length wave frequencies. In orbit the Olympus experimental satellite continued to provide data on direct broadcast satellite services and superhigh-frequency communications.

Earth observation satellites. This category includes meteorologic (weather), Earth resources, and military early warning surveillance and reconnaissance satellites.

Weather satellites. Continuous global weather observations were obtained during the past year from U.S., European, and Japanese weather satellites in high-altitude geostationary orbits and from U.S., Russian, and Chinese satellites in polar or near-polar orbits at lower altitudes.

To maintain complete national and global weather coverage, the U.S. Department of Commerce, through its National Oceanic and Atmospheric Administration (NOAA), operated two meteorologic Geostationary Operational Environmental Satellites (GOES) in high-altitude geostationary orbits above the U.S. east and west coasts and at least two operational NOAA weather satellites in low-altitude polar orbits. To replace a failing GOES, the Department of Commerce leased Meteosat 3 at a cost of $13.5 million over three years from Europe's weather satellite agency, Eumetsat, and moved it west to cover the U.S. east coast and the Caribbean. GOES 7, previously in that position, was moved west to cover Pacific weather. (Two other Eumetsat weather satellites, Meteosat 4 and 5, remained in orbit serving the European Communities.) NOAA's replacement satellite, GOES-Next, delayed by technical problems, was not scheduled to be launched before 1994.

U.S. low-altitude civil and military weather satellites in polar orbit and their civil counterparts in geostationary orbit greatly minimized loss of life by providing ample advance warning of Hurricane Andrew, which ravaged southern Florida and Louisiana in late August. In November direct transmission of real-time cloud images from satellites to aircraft was demonstrated by NASA. The continuous 137-MHz

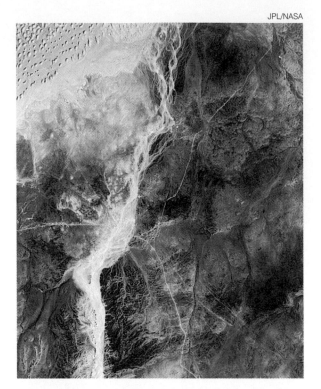

JPL/NASA

Enhanced image obtained by Landsat reveals light-colored roads converging on the village of Shisr in Oman (center) and also discontinuous tracks that are ancient trails and indicate that Shisr is on the site of the ancient city of Ubar.

signals from NOAA polar-orbiting satellites were presented on a screen overlaid with latitude and longitude. (One megaHertz equals one million cycles per second.) The two Defense Meteorological Satellite Program spacecraft supported U.S. and UN military forces operating in Somalia and the Persian Gulf.

Earth-resources satellites. This class of remote-sensing spacecraft observed the Earth and transmitted images in several spectral bands. Among other applications, they provided information on changes in the physical, chemical, and biological processes in the Earth's ecosystem, and the influence of human activity. The use of these vehicles to assess the world's environment for the purpose of its protection assumed a higher priority among nations during the past year.

In Europe the ESA's Earth Remote-Sensing Satellite (ERS 1) SAR images began to be marketed in quantity during July. ERS 1 images proved of exceptional quality and of great benefit in locating icebergs in maritime sea lanes. Indeed, in calm, shallow seas the SAR on ERS 1 furnished details of the topography of the seafloor. Russia encountered bureaucratic difficulties in marketing and rapidly disseminating images generated by the Almaz SAR satellite launched in July 1991. In October 1992, when the spacecraft encountered technical problems that threatened its

orbit, the RSA chose to deorbit the vehicle into the Pacific Ocean, thereby eliminating the risk of eventual uncontrolled reentry. Notably, the discovery by a team of remote-sensing experts and archaeologists of the lost city of Ubar in southern Oman, called by some the "Atlantis of the sands," was reported during the year. Images in various spectral bands from several spacecraft were used to detect the ruins.

In August the French Centre National d'Études Spatiales and NASA launched their Topex/Poseidon oceanographic satellite on an Ariane 4 rocket from Kourou, French Guiana. Equipped with French and U.S. radar altimeters, this satellite measured sea-surface height and ocean-current circulation as they affected the Earth's climate. Placed in a polar orbit, Topex/Poseidon contributed important data about the ocean during Hurricane Andrew.

Japan launched its first Earth-resources satellite (JERS-1) in February atop a three-stage H-1 rocket. The satellite carried as its primary instrument a synthetic aperture radar (SAR) with an imaging resolution of 18 m (60 ft). After the high-gain antenna was fully deployed in April, JERS-1 began returning images of great clarity. India, meanwhile, continued to operate and use data for state planning from its two remote sensing satellites (IRS-1A and -1B) launched by the Soviet Union in 1988 and 1991, respectively.

Military reconnaissance/surveillance satellites. Reconnaissance satellites provided optical and radar images of the Earth and monitored electronic emissions of terrestrial and airborne communications and radar systems. "Early-warning" surveillance satellites were equipped with infrared sensors that could detect missiles within moments of their launch from land or sea and record nuclear explosions above ground or in space. In a peacekeeping role, these U.S. and Russian spacecraft monitored compliance with international treaties and furnished warnings of imminent hostilities.

Russia operated all forms of instrumented reconnaissance and surveillance spacecraft in its Cosmos series. Some of those satellites were believed to be equipped with electro-optical devices that transmitted images to the Earth as digital data; others carried SARs that penetrated cloud cover and were used primarily to track maritime movements; others were instrumented for electronic eavesdropping of communications. A constellation of nine Russian surveillance satellites in Molniya orbits was deployed to furnish early warning of ballistic missile launches.

The U.S. likewise operated all forms of reconnaissance and surveillance satellites. In September the Department of Defense acknowledged for the first time the existence of the organization that developed and operated space reconnaissance assets: the National Reconnaissance Office (NRO). On the basis of lessons learned in Operation Desert Storm, the Department of Defense established a Central Imagery Office to channel requests from and improve delivery of imaging data to tactical military commanders. The U.S. Air Force remained responsible for the Defense Support Program early-warning surveillance satellites in geostationary orbits. Early in the year air force officials approved a follow-on early-warning system to be launched by the 21st century.

The French Defense Ministry during the past year increased funding for military space support systems, with particular emphasis on reconnaissance satellites. Defense Minister Pierre Joxe confirmed programs to develop a SAR satellite and an electronic eavesdropping satellite. Known as Osiris and Zenon, respectively, these spacecraft were to be launched around the turn of the century. They would augment the Helios visual imaging satellite developed with Italy and Spain, presently scheduled for launch in 1994.

Navigation satellites. Both the U.S. and Russia continued to operate in high Earth orbits navigation satellites that provided those equipped with receivers both geographic position and velocity with a high degree of accuracy. Near-identical twins, the U.S. GPS system and Russian Global Navigation Satellite System (GLONASS) would, when completed, each be composed of 21 active satellites and 3 spares. The GPS was scheduled to be fully operational in 1993 and GLONASS probably in 1995. Both systems seemed certain to have almost immediate commercial applications. During 1991 the world market for commercial GPS receivers rose to $500 million, and it was believed to have doubled in 1992 as numerous firms and organizations moved to exploit this technology. New studies prompted civil aviation leaders to consider navigation satellites as the primary element in a worldwide space-based air traffic control system.

Because the freely radiated signals of navigation satellites could be used by an enemy to guide weapons, the U.S. military designed the GPS system for "signal encryption." This denied highly accurate position data to unauthorized users without a decoding device. Because most commercial users demanded the more precise data for navigation, the U.S. Coast Guard in 1992 provided funds for marine radio broadcasts in coastal waters that would correct inaccuracies in the satellites' signals created by the military. The U.S. Federal Aviation Administration and Federal Highway Department also began to investigate these "differential stations" that rebroadcast "corrected" GPS signals. Aerospace companies in 1992 likewise investigated the market for differential receivers, as well as building and launching commercial navigation satellites. Thus, although military leaders might protest, it appeared that worldwide demand and economic competition would prove irre-

Rockwell International Corporation

Artist's drawing shows a U.S. Global Position System (GPS) navigation satellite. Operating in high Earth orbits, these satellites provided, to those equipped with receivers, geographic positions with a high degree of accuracy.

sistible, redirecting this military satellite application toward commercial ends.

In a related application, the humanitarian international search and rescue satellite system (Cospas-Sarsat), operated by the U.S., France, Canada, and Russia, mounted a secondary payload on board spacecraft in a low Earth orbit frequently visible to ships and aircraft equipped with Cospas-Sarsat beacons. When activated, the beacon's distress signal was relayed from the satellite to Earth stations (when in line of sight), providing accurate position data for rescue operations.

Inmarsat announced during the year a competitive system featuring a distress radio beacon in buoy, which would relay SOS messages through any of Inmarsat's four communications satellites in equatorial geostationary orbit. In 1992, underscoring the growing importance of satellite-aided rescue, the International Maritime Organization ordered all ships of more than 300 tons to install either Cospas-Sarsat or Inmarsat emergency position-indicator radio beacons by August 1993.

—F.C. Durant III; R. Cargill Hall

See also Feature Articles: INTELLIGENT VEHICLE-HIGHWAY SYSTEMS; COMPUTER-AIDED MOLECULAR DESIGN.

345

Energy

By 1993 the energy crisis of the early 1970s had evolved into a more complex and subtle situation. Some fuels, gasoline in particular, were actually cheaper in real terms than they had been before the crisis, and none showed any sign of an imminent shortage of supply. Energy was being used with far greater efficiency and with less environmental damage. However, the long-term problems—accumulating environmental degradation and increasing world dependence on Middle Eastern oil—were as intractable as ever.

Improved technology was a major reason for the defusing of the energy crisis. As energy prices rose, users found new ways to reduce the amount they needed. The U.S. economy grew almost 40% from 1972 to 1985 with essentially no increase in energy consumption. New technology also improved the production of oil, natural gas, and other sources. As a result, there was much less stress on world energy supplies than had been predicted in the 1970s. To a large extent, energy technology was a victim of its own success. Energy abundance led to low prices, which inhibited further efforts to improve efficiency as well as research and development in alternative energy sources.

However, the need for new energy technology grew no less pressing because environmental concerns were increasing. Global warming could mandate reductions in the use of fossil fuels, but disadvantages of nonfossil technologies continued to preclude them from playing a larger role in the overall supply of energy. Furthermore, it could take decades to change significantly the energy system. For example, after 30 years of development, nuclear power provided only about 7% of the U.S. energy supply. Problems such as resource depletion, which were unlikely to be critical for at least 20 years, would be increasingly difficult to manage if ignored until they became more apparent.

Many new technologies for the production, conversion, and use of energy were nearly ready for commercial use. Others were well along in the development process and could be expected to achieve cost competitiveness as they were further refined or as energy prices increased. However, all these technologies entailed compromises. In fact, there probably never will be an ideal energy option.

Environmental constraints. Energy development is often driven by environmental policy. Three (among others) environmental concerns—global climate change, urban air pollution, and electric/magnetic fields—had the potential for forcing significant changes in energy systems.

Global climate change. The greatest uncertainty confronting energy planners was how to respond to global warming. At the "Earth Summit" in Rio de Janeiro in June 1992, nations agreed to try to limit emissions of carbon dioxide—the major greenhouse gas, which is produced by the combustion of fossil fuels—to the levels of 1990. This was a compromise position, largely because the U.S. resisted calls for further reductions. However, even this modest goal would require deliberate changes in the energy system. Economic growth would raise demand for energy services, and there were only three nonfossil options to compensate for a reduction in fossil fuels: increases in efficiency of energy use, renewable energy sources, and nuclear power.

Many opportunities existed for efficiency improvements, particularly in the former Soviet Union and other centrally planned economies. Less developed countries also tended to use energy inefficiently, and their needs were growing rapidly. The U.S. with its history of cheap, abundant energy prior to 1973, had developed patterns of energy use much less efficient than those in Japan and Europe. Improved efficiency had been the major U.S. energy success story since 1973 and probably would continue to be so. However, it could not be counted on to eliminate an increase in carbon dioxide, even in the U.S., unless energy prices rose significantly.

Several forms of solar energy had become economically competitive but only under specific conditions that were not widely duplicable. Hydroelectric power was encountering increased opposition for environmental reasons, and growth was likely to be slow. Biomass—plant materials and animal waste—as a source of fuel was important locally, especially in less developed countries, but was inconvenient and difficult to transport. Wind power remained restricted to highly favorable sites, though recent developments were promising to expand its potential.

Nuclear power was competitive with fossil plants in some countries. In the U.S., where no new plants had been ordered since 1978, unhappy experiences with many (though not all) first-generation plants and uncertainties over economics, regulation, public acceptance, and operability left great doubts about future growth.

Current technology for all three options might be adequate to meet the goal of stabilizing the levels of carbon dioxide but only at significant cost. If further reductions were required, as thought by some researchers, technology would have to be improved to reduce costs and address other problems.

Urban air pollution. Automobiles were the largest source of air pollution in most urban areas and also the source most difficult to clean up. By 1993 several states in the U.S. were mandating the production within a few years of automobiles that used methyl alcohol (methanol) or other unconventional fuels that burn more cleanly than gasoline. The development of electric vehicles was spurred by such mandates, because it was the only technology that could operate with zero emissions at the point of use.

Alternative fuels, including electric vehicles, would require major changes by manufacturers, fuel suppliers, and users. None was expected to be competitive with gasoline in the near future without policy support.

Electric and magnetic fields (EMF). Research suggested that there might be a link between human health and exposure to EMF. Two Swedish studies

The National Energy Policy Act of 1992

Just before adjourning for the 1992 national election, the U.S. Congress passed the nation's first major energy policy legislation in more than a decade. The National Energy Policy Act was expected to affect almost all facets of the energy industry. A major goal was to reduce oil imports, which the Gulf war had shown again to be vulnerable to disruption. However, two key elements—increasing automobile fuel economy and allowing drilling in the Arctic National Wildlife Refuge—had to be deleted for a compromise to be reached. Major provisions with implications for energy technology include:

Global Warming: Plan to stabilize or cut emissions of greenhouse gases; promote efficiency in the U.S. and in other nations.

Alternative Vehicle Fuel: Mandate some nongasoline vehicles; demonstrations of electric vehicles.

Renewable Energy: Promote commercial development and exports of renewable technologies.

Energy Efficiency: Set standards for federal buildings and help states raise standards; set standards for electric motors and lights; encourage electric utilities to promote conservation.

Nuclear Power: Streamline licensing for new nuclear reactors; expand research and development for advanced, safer reactors; restructure the government uranium-enrichment program and study privatizing it; provide joint federal-private funding for the cleanup of enrichment plants; expedite nuclear-waste disposal at the Yucca Mountain site in Nevada.

Electricity: Remove restrictions on those who can generate power; expand access to the transmission system.

Research and Development: Emphasize programs—advanced oil recovery, unconventional gas, efficiency, and clean coal—that could reduce imports of oil; reduced environmental impact is also a major goal.

High-voltage power lines expose people living nearby to electric and magnetic fields (EMF). Two recent studies in Sweden linked exposure to EMF with an increased risk of leukemia.

released in September 1992 found a weak relationship between leukemia and the strength of exposure to magnetic fields. Both these studies were based on detailed exposure data, avoiding deficiencies of earlier epidemiological studies. Evidence of health effects, however, remained ambiguous. Even a mechanism for causing biological damage had yet to be identified. The U.S. Energy Policy Act, passed in October 1992, authorized a five-year, $65 million research program.

Many people had become concerned about EMF, especially in regard to high-voltage transmission lines, even though most exposure was from wiring and appliances in the home and workplace. Partly because of these concerns, the siting of new lines became difficult. Two possible remedial measures were wider rights-of-way and underground transmission, both of which were expensive. New technologies such as fuel cells that could be located near load centers, avoiding transmission altogether, became more appealing because of EMF concerns.

Commercial technology. Energy technology was evolving continually. Products were introduced and improved, frequently over a period of many years. Sometimes a breakthrough might be indirect, such as a demonstration that a perceived problem (such

Controlled by computers, wind turbines in Livermore, Calif., produce a steady flow of current regardless of changes in the wind's speed. This lowers the cost of the electricity so that it is competitive with that generated by fossil fuels.

as a public health or safety concern) was less important than previously thought. Technologies that recently changed significantly or grew rapidly are discussed here.

Energy-conversion technologies. Combustion turbines, essentially stationary jet engines, have long been used for electric power generation, primarily for meeting peak power needs. A new generation, incorporating the advances of modern jet engines, was achieving unprecedented efficiency and economy. One model introduced in 1992 had a thermal efficiency of more than 50% when operated in a combined cycle, where the hot exhaust gases produce steam that drives another turbine. (Thermal efficiency is the ratio of the work done by a heat engine to the heat energy absorbed by it.) Improvements expected later in the 1990s (such as intercooling between the compressor and the combustor) might raise efficiency to 55%.

Since combustion turbines cost much less than new coal plants and could be installed rapidly in small increments, they were becoming the favorite choice of the power-generation industry. The major limiting factor was concern about the long-term price of natural gas. Some turbines were designed to be fueled by coal via a gasification plant should the economic situation change.

Fuel cells convert chemical energy directly to electricity as does a battery, but the fuel is continually replenished in the fuel cell. Because no combustion is involved, the process can be very efficient and virtually pollution free. Fuel cells had been prohibitively expensive in generating power for utilities until recently, when small fuel cells using phosphoric-acid technology became available for on-site power and heat generation. Among other new activities, a government/utility group announced in 1992 that it would cooperate to demonstrate a two-megawatt molten carbonate fuel cell by 1994. Other utilities agreed to buy and operate subsequent fuel cells of this type in order to provide the necessary market for commercialization. Rapid expansion of the technology could occur by the end of the century. Eventually, fuel cells might be used in place of engines in vehicles, but that application was expected to be much more difficult to achieve than that for utility use and was unlikely during this century.

Energy end use. Traditionally, electric utilities generated and sold as much power as they could. In recent years state regulatory agencies had been influential in persuading utilities to think of themselves as energy service companies in order to minimize costs to customers. This had involved assistance by utilities to their customers to help them reduce their consumption so that the utilities could delay the construction of new (and expensive) generating capacity. During the past several years these activities had grown rapidly. For example, utilities offered energy audits for houses, with recommendations for improvements; subsidized the purchase of efficient compact fluorescent light bulbs and efficient refrigerators and other appliances; and cooperated with industry to reduce demand.

One product—high-efficiency windows—deserves mention because of its rapidly increasing use. In most buildings windows are disproportionally responsible for heat loss. It is relatively easy to insulate a wall, but windows must be clear and usually openable. New technology, however, raised the thermal resistance of windows to a level almost as high as that of walls. Coated glass restricted nonvisible light transmission; thin films were installed between the glass panes to add thermal barriers; and the sealed window was filled with an inert, high-resistance gas such as argon or krypton. Windows with all these features were too expensive to be cost-effective except in severe climates, but simpler versions were becoming popular.

Renewable energy. Next to hydroelectricity, wind power was the form of renewable energy most nearly commercial. By 1993 about 3,000 MW were operating worldwide, and that number was increasing rapidly. Costs had dropped to the point that wind power was highly competitive in places where strong, steady winds persisted. For the most part, incremental progress—improved blades, better manufacturing, reduced maintenance, larger turbines, economies of scale—was responsible for the cost reduction. A major innovation was the variable-speed turbine, which could operate optimally for any conditions while producing power of constant frequency. In 1993 the first large-scale variable-speed turbines began coming onto the market.

Photovoltaic (PV) cells convert sunlight directly to electricity without any moving parts. They had been used for years in space satellites and calculators and also for buoys and highway signs where it would be too costly to run power lines. PV systems had been much too expensive to compete with conventional utility power, but that appeared to be changing, at least for specialized markets. Manufacturers were reducing the cost of production, and cells of higher efficiency, such as those made with cadmium telluride, were emerging from laboratories. In January 1993 a government-utility consortium started operating a 400-kw demonstration plant in California. Despite these improvements, PV costs were still several times too high to play a large role in energy production, but major reductions appeared possible with improved technology and economies of scale.

Nuclear power. One of the last U.S. nuclear power plants still under construction, Commanche Peak in Texas, started low-level operations in February 1993. Three older plants were closed down because they had become too expensive to operate. Despite the lack of current orders, the nuclear industry was preparing designs for the next generation of light-water reactors. Future reactors were expected to be simpler and safer to operate and much less prone to cost overruns during construction.

In March 1992 Tokyo Electric Power broke ground for the first advanced boiling-water reactor. Funding for detailed design for U.S. licensing was announced in January 1993 by the U.S. Department of Energy, a consortium of utilities, and two manufacturers (General Electric Co. and Westinghouse Electric Corp.). If licensed, the reactor and most systems affecting safety would be largely preapproved. One of the major difficulties the industry suffered in the 1970s and early 1980s was frequent changes in safety requirements. This stemmed largely from the starting of construction before technology was mature and before the specific design was fully approved; many safety questions had not yet been resolved or even identified. The more orderly approach anticipated for the future should address most of these problems, but it remained uncertain as to whether the new reactors could be economically competitive and acceptable to the public.

Research and development. The Clean Coal Technology Program of the U.S. Department of Energy initiated its fifth and presumably last round of funding in 1992. This $6 billion program, about half funded by industry, emphasized very efficient and clean advanced technologies such as coal-powered fuel cells, pressurized fluidized-bed combustion (in which fuel particles burn in a mixture of ash and limestone suspended in upward-moving air), integrated gasification-combined cycles (in which coal is gasified, then burned in a combustion turbine that exhausts to a steam generator), and liquid fuels. The technologies offered some significant advantages for meeting the requirements of the Clean Air Act. Most could be commercially available within a decade. However, even the most efficient ones would release into the atmosphere more carbon dioxide than equivalent units fired by natural gas. Thus, if it became necessary to reduce emissions of greenhouse gases, these technologies would have limited application.

A major effort was under way to develop improved batteries. A consortium of automakers and the government awarded its first development contracts in 1992. The goal was to develop batteries with twice the performance of today's lead-acid technology. Some of the candidate types were nickel-hydride, lithium-polymer, and lithium-metal sulfide. The low capacity of batteries for storing energy, relative to gasoline, had been the main factor limiting the appeal of electric vehicles.

Another technology creating interest was superconducting magnetic energy storage (SMES). This is simply a coil with current circulating through it. The magnetic field it generates stores energy that can be tapped as needed and then replaced. If superconducting wire, which has zero resistance, is used, the current keeps flowing without losses. By 1993 SMES units were available commercially, but they had to be kept at a temperature near absolute zero. Materials developed during the past decade that exhibit superconductivity at higher temperatures were expected to reduce costs greatly.

Development of a new light bulb, the E-Lamp, was announced in June 1992. Similar to the existing compact fluorescent bulb in projected price and efficiency, the E-Lamp might be somewhat smaller and longer lived. It operates on a different principle, using a radio signal to excite a plasma that activates a phosphor coating on the inside of the glass. Commercial production was expected in the near future.

An intriguing program to foster research and development for improved efficiency was announced in 1992. A consortium of utilities offered an award

Using a radio signal to excite a plasma that activates a phosphor coating on the inside of the glass, the E-Lamp was designed to produce 20,000 hours of light, about 14 years of average use. It will fit standard sockets and cost homeowners about $10.

Fusion is the ultimate form of nuclear energy. The goal had been elusive, despite the expenditures of billions of dollars, because the technological problems were formidable. However, progress was evident. Researchers at Princeton University produced a record amount of energy from a fusion reaction, although they used a deuterium-tritium reaction that might not be applicable to commercial units. Because development costs would be prohibitively high for any one country, international collaboration was already an important part of the program. The next step in reactor design was to be the International Thermonuclear Experimental Reactor (ITER). Joint funding was announced in July 1992 by the U.S. Department of Energy, the European Communities, Russia, and Japan.

—Alan T. Crane

Environment

Three of the most obvious global environmental problems during the past year were drought, violence, and AIDS. In each case, this discussion begins with a review of important facts and then seeks a deeper understanding by imbedding the issue in a broader, more analytic context.

Drought. Drought was important during the year in a variety of types of society ranging from desperately poor Third World countries, such as Somalia, to rich developed areas, such as the United States west of the Rocky Mountains. This problem has multiple origins, and the following discussion has two goals. The first is to seek root causes for the situation in Somalia and to present a realistic proposal for fixing the problem, given what is known to be technologically feasible. Certain fundamental truths emerge from that analysis, leading to the second goal: finding whether all the drought-stricken areas represent different stages along a continuum, with the western U.S. representing an early stage of a process for which Somalia is a late stage and the ruins of Palmyra in northern Syria are at the end stage. The question arises as to whether all stages along such an imaginary continuum have certain fundamental features in common.

It should be mentioned at the outset that nothing in the Somalia situation would surprise the many people who have studied civilization in semiarid areas or have been tracking the situation in Africa. Karl Wittfogel had by 1957 gained a profound understanding of the relation between a precarious water supply and the required form of governmental organization. He understood that to prosper in such an environment a society required a high degree of organization on a national scale, highly competent planners and engineers, and the central control

of $30 million to the first company to develop and market a more efficient refrigerator. The prize, called a "golden carrot," was for a refrigerator that used about half the electricity required by the average new model and no ozone-depleting chlorofluorocarbons, used now as refrigerants and in insulation.

The advanced light-water reactors discussed above offered many advantages over current technology, but it was not clear if they would be sufficiently superior to allow a revival of the industry. An alternative concept, gas-cooled reactors, had been under consideration for many years. They appeared to be significantly more resilient to accidents, with a much lower risk of releasing radioactivity off-site. They also should operate at higher thermal efficiency than light-water reactors. In addition, they could be supplied as small, factory-built units that were added as modules as demand grew. What was not clear was whether they could be competitive from a cost standpoint and whether the additional safety—reducing the risk to the public from very low to extremely low—would lead to gains in public acceptance.

A design variation suggested recently—a closed-cycle helium turbine modular gas reactor—would help address the first concern. The conventional gas reactor uses helium to remove heat from the reactor. The hot helium passes through a steam generator, which drives a steam turbine. The new design would eliminate the steam cycle and replace it with a gas turbine. Helium can be handled at higher temperatures than can steam, and so the cycle would operate at a higher thermal efficiency, perhaps more than 50% eventually. The simpler cycle also should lower plant costs, making it competitive with fossil and other nuclear technologies.

350

needed for the careful allocation of scarce resources among regions. He understood, for example, that the curtailment of resource supplies by natural catastrophes and a breakdown in social organization for water management would lead to banditry. Every aspect of situations such as Somalia has been considered comprehensively and with great insight by both the International African Institute and the Club of Rome.

Viewers of television coverage of the Somalia drought might have noticed several aspects of the situation that appeared repeatedly. When women were asked about the number of children they had, the numbers mentioned were large: from 6 to 26. Also, the climate is clearly not conducive to high agricultural or forest productivity: there were few clouds in the sky; there was little standing water in sight; and it rained only occasionally. Foreign soldiers referred with astonishment to the dustiness of the environment. Vegetation was sparse and dried out. Much of the soil appeared degraded, ruined, and unsuitable for productive agriculture. The country was also characterized by a poor transportation infrastructure. The cost in energy of providing food from outside the country and protecting supply convoys against attack by bandits was enormous.

Somalia in 1993 was obviously bedeviled by a high degree of societal disorganization, with no institution having the capacity, authority, responsibility, or power to engage in rational planning or management on a nationwide basis. It was not clear that anyone, including the chiefs of the rival gangs, had the power to issue an order that would be obeyed by all members of the gang. Clearly, there was no capacity to balance a rapidly growing population with supplies of water and food.

Recent statistics and projections into the future reinforced those observations and provided additional insights. Relative to other Third World countries, only some of the demographic statistics for Somalia were particularly surprising. The high population growth rate and high birthrate were not extraordinary. Unlike Latin America or Asia, but like some other African countries, the population growth rate appeared to be accelerating. The annual rise was estimated at 2.1% from 1985 to 1990 and was expected to be 3.5% from 1990 through 2000. However, it rose only 0.83% from 1990 to 1991. The low recent population growth rate was explained by the death rate: 2.26% per year from 1985 to 1990, the second highest death rate of any country. The rate for 1992 was expected to be much higher than that, but because of the social chaos it would probably remain unknown.

These figures are significant for two reasons. First, for the living conditions of the Somalian population to improve, the rate of increase in food production

or importation needs to be greater than the projected rate of increase in population. Second, the discrepancy between the projected and actual recent population growth rates illustrates a widespread phenomenon in the modern world: all forecasts represent "best case," or optimistic, scenarios rather than likely, realistic ones. The discrepancy in this instance arises from the implicit assumption that food availability could be made to increase faster than population growth rate.

To satisfy the objections of technological optimists, one can postulate that a veritable miracle in increased food production will be achieved in Somalia. The question then arises as to what is the absolutely greatest such miracle for which the most optimistic people could reasonably hope. Exploring international statistics for the last several years, one finds that the most startling large-scale example of the Green Revolution that continued for any extended period was that of India; wheat production increased 6.6% per year from 1974 to 1986, and rice production rose 4.5% per year from 1974 to 1985. Given the 3.5%-per-year population growth projected for Somalia on the assumption of adequate food, an Indian-scale miracle is the minimum required for improving the famine problem in Somalia. How likely is such an improvement in food production? For all of sub-Saharan Africa total food production increased only 1.5% per year from 1980 to 1987. During the last year of that period it actually declined 4%. The inescapable conclusion seems to be that no amount of technological miracle will deal with the famine problem by increasing food supply alone; a solution also requires management on the demand side. The population growth rate must be decreased.

In regard to the climate in Somalia, the International African Institute and other scholars, such as Reid Bryson, have given much thought to drought in Africa. Several of these scholars postulated that the processes associated with civilization might be modifying climate on a large scale. Further, H.H. Lamb concluded that the recent climate cycles producing African drought were not short. Rather, he thought that the climatological processes implicated in the drought had cycles of at least 50 to 90 years. If that is the case, the drought in Africa might last for a considerable period.

Further, the environment is gradually being degraded, and the desert is increasing because of excessive human populations and grazing by livestock. This process could be stopped and reversed if human population were to decline. Even in dry lands with low and sporadic rainfall, the environment can be restored with wise management and fertilization.

In dealing with this situation another option can be considered. How realistic would be the assumption of sustained mass importation of food? To guard against large-scale surprise attacks by bandits on food-supply convoys, helicopter gunships would appear to be a requirement for some time. The economic and geopolitical implications of this option have received insufficient attention. Helicopters are an extraordinarily energy-intensive mode of transportation. They have only one-sixth the propulsion efficiency of such jet transports as the DC-10 and only 4% the energy efficiency of a highway bus. Also, an enormous amount of transportation was involved in shipping food and manpower into Somalia.

The energy situation of the principal supplier, the U.S., needs to be considered when options for Somalia are evaluated. A revealing statistic is the ratio of proven domestic crude oil reserves to the annual crude oil input to U.S. refineries. This ratio measures the number of years that U.S. refineries could continue to operate if the only available supply were existing domestic reserves. The ratio dropped from 9.82 years in 1970 to 5.37 years in 1990.

There are, indeed, few countries that will be able to export crude oil on any significant scale for more than a decade. The oil demand-to-supply balance is rapidly becoming precarious for both Russia and China. Thus, it appears that the domestic energy situation of many countries is sufficiently precarious to give pause to anyone proposing the continuation of a mass food-relief program for Somalia.

A realistic solution must involve a dramatic, intensive, and serious change in the societal infrastructure and organization within Somalia itself. There is a circular causal relationship between societal organization and food production; the former affects the latter, but the latter also affects the former. As Wittfogel wrote, in semiarid regions overpopulation relative to food supply leads to banditry, and natural calamities weaken the control and authority of government.

The basic message from the Somalia situation appears beyond dispute; if the standard of living in a country is to increase, the availability of critical limiting resources must increase faster than local population. A deeper message, applicable in all societies, is that human beings seem to expect optimistic rather than realistic scenarios for the future. In terms of precipitation, this implies that human population densities in each part of the world increase to levels that can be supported by the environment under maximal, not average, likely rainfall. Consequently, population builds to a density at which there will be hard times when rainfall is less than maximal.

To determine if this is indeed a widespread phenomenon, one can turn to the western United States in general and California in particular. Fortunately, this issue has been of sufficient concern that the U.S. Department of the Interior and the Department of Water Resources of the state of California publish detailed statistics and maps on trends in precipitation, runoff, and water-storage in reservoirs. The water-storage figures are updated daily. If population and water input are in balance, this is reflected in a stable or rising amount of water in all reservoirs.

A gaunt camel trying to forage for food in Somalia reveals that the nation's long-term severe drought brought hardship to livestock as well as humans.

If population increase is imposing a dangerous level of demand on available water supplies, there will be a long-term declining trend in the amount of water in storage.

In fact, the entire western U.S. has been flirting with a region-wide drought disaster in recent years. One way of expressing the situation is with maps of the Palmer drought-severity index. This is a measurement that expresses relative dryness or wetness of a region and indicates prolonged and abnormal deficiencies or excesses of moisture. It is computed from a variety of other indexes, such as measurements of precipitation totals, temperature, moisture content of the soil, and evaporation. The index is designed so that values greater than +4 represent extremely wet conditions and values lower than −4 represent extreme drought.

The region of concern is a huge landmass, cornered by four states: Washington, North Dakota, Texas, and California. The area affected by drought increased steadily during 1990 until by October of that year extreme drought conditions (Palmer index below −4) were found in much of California, Oregon, Washington, Nevada, Utah, Idaho, Montana, Wyoming, Colorado, North and South Dakota, and Nebraska.

Some reservoirs are large enough to meet the demand for water even if there are three consecutive years of inadequate snowpack. For most reservoirs carryover storage is no longer available when drought extends beyond three years. By late 1990 that danger condition, four or more consecutive years of drought, had occurred in some areas of the western United States. Under conditions of prolonged drought, entire reservoir systems would simply run dry. To show just how serious the situation had become, the most up-to-date statistical compilation for all 155 major reservoirs in California was issued by that state's Division of Flood Management on Nov. 12, 1992. The reservoir storage had decreased almost steadily, from 33 billion cu m (26.8 million ac-ft) in 1986 to 15.7 billion (12.7 million) as of Sept. 30, 1992. Heavy precipitation in late 1992 caused the snowpack in the Sierra Nevada in California and Nevada to reach 120% of normal as of Dec. 31, 1992. Even so, as of that date at four of the largest dams in California, the water in storage was still only 59% of the historical average.

The question then arises as to whether population in the U.S. West is becoming dangerously high. To simplify this problem, this discussion focuses on California. Curiously, coincidentally with the impending drought, the rate of population growth in California increased until quite recently. From 1970 to 1980 the state's population grew at an average rate of 1.71% per year, but in the next decade that rate accelerated to 2.32%. Only in 1991 did the population growth rate begin to slow, to 2.08%. Davis is the weather station in California with long runs of weather records most correlated with those that measure conditions in the mountains that feed the state's large reservoirs. From 1929 to 1934 total precipitation at Davis was only 61% of that during 1965–70, a relatively wet spell. Given recent California population size and growth rates, a repeat of 1929–34 precipitation would deplete California reservoirs dangerously.

This issue has implications that go far beyond California. That state earns about 12% of all U.S. net farm income, and California is a major food supplier, particularly of fruits and vegetables, to the rest of the nation. In light of the recent precariousness of the situation, it is curious how little attention has been attracted by this issue of the balance between human population and the carrying capacity of the region for people, which is set by inflow rates of fresh water.

A variety of phenomena related to this long-term drought in the western U.S. attracted media attention during the last year. Overbuilding of residences in regions of very high fire risk slows the process of fighting regional-scale fires because saving life always takes priority over extinguishing fires. The drought in Nevada is drying up bird-breeding marshes. As the drought kills trees, there is less high-quality wood for building homes, furniture, and all other uses. As pointed out by John Perlin, a superabundance of healthy trees has a diversity of hidden beneficial effects on economic health and sustainability that have received inadequate attention. Vast forests were certainly an important factor in the shifting of economic preeminence from Europe to North America from 1800 to 1950.

One scholar did attract attention to drought as a global issue during the past year. Sandra Postel of the Worldwatch Institute pointed out that many regions of the world are at risk from drought: western North America and South America, much of Africa, the Middle East, the southern region of the former Soviet Union, and Australia. *Last Oasis* highlighted several fundamental issues related to the limits imposed on human population growth by the availability of fresh water. One fact that she pointed out is of extreme importance, although few people had noticed it or grasped its significance. The land area under irrigated agriculture per person, worldwide, has been declining since 1978. This means that food security will continue to erode in a large portion of the less developed world since irrigation is required for boosting agricultural production.

Two themes appear throughout her book. First, in order to surmount the limits to population and economic growth imposed by water, it is necessary to expend both capital and energy. However, these

The Yosemite toad, a native of the Sierra Nevada, is one of many species of amphibians throughout the world that have been declining in numbers during the last 50 years. The Declining Amphibian Populations Task Force, involving more than 1,000 researchers in 40 nations, was established to investigate the phenomenon.

are both becoming limited themselves, and so human population growth is encountering real limits to carrying capacity. Second, confusion about the number of people a region of the world can support has resulted from the failure of political leaders to understand the difference between stock resources, or quantities stored in systems, and flow resources, or quantities steadily flowing into systems. The former can be depleted; the latter cannot. In many parts of the world, an increase in human population is being made possible by the pumping of underground aquifers to depletion. When those storages are depleted, the human populations will be excessive, and the societies will be unsustainable. When that happens, it will be economically infeasible to make up the shortfall by desalinating seawater; the price of energy will have become prohibitive by that time. As Postel observes, obtaining drinking water from ocean water is currently four to eight times more expensive than the average present cost of urban water supplies. Desalination increases the cost of farm water supplies 10 to 20 times.

The fundamental question that must be asked of any region is, "Can water availability be increased fast enough to balance population growth rates, and growth in standard of living per person, at a price the average person can afford to pay?" If the answer to this is negative, then population growth in that area is an issue, and it has already become an issue in most places. It is noteworthy that every civilization prior to this one ultimately collapsed, and mismanagement of water is a clear explanation for the fall in most instances.

Violence. During the past year violence became an increasingly important part of the environment for many people in many countries. In considering this phenomenon, researchers asked if they could improve their understanding of violence by looking at it from an entirely different perspective. For example, if the statistics on violence were labeled as measures of a disease and presented to any epidemiologist as a medical phenomenon, the physician would seek an explanation in the form of some pathogen, or physical or chemical causative agent.

In 1993 the U.S. National Research Council issued a new report on violence that represented a first step in shifting to that type of perspective. As the report stated, no comprehensive assessment of violence as a phenomenon had been attempted by a scientific panel. Previous assessments had involved reviews of work in only one or two social sciences. In this new study there was a significant attempt to review knowledge from biomedical and biobehavioral disciplines that might contribute to an understanding of violence.

The report presented four sets of statistical findings that suggest the notion of an epidemic with some underlying medical cause. First, the incidence of violence is very different from one country or place to another. Particularly puzzling is the fact that the United States has much higher rates for many types of violent crime than are found in other countries that superficially appear very similar to it, both economically and culturally. For example, the homicide rate in the U.S. is four to eight times higher than in many European countries. This suggests that environmental factors may be operating in the U.S. that are not found in the other places and indicates the value of a search to discover such factors.

Second, many measures of violent crime in the U.S. have increased markedly since the mid-1960s, and for some measures, such as aggravated assault, the rate is clearly accelerating. This suggests that one or more causative agents in the environment may have occurred in increased intensity or concentration during recent times.

Third, violent criminal behavior is more likely as city size increases. This suggests the notion of some causative agent that occurs with higher intensity or concentration in places of high human population density. Many such causative agents fit that description; pollutants occur at higher concentrations in air and water where human population density is highest. Also, the stresses on human populations, which lead to the use of drugs or medicines, are greater where population density is greater.

Fourth, the new report notes that aggressive children tend to become violent teenagers and adults. This means that it would be profitable to focus attention on the causes of aggression that affect humans at an early age. In fact, the report calls attention to the significance of factors affecting the fetal environment that could produce violent behavior after birth. Exposure of the fetus to abnormally high testosterone levels permanently alters the relationship between aggressive behavior and steroid hormones.

More generally, the report calls attention to a wide variety of biological substances, phenomena, and mechanisms that seem to be associated with violent behavior, including lead poisoning, alcohol or cocaine use or tobacco smoking by expectant mothers, and hypoglycemia. The last-named condition is a defect in the regulation of the blood sugar level by the body in which the blood sugar level drops very low after glucose ingestion. A researcher from Finland, Matti Virkkunen, for many years conducted a program on hypoglycemia in violent criminals. He found that violent criminals, on average, are hypoglycemic and that those with behavior most unlike other humans are the most hypoglycemic of all.

AIDS. Several aspects of the AIDS (acquired immune deficiency syndrome) pandemic attracted a great deal of attention during the past year. Gena Corea published *Invisible Epidemic,* a book about AIDS in women that was revealing about the perception of information as a scientific issue. In the case of AIDS the way the population at large and the medical profession in particular have perceived the severity of the pandemic has been consistently affected by factors other than data. Corea pointed out that male physicians for a long time underestimated the importance of AIDS in women, not having realized that cervical cancer, pneumonia, influenza, tuberculosis, and a variety of other conditions might in fact be clinical expressions of AIDS. The conviction that AIDS would be unimportant in the female population was so strong that for many years it was difficult for female doctors or epidemiologists to obtain grant or contract money for research on AIDS in women.

Corea's book reinforces an observation that has been made in regard to other medical problems, such as premature death due to air pollution. When a disease may reveal itself in a diversity of symptoms, the best measure of the real severity of the disease may be the rise of the total death rate from all causes, rather than the increase from a narrow range of causes believed to be expressions of the disease.

AIDS as a worldwide pandemic had begun to appear much more serious by the end of 1992. The number of people infected with the AIDS virus first grew most rapidly in Africa and North America. The rate of infection appeared to have peaked on those continents, at least temporarily, but in Asia it was rising rapidly and was expected to average about 1.3 million people per year by the year 2000.

An important research finding with implications for the AIDS pandemic appeared during the past year. According to a study from the Alan Guttmacher Institute, sexually active teenage girls were almost twice as likely to have multiple partners than they had been in the mid-1970s, despite the dramatic increase in their vulnerability to AIDS. This would appear to support the argument that a much more aggressive program of sex education among the young would be justified.

Frogs. Scientists have been aware for at least three decades that frogs, toads, and salamanders are among the first living animals to disappear from an environment when civilization moves in. However, this disappearance of amphibians has now become an international phenomenon. The Declining Amphibian Populations Task Force was established internationally as a unit of the World Conservation Union in Switzerland and involves more than 1,000 researchers in 40 countries.

It is disturbing that, although frogs have survived on this planet for at least 200 million years, they now seem to be in the midst of a global disappearance in the space of half a century or less. The explanation for this has not yet become clear, but early indications are that the disappearance may be related to a collapse of the immune system in frogs, which shows up as a condition called red-leg disease, and may reflect the combined effect of a variety of kinds of environmental threats.

Global greenhouse warming. The most complex theory to emerge from the environmental sciences is that of global greenhouse warming. It has attracted a great deal of attention from scientists in a wide diversity of disciplines because it has implications for an enormous array of phenomena, from lake and ocean levels to the physiology of forest trees and desertification. An important new book on the debates surrounding this theory, by Robert C. Balling, appeared during the past year.

One issue discussed in his book, desertification, is of interest in connection with the global drought discussed above. Balling explains that some of the global warming of the last century is not associated with or caused by the increased concentration of greenhouse gases in the atmosphere. Part is due to the local warming associated with the buildup of cities. Another part results from overgrazing and the resultant desertification. Data analyses from pairs of closely located sites where there are differences in removal of vegetation by overgrazing show how much overgrazing has contributed to an atmospheric warming trend that has extended over several decades. Desertification produced a "warming signal" of almost 1% of 1° F (0.006° C) per year. Or, to return to the Somalia example, part of the reason there is low agricultural productivity in a region because of drought is that prior overgrazing has affected the climate. Thus, this situation demonstrates a circular causal positive feedback mechanism; past mismanagement of the land alters the climate, which in turn makes it more difficult to manage the land wisely now.

—Kenneth E.F. Watt

See also Feature Articles: BAIKAL—THE GREATEST GREAT LAKE; THE SAVANNAH RIVER ECOLOGY LABORATORY.

Food and agriculture

Worldwide production of food and fiber rose during the year, and so did demand for many agricultural products. As world population continued to increase, real world economic growth was expected to reach nearly 3% during 1993. Stronger economic growth and an easing of trade barriers could boost trade in food and fiber, benefiting U.S. farmers, who are very competitive internationally. However, the change of administrations in the U.S. and opposition from various interest groups in both the U.S. and Europe threatened to delay world trade accords. Meanwhile,

consumers could look forward to the appearance of wildly colored food products and genetically engineered foods on grocery shelves. The future was also likely to bring a new class of crops and animals grown for their pharmaceutical value rather than for food, fiber, or fuel.

World production of most crops rose in 1992–93, thanks to favorable weather conditions in some major producing areas, including the U.S., the former Soviet Union, and India. Animal output reached a record high as pork and poultry supplies continued to increase. World commodity demand strengthened in response to real economic growth and population increases. However, shorter supplies in such regions as eastern Europe, combined with higher prices, dampened growth in global consumption of grains. U.S. grain exports rose slightly, restrained by large supplies in other countries, but greater use of grains and high protein meals boosted domestic demand.

GATT. After six years of squabbling over agricultural trade barriers, the nations participating in the Uruguay round of talks under the General Agreement on Tariffs and Trade (GATT) had resolved most of their differences. However, before the agreement could be clarified and signed, the text—which had been on the table for more than a year—began to unravel.

As the U.S. changed administrations, Agriculture Secretary Edward Madigan left office in January 1993 warning that failure to sign the accord quickly could spell its doom. Nevertheless, GATT Director General Arthur Dunkel reopened negotiations in mid-December on areas where there had been implicit agreement, thus opening the door for U.S. and French farm interests to try to gain concessions that would compensate for those made to the European Communities on farm subsidies.

Farmers in Strasbourg, France, demonstrate to protest a trade agreement reached in November between the U.S. and the European Communities. The agreement would reduce European production of oilseeds, including soybeans.

AFP

Agricultural issues were generally blamed for delaying agreement in the Uruguay round, although at times there had been other sticking points. As President-elect Bill Clinton prepared to take office on January 20, Madigan declared that there were no outstanding agricultural issues remaining to prevent a quick GATT agreement. However, he said, agreement on agricultural issues had brought to light disagreements in other areas, among them protection of intellectual property, dumping of industrial goods, and environmental issues. Even before his inauguration, Clinton was under pressure to make his mark on the Uruguay round before submitting it to Congress. Nor would signing of the GATT agreement end the story. Bilateral agreements would have to be signed to establish each nation's commitment to open markets.

There had been seven previous GATT negotiation rounds, beginning in 1947. The Uruguay round, which began in 1986, had focused largely on agriculture, although questions regarding services, intellectual property, and investments were also hotly debated.

NAFTA. The new U.S. administration took over while Congress was reviewing the provisions of the North American Free Trade Agreement (NAFTA), which would gradually knit the three nations of the North American continent—the U.S., Canada, and Mexico—into a large and rich free-trade zone. Clinton and many new Democratic members of Congress had expressed reservations about NAFTA, and this could make it difficult for the pact to go into effect as scheduled on Jan. 1, 1994. Clinton called for parallel talks on NAFTA-related social issues. For example, he wanted more money spent on environmental cleanups, a trinational environmental protection commission with powers to prevent and clean up pollution, and more money to help U.S. workers who lost their jobs because of imports. Mexico, in turn, called for a binational commission to clean up the Gulf of Mexico.

Probably no other U.S. industry was as divided over NAFTA as agriculture. Overall, agriculture would probably benefit from the agreement, but some sectors would experience losses. Under NAFTA's agriculture provisions, Mexico would have separate bilateral agreements with Canada and the U.S. but, in general, most product tariffs would be phased out either immediately or in five years. Tariffs for some items would be phased out over 10 years or, in a few cases, 15 years. Canada's most protected items include poultry and dairy industries, for which it claims protection under GATT. Mexico's most protected list includes corn, edible beans, and dairy products, and the U.S. list includes orange juice concentrate, most tomatoes, asparagus, broccoli, cauliflower, and onion products. The NAFTA pact would allow Mexico and

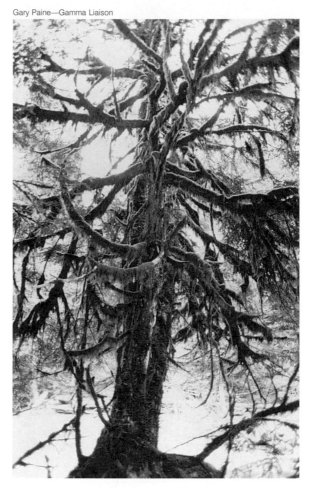

The Pacific yew has been the primary source of the cancer-fighting drug taxol. Because the yew is in limited supply and grows slowly, research was under way to find other sources of taxol.

the U.S. to ship determined amounts of specific products—such as Mexican orange juice and U.S. corn and sugar—to the other country immediately, duty-free or with a very low duty.

Taxol. As research advanced, a new class of crops grown for their pharmaceutical uses could emerge in the U.S. Meanwhile, environmentalists were battling pharmaceutical companies over use of the bark of the Pacific yew (*Taxus brevifolia*) to produce the cancer-fighting drug taxol. The drug was approved in December 1992 by the Food and Drug Administration (FDA) for use in treating women with advanced ovarian cancer. Although not a cure, it had shown great promise in treatment of advanced ovarian, breast, and other cancers. However, initial supplies were limited because the only source was the Pacific yew tree. Yews are slow-growing evergreens, and the procedure required for obtaining taxol was difficult and expensive and yielded only small amounts. Using bark-extraction procedures, the National Cancer

Institute (NCI) estimated that it would take up to three of the 150- to 200-year-old trees to provide enough drug to treat one patient, and the procedure required killing the trees to harvest the bark. The NCI said 8,000 to 10,000 patients received taxol during 1992. Environmentalists opposed increasing the harvest of Pacific yews because of the tree's slow growth and the risk of damage to old-growth forests, which included the habitat of the endangered spotted owl.

Because of the limited supply of taxol, the NCI made finding additional sources a top priority, and researchers around the world were racing to develop synthetic and natural alternatives. Development of a synthetic drug was several years away, and the cultivation of domestic nonbark sources of taxol and related taxanes now appeared to offer the best prospects, according to studies sponsored by the U.S. Department of Agriculture (USDA). Scientists hoped to develop the drug eventually from several alternative sources, including yew-tree needles and clippings and the bark and leaves of other plant species found in the United States, Europe, and Asia. Bristol-Myers Squibb Co., codevelopers of taxol with the National Cancer Institute, hoped to obtain all of its taxol from sources other than Pacific yew tree bark by 1995.

In a relatively short time, U.S. agricultural researchers concluded that they had found practical alternatives to Pacific yew tree bark—harvesting clippings from ornamental yews, increasing production of clippings, and improving greenhouse cultivation of yews. The USDA's Cooperative State Research Service (CSRS) funded a demonstration project in cooperation with the NCI that involved Ohio State University (OSU), the University of Mississippi, and Zelenka Nursery Inc. of Grand Haven, Mich. Zelenka, the nation's largest producer of ornamental yews, collected clippings for the project. The University of Mississippi's Research Institute of Pharmaceutical Science–Natural Products conducted pharmacological studies and provided information on processing technology and on the concentration and quality of taxanes in materials from *Taxus* species.

Several common types of ornamental yew were found to contain higher levels of taxol than the Pacific yew, though determining the purity and quality of this source would require further research. OSU's Ohio Agricultural Research and Development Center (OARDC) provided expertise in handling and drying technology and in the identification and verification of *Taxus* species.

Blood clotting. The era of raising animals that produce drugs was also moving closer. A research team at Virginia Polytechnic Institute and State University created pigs that produce Protein C, a potentially lifesaving but scarce human protein, in their milk. Protein C appeared promising as an anticoagulant, but supplies from human sources are limited. Researchers believed the pig technology, if it worked on a large scale, could help solve the supply problem. While similar proteins had been produced through similar technology, the researchers said this was the first time a protein as complex as Protein C had been produced in amounts large enough to be commercially feasible.

Humans produce Protein C in trace amounts and, under normal conditions, it regulates blood clotting by attacking other proteins that are necessary for the clotting process. A deficiency of the protein can result in excessive production of clots, increasing the risk of heart attack or stroke. Currently, aspirin,

Drawing by Ed Fisher; © 1992 The New Yorker Magazine, Inc.

coumadin, and heparin are used to prevent excessive clotting, but they can cause other problems, such as extending episodes of bleeding. Encouraged by studies that show human Protein C can prevent excessive blood clots in animals, scientists working with the Red Cross were testing Protein C derived from human blood plasma in human subjects. If the drug works and regulators approve its wide use, it is possible that more Protein C will be needed than can be produced from human plasma. That would be where the pigs come in.

The technique of introducing new genetic material into animals was being used elsewhere, although researchers said drugs from this source were years away from commercial production. GenPharm International Inc. of Mountain View, Calif., was developing cows to produce human milk proteins for use in infant formula and mice to generate human monoclonal antibodies. In 1991 DNX Corp. of Princeton, N.J., said it had spliced the human hemoglobin gene into pigs.

Edible vaccines. Scientists at Texas A & M University reported research indicating that it may be possible to produce an edible vaccine in an edible plant. Consumers would then be able to gain protection from disease along with their dinner. Using a hepatitis B antigen and tobacco plants, the researchers inserted certain genes into naturally replicating plant DNA, with encouraging results. The researchers were now trying to increase the accumulation of the antigen in the plant. They also put the gene into tomatoes and lettuce, which would be fed to mice to determine whether it produced an immune response. Researchers were not sure whether this would work in humans, but if it did, the impact would be felt worldwide.

Genetic engineering. The USDA proposed a new system for dealing with genetically engineered crops that would make it easier and less expensive for companies or research institutions to field-test their products. Under the plan, the department would no longer require companies to obtain specific permits before growing or moving their crops. Instead, companies could simply notify the agency of field tests, provided their products met certain guidelines. The USDA had overseen about 300 field tests without major problems and therefore believed that test requirements for the crops with which it had had the greatest experience, including tomatoes, potatoes, corn, soybeans, and tobacco, could be greatly simplified. The biotechnology industry applauded the proposal, but opponents called it negligent and illegal, and a battle over regulations and food labeling was in full swing.

The Flavr Savr tomato developed by Calgene Inc. of Davis, Calif., was the first genetically altered plant product to be approved by the USDA for commercial

Agricultural Research Service, USDA

Potatoes with orange flesh and white or red skins were produced in a U.S. Department of Agriculture test plot containing plants from the Andes Mountains of South America.

food production. It was resistant to spoilage, could be picked and shipped at a tasty, red-ripe stage, and was said to have that summertime, farm-fresh taste. The company expected to market the tomato commercially by the late summer of 1993, but first the FDA would have to declare it a food.

New products. Black strawberries and orange cauliflower were already on the market, so orange potatoes were not out of step with the trend. A diminutive potato with orange flesh could become a novel addition to the current selection of potato chips. The egg-size tubers turned up in a USDA test plot of potatoes originating from samples from the Andes Mountains of South America. Breeders from several snack food companies requested samples of the orange potato and crossed the plants with their own varieties. Their aim was to come up with a new variety suitable for making orange or orange-yellow potato chips or other snacks. Surprisingly, the potatoes contain little beta carotene, the natural pigment—converted into Vitamin A by the human body—that gives carrots, sweet potatoes, and yams their orange color. The potatoes do contain high levels of related carotenoids, called zeaxanthin and lutein, that are also found in corn, squash, citrus, and leafy green vegetables. To date, the nutritional value of these carotenoids is unknown, but scientists say further research may reveal their potential as antioxidant compounds, thought to retard aging and possibly protect against cancer.

Agricultural experiment station researchers at the University of Georgia thought they might have the secret to snacking without guilt. The scientists had developed the technology for processing vegetable- or fruit-based, nonfried snacks that have the texture of a fried snack but retain the nutrients and flavor of the raw food.

—John Patrick Jordan; Patricia Brazeel Lewis

Life sciences

Among highlights in the life sciences during the past year were the identification of several key plant genes, the growing recognition of the importance of microbial activity to geochemistry taking place below the Earth's surface, the recovery of DNA from preserved insects 30 million years old, and the unearthing of two new dinosaurs, one fearsome and the other primitive. Publication of the most detailed maps to date of the human chromosomes represented a major step toward identifying the genes responsible for a number of important hereditary diseases.

Botany

The steady progress in botany during the past year was characterized by applications of genetics in many areas of research. The rapid progress in working out the genome of *Arabidopsis* and a number of applications of chloroplast DNA study seemed to be typical. Another dominant theme involved the concern about worldwide forest depletion and its effects.

Arabidopsis. This may have been the year of *Arabidopsis thaliana,* as the diminutive member of the mustard family came into its own as an object for the genetic study of plants. It proved to be extremely useful because of its small size (up to 30 cm [12 in]), ease of culturing, short life history (five to six weeks), prolific seed production, and relatively small genome (amount of genetic material).

As a result of the Multinational Coordinated Arabidopsis Genome Research Project and other efforts, plant geneticists were identifying and mapping more and more genes that control specific traits such as the production of metabolic enzymes. While such findings characterized the study of a number of other plants, botanists hoped that *Arabidopsis* would be much more useful for the discovery of homeotic genes, those that control developmental steps in the organism such as formation of the embryo and later differentiation of tissues and organs. Early work suggested that some of these appear to be similar to those known in animals and that some may be different. Examples of some findings concerning *Arabidopsis* published during the past year follow.

Alan M. Lloyd, Virginia Walbot, and Ronald Davis of Stanford University reported on the ability to affect the anthocyanin pathway of *Arabidopsis* by transplanting genes from *Zea mays* (maize). Developing *Arabidopsis* plants that received regulatory genes *R* and *C1* produced anthocyanins in roots, petals, and stamens where pigment is not normally produced. Plants deficient in normal anthocyanin were also restored by receiving these genes. (Anthocyanins are glycoside pigments producing blue to red coloring in flowers and other plant tissue.)

John Celenza, Whitehead Institute

The diminutive Arabidopsis thaliana, *shown about one-third of life size, has become a focus of studies in plant genetics because of its small size, ease of culturing, five-to-six-week life history, and relatively small genome.*

Daniel P. Schachtman of the University of California at San Diego and his associates reported that an *Arabidopsis* gene, *KAT1,* controls the formation of a cell-membrane feature called a K^+ (potassium ion) channel. This channel provides for the passage of potassium ions from the outside to the inside of cells.

Z.R. Sung and associates from the University of California at Berkeley reported the discovery of a gene, *EMF,* that promotes the growth of the vegetative shoot in *Arabidopsis.* If the allele (alternative gene), *emf,* is present instead, the plant produces flowering stems only.

N. Murata and associates from the Central Laboratory for Basic Biology in Japan demonstrated that an *Arabidopsis* chloroplast gene can be transferred to tobacco plants (*Nicotiana tabacum*), where it will provide protection from chilling. This gene controls the level of unsaturated fatty acids involved in the synthesis of phosphatidylglycerol, which acts as an "antifreeze" or at least an "antichill." It is understood to be responsible for the resistance to chilling in *Arabidopsis.*

Flower research. Early researchers proposed that a single kind of plant pigment made roses red and cornflowers blue. This pigment group came to be called the anthocyanins, and it was believed that cellular chemistry determined which color is expressed: red under acid and blue under basic conditions. However, since a large array of color shades of this type occurs in plants, researchers have thought for a time that blue-color determination must be more complex.

Using X-ray crystallography, Tadoa Kondo of Nagoya (Japan) University and a number of associates were able to show that the blue color in the petals of *Commelina communis* (day flower) is caused by a super molecule. This consists of a magnesium core surrounded by precisely arranged and vertically stacked anthocyanin and flavone ($C_{15}H_{10}O_2$) molecules. Further study of such pigments revealed that a variety of anthocyanins and other organic compounds, with or without the metal core, participate in the making of these pigments in various plants. Continued study by the Japanese workers involved the recognition process—how the specific arrangement of the constituents is determined in each plant species.

The flowers of the arctic poppy (*Papaver radicatum*) demonstrate heliotropism; that is, they tend to keep turned toward the Sun. Three researchers from Queen's University, Kingston, Ont., went to Baffin Island to investigate ways in which this phenomenon might benefit the plant, particularly in alpine regions with short growing seasons. Andrea Corbett, Paul Krannitz, and Lonnie Aarssen removed the petals from some poppy flowers and compared them with normal flowers, sometimes from the same plant. They measured light intensity, ovary temperature, seed weight, and number of seeds produced. Flowers without petals did not track the Sun; their ovary temperatures were significantly lower than in flowers with petals, and the ovaries produced fewer and smaller seeds.

Corbett, Krannitz, and Aarssen found that irradiance was actually higher when measured with a photocell held at the angle of the petals than when the cell was held in a horizontal position. (Irradiance is the amount of radiant energy falling on a specific area.) The investigators concluded that the poppy petals tend to concentrate light on the ovaries. Just how this results in increased seed number and larger seeds depends on whether increased temperature results in greater ovule survival and whether the ovary is capable of photosynthesis that utilizes the directed light.

This study illustrates the fact that research on the enhancement of reproductive success tends to focus on the female component of the flower. Sometimes, however, an interesting adaptation of the male flower parts becomes known. Joan Edwards and James R. Jordan of Williams College, Williamstown, Mass., observed flowers of the wood lily (*Lilium philadelphicum*) growing on Isle Royale in Lake Superior. They noticed that the flowers' anthers opened up (dehisced) so that pollen would be available to pollinators. (Anthers are the pollen-producing parts of flowers.) They also noticed that the anthers closed up again on rainy days. The result of this behavior is that pollen becomes available to the large butterflies that cross-pollinate lily flowers on sunny days and is conserved on rainy days, when butterflies do not fly. Since the pollen would be otherwise washed away by rain, the ability of the flowers to close the anthers prolongs the period of pollen availability. The researchers feel that this may be the first case discovered of anthers with longitudinal dehiscence reclosing after opening.

Seedling shadow. The dispersal of seeds around individual plants is called the seed shadow. It has been studied frequently in an effort to understand the characteristic distribution of plants in ecosystems such as the rain forest. John M. Pleasants and Thomas W. Jurik of Iowa State University found that very few studies have been done on seedling shadows, which they believed may also be important. They observed seedlings of the prairie compass plant (*Silphium laciniatum*), a composite plant growing in a small prairie remnant south of Ames, Iowa. (A composite plant is characterized by florets arranged in dense heads that resemble single flowers.) They found that the compass plant flowered abundantly during the years following years of dry growing seasons, that approximately 1% of the seeds survived to

A study of the ways in which Sun-tracking behavior benefits the arctic poppy (below) revealed that its flower petals concentrate light energy on the ovary, a feature that in some way results in the production of more and larger seeds.

Andrea L. Corbett

produce seedlings the following year, and that the average seedling distance from the nearest stalk was one meter (3.3 ft).

The short dispersal distance is related to the fact that this species does not produce seeds with a pappus, a parachute-like structure that catches the wind, as is found in many other composites. Because of this, subtle differences such as height of the flowering stalk and any tendency of the tall stalk to fall down may be instrumental in increasing the dispersal distance.

Chloroplast genes. Chloroplast DNA was used during the past year to explore plant-group relationships. (Chloroplasts are cell organelles occurring in the green parts of plants and are responsible for photosynthesis.) One example was a study of *Codium*, a fairly large genus of green algae, by Linda J. Goff of the University of California at Santa Cruz and her associates. About 100 species of these plants exist in tropical and temperate waters, where they occupy narrow geographic ranges and exhibit little structural variability. However, a few species or subspecies have a broader distribution, apparently facilitated by rapid growth, parthenogenetic reproduction, and the tendency to grow in sheltered habitats where they may "hitchhike" on boats and other objects. These are called "weedy" by some botanists. *C. fragile* subspecies *tomentosoides* is one of the latter. It arrived in San Francisco Bay in 1979, at a place not far from the habitat of a nonweedy subspecies, *C. fragile* subspecies *fragile*.

Goff and her associates examined the chloroplast DNA of both groups to try to determine if it was similar enough to conclude that the weedy species had originated from the nonweedy one. Using a technique called restriction mapping, they concluded instead that the two *C. fragile* subspecies were significantly different from each other and from other species of *Codium*. Interestingly, the restriction map of the San Francisco subspecies *tomentosoides* was indistinguishable from that of the same subspecies growing in the Atlantic. This left open the question of the origin of the weedy subspecies, but it did indicate that its recent source was not its neighbor subspecies.

Phylogeny. Many introductory botany books arrange the lineage (phylogeny) of plants according to the belief that mosslike plants (Bryophyta) gave rise to higher plants (Tracheophyta). The transition is a significant one because the moss group does not generally have vascular tissue, while the higher plants do. Vascular tissue is specialized into xylem and phloem, which conduct materials throughout the plant. Botanists continued to be interested in identifying transitional forms whether the plants are extinct or not. Two alternative transitions have been favored: through the psilopsids and through the lycopsids. Psilopsids, belonging to the division or subdivision Psilopsida, tend to have a rather simple structure for vascular plants; while the vascular tissue is fairly well developed, these plants have no roots, may not have leaves, and send up shoots from an underground rhizome (horizontal stem). Lycopsids, belonging to the division or subdivision Lycopsida, are somewhat more complex, having both roots and leaves.

Evidence that may place the lycopsids in the gap was suggested by Linda A. Raubeson, then working at Yale University, and Robert K. Jansen, then working at the University of Connecticut. They studied DNA from certain bryophytes, psilopsids, lycopsids, ferns, and higher plants. They were aware of previous reports that showed the chloroplast DNA of certain bryophytes and higher plants to be very similar except for a section that is inverted. This means that a section found in the higher plants is reversed in the bryophytes. Further investigation revealed that the psilopsids have the higher-plant arrangement and the lycopsids have the bryophyte arrangement. Raubeson and Jansen interpreted this finding to indicate that the lycopods were more likely to be in the lineage between the bryophytes and the tracheophytes and that all other vascular plants, including the psilopsids, are derived from that lineage. In other words, they concluded that the psilopods are not the transitional group between bryophytes and tracheophytes.

Forestry. The American chestnut (*Castanea dentata*) is remembered by some as the ideal eastern deciduous forest tree. In the former oak-chestnut forests of the entire Appalachian region and as far west as southern Illinois, the chestnut was known for its versatility and virility. It constituted up to 25% of the dominant trees, supplied fine hardwood, and provided desirable fruit. However, the relative smallness of the fruit led to the downfall of the species when Asiatic chestnuts were brought in to cross with the American species in order to produce a large-fruited hybrid. The Asiatic trees brought in a blight-producing fungus (*Cryphonectria parasitica*) to which the native trees were highly sensitive. Most of the eastern American chestnut trees died. The largest known survivor is in Oregon, apparently out of reach of the fungus.

Today a meager number of American chestnuts exist as root sprouts and somewhat older trees in isolated ravines. Gary Griffin of Virginia Polytechnic Institute and State University searched 17 selected forest sites in Virginia, North Carolina, and Tennessee. He recorded numerous small chestnut trees in many of the coves and studied five of the sites in detail. He found that survival seemed to be associated with the frequency and size at each site of red maples (*Acer rubrum*) and concluded that such sites may be the best for experiments on control of the blight.

In addition to the attempt to hybridize an American strain of trees with blight-resistant foreign trees, for some time research focused on developing a way to introduce hypovirulence (decreased infectiousness) into the fungus so that young trees would no longer be sensitive. Limited occurrences of such strains already existed in nature but did not seem to be spreading. Researchers were considering the possibility of producing hypovirulent strains experimentally and then introducing them into nature, where they would be expected to hybridize with the virulent strains and cause the latter to become ineffective. An example of current research was reported by Gil H. Choi and Donald L. Nuss of the Roche Research Center in Nutley, N.J. They established that one cause of hypovirulence in the blight fungus is a certain kind of double-stranded viral RNA. They were able to reverse-transcribe this to DNA and thereby transform cells of *C. parasitica* from their normal virulence to hypovirulence. Their hope was that such laboratory-produced strains would hybridize when released.

World attention was increasingly drawn during the past year to the status of tropical rain forests. Their welfare was commonly discussed as more people became aware of the destruction of vast areas to provide space and employment for burgeoning populations, to boost ailing economies, and to attempt satisfaction of the global appetite for wood and agricultural products. There were, however, other forests fully as extensive as tropical rain forests and probably as fully threatened. These included the magnificent boreal forests (taiga) of Siberia. According to some estimates, they covered an area the size of the continental U.S. and contained up to 57% of the Earth's coniferous trees and 25% of its total wood volume. Of the 6 million sq km (2.3 million sq mi) of these forests, 40,400 sq km (15,600 sq mi) are harvested each year, and pressure to harvest more rapidly seemed almost certain to be applied by forces within Russia to shore up the republic's sagging economy and attract foreign investment.

The current logging practice in Siberia of clear cutting (felling and removing all trees in a forest area) resulted in erosion, loss of water retention, and poor regeneration of trees. Inefficient technology required three times as much timber for finished product as was needed by the North American and Western European forest product industry. Given the political uncertainties in Russia, it seemed unlikely that modifications in practice would be implemented soon.

In the U.S. during the year, probably the broadest concern was over forest health. Widely throughout the West, insects and disease killed trees across mil-lions of hectares of forest. Many foresters believed that the recent history of forest management coupled with years of drought combined to make trees more susceptible to disease. In many forests logging practices altered the species makeup of the forest, replacing disease-resistant trees with more vulnerable ones. In addition, fire was not allowed its natural and regular function of repressing invading species and reducing surface debris. Under consideration by the U.S. Forest Service were practices that might be somewhat controversial but were aimed at long-range improvement in forest health: salvaging dead trees, planting insect-resistant trees, thinning crowded stands, applying insecticide to disease-ridden areas, and allowing controlled burning. More and more, foresters were convinced that forests are complete ecosystems, that problems in any part of the forest are problems of the whole system, and that any management technique cannot be applied without careful study of its effects on the whole system.

—Albert J. Smith

Microbiology

During the past year there were numerous exciting (and sometimes frightening) discoveries in microbiology. In this review they have been divided into three sections: environmental microbiology, medical microbiology, and biotechnology.

Environmental microbiology. Toxic algal blooms, sometimes referred to as red tide, have occurred throughout the ages. Indeed, the Bible may have one of the earliest references to red tide in its story of Moses sending a plague upon the Egyptians that turned the water blood red, killing the fish. During the last five years a number of novel algae have been discovered in toxic blooms. One of the most elusive of these is a dinoflagellate with phantomlike behavior that was recently discovered in the Pamlico Estuary of the southeastern United States. This microorganism was present in the water during a kill of nearly one million Atlantic menhaden (*Brevoortia tyrannus*) but virtually disappeared one day after the kill. Apparently the lethal vegetative algal cells had moved from the sediment to the water, where they produced a neurotoxin that caused fish suffocation. The dinoflagellates then attached to sloughed tissue from dying fish and became dormant cells known as cysts that vanished back into the sediment. The Pamlico Estuary receives high levels of phosphorus and nitrogen from human sources. Water pollution and the spread of toxic organisms in the ballasts of oceangoing cargo ships were being studied as factors that may contribute to the growth and spread of toxic algae.

Until recently, biological weathering of minerals was thought to occur exclusively at the Earth's sur-

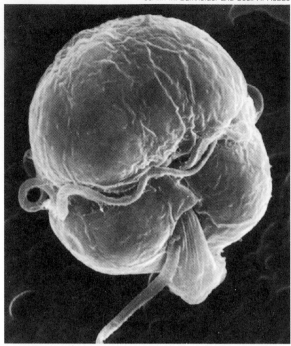

JoAnn M. Burkholder and Cecil H. Hobbs

A newly discovered species of microscopic dinoflagellate was shown to cause major fish kills by swarming suddenly and in large numbers from the bottom sediment in the presence of live fish and then releasing a potent water-soluble neurotoxin.

face. Opinion began to shift when bacteria were discovered in cores taken thousands of meters below the surface. Microbes in deep sediments may have been entombed when the rock was first deposited tens or hundreds of millions of years ago. Some of these bacteria appear to be dissolving the rock on which they live. Bacteria adhering to rocks well below the Earth's surface metabolize organic molecules such as petroleum and release organic acids that etch and pit the surface of quartz and other minerals. Over geologic time such microbial activity could form large underground channels and might explain the network of pores found near oil wells and underground aquifers. Subterranean bacteria may open and close flow paths for groundwater. For example, some bacteria transform insoluble ferric iron to the soluble ferrous form, which could open pores and enhance water flow. But when the dissolved iron encounters sulfide, produced by other kinds of bacteria, the sulfide and soluble iron precipitate, forming layers of pyrite (fool's gold) that obstruct water flow. Thus, the activity of subterranean microorganisms may represent a previously overlooked factor in subsurface geochemistry.

Termites have a diverse community of microbes living in their hindguts that aid in the digestion of wood polysaccharide, principally cellulose. During the course of cellulose digestion, the microbes produce a number of fermentation products, including acetate, methane, and hydrogen gas. The acetate molecules are absorbed from the termite hindgut and serve as the principal food source for the termite. The methane and hydrogen gas are emitted into the atmosphere, and termite emissions are currently estimated to account for 5–40% of the total annual global methane production.

Gradually increasing concentrations of methane in the atmosphere, and the potential contribution of methane to global warming, have placed added importance on the quantification of methane emissions by termites. Such emissions were measured from 24 different termite species and found to vary more than 100-fold with the termite species. Acetogenesis (acetate synthesis from carbon dioxide and hydrogen gas) and methanogenesis (methane synthesis from carbon dioxide and hydrogen gas) are competing chemical reactions in the termite hindgut owing to the limited supply of carbon dioxide and hydrogen. Acetogenesis was found to be more prominent than methanogenesis, even though the latter is the thermodynamically favored process. In fact, yields of methane were less than 10% of the theoretical maximum. These results suggest the presence of other unknown factors in the termite that determine the relative rate of these two competing processes. Because of uncertainties in global estimates of termite numbers, and uncertainties about methane utilization by soil bacteria around termite mounds, more work is required for determining how much methane termites contribute to the atmosphere.

Medical microbiology. Bacteria exhibit forms of motility (movement) that are adapted to their particular habitat. Aquatic bacteria with flagella swim rapidly but are less adept at moving on solid surfaces. Conversely, gliding bacteria in soil move well on surfaces but are nonmotile in liquid. The recent discovery of a new form of bacterial motility serves to underscore the versatility of bacteria in adapting to their specific habitats. *Listeria monocytogenes* is a human pathogen that causes a variety of diseases, including meningitis. While invading *Listeria* cells are readily recognized by a person's immune system and ingested by macrophages (cells that protect the body against infection and noxious substances), they subvert the immune system and multiply inside the macrophages, where they live as intracellular parasites. *Listeria* can move at a rate of 0.2 micrometer (millionths of a meter) per second inside the host cell cytoplasm by a unique motility system. (Cytoplasm is the protoplasm of a cell external to the nuclear membrane.) A host cell protein known as actin is polymerized behind a moving *Listeria* cell and remains stationary in the cytoplasm as the bacterium moves forward. The rate of actin polymerization is roughly proportional to the rate of movement. Al-

364

though it seems apparent that actin polymerization provides the driving force for bacterial propulsion, the manner in which a propulsive force is generated is not yet known.

The importation from Asia of used tire casings containing *Aedes albopictus* larvae resulted in the introduction of this mosquito species to Houston, Texas. During the past eight years this mosquito has become established in 21 states of the U.S. Public health officials became concerned about the establishment and spread of this species in the U.S. because of the ability to transmit dengue fever viruses that it demonstrated in Asia. To determine viruses that this mosquito may transmit in the U.S., specimens from Polk county, Florida, were examined for the presence of viruses. More than 9,000 *A. albopictus* specimens were collected from vegetation swept with a mechanical aspirator. At least 14 mosquitoes were infected with eastern equine encephalitis virus. In the United States, eastern equine encephalitis is the rarest of the mosquito-borne viral encephalitides, but it has a high fatality rate of about 30%. The virus is normally maintained in freshwater swamp habitats in a cycle involving a native mosquito, *Culiseta melanura,* and several bird species. What makes *A. albopictus* a particularly worrisome pest is that it has a wider variety of hosts than *C. melanura.* Blood meals from 43 engorged *A. albopictus* collected at a Polk county tire dump were identified as follows: 31% bovine, 19% deer, 14% human, 7% raccoon, 5% rabbit, 24% unidentified mammal, and 2% bird. These results suggest that *A. albopictus* could pose a threat to humans as a carrier of eastern equine encephalitis virus.

A crisis emerging in medical microbiology may shape the quality and cost of health care in the future. During the past several years the frequency of infections resistant to antimicrobial therapies has increased in both the hospital and the community. To place this crisis in perspective, a hospital ward in 1930, the preantimicrobial era, was populated by patients with infectious diseases: pneumonia, meningitis, bacteremia, typhoid fever, endocarditis, mastoiditis, syphilis, tuberculosis, and rheumatic fever. Although the patients were often young, many would die from those diseases or their complications because there were few effective treatments. The introduction of antimicrobial agents in the mid-1930s initiated the antimicrobial era, sparing the lives of millions of people. The result was a striking transformation in the types of patients found in hospital wards. In the early 1980s hospital wards were filled with patients with noninfectious diseases: cancer, heart disease, and complications of diabetes or hypertension. Sadly, however, the trend was beginning to be reversed, leading some to predict the beginning of the postantimicrobial era.

This reversal of fortune was caused primarily by two problems. The first was the emergence of multiple-drug resistance in many pathogenic bacteria, such as *Mycobacterium tuberculosis, Streptococcus pneumoniae, Staphylococcus aureus, Enterococcus,* and *Shigella dysenteriae.* The emergence of these strains made most currently available antimicrobial drugs ineffective, and in certain instances these multiply-resistant organisms were posing public health problems. Antimicrobial resistance increases the mortality associated with the disease because precious time is used looking for alternative drug therapies, and it also leads to an increase in the incidence of the disease because patients who are not effectively treated may continue to transmit it. The substitution of newer and more expensive antimicrobial agents can dramatically increase the cost of treatment. For example, the estimated cost of treating a case of tuberculosis increases from $12,000 for a drug-susceptible strain to $180,000 for a strain resistant to many drugs. Tuberculosis remains the leading cause of death in the world from a single infectious disease (2.9 million deaths worldwide in 1992), and the incidence of tuberculosis has been rising steadily since 1985, especially among AIDS patients.

The second problem was that fewer new antimicrobial drugs were under development in the U.S. because of the high costs associated with drug development and the lack of a comprehensive health care plan for the country. An effective mechanism for dealing with the emergence of antimicrobial resistance would be the development of vaccines to prevent diseases that are difficult to treat. Incentives to develop new drugs from novel groups of bacteria such as the myxobacteria also appeared to be necessary to provide new antimicrobial agents.

Biotechnology. One of the earliest biopesticides was *Bacillus thuringiensis* (Bt), which has been commercially available since the 1950s. This bacterium produces crystal proteins that destroy the gut of insect larvae that ingest them. Each strain is active against only a narrow group of insects and causes no known side effects on nontarget organisms, including humans. However, resistant insects began to emerge; the Indian meal moth in 1985, the tobacco budworm in 1989, and the diamondback moth in 1990. By 1991 reports of resistance were commonplace. However, several recent findings offer some encouragement for the future. First, there appear to be at least three genes that are involved in conferring Bt resistance to the tobacco budworm. Mutations in two of those three appear to make the insects less fit, offering hope that Bt resistance may partially disable the insect. Second, the determination of the toxin crystal structure and the identification of the toxin receptor may enable genetic engineers to produce more potent varieties of Bt.

Microbiology was providing useful tools for assessing human-generated damage to the environment and for repairing the damage. A good example was bioremediation, which used living microbial systems to dispose of toxic environmental waste. The projected bioremediation market for 1995 was estimated to be $300 million.

Another important aspect of microbial biotechnology was the development of sensors for detecting environmental damage and monitoring it during the cleanup process. Sales of environmental sensors were expected to be about $40 million in 1995, even though sensor development was in its infancy. Such sensors must be capable of interacting with any compound that is poisonous. Bacteria are ideal choices for these tools because they can be maintained in a viable state even in the absence of nutrients and because sensitive assays exist for measuring bacterial metabolism. A number of different biosensor systems in which some aspect of bacterial metabolism was linked to some form of electronic monitoring were being developed. One of the most sensitive detection systems measures the luminescence of *Photobacterium phosphoreum,* which serves as an indicator of the health of the cells. The light-generating bacterial enzyme luciferase needs a high level of adenosine triphosphate (ATP) to operate but is not given preference in the use of this metabolite. Any toxin that interferes with intracellular energy generation will reduce the amount of ATP, causing an immediate drop in light intensity. A significant advantage of light detection over nonluminescent detection systems is that the former is exquisitely sensitive and involves the use of inexpensive and portable photodiodes as photodetectors. Similar bioluminescence systems can be used to measure specific environmental contaminants. For example, genetically modified strains of *Escherichia coli* have been developed that glow when exposed to aluminum or mercury.

—Lawrence J. Shimkets

Molecular biology

The pace of accomplishments in science is so rapid today that it has become impossible for a single scientist to keep up with even the primary publications in his or her own field. Each year there are more primary journals, each publishing more pages. Consequently, there is now a market for new journals that publish reviews of current work in well-defined areas of research; these are in addition to the older quarterly and annual reviews that summarize several years of work in a given area. It would be possible to fill this article with just the names of topics in molecular biology that might be covered.

The human genome. One of the most significant accomplishments of the past year was the assembly of physical maps for all of the human chromosomes, a collaborative effort coordinated by the Human Genome Project of the U.S. National Institutes of Health. This field is changing so rapidly that every new map is out of date before it is published. Nevertheless, a quick look at the methods being used and a snapshot of the project status at the beginning of 1993 is edifying.

Every human cell begins its life with 23 pairs of chromosomes, which include one pair of sex chromosomes. A male has one X and one Y sex chromosome; a female has two X sex chromosomes. The X chromosome contains 160 million pairs of nucleotide bases, or base pairs, on its double strand of DNA, while the Y chromosome contains only 60 million base pairs. (The nucleotide is the smallest building-block unit in a molecule of DNA; a gene consists of an chain of nucleotides whose sequence of nitrogen-containing groups, called bases, specifies the sequence of amino acids in a protein.) Most of the Y chromosome had been thought to contain "junk" DNA (DNA that does not code for proteins) because few genes had been mapped to the Y. However, the recent physical mapping of the Y shows that about a third of its DNA is similar to sequences on the X chromosome; about half consists of various forms of repetitive DNA, which does not code for proteins; and the rest, as much as 10 million base pairs, is uniquely Y chromosome DNA that probably corresponds to real, coding genes. Of the greatest importance is a gene called *SRY,* which encodes a testis-determining factor. It is the presence of this gene on the Y chromosome that determines whether an embryo will develop as a male or a female. An individual whose sex chromosome constitution is XY but who lacks the *SRY* gene develops as a female.

Physical mapping means the assignment of physically detectable markers along the entire length of the chromosome. These markers can be restriction sites (places in the DNA where the nucleotide sequence is recognized and cleaved by an enzyme called a restriction endonuclease; see *1988, 1989,* and *1991 Yearbook of Science and the Future* Year in Review: LIFE SCIENCES: *Molecular biology*) or places where a particular sequence of DNA can be assigned on the basis of hybridization with a DNA probe (a short DNA fragment of known sequence whose nucleotide bases pair up and bind with a specific base sequence on the chromosome). Genetic maps are constructed on the basis of the frequency of coinheritance, among offspring, of markers that define the location of genes. The recent and remarkable progress in DNA technology provided by the polymerase chain reaction, which permits the repeated copying, or amplification, of specific DNA sequences to make useful quantities, has provided thousands of probes (called sequence tagged sites) that permit the merging of the physical and genetic maps of the human chromosomes.

The final piece of technology that enabled the physical maps to be made was provided by the creation of yeast artificial chromosomes (YACs). Consider the human X chromosome of 160 million base pairs. The largest bacterial cloning vector (a molecule that carries inserted fragments of foreign DNA into bacteria for replication) in wide use for the construction of libraries of chromosomal DNA fragments, the cosmid, can accept an insert of 40,000 base pairs. Thus, preparing a set of cosmids that contains a full representation of the DNA in the X chromosome would require more than 4,000 cosmids—actually at least twice that number. Then the set would have to be aligned, determining by hybridization which of the cosmids overlap with which others in terms of their inserted base pairs. The use of YACs reduces the logistic problem at least 10-fold. It turns out that a yeast cell can be fooled into accepting foreign DNA as one of its own chromosomes, and into faithfully replicating and distributing it to daughter cells, if the DNA contains the base-pair sequences that make up the yeast cell's centromere (to which the mitotic spindle attaches) and the two telomeres (the ends of the chromosome). Maynard Olson and his colleagues at Washington University, St. Louis, Mo., constructed DNA vectors into which very large pieces of DNA, as large as a million base pairs, could be inserted and then introduced into yeast cells. The yeast cells then propagate these molecules as YACs.

Within the past year, complete overlapping YAC maps were obtained for the human Y chromosome and much of the human X chromosome. The significance of the accomplishments lies in the fact that so many important diseases are due to mutations of genes on the X chromosome. For some of these diseases, the relevant gene already has been cloned and sequenced, but for many others the physical map will provide a great step toward identifying the gene. Duchenne muscular dystrophy is an X-linked disease for which the gene was cloned several years ago. The affected gene encodes a muscle protein called dystrophin. In persons with the disease, a portion of the gene is deleted, resulting in the production of a much shorter protein than in normal individuals. More recent cloning successes include the genes for fragile-X mental retardation, spinobulbar muscular atrophy, and Huntington's chorea. In each case the mutation appears to be due to the expansion of three-nucleotide (trinucleotide) repeat sequences. Fragile-X syndrome, for example, results from an increase in the number of tandem repeats of the base sequence CGG near the beginning of a gene called *FMR-1*. (C and G represent the nucleotides cytosine and guanine. Two other nucleotides, abbreviated T

for thymine and A for adenine, are also present in DNA.)

Myotonic dystrophy, a common form of muscular dystrophy that is more severe in successive generations, is due to expansion of a repeated trinucleotide sequence in a gene encoding a protein kinase. Protein kinases are enzymes that regulate the function of other proteins by adding a phosphate group to one or more of the target protein's amino acids. In some cases this phosphorylation increases the activity of the target protein, whereas in other cases it decreases it. A curious finding in the molecular biology of myotonic dystrophy is that the expanded triplet sequence is not inside the coding region of the protein kinase gene but rather is in the tail of the messenger RNA (mRNA) transcript, a part of the mRNA that is not translated into protein. Possibly this tail determines how stable the mRNA is or how efficiently it is translated. The work leading to this discovery was carried out by an international team comprising six laboratories, all funded by the Muscular Dystrophy Association.

Hormone regulation of gene activity. Significant progress was also made in studies of the mechanisms by which hormones control cellular behavior. There are many categories of hormones, defined simply as molecules elaborated by one type of cell that influence the behavior of another. The sex hormones, for example, determine the development of reproductive organs and their function; other hormones, like thyroid hormones and insulin, control the metabolic activities of cells. Some hormones function by attaching to receptor proteins embedded in the membranes of target cells. The receptors then initiate a chemical cascade of events that finally signal the cell nucleus to activate certain genes. Other hormones bypass the cell surface receptors. Rather, they enter the cell directly, bind to a receptor protein in the cytoplasm, and are transported to the nucleus, where the hormone-receptor complex directs the DNA to activate gene transcription. The genes to be activated by this process contain specific sequences upstream of their coding regions called hormone-response elements, to which the hormone-receptor complexes bind. Nevertheless, the number of hormones in the body is limited, whereas the number of genes and cell types that have to be regulated is very large. How is this apparent paradox resolved? Part of the answer seems to reside in the ways that the constituents of the hormone-receptor complex are combined and in simple variations in base-sequence spacing within the response element.

The hormone receptors present in the cytoplasm are a family of similar proteins with related architectures. Each receptor protein has three domains: one that is responsible for binding the hormone, one that binds to DNA, and one that participates

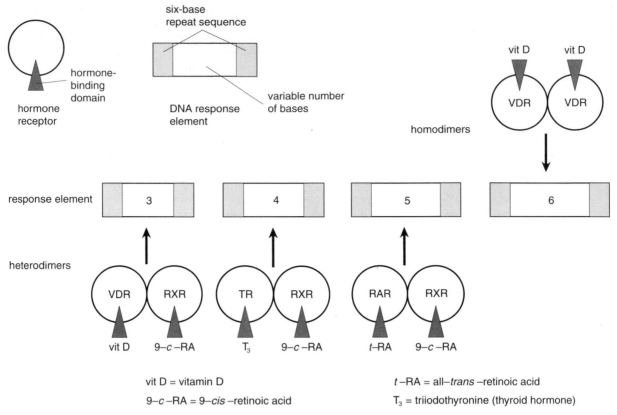

The mechanism that allows a limited number of hormones to regulate a large number of genes and cell types seems to depend on the different ways that hormone-receptor proteins can form complexes and on the presence of simple spacing variations within the DNA sequences that respond to those complexes. See text.

in dimerization, either forming homodimers (two of the same protein joining to form a dimer) or heterodimers (two different proteins joining). The hormone-response elements in DNA are short sequences of six nucleotide bases either directly repeated or repeated with inversion (*i.e.,* the sequence appears on the opposite DNA strand, creating a palindrome), with a variable number of nucleotides between the repeats. For example, the DNA element that responds to the vitamin D receptor (VDR) has the base sequence AGGTCAnnnnnnAGGTCA, in which n is any nucleotide; the VDR response element thus consists of a direct repeat separated by six nucleotides. On the other hand, the response element for the steroid hormone receptors (receptors for mineralocorticoid, glucocorticoid, progesterone, and androgen hormones) is GCTACAnnnTGTTCT, which approximates an inverted repeat separated by three nucleotide bases.

The steroid hormone receptors bind to their response elements as homodimers. The three-dimensional structure of one such complex was determined in the laboratory of Paul Sigler of the Howard Hughes Medical Research Institute at Yale University by X-ray diffraction studies of crystals of the DNA-

protein complex—with striking results. In addition to demonstrating exactly which parts of the protein contact which nucleotides in the response element, the structure showed why precisely three nucleotides are needed between the inverted six-nucleotide repeat sequences in the response element. When four nucleotides were present instead of three, the resulting crystals were better organized and easier to resolve structurally, but the protein-DNA contacts for one of the protein subunits of the dimer were "wrong"; when the contacts are correct, the DNA is forced to bend. Presumably this bending has something to do with the activation of transcription.

In addition to the steroids and vitamin D, another class of recently appreciated hormones are the retinoids. These are derivatives of vitamin A and consist of two major species: all-*trans*-retinoic acid and 9-*cis*-retinoic acid. The protein receptors for these compounds are called retinoic acid receptors (RAR), which bind all-*trans*-retinoic acid, and retinoid X receptors (RXR), which bind the *cis* species. The RXR family was discovered only recently as a nuclear factor needed for the other receptors (RAR; thyroid hormone receptor, TR; and vitamin D receptor, VDR) to bind to DNA in the test tube. This work was carried out at several institutions, including the laboratory of Pierre Chambon of the Institute of Biological Chemistry, Strasbourg, France. These other hormone receptors, unlike the steroid receptors, do not generally bind to their targets in DNA as homodimers. Instead, each forms a heterodimer with RXR (*see* Figure). The different heterodimers recognize their different respective targets on the DNA on the basis of the spacing between the six-nucleotide repeat sequences. Thus, the complex of VDR:RXR binds to six-nucleotide sequences separated by three nucleotides; the complex of TR:RXR binds to those separated by four nucleotides; and the complex of RAR:RXR recognizes a space of five nucleotides. This picture is certainly oversimplified, but it gives a hint of the wealth of possibilities for gene control by hormones and their nuclear receptors. Very simple motifs in the DNA can be made to respond to one or another hormone by small adjustments in the spacing of the repeat sequences to which the receptors bind and by switching from the homodimer binding that characterizes steroid receptors to heterodimer binding for the other receptors.

Further variations in the levels of physiological regulation that are possible were revealed by experiments showing that steroid receptors vary in their ability to interact, positively or negatively, with components of the transcription apparatus. Recall that the purpose of binding to the response elements is to control transcription of a gene near the response element. That control can be negative, for example, by tethering a protein that normally is required for attracting the enzyme RNA polymerase to the start site for transcription, or positive, for example, by changing the conformation of the DNA to one that favors the escape of RNA polymerase from its initial binding site.

Structure of a photosynthetic reaction center. Photosynthesis begins with the absorption of light energy by chlorophyll molecules embedded in a protein complex—the reaction center—that spans a membrane system in the chloroplasts of green plants and algae or the internal membranes of photosynthetic bacteria and cyanobacteria (blue-green algae). The absorbed light energy results in the excitation of special chlorophyll molecules in these reaction centers. The excited chlorophylls give up an electron that is ultimately transferred across the photosynthetic membrane, resulting in an electrochemical gradient across the membrane.

Two kinds of photosynthetic reaction centers are known. Green plants and cyanobacteria have both, termed photosystem I and photosystem II (PS I and PS II). Purple bacteria have reaction centers evolutionarily related to PS II; these centers transfer electrons from a special chlorophyll to an intermediate called phaeophytin (a chlorophyll molecule

without a magnesium ion in its center) and then to a quinone molecule. Green photosynthetic bacteria such as *Chlorobium* and the recently discovered *Heliobacterium* contain reaction centers related to PS I, which is an "iron-sulfur" type. PS I also contains a quinone that accepts electrons from a special chlorophyll, through the intermediate phaeophytin, but then the electron is passed to an iron-sulfur protein rather than to a second quinone. The iron-sulfur centers are so-called Fe_4S_4 centers of the type found in ferredoxins, which are low-molecular-weight, soluble, electron-transfer proteins used in a large number of oxidation-reduction reactions in cells.

Protein complexes containing the PS II reaction centers from green plant chloroplasts have been purified, but none has yet been crystallized. Structural information about the reaction centers is limited to the purple bacteria *Rhodopseudomonas viridis* and *Rhodobacter sphaeroides*, from both of which the reaction centers were crystallized in the mid-1980s. The three-dimensional structures determined by X-ray diffraction analyses showed two related proteins, L and M, spanning the membrane five times each. Within the membrane spans are located the so-called special pair of chlorophylls that form the trap for light energy, another pair of chlorophylls nearby, a pair of phaeophytin molecules, and the two quinones. PS II reaction centers from green plants are believed to have structures analogous to reaction centers from cyanobacteria, in part because analysis shows that they have the same pigment and quinone composition and that their proteins are very similar in amino acid sequence to the L and M components of the bacterial reaction centers.

PS I remained more of a mystery until the past year. The breakthrough came from the study of thermophilic (heat-loving) cyanobacteria. Wolfram Saenger of the Free University of Berlin, Horst T. Witt of the Technical University of Berlin, and their colleagues in Germany succeeded in purifying PS I reaction centers from a cyanobacterium that thrives at 65° C (150° F) and in crystallizing them. The X-ray structure was solved to low resolution only, but it was still possible to see remarkable features in the structure. There are two symmetry-related proteins, as in PS II, but the proteins of PS I are much larger, traverse the membrane 12 times instead of 5, and have more than 40 chlorophyll molecules associated with each. As in PS II, there is a special chlorophyll pair, a nearby phaeophytin, and then a quinone. But thereafter the picture changes; there are three iron-sulfur centers more or less in line with the quinone. Thus, whereas the PS II center is built with the goal of adding electrons to a quinone to effect the charge separation that can do useful work, the PS I center uses iron-sulfur clusters for that purpose. (For a discussion of related findings about nitrogenase, the

369

Life sciences

enzyme responsible for biological nitrogen fixation, *see* CHEMISTRY: *Inorganic chemistry.*)

—Robert Haselkorn

Zoology

Amazingly, each year brings forth more and more remarkable observations and exciting discoveries in zoology. Examples during the past year included the discovery of two new dinosaurs, the isolation of ancient DNA from preserved insects in amber, the location of the Japanese eel spawning ground, the demonstration of learning behavior in octopuses, the discoveries of poisonous birds in Papua New Guinea, the use of ultraviolet trickery in spider web decorations, ballooning behavior in a deep-water octopus, unusual survival methods of desert silver ants, and the enlargement of a fish belly to deter its predators.

Two new dinosaur discoveries. Unearthed in Utah was a dinosaur fossil that may represent the most vicious killing machine ever known in the animal world, even surpassing the infamous *Tyrannosaurus rex.* Discovered by Carl Limoni at the College of Eastern Utah, and identified by James Kirkland and colleagues with the Dinamation International Society, the beast, designated *Utahraptor,* was 6.1 m (20 ft) long and weighed 680 kg (1,500 lb). It was armed with a vicious array of teeth and possessed a bipedal body designed for speed. In comparison with *T. rex,* *Utahraptor* had larger forearms, with each bearing three 26-cm (10-in) claws. The animal's most unusual feature was a large 30-cm (12-in) upward-protruding, sickle-shaped claw on each hind foot. The creature is believed to have attacked its prey by ripping and tearing flesh with its foreclaws and teeth while disemboweling it with the specialized hind claws.

To make matters worse for the victims, evidence indicates that *Utahraptor* traveled and hunted in packs. The fossil was found in the early Cretaceous sediments of approximately 125 million years ago, 50 million years before *T. rex* appeared in the fossil records, and so a showdown between those two animals never occurred. As stated by Kirkland, the real wonder of this find is why such an effective carnivore disappeared before the general dinosaur extinction at the end of the Cretaceous Period.

From the Late Triassic of Argentina came another noteworthy dinosaur skeleton, one whose lack of specialized adaptations made it the most primitive dinosaur known. Found by Paul Sereno and colleagues Catherine Forster and Raymond Rogers of the University of Chicago and Alfredo Monetta of the National University of San Juan, Argentina, the new fossil, named *Eoraptor lunensis,* is about 230 million years old. Skeletal evidence indicates that *Eoraptor* was about a meter (three feet) long, carnivorous, and bipedal, supporting the hypothesis that dinosaurs diverged rapidly from a common ancestor having just these characteristics.

Ancient DNA. Michael Crichton's novel *Jurassic Park* describes a group of scientists cloning an array of dinosaurs from isolated dinosaur DNA ranging in age from 65 million to 100 million years. The DNA was extracted from dinosaur blood found in the stomachs of biting insects that were nearly perfectly preserved in clear amber (ancient tree sap). Although the cloning of any whole animal or organism from DNA sequences is presently impossible, the isolation of DNA from ancient animals and plants, particularly those preserved in amber, is a growing area of research. In fact, a scientific race was under way to isolate the oldest DNA. Notably, two separate research laboratories, under the auspices of George O. Poinar, Jr., of the University of California at Berkeley and Dave Grimaldi of the American Museum of Natural History in New York City, isolated DNA sequences from insect tissues approximately 30 million years old. These reports described the oldest DNA yet characterized, a record destined to be short-lived. Both groups extracted small portions of DNA, amplified the DNA by polymerase chain reaction (PCR), and then sequenced the nucleotides composing the DNA. (A polymerase is an enzyme that links nucleotides to form polynucleotide chains.) The DNA isolated by this process was then compared with similar sequences of extant (living) species of insects. Poinar and colleagues Raul J. Cano, H.N. Poinar, and D.W. Roubik extracted DNA from five specimens of an extinct stingless bee (*Proplebeia dominicana*). Comparisons with extant species convinced them that the isolated DNA was from the preserved bee rather than contaminants of DNA from other sources, such as microorganisms. The researchers were using this study as a foundation for pursuing the evolutionary history of stingless bees.

Grimaldi and his colleagues, Rob DeSalle, John Gatesy, and Ward Wheeler, obtained DNA sequences from a fossil termite (*Mastotermes electrodominicus*) in a process similar to that used by Poinar's group. This fossil termite is believed by some scientists to be a missing link between termites and cockroaches. However, the obtained sequenced pattern showed a more favorable comparison with the DNA of extant termites than with that of cockroaches, indicating that these two groups had separate origins. This procedure of ancient DNA isolation was providing data to support, modify, or enhance more traditional studies. Since insects and other small animals have been found in amber that is more than 100 million years old, the knowledge yet to be gained from these gems should be astounding.

Spawning site for the Japanese eel. In 1922 Johannes Schmidt, a Danish oceanographer, reported

370

the Sargasso Sea as the area to which adult Atlantic eels (*Anguilla*) migrated from freshwaters of America and Europe to spawn. However, the spawning location of the Japanese eel (*Anguilla japonicus*) had until the past year remained undetected. From extensive data collected in 1991 and from earlier expeditions, Katsumi Tsukamoto of the Ocean Research Institute of the University of Tokyo determined the spawning site to be in the westerly flowing North Equatorial Current of the Pacific Ocean between the Mariana Islands and the Philippine Islands north of a tropical salinity front broadly located near latitude 15° N and longitude 140° E. He determined the site by collecting leptocephali, the leaflike eel larvae, which are found only in the spawning area. These were collected at night by trawl nets involving oblique tows from the surface down to depths of 300 m (984 ft) and horizontal tows at selected depths. By measurements of the lengths of the larvae from each collection site, taking into account the rate of larval growth and the movement of the larvae by ocean current flow, the spawning area was determined.

The spawning area was found to be broad but closely associated with a region of high salinity representing the separation of tropical water from the North Equatorial Current into its northeasterly flowing continuation, the Kuroshio Current. The latter carries the larvae to coastal waters in eastern Asia. As suggested by Tsukamoto, the selection of spawning sites by both the Atlantic and Japanese eels was dependent on currents that could transport larvae to growth habitats.

Octopus learning and behavior. Two Italian scientists, Graziano Fiorito and Pietro Scotto, documented for the first time a learning behavior in the octopus *Octopus vulgaris*. Although octopuses have highly advanced brains for invertebrates, they are normally asocial animals that live independently. Thus, they were not believed to exhibit learning behavior.

To demonstrate the existence of this behavior, the investigators collected from the Bay of Naples specimens weighing from 200 to 650 g (about ½ to 1½ lb). A group of octopuses was placed one at a time into tanks and trained to attack either a red or a white ball. When it attacked the correct ball, the animal was rewarded with a small piece of fish, but it was punished with an electric shock when it choose the incorrect ball. Once this group was trained, the remaining octopuses were placed individually in separate tanks so that they could observe demonstrations from the first group. These observers were then exposed to the two balls and were found to make the correct choice, proving that they had learned by observing. Since the mother dies shortly after egg laying, young octopuses must survive alone after hatching. Quite possibly the young octopus learns by watching others, thus increasing its survival potential.

Rarely observed are the deep-sea finned octopuses belonging to the order Cirroctopoda. The cirrate octopus, unlike its better known cousins, has webs between the eight arms. Since little is known about the behavior of this group, a recent observation in the French deepwater submersible *Cyana* provided a rare firsthand opportunity to study one behavioral pattern. The investigators videotaped a ballooning reaction in a species of the genus *Cirrothauma* while the animal was hovering over the sea bottom at a

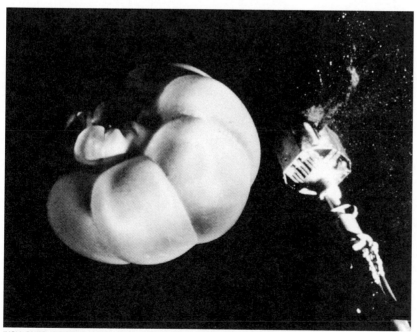

A deep-sea octopus of the genus Cirrothauma *balloons into the shape of a pumpkin in response to a touch from the grab arm of a submersible. Scientists believe that this newly observed behavior, which gives the animal an uncharacteristic shape, helps deter predators.*

INSU–CNRS, IFREMER, CALSUB cruise, Diving saucer CYANA, observer Michel Rio, Lyon, France depth of 2,880 m (9,446 ft) off the northeastern coast of Lifou Island in the southwestern Pacific. While the octopus was being taped, the grab arm of the submersible touched the animal, which immediately underwent a remarkable change. When hovering, the octopus resembled an inverted umbrella in which the octopus arms represented the ribs and the webs represented the fabric. The touch initiated a response whereby the arm tips moved outward and downward until they touched, producing a puffing out of the web. This gave to the octopus a ballooning appearance resembling a pumpkin, certainly a shape not characteristic of this animal. The scientists concluded that this response is a predator-avoidance behavior, which in that world of darkness acts as a deterrent to predators that depend on familiar tactile responses.

Frying pan ants. The Sahara silver ant (*Cataglyphis bombycina*) lives in the African Sahara, where the ant-height (four millimeters above the surface) temperature can exceed 60° C (140° F). These ants prey on arthropods that are under heat stress and at the same time must avoid their predator, the desert lizard *Acanthodactylus dumerili*. As observed by R. Wehner and S. Wehner of the University of Zürich, Switz., and A.C. Marsh of the University of Namibia, Windhoek, the foraging habits of the silver ant are unusual. Most of the time they reside in their burrows. However, when the surface ant-height temperature reaches 46.5° C (115.7° F), they explode onto the sand and forage until the temperature reaches 53.6° C (128.5° F), whereupon they return to the safety of their burrows; this is a time period of approximately 15 minutes.

Other species of desert ants are more conservative and retreat to their burrows in a temperature range between 35° and 45° C (95° and 113° F). But the silver ants are scavengers and search for other species of ants and arthropods that have failed to reach the safety of burrows or have succumbed to rising temperatures. With such foraging habits, the silver ants not only have available food but also avoid their desert lizard predator, which burrows at about the same temperature the silver ant begins foraging. This temperature of 53.6° C is the maximum recorded for any terrestrial animal.

Spider webs and bee entrapment. Can spiders use visual tricks to trap unsuspecting insects? Apparently so, judging from a study by Catherine L. Craig and colleagues Cheryl Hayashi and Jennifer Coddington of Yale University. The common garden spider (*Argiope*) spins a web and then places in the center of the web a brightly colored silk decoration that reflects ultraviolet radiation. Presumably, insects are attracted to the decoration and, on contact, adhere to the web threads. The spider reacts by rolling up the prey in more silken threads and injecting into

John P. Dumbacher

The hooded pitohui (Pitohui dichrous), an orange and black songbird from New Guinea, and two related species became the first birds known to be poisonous. From the feathers, skin, and other tissues of the birds, scientists isolated an alkaloid of the same type found in the skin of poison-dart frogs of Colombia.

the insect digestive juices to liquefy its tissues, which can then be leisurely sucked up by the spider.

To prove this hypothesis of entrapment, the investigators studied a Panamanian garden spider (*Argiope argulus*) and the behavior of one of its prey, a nonstinging bee. This bee can identify ultraviolet-reflecting objects such as flowers. In examining a spider web by means of ultraviolet detectors, the investigators noted a bright ultraviolet spectral pattern emanating from the threads composing the decoration but not from the web. The decoration looked very much like a flower. The investigators moved the web into a laboratory, where they then marked bees with colored paint and studied their behavior as they flew toward a sugar source placed behind a decorated web. In their first flights the bees were caught in the web, but if they were allowed to escape, they soon learned to avoid the web on approaching the food source. However, if a different decoration was added to the web, the bees once again flew into it, presumably again believing that a flower was present. In nature the spiders maintain their trickery by constantly changing their decorations, thus assuring a continuous supply of nutrients.

Poisonous birds. Three species of birds in the genus *Pitohui* found in the Central Province of Papua New Guinea contain in their feathers and skins a toxin that causes numbness, burning, and sneezing in human nasal tissues. The local New Guineans call them "rubbish birds" and eat them only when the birds have been skinned and specially prepared.

To examine this toxin, J.P. Dumbacher of the University of Chicago, B.M. Beehler of the Smithsonian Institution in Washington, D.C., and T.F. Spande, H.M. Garraffo, and J.W. Daly of the National Institutes of Health in Bethesda, Md., collected specimens of the hooded pitohui (*P. dichrous*), variable pitohui (*P. kirhocephalus*), and rusty pitohui (*P. fer-*

rugineus). From these specimens the feathers, skin, striated muscles, uropygial gland, heart-liver, and stomach with contents were removed. The toxin was isolated and identified. Then, to test the toxicity, extracts from each tissue were injected subcutaneously into the hindquarters of laboratory mice, and the effects were monitored.

The investigators described the toxin as a homobatrachotoxin, a steroidal alkaloid similar to the toxin described in the poison-dart frogs (*Phyllobates*), whose skins are used by native Colombians for poisoning blowgun darts. Homobatrachotoxin activates sodium channels in cells, preventing the polarization of membranes, and, depending on the dosage, it caused in the mice paralysis in the hind limbs, locomotor difficulties, prostration, convulsions, and death. Of all tissues tested, the feathers and skins were the most toxic, and those of the hooded pitohui were the most powerful of all three species. The investigators believe that the toxin acts as a protection against natural predators such as snakes, birds of prey, and, possibly, tree-dwelling marsupials. If so, this is the first description of a poison in birds that aids in the protection of the species against predation. The pitohuis are also brightly colored in black and contrasting orange-brown and emit a strong sour odor. Possibly these factors also identify the birds to potential predators as an undesirable prey.

Potbellied carp. Two Swedish scientists reported a fish that can change its shape from streamlined to potbellied to avoid predation, a change that previously had been described only in some invertebrates. Christer Brönmark and Jeffrey G. Miner of the University of Lund, Sweden, demonstrated an increase in the body depth of the crucian carp (*Carassius carassius*) when in prolonged presence of its predator, the pike *Esox lucius*. The carp was already known to have two body shapes, but the potbelly form was believed to be a result of having more food available.

To prove the predator hypothesis, Brönmark and Miner selected two suitable ponds and divided them into halves with plastic curtains that were anchored into the soft bottom sediments and extended 30 cm (11.8 in) above the pond surface. Crucian carp raised under similar conditions were placed into both halves of each pond. Pike that preyed on the carp were then placed into only one half of each pond. In both ponds the carp lengths and body depths were measured before the introduction of pike and 12 weeks after the introduction. The results showed that the body depth of carp exposed to pike was greater than the body depth of those not exposed. The investigators concluded that the crucian carp grows a deeper body to make predation by pike more difficult because a deep-bodied fish does not fit well into a pike's mouth.

In order to prove that overeating was not the reason for the deeper body, but that the presence of the pike was, other experiments were performed with low food or high food with pike groups. In the high food experiments, carp were placed in several laboratory

Two specimens of crucian carp (Carassius carassius) are compared. Although both fish were raised under similar conditions, the top one was exposed for 12 weeks to predatory pike, whereas the bottom one was not. The deepening of the body in the pike-exposed carp was thought to have a defensive purpose—to make the fish harder to fit in the pike's mouth.

The invertebrate known as the onychophoran, or velvet worm (right), was long thought to represent the evolutionary missing link between the segmented worms (annelids) and the arthropods. From an RNA analysis of 39 invertebrate species, scientists determined that onychophorans are arthropods related to spiders and scorpions.

tanks, half of which contained pike. Both the carp and the pike were fed abundantly, and so pike did not prey on the carp. However, as before, the carp that were kept in the presence of pike grew significantly deeper bodies than those not exposed. Thus, the presence of pike affected the body morphology of the crucian carp. Although a deeper body was an advantage to the carp in decreasing the risk of predation, the mobility of those fish was reduced. The stimulus for this morphological change remained unknown, although some scientists believed that the carp may receive a chemical cue from the pike.

Onychophorans. An enigma of invertebrate evolution is the relationship of onychophorans, velvet worms resembling slugs with legs, to other invertebrates. One hypothesis proposed that onychophorans are a missing link between annelids and arthropods. In an extensive study J.W.O. Ballard, W.A. Odgers, and P.W. Atkinson of the Commonwealth Scientific and Industrial Research Organisation in Canberra, Australia, along with other colleagues, analyzed ribosomal RNA sequences on 5 species of onychophorans and 34 species of other invertebrates, including annelids and arthropods. They determined from their data that onychophorans and arthropods are not only closely related but also monophyletic (developed from a single, common parent form).

Shipwrecked tube worms. The vestimentiferan worms, or bearded worms, are a zoological oddity first discovered in 1969 on deep-water hydrothermal vents in the northeastern Pacific Ocean. The worms are peculiar in lacking a digestive system and in

obtaining energy from chemoautotrophic symbiotic bacteria housed in their tissues. The worms transport hydrogen sulfide from the outflow of hydrothermal vents or of cold water seeps to the bacteria, which oxidize the chemical and produce high-energy phosphorus compounds that are incorporated by the host worm.

Until the past year these worms had been detected only at hydrothermal vents and cold water seeps in the Pacific and the Gulf of Mexico. However, P.R. Dando, A.J. Southward, and E.C. Southward of the Marine Biological Association of the United Kingdom; D.R. Dixon of the Plymouth (England) Marine Laboratory; and A. Crawford and M. Crawford of Deep Water Recovery and Exploration Ltd. at Newport-on-Tay, England, discovered the worms on a sunken cargo ship (*François Vieljeux*) located approximately 50 km (30 mi) west of Vigo, Spain. Since this was a ship rich in organic material, including sunflower seeds, pineapples, and beans, and had sunk to a depth of 1,160 m (3,805 ft), the conditions were right for the existence of chemoautotrophic symbiotic bacteria and, therefore, vestimentiferan worms. The discovery extended the known range of this animal and suggested that the larvae came from yet-to-be-discovered colonies of worms in the eastern Atlantic.

—George G. Brown

See also Feature Articles: THE ANIMAL THAT WALKS BY ITSELF; BAIKAL—THE GREATEST GREAT LAKE; COMPUTER-AIDED MOLECULAR DESIGN; DEAD MEN'S MOLECULES; IMAGINING ALIENS; THE SAVANNAH RIVER ECOLOGY LABORATORY.

374

Materials sciences

Increasing the strength and efficiency of ceramic materials and metals was a major focus of research and development during the past year.

Ceramics

Major advances were made in the areas of structural ceramics and high-temperature ceramic superconductors. One of the major applications of structural ceramics was expected to be as materials for future automobile engines.

Automobile engines. Automotive gas turbine engines offer the promise of improved fuel efficiency and reduced pollutant emissions. These benefits accrue most significantly as the operating temperature of the engine rises, necessitating the use of such materials as ceramics in the hottest sections of the engine. The capabilities of structural ceramics to fulfill this need were being evaluated in the U.S. Department of Energy's Advanced Turbine Technology Applications Project (ATTAP). Begun in 1987, this program sought to develop and demonstrate structural ceramic components that could operate in the turbine engine environment at temperatures up to 1,370° C (2,500° F) for 3,500 hours.

Significant progress was made during the year by the Allison Gas Turbine Division, in conjunction with the Advanced Engineering Group, of the General Motors Corp. Their AGT-5 (Advanced Gas Turbine #5) featured a combustor, heat regenerator, gasifier assembly, and power turbine, all made from ceramics. In this design intake air is compressed by a metallic impeller wheel and routed through the regenerator for preheating. The air is then mixed with fuel and burned in the combustor before entering the gasifier section. This complex assembly consists of a spiral duct termed a scroll, guide vanes to direct the gases exiting from the scroll, and a rotor (a bladed wheel) that conveys the gas to the power turbine wheel. Exhaust from the turbine section passes through the regenerator for heat recovery before exiting from the engine.

Test rigs based on the AGT-5 design were built to mimic the real engine. These are essentially engines in which the power turbine section has been removed and replaced by observation and instrumentation ports. Such rigs provide a good simulation of the actual engine environment and were used for evaluation and testing of ceramic components before full-scale engine testing began.

At the heart of the engine is the gasifier rotor. It must be capable of operating at a gas inlet temperature of 1,370° C (2,500° F) and at a rotational speed of 80,000 rpm. The initial design featured 38 blades and was made of silicon carbide. However,

this configuration was extremely sensitive to damage when struck by other objects. A second-generation rotor was fabricated by Kyocera Corp. of Japan from tougher silicon nitride. The component was shaped by slip casting (the pouring of liquid suspensions of ceramic particulate into porous molds) and densified by gas pressure sintering (the application of heat in a pressurized gaseous environment). Equipped with 15 thick blades, this rotor was successfully tested to 1,370° C at full rotational speed, even after experiencing foreign-object impacts during 350 hours of operation. A more recent 20-blade rotor with improved aerodynamic efficiency was fabricated by Kyocera and tested by General Motors with great success. The running time of one such rotor accumulated during the past year to 1,000 hours, including 5,170 starts. Another silicon nitride rotor, made via slip casting by Norton/TRW Ceramics in the U.S., was successfully tested for 220 hours.

At present, researchers are focusing on the design, fabrication, and test of a 26-blade rotor with still better aerodynamic efficiency. Eight such rotors fabricated by Norton/TRW were successfully tested to full speed during the past year. This rotor was also supplied by Ceramic Process Systems (CPS) of the U.S. and used a silicon-aluminum-oxygen-nitrogen composition. CPS employed a newly developed process termed Quickset injection molding. In this method ceramic powder is forced into a mold shaped to the component geometry. Traditionally, the powder had to be mixed with a flowable molten polymer, which, after solidification, was burned out before the ceramic is densified at high temperature. The polymer-removal step is often difficult and must be carefully performed to maintain shape tolerance and permit successful densification. The Quickset process eliminated the need for the polymer, thus improving yield and reducing cost. The ceramic can be densified at elevated temperature without the assistance of pressure, and the excellent surface finish and dimensional control allow shape fabrication with minimal machining. Rotors with 26 blades were successfully fabricated by CPS for testing.

Significant progress in improving the processing and quality of the gasifier turbine scroll was made during the past year. This complex part was processed by Norton/TRW. A modified silicon carbide slip (slurry) formulation was developed for pressure casting with reusable, porous plastic molds. This resulted in a 20-fold reduction of casting time in comparison with standard plaster molds. Excellent mechanical properties were attained with this material, in which the cast silicon particulate was converted to silicon carbide at elevated temperature in a gaseous environment. The reaction occurs with minimal shrinkage, permitting better dimensional control of this large, complex component. Scrolls were also successfully made of slip-cast silicon nitride by Kyocera.

Along with the rotor and scroll, the flow-path directional vanes complete the gasifier assembly. Design advances during the last year led to the successful attachment of the vanes to the scroll without the use of potentially weak ceramic-to-ceramic bonds. The new design featured nonbonded mechanical attachment through the use of a vane platform and retaining ring. These components were made of silicon nitride and, for the ring, silicon carbide as well.

The most dramatic achievement of the past year was the successful operation of an all-ceramic gasifier assembly through 100 hours of durability rig testing to temperatures of 1,370° C; the rig simulates full power trains (driveshaft, clutch, transmission, and differential). The durability cycle included numerous starts, stops, accelerations, and decelerations in each hour of testing. Though some damage occurred, the components maintained structural integrity for the duration of the test. A new gasifier was assembled in preparation for an upcoming 300-hour test.

It is clear that the advances made on the AT-TAP program resulted in large measure from the

High-temperature superconducting electromagnetic coils, which form the heart of motors and energy-storage devices, feature wire that is flexible enough to withstand automated winding operations.

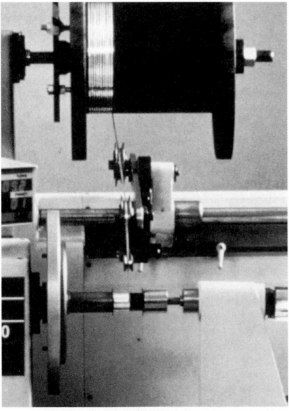

American Superconductor Corporation, Westboro, Mass.

significant enhancement of ceramic material performance on the part of the component producers. Improvements in the processing of these materials and control of their microstructures led to superior toughness, time-dependent properties, resistance to mechanical loads, and environmental stability. The positive results pointed toward real future application of ceramics in automotive turbine engines.

Ceramic superconductors. High-temperature superconductors (HTS) based on copper-oxide compositions have excited the materials community since their discovery in 1986. During the past year dramatic advances were made in developing HTS in bulk form for a variety of potential applications. Efforts were focused on improving the current-carrying capability, making wires and tapes, and demonstrating prototypical devices.

Activities centered on the three major classes of HTS: (1) yttrium barium copper oxide (YBCO) with a superconducting transition temperature (T_c)—the temperature below which the material becomes a superconductor—of 92 K (0 K = −273° C [−460° F]); (2) bismuth strontium calcium copper oxide (BSCCO) with T_c up to 110 K; and (3) thallium barium calcium copper oxide (TBCCO), which exhibits T_c as high as 125 K.

In general, the amount of current the superconductor can carry (J_c) will decrease with increasing temperature and with increasing magnetic field. For many electrical power applications, it will be necessary for HTS to carry large currents in strong magnetic fields. HTS materials exhibit sheetlike structures, with current carried largely by parallel copper-oxygen atomic planes. Superconducting properties perpendicular to these planes are poor. Bulk forms of HTS, such as wires, are polycrystalline; they are a collection of many grains (microcrystallites) joined at grain boundaries. Misalignment of these grains will reduce J_c. Also, boundaries that contain nonsuperconducting inhomogeneities—known as weak links—will further reduce J_c. Considerable progress toward improved J_c was made during the year through the development of microstructures with aligned grains and cleaner grain boundaries. For YBCO, alignment was accomplished by the solidifying of molten material in the presence of a temperature gradient (melt texturing). BSCCO behaves much like sheets of mica and was successfully aligned by mechanical deformation. These alignment techniques were refined and, along with improved control of composition, led to increasingly better J_c.

The presence of magnetic fields degrades J_c through a phenomenon known as flux creep. The fields create an array of magnetic flux lines (fluxons) in the HTS. Sufficiently high currents or thermal fluctuations cause the fluxons to move, thus reducing J_c. If the fluxons can be pinned (stopped

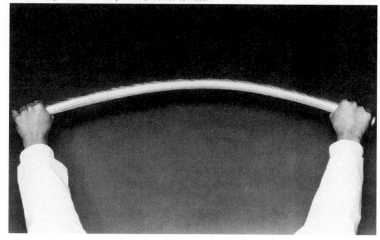

A prototype of a flexible multistranded superconducting power-transmission cable was demonstrated during the past year. Made from bismuth strontium calcium copper oxide, the cable could carry up to 500 amp at a temperature of 77 K.

or hindered from moving), current capacity will increase. Promising approaches to achieving this were pursued during the past year and included the use of small particles of nonsuperconducting material as pinning sites. Researchers at CPS Superconductor in the U.S. reported high J_c in YBCO treated in this manner. A second approach involved the creation of microscale damage by neutron irradiation. Demonstrated by IBM Corp. in the U.S., it led to dramatic increases in J_c at 77 K for YBCO. A third avenue was the substitution of smaller atoms in the chemical composition to reduce the distance between copper-oxygen planes. Researchers hoped that this would lead to improved pinning.

Superconducting devices can generate, transmit, and store energy more efficiently than can traditional ones. According to the Electric Power Research Institute, a 1% increase in system efficiency would save nearly $2 billion of energy per year in the U.S. alone. HTS technology advanced to the point where numerous prototype power devices were fabricated and tested. These successes resulted from improvements in the fundamental understanding of materials coupled with significant advances in making long (100-m [328-ft]) wires and tapes with useful properties.

Developed in 1989 by Vacuumschmelze GmbH. of Germany for BSCCO, the powder-in-tube (PIT) process was shown during the past year to be capable of producing wire in excess of 100 m in length, with J_c near 12,000 amp per sq cm of wire thickness at 77 K. Similar results were reported by the American Superconductor and the Intermagnetics General corporations in the U.S. and by Sumitomo Electric Industries in Japan.

The PIT process involves loading an oxide precursor powder into a silver tube, which is then drawn through a die to reduce its cross section. The wire is heat-treated in a furnace, followed by repeated deformation and annealing steps to optimize the HTS structure and composition and to shape the product to the desired geometry. The wire-drawing process causes the BSCCO grains to align, thus improving J_c. An interesting variant of this method, announced during the year by American Superconductor, utilizes metallic precursor powder in lieu of the oxide precursor. This allows the wire to be deformed more easily before the metal is converted to the brittle oxide state on subsequent heat treatment.

In an exciting development, researchers at General Electric Co. in the U.S. fabricated thick films of TBCCO by spraying the superconductor onto a silver substrate. The process was termed spray pyrolysis, and the addition of the silver was said to reduce weak links. The films showed excellent resistance to flux creep, an inherent advantage of TBCCO HTS. The technique holds particular promise if suitable flexible substrates can be identified and employed.

Superconducting power-transmission cables represent a promising application with the potential to reduce significantly the resistive losses in conventional cables. American Superconductor, in conjunction with Pirelli Cable of Italy, successfully demonstrated a flexible, multistranded cable one meter in length. Made by PIT from BSSCO, the cable carried up to 500 amp of current at 77 K. Similar results were obtained by Sumitomo and the Tokyo Electric Power Co. Working with Pirelli, Underground Systems Inc. in the U.S. designed a superconducting power-transmission system that could operate at liquid nitrogen temperature (77 K), and the feasibility of the system was being assessed.

Motors, generators, and energy storage devices utilizing superconductors will require magnets wound from HTS. Prototype magnets with promising properties were fabricated during the past year from pancake coils. These coils are made from multiple lengths of BSCCO wire wound around each other concentrically and separated by insulation. Several such coils are stacked to create higher magnetic fields. The best results have been achieved through the wind-and-react approach, in which a final heat treatment is performed after winding. This helps to heal any cracks created during the winding step. Coils of this type were demonstrated by American Superconductor and Intermagnetics General in the U.S. and by Sumitomo Electric, Showa Electric, and Kobe Steel in Japan. One such high-performance coil, made by American Superconductor and consisting of five lengths of BSSCO wire joined to a total length of 293 m (961 ft), produced an impressive peak magnetic field of 0.3 Tesla at 20 K.

In the first demonstration of an HTS motor with usable power output, an American Superconductor BSCCO coil was employed by Reliance Electric of the U.S. to build a 25-w motor. It operated at 77 K, with power comparable to that of a desktop computer's cooling fan.

—Allan P. Katz

Metallurgy

Irradiation-assisted stress-corrosion cracking. Stress-corrosion cracking (SCC) is the fracture-based failure of materials exacerbated by environmental effects. SCC can result in catastrophic brittle failure of materials that are usually highly deformable. The brittle failure observed in many cases of SCC is caused by cracking of the individual planes within the many crystals of polycrystalline materials. This separation of crystal planes without associated plastic deformation is termed cleavage or brittle transgranular failure. Certainly, the potential for SCC failure of materials in nuclear reactor applications is of great concern to designers and operators of reactors. SCC in nuclear reactor materials is well known. Less well known is the effect of irradiation in accelerating stress corrosion damage. Irradiation is the treatment of an object by exposure to radiation. In a recent article in *Journal of Metals*, Gary Was of the University of Michigan and Peter Andresen of General Electric outlined problems in isolating the precise effects of irradiation on SCC.

The main type of SCC that occurs in reactor systems is the failure of austenitic stainless steels. Austenitic stainless steels, alloys of iron with nickel and chromium as the primary additions, have a crystal structure called face-centered cubic. They typically contain, by weight, on the order of 18% chromium and 8% nickel. These alloys are easily welded, can be shaped by forming processes, and can be strengthened by working processes. However, failure can occur in the 275°–300° C (527°–572° F) steam environment of reactors because of intergranular cracking between the individual crystals rather than by cleavage of individual planes. This type of SCC is called intergranular stress-corrosion cracking (IGSCC). Because this type of failure is possible without radiation, just how irradiation may accelerate the phenomenon is not well understood. The mechanisms of irradiation-assisted stress-corrosion cracking (IASCC) in nuclear reactor components have been attributed to radiation effects on corrosion, radiation hardening, radiation-induced segregation, and radiation-enhanced creep. (Segregation is the nonuniform distribution of alloying elements, and creep is a time-dependent strain of solids caused by stress.)

Irradiation can induce a number of defects in materials. High-energy neutrons can interact with atoms by either knocking an atom out of its normal position within a crystal or by changing the energy level of the atom. When the atom is displaced from its normal site, a vacant site is created with an associated atom sitting in an interstitial site (a position between the normally allowed positions of the atoms). This vacancy-interstitial pair is called a Frenkel defect, after Russian physicist Yakov Frenkel (1894–1954). The permanence of the Frenkel defect depends on the energy of the neutron that collides with the atom. If the energy level is sufficient only to create a neighboring vacancy and interstitial atom, then the atom is likely to move back into the site it left, eliminating the Frenkel defect. If the energy of the neutron is high enough to displace the interstitial atom at least two or three interatomic distances, the Frenkel defect will be fairly stable. The minimum energy level of neutrons necessary to cause this type of damage is usually greater than one million electron volts.

The probability of a neutron colliding with an individual atom is quite small; however, each high-energy neutron can produce many collisions and, therefore, a large number of vacancies. The presence of these defects can cause hardening of the material and an associated reduction in its ductility. These defects can also lead to growth of small voids that can expand under applied stress. For the conditions under which IASCC occurs, the loss of ductility because of the increase in defects is probably the most harmful effect.

IASCC was reported more than 30 years ago as the cause of intergranular cracking of the stainless steel jacket that contains nuclear fuel. Subsequently, irradiation-assisted damage was identified in a number of other reactor components. Recent work has frequently been directed at the problem of radiation-induced segregation of impurities to grain boundaries (the surfaces between individual grains in a metal). Impurity elements can become concentrated in the boundaries between the individual crystals. Because the concentration of defects is increased in the irradiated material, the motion of impurity elements to or away from grain boundaries can be enhanced. Defects are essential to motion of atoms of any one type within a material. Also, grain boundaries can act as low-energy traps or sinks for impurity atoms. That irradiation might enhance segregation is not surprising, since scientists have already confirmed that a tendency for grain-boundary segregation is prevalent in stainless steels. Radiation-induced segregation experiments revealed that nickel segregates preferentially to grain boundaries, whereas chromium and iron content is reduced there. Stainless steels also contain impurities besides the base components of nickel, chromium, and iron. The common impurities sulfur, phosphorus, and silicon all segregate to the grain boundary, but molybdenum and titanium become depleted from grain boundaries during irradiation.

Sulfur and phosphorus are known in other iron-based alloys for their harmful effects on grain-boundary strength and resistance to brittle failure. SCC data on stainless steel alloys containing sulfur and phosphorus that have been segregated by heat treatments rather than by irradiation suggest that those segregated alloys are not susceptible to SCC in the type of steam environments often found in nuclear reactors. Similar experimental results regarding silicon were inconclusive.

The most likely culprit in grain-boundary segregation is the depletion of chromium from the grain boundaries. The main contribution of chromium in stainless steels is as an oxidation and corrosion inhibitor. Corrosive or environmental cracking of austenitic stainless steels that have reduced chromium content at grain boundaries is well known.

Research into the mechanisms behind IASCC has been difficult because the residual radioactivity of the materials after irradiation can be hazardous. Components from the core of nuclear reactors must be analyzed by means wherein the human investigators work indirectly with materials kept in shielded "hot cells." Although performing trial experiments in components of operating reactors might seem like a good idea, the safety considerations and overall complexity of an operating reactor make such experiments difficult to perform. Only recently have scientists performed instrumented experiments wherein continuous monitoring of the stress-corrosion process can be performed in a reactor core. Research into IASCC is expected to become more important in future years to ensure reliability of operating reactors, provide better design for future reactors, and enable design of storage systems for radioactive waste.

Mechanical alloying to produce metal powders. Mechanical alloying is a process wherein readily deformed powder materials of different composition are subjected to extreme levels of plastic deformation and fracture. Through a combination of cold welding, particle coalescence, and refinement, alloying of two or more constituents takes place. In the processing of materials, the benefits of mechanical alloying in comparison with solidification-based mixing of liquid elements are primarily realized by the elimination of the segregation that prevails when a liquid mixture of elements is solidified. Also, the melting temperature of many materials can be so high that it is not possible to contain and handle the liquid material inexpensively.

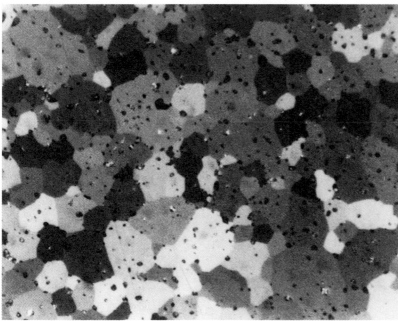

Los Alamos National Laboratory

Composites based on molybdenum disilicide show considerable promise for high-temperature applications because they deform rather than break when exposed to extreme heat. At the left is a microstructure of such a composite. By modifying the microstructures, researchers can increase the fracture resistance of these composites.

An example of the benefits of mechanical alloying is found in the synthesis of refractory (heat-resistant) metal disilicides. Molybdenum disilicide ($MoSi_2$) and similar compounds based on niobium, tungsten, tantalum, and chromium have been of great interest because of their potential in high-temperature applications. These materials have been made by a large number of methods, including conventional arc-melting, sintering, and hot-pressing.

Conventional melting processes pose problems because of the high melting temperatures of the metal disilicide compounds (for $MoSi_2$ the melting temperature is over 2,100° C [3,812° F]) and also the large differences in the melting temperatures of the two metals (for pure molybdenum the melting temperature is 2,623° C [4,753.4° F], while for silicon, Si, it is approximately 1,414° C [2,577° F]). In all known processing techniques, oxygen is incorporated into the material in the form of a glassy coating of silica (SiO_2). Although SiO_2 is responsible for providing a protective coating to the external surfaces of refractory metal disilicides, thereby inhibiting catastrophic oxidation at high temperatures, it degrades the low-temperature fracture resistance and the high-temperature strength of those materials when it is present internally.

To inhibit the formation of SiO_2 coatings on the surface of powder particles, mechanical alloying experiments can be performed on starting materials of high purity in the presence of very little oxygen. Since oxide coatings tend to coat a material to a particular thickness, producing fine powders usually increases oxide content by an increase in the ratio of the surface area to the volume of the material. Performing mechanical alloying at low temperatures, conditions under which the kinetics of oxidation are slow, and in a nearly oxygen-free environment can keep the amount of SiO_2 in the final products low.

Researchers at Los Alamos (N.M.) National Laboratory were successful in producing substantially improved processing for powders synthesized by mechanical alloying of elemental Mo and Si starting materials. Internal grain-boundary pockets of SiO_2 were apparently substantially reduced. Whether improved properties can be obtained by use of such materials has not yet been determined.

—Keith J. Bowman

Mathematics

Mathematical research in 1992 revealed a surprising connection between a newly discovered means of checking proofs and the intrinsic difficulty of certain optimization problems. A problem dating to 1910 was finally solved, revealing that there are an infinite number of exceptions to a much-used method of testing whether a number is prime. Two conjectures about higher-dimensional spaces were refuted, leading mathematicians to conclude that intuition about the familiar spaces of two and three dimensions can lead one astray in higher dimensions. A well-known combinatorial problem, with applications to the design of experiments, was solved. Fermat's "last theorem" was confirmed for additional cases; a new Mersenne prime was discovered; physics provided a new method of cryptography; a human defeated a computer for the world checkers championship; calculations showed that the solar system is chaotic in the mathematical sense; questions were raised concerning random-number generators; and research suggested that babies may have some numerical understanding.

Holographic proofs and hard problems. Verifying that a mathematical proof is correct is much easier than devising it. However, even verification can be difficult and time-consuming. A recent conceptual breakthrough, holographic proofs, however, now offers the prospect of easy checking of hard proofs by computers. Moreover, holographic proofs have already been exploited to yield the surprising result that for some difficult problems it is no easier to find approximate solutions than exact solutions.

The idea behind a holographic proof is first to write out the proof in a formal logical style and then to alter it to a "transparent" or "holographic" form in which any error or inconsistency is "amplified" so as to contaminate virtually all parts of it. Much as the entire image of an optical hologram is stored in every part of the hologram, any error in a holographic proof will be detectable in almost any part of the proof as an inconsistency. The verification of the holographic proof consists of random checking of parts of the proof for consistency. If an inconsistency is found, the original proof is defective (or else there was an error in transforming it). If the holographic proof passes a certain number of consistency spot checks, there can be a high degree of confidence that the original proof is correct.

Surprisingly, the number of checks required for a given level of confidence does not depend on the length of the original proof, and so a very long proof is no harder to check than a short one. Despite this encouraging fact, the main obstacle to the practical application of holographic proofs is the length of the holographic proof, which can be considerably greater than that of the original formal proof.

This research into holographic proofs produced a surprising result. By modeling the spot checks as vertices in a mathematical graph and connecting two vertices if the checks were mutually consistent, mathematicians were able to transform the question about consistency of all of the spot checks into a question about the approximate size of the largest clique (collection of connected vertices) in a graph. That clique must be either extremely large (all the vertices in the graph, if the holographic proof is correct) or else relatively small (if the proof is not correct). If there was an efficient algorithm (set of well-defined rules for the solution of a problem in a finite number of steps) to find the largest clique in a graph or even to approximate its size, then it could be determined with certainty whether the original proof was correct.

The problem of finding the largest clique in a graph belongs in the class of NP-complete problems, a large group of difficult problems for which there are no known efficient algorithms. An efficient algorithm to approximate the size of the largest clique in a graph (because of its special role in verifying proofs of solutions) would allow mathematicians to solve efficiently all NP-complete problems. For some NP-complete problems, there are algorithms to find approximate solutions, but many face the same situation as the largest clique problem, that there is no known efficient approximation scheme.

Carmichael numbers. Contemporary cryptography uses very large prime integers (those having no divisors except themselves and one) that are often several hundred digits long. It is impractical to verify that integers of such length are prime by examining all potential factors; instead, probabilistic algorithms are used. These are algorithms that allow one to verify easily, to any degree of confidence desired (except certainty), that an integer is prime.

One widely used probabilistic algorithm relies on a result obtained by Pierre de Fermat in 1640. Fermat

"Oh, dear! Another tragic case of math anxiety!"

Sidney Harris

observed that for a prime p, the number $a^p - a$ is divisible by p for any value of a whatsoever. For the prime 3, for example, $2^3 - 2 = 6$ is divisible by 3, as is $1{,}000^3 - 1{,}000 = 999{,}999{,}000$. Therefore, one test for the primality of a number n is to calculate $a^n - a$ for a collection of values of a chosen at random. If for any of those values the number $a^n - a$ is not divisible by n, then n fails the test and is not prime.

However, there are numbers n that can pass the test for any a whatsoever but are not prime. They are called Carmichael numbers, after mathematician R.D. Carmichael, who investigated them in 1910 but was unable to ascertain if there were infinitely many. Since Carmichael numbers are exceptions—obstacles in this important test for primality—mathematicians were grateful that they seemed to be rare (the smallest is 561) and even hoped that there might be only a finite number of them. Those hopes were dashed during the past year when William R. Alford, Andrew Granville, and Carl Pomerance at the University of Georgia proved that there are infinitely many. Specifically, they showed that for n sufficiently large, there are at least $n^{2/7}$ Carmichael numbers less than n.

Two conjectures fall. Much of mathematicians' intuition for geometric properties in the fourth and higher dimensions comes from experience with dimensions one, two, and three. However, many properties that hold in the lower dimensions do not extend to higher ones, and it is always exciting to mathematicians to find simple properties that do not. In 1992 two such conjectures, dating from the 1930s, that certain simple properties that hold in dimensions one through three also extend to higher dimensions, were refuted.

The first, Keller's conjecture (by Otto-Heinrich Keller in 1930), supposed that completely filling n-dimensional space with n-dimensional cubes of the same size would force at least two such cubes to share a complete $(n - 1)$-dimensional side. Jeff Lagarias and Peter Shor of AT&T Bell Laboratories showed that this need not happen in 10 or more dimensions. Since it is known that the conjecture is true in dimensions four, five, and six, the only remaining open questions are what happens in dimensions seven, eight, and nine.

Borsuk's conjecture (by Karol Borsuk in 1933) also fell. It concerns using straight cuts to carve a geometric object into pieces and asking whether the pieces are "smaller," in a particular mathematical sense, than the original. The measure of size is its diameter, the greatest distance between points in the object. In dimension one, the diameter of a line segment is its length; cutting a line segment in two produces two pieces, both of which are "smaller" (have smaller diameter) than the original object. Cutting a circular disk into two pieces, however, always results in at least one piece possessing a diameter of the original disk and, therefore, having the same diameter. However, the disk—in fact, any bounded two-dimensional object—can be cut into three pieces, all of which are smaller than the original. Similarly, for any three-dimensional object, four carefully chosen cuts will suffice to obtain smaller pieces, a fact proved in 1946.

Borsuk's conjecture was that any n-dimensional object could be cut into $(n + 1)$ smaller pieces. However, Jeff Kahn of Rutgers University, New Brunswick, N.J., and Gil Kalai of Hebrew University of Jerusalem were able to demonstrate that the conjecture is false in all dimensions greater than 10,000 and that the number of pieces required, in fact, grows exponentially. Still, it remained unknown what happens even in dimension four.

Fermat's conjecture holds up. Pierre de Fermat stated in the 1600s that there are no solutions in positive integers to $a^n + b^n = c^n$ for $n > 2$. In other words, there is no cube that is the sum of two cubes, no fourth power that is the sum of two other fourth powers, etc.

Fermat claimed to have a proof of this conjecture, which has become known as Fermat's last theorem despite the fact that no proof has ever been discovered. Mathematicians devised proofs for special cases, and it has been known since 1978 that any counterexample—an example that disproves the conjecture—must have $n > 125,000$. During the past year it was established, by Joe Buhler of Reed College, Portland, Ore., and Richard Crandall of NeXT Computer, that any counterexample must have $n > 4,000,000$. Consequently, if there is a counterexample, it must involve numbers so large that they could never be written down.

New Mersenne prime. David Slowinski and Paul Gage of Cray Research, Inc., announced the discovery of the 32nd Mersenne prime, $2^{756839} - 1$, which has 227,831 decimal digits and is the largest integer known to be prime. Mersenne numbers, integers of the form $M_p = 2^p - 1$ (one less than 2 raised to a prime power), are named after Marin Mersenne (1588–1648), a French monk who was an amateur mathematician.

It is impossible to prove that a very large number is prime by trying all potential divisors, and pure mathematicians would not be satisfied with a probabilistic proof (such as the Fermat test described above). However, because of the special form of Mersenne numbers, special methods apply. In particular, the Lucas-Lehmer test, devised by Édouard Lucas (1842–91) and Derrick H. Lehmer (1905–91), states that M_p is prime if and only if it divides U_p—the pth number in the sequence with $U_2 = 4$—and subsequent terms defined by $U_n = U^2_{n-1} - 2$. For example, the third term is $U_3 = 14$, which is divisible

by the Mersenne number $M_3 = 2^3 - 1 = 7$, which therefore must be prime. Other Mersenne primes may yet lie between the previous largest Mersenne prime (M_{216092}) and the new one. In particular, there are unchecked gaps from 370,000 to 430,000 and from 524,000 to 750,000.

Each Mersenne prime corresponds to an even perfect number, one that equals the sum of all its factors except itself (for example, 6, 28, and 496); perfect numbers were studied by the ancient Greek mathematician Euclid, who showed that an even number is perfect if it is of the form $2^{n-1}(2^n - 1)$ with $(2^n - 1)$ prime. Leonhard Euler (1707–83) proved that every even perfect number must have this form. There may be odd perfect numbers, but none has been discovered.

Quantum cryptography. Traditional cryptography depends on the secure distribution and secure possession of keys to the code that is being used. The renascence of cryptography during the 1980s produced novel public-key cryptosystems, which completely avoid the problem of distribution of keys but depend for their security on the mathematically uncertain difficulty of factoring integers. Coming to the fore in 1992 was quantum cryptography, the use of quantum objects (such as light photons) to transmit keys. These systems are based on the Heisenberg uncertainty principle in quantum mechanics, which in this context causes any attempt to eavesdrop on the communication to produce changes in it that will be detected.

Practical systems have been developed that work over short distances. The question that remained to be answered was whether cryptosystems depending on quantum mechanics would eventually completely displace mathematical systems.

Human versus computer. Computers can now play chess at the Grand Master level but do not yet seem close to competing for the world championship. While chess has received the lion's share of attention, the human-computer battle has also been contested in the game of checkers, whose world championship match in 1992 was between a human and a computer. In this contest Marion Tinsley, a mathematician who had completely dominated the game of checkers and its championship for the past 42 years (losing only 5 games), played a match of 40 games against a computer program called Chinook, developed by researchers at the University of Alberta. Chinook took an early lead of two wins to one, but at the end Tinsley won four to two. Because two of Chinook's losses were a result of errors that are correctable (an erroneous line of play was programmed from a respected source, and another game was lost by unaccountable stalling until time ran out), its creators were eagerly looking forward to a rematch.

Chaos in the universe. Isaac Newton in the 17th century had a vision of the solar system as a great mechanical clockwork, playing out a regular and predictable motion to the end of time. However, computer simulations for 100 million years in the future have revealed an entirely different kind of universe. The orbits of all of the planets in the solar system are chaotic in the mathematical sense, which means that the slightest imprecision or change in position or velocity makes their positions totally unpredictable in the far future. A major source of some of the chaos seems to be a complex interaction between the Earth and Mars. Why the solar system is chaotic, and why it has survived five billion years despite that fact, remain mysteries.

Bad random numbers. A group of physicists experimenting with several traditional computer pseudorandom-number generators and more recently developed ones (such as the extended-period ones of George Marsaglia and Arif Zaman of Florida State University) got, to their surprise, wrong answers for a problem for which the exact answer is known. The pseudorandom-number generators had passed a battery of statistical tests for randomness but nonetheless apparently possessed subtle patterns of nonrandomness. The moral appeared to be that scientists should be more skeptical about random-number generators and need to test a particular one to be sure that it works well for the specific application at hand.

Can babies count? Karen Wynn of the University of Arizona suggested that babies at five months may possess a rudimentary ability to add and subtract. Basing her work on the tendency of babies to look longer at new, unusual, or unexpected scenes, she examined their reactions to correct and incorrect addition and subtraction of small numbers. After studying these reactions, she concluded that babies have numerical concepts and can calculate. However, further experimentation was needed to test an alternative interpretation, that the results can be explained purely by perceptual discrimination without imputing number concepts, counting, or arithmetic to babies.

—Paul J. Campbell

Medical sciences

Fulfilling a promise made during his campaign for the presidency, U.S. Pres. Bill Clinton in January 1993 appointed the Task Force on National Health Care Reform, to be headed by his wife, Hillary Rodham Clinton. In making the announcement Clinton said, "It's time to make sense of America's health care system. It's time to bring costs under control and to make our families and businesses secure."

General medicine

A resurgence of tuberculosis, new treatments for AIDS and multiple sclerosis, and the discovery of the locations of genes responsible for several serious diseases were among the highlights of the past year in medicine.

Tuberculosis. Recognition of the astonishing reemergence of pulmonary tuberculosis (TB) in the big cities of the U.S. and Europe was a major development during the past year. The resurgence followed a century during which the disease had been repelled, initially as a result of improved nutrition and hygiene, then by immunization, and, most spectacularly in the 1940s and '50s, by antibiotic drugs such as streptomycin.

In the U.S. the number of new cases of TB reported annually grew by 16% during the past six years, reversing the trend of the previous three decades, which saw an average annual decline of 6%. Several factors contributed to the growing American epidemic; homelessness, drug abuse, increased immigration from countries with a high prevalence of TB, and overcrowding in prisons, shelters, and the homes of the poor were each partly to blame. The mechanisms linking those social determinants with the actual disease included malnutrition, impaired immunity, and enhanced dissemination of the tubercle bacillus, the disease-causing organism.

On a worldwide scale, the resurgence of TB could be attributed in large part to the spread of the human immunodeficiency virus (HIV), the virus that causes AIDS. Although not everyone infected by the tubercle bacillus would go on to develop tuberculosis, the chances of doing so were much higher if the individual's immune system was compromised by HIV. Thus, while only about 30% of people with normal immune systems who were exposed to the bacillus became infected—and only about 10% of those became ill—up to 40% of people with AIDS had active TB. In the U.S. outbreaks of TB among HIV-infected individuals reported during 1992 were characterized by their rapid spread and by the speed with which the TB progressed. The inexorable, concurrent spread of those two microbes could pose an even greater public health threat in many parts of the Third World, particularly Africa.

The picture was complicated further by a pronounced increase in the resistance of the tubercle bacillus to the drugs normally given to treat the disease. In many less developed countries this occurred because antituberculosis drugs had been freely distributed without controls over the way they were used. Elsewhere, especially in the U.S., the cause seemed to be that many patients discontinued treatment before the bacillus was completely eradicated from the body, a process that might take up to 18

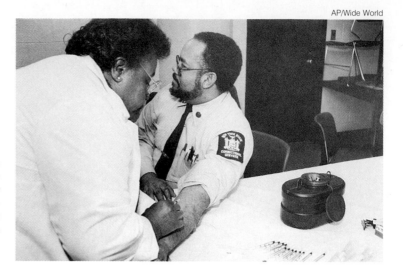

Corrections officer at Queensboro State Prison in New York City is tested for tuberculosis after testing for TB was made mandatory among officials and inmates in the state prison system. A number of the prison deaths that had recently occurred were believed to have been caused by a drug-resistant strain of tuberculosis.

months. In each of these situations not only did the infection continue to spread, but the emergence of resistant strains of disease-causing organisms was encouraged, too.

Another feature of the resurgence of TB was that, having ostensibly been defeated as the great social scourge of past centuries, the disease had been marginalized both as a challenge to medical science and as a target of public health efforts. With TB under control, there had been no reason for pharmaceutical companies to develop new drugs that could be used against resistant strains. In the U.S. production of streptomycin had declined to the point where it was virtually unobtainable. Moreover, with the decline in the number of cases of TB in the U.S. since the 1950s, the medical community had become increasingly unfamiliar with the subtleties of diagnosis and treatment of the disease.

AIDS. Although they disagreed on the exact numbers, two international organizations were in concert during the year in issuing bleak predictions of the worldwide spread of AIDS. The World Health Organization (WHO) estimated that approximately 10 million people were already infected with HIV, while the Harvard University-based Global AIDS Policy Coalition said the figure was more like 13 million. According to WHO, by the year 2000, 30 million to 40 million would be infected; the Harvard group believed that the number could be as high as 110 million. Major epidemics were emerging in Asia and Latin America.

In the U.S. concern grew over the increasing spread of HIV infection among teenagers; AIDS was reported to be the sixth leading cause of death among 15- to 24-year-olds. A continuing concern was the infection of newborn infants by their HIV-positive mothers. However, one small study showed that zidovudine (also called azidothymidine, or AZT) given

during pregnancy was well tolerated by mothers and fetuses and could apparently interrupt perinatal HIV transmission; a larger national study was under way. Another proposed study, sponsored by the National Institutes of Health, was to assess whether giving HIV immune globulin (a blood product containing antibodies to HIV) to infected pregnant women and to infants after birth would prevent transmission. Other research was aimed at developing better methods of detecting infection in newborns so that treatment with potentially toxic anti-AIDS drugs could be given only when truly needed.

A report in the *New England Journal of Medicine* showed that early treatment of HIV-infected people with zidovudine could, as hoped, delay the onset of AIDS and prolong survival. Zalcitabine (also called dideoxycytidine, or ddC) received the approval of the U.S. Food and Drug Administration (FDA) for use in conjunction with zidovudine and, under the FDA's expanded access program, a still-experimental drug, stavudine (also called D4T), was being made available to patients who were unable to tolerate approved anti-HIV drugs.

The Centers for Disease Control and Prevention (CDC) finally expanded the official case definition of AIDS, a measure that was expected to double the number of reported cases. The revised definition included HIV-positive persons who had fewer than a certain number of immune cells (called CD4 lymphocytes) and added three more maladies often found among HIV-infected women and drug abusers to the list of complicating conditions: invasive cervical cancer, pulmonary TB, and recurrent bacterial pneumonia.

The public reacted with alarm to reports of a mysterious new AIDS-like illness whose victims showed no evidence of HIV. Whether some other microorganism was causing the disease was not clear. A

384

meeting convened by WHO revealed that the incidence of the disorder was very low—some 100 cases worldwide—but research was scheduled to continue. There were also reassurances that the blood supply was safe.

Heart disease. Several issues in 1992 stood in sharp contrast to previous years. Perhaps chief among them was the worry about the possible ramifications of low cholesterol levels (below 160 milligrams per deciliter [mg/dL]) and whether the efforts at decreasing total cholesterol by means of drugs may have been somewhat misguided. Several studies had shown that lowering total cholesterol (with diet or drugs) below 160 mg/dL not only failed to decrease the rate of death from heart disease but was associated with increased mortality from noncardiac causes, including cancer, lung disease, suicide, and alcoholism. One possible reason for the slight— or absent—improvement in cardiovascular mortality was that lowering total cholesterol also lowers levels of the "good" cholesterol, high-density lipoprotein (HDL) cholesterol. One study published in the journal *Circulation* during the year showed that even in heart disease patients with a total cholesterol level of 175 mg/dL or under—a desirable level—those with low HDL levels (under 35 mg/dL) had twice the risk of suffering a subsequent heart attack or possibly dying from heart disease as those with higher levels.

If there was less interest in the drastic lowering of total cholesterol, this change in attitude might have been partly attributed to the discovery of rival risk factors for coronary heart disease. According to a Finnish report published during the year, high levels of stored iron were one such factor. A five-year study of nearly 2,000 men showed that every 1% increase in stored iron was associated with a greater than 4% increase in heart attack risk. The report seemed to confirm a theory advanced 11 years before by Jerome L. Sullivan of the Veterans Affairs Medical Center, Charleston, S.C., which suggested that the relatively low level of iron in the bodies of menstruating women accounts for that group's lower risk of heart attack compared with men or postmenopausal women.

A study of men under 55 found that those with bald spots on top of their heads have a 40–340% greater risk of suffering a heart attack than men with full heads of hair, depending on the extent of the baldness. The researchers pointed out that this was a statistical association and that further research on the possible connections between the two phenomena was necessary.

In other research, studies published during the year indicated that intravenous injection of magnesium might be helpful to victims of heart attack. According to these data, treatment begun as soon as possible after a heart attack might reduce mortality by about 25%. An attractive feature of magnesium is that it is inexpensive. Two additional studies concluded that opening plugged arteries with balloons (balloon angioplasty) is more effective than injecting clot-dissolving drugs.

Prospects improved substantially for those heart attack victims in danger of a subsequent attack due to malfunction of the left ventricle, the heart's main pumping chamber. A study involving over 2,000 such patients, based at Harvard Medical School and other centers in the U.S. and Canada, showed that captopril, a member of the group of drugs known as angiotensin converting enzyme (ACE) inhibitors, greatly improved their chances of surviving and reduced

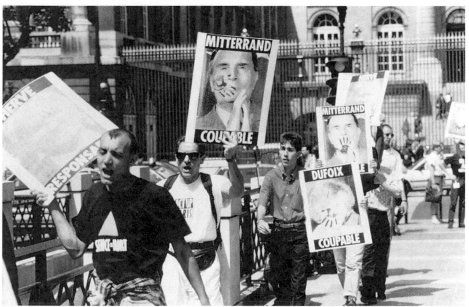

Christian Vioujard—Gamma Liaison

Demonstrators charge complicity at the highest levels of the French government as they march outside the courtroom where four former health officials were on trial for authorizing the distribution of blood products known to be contaminated with the AIDS virus. In October three of the officials were found guilty.

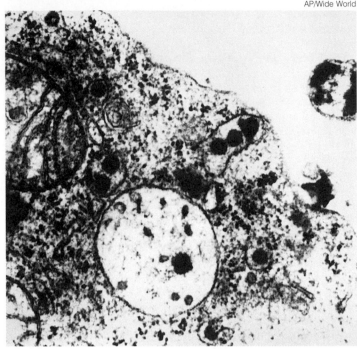

Magnified photograph reveals a white cell infected with a virus (heavy black spots) that causes AIDS-like symptoms but is not the human immunodeficiency virus. Research on the disease, which struck only about 100 people throughout the world, continued during the year.

the likelihood of death or further illness due to the heart condition. This conclusion was supported by the results of an even larger study with another ACE inhibitor, enalapril, carried out at the U.S. National Heart, Lung, and Blood Institute, Bethesda, Md.

Finally, two possibly improved methods of cardiopulmonary resuscitation (CPR) were reported during the year. One called for the application of rhythmic abdominal pressure along with the standard method of chest compression (at least two people would be needed to do CPR); the other involved substitution of a device similar to a toilet plunger that would compress and decompress the chest.

Genetics. Several major advances occurred in the location of genes responsible for particular diseases—advances that should help in screening for those conditions, prevention, and possibly treatment, too. Researchers in London and Cardiff, Wales, announced that they had identified, on human chromosome 19, the genetic defect that causes myotonic dystrophy, the most common form of adult muscular dystrophy. Research in Britain also indicated that deletions of genetic material in chromosome 22 are an important cause of familial congenital heart defects, while a U.S. study showed that DNA markers could be used to make a diagnosis in some families affected by the type of potentially fatal heart arrhythmia known as long QT syndrome. Early in 1993 researchers also found the genes in which the defects occur that cause three severe progressive ailments: Huntington's disease, amyotrophic lateral sclerosis (Lou Gehrig's disease), and adrenoleukodystrophy (ALD).

A collaborative investigation in the U.S. and the U.K. suggested that Marfan's syndrome is attributable to mutations in a particular gene on chromosome 15. As a result, this common hereditary disease, characterized by skeletal anomalies, vision problems, and life-threatening circulatory complications, could now be diagnosed in many affected families. Another U.S.-U.K. collaboration, supported by work in France, pinpointed defects in a particular gene in the causation of the variety of diabetes known as maturity-onset diabetes of the young. The gene is one that normally produces an enzyme responsible for regulating sugar metabolism in the pancreas and liver.

Studies in Oxford and Paris threw light on the genetic basis of atopy, an inherited state of hypersensitivity that underlies allergic asthma and rhinitis. Although the condition had been traced to a gene on chromosome 11, the trait was detectable only when transmitted through the mother. This appeared to be an example of the recently recognized phenomenon of genomic imprinting, in which a particular gene behaves differently when passed down through the maternal or paternal line.

Further complicating the ongoing research into Alzheimer's disease, a progressive, irreversible dementia, researchers at the University of Washington announced the finding of a gene defect on chromosome 14 that is associated with an early-onset form of the disease in a few families. Earlier studies had implicated sites on chromosomes 21 and 19 in families with a history of Alzheimer's.

Previously, once researchers had located genes responsible for particular diseases (or marker genes very close to them on the same chromosome), tests for those genes were used principally as a basis for selective abortion of affected fetuses. In 1992, however, there was the first detailed report of the birth of a normal, healthy baby following a more positive type of screening to eliminate the possibility of a genetic defect. Collaborators at the Hammersmith Hospital, London, and Baylor College of Medicine, Houston, Texas, used the new approach, termed preimplantation diagnosis, to screen embryos fertilized in the laboratory prior to implantation in the mother's uterus. In this case, both the husband and the wife were carrying a genetic defect known to be associated with cystic fibrosis. Cells removed from the embryos three days after fertilization were screened for the genetic abnormality. Some were affected and some unaffected. Following reimplantation of an unaffected embryo, the woman gave birth to a girl who thus was free of both cystic fibrosis and the aberrant gene.

Other developments. The era of animal-to-human transplants may have begun in 1992 with the transplantation of a baboon's liver into a man whose liver had been almost destroyed by hepatitis B. The patient died of a brain aneurysm 71 days after surgery; a second patient died 26 days after a transplant in early 1993. Soon after this, as a temporary measure until a human liver could be found, doctors at Cedars-Sinai Medical Center in Los Angeles transplanted a pig liver into a woman dying of liver failure. Unfortunately, the woman died of complications of liver failure just before a newly obtained human liver could replace the pig liver.

A number of pediatric issues were in the news in 1992. Confirming what many parents had long suspected, U.S. researchers reported in the journal *Science* that babies grow in spurts—sometimes as much as 2.5 cm (one inch) in 24 hours—rather than steadily and continuously. Following a reduction in the CDC's official threshold for potentially dangerous levels of lead in the blood—from 25 micrograms per deciliter to 10 micrograms per deciliter—it was announced in 1992 that virtually all children on Medicaid would undergo blood screening for lead poisoning. It was estimated that more than six million children under age six would be eligible for the screening. That intellectual development can be significantly impaired by lead exposure—independent of any detrimental influences exerted by socioeconomic factors—was confirmed by an Australian study that documented the adverse effects on cognitive abilities of low levels of lead in school-age children in a middle-class community. It was the largest long-range investigation of the effects of lead exposure ever conducted.

In March 1993 an advisory committee to the FDA recommended that a new drug to treat multiple sclerosis be approved. The drug, Betaseron, was the first among hundreds previously tested that was found to be effective in slowing the course of the progressive neurological disorder. An immune-system hormone, it reduced the number of acute episodes of multiple sclerosis significantly and lessened the severity of those that did occur. Also, in a small test an oral vaccine against the disease was determined to be promising enough to merit further tests.

A recently introduced vaccine against the bacterial infection haemophilus influenzae type B, the leading cause of meningitis in children, was shown to be exceedingly effective, reducing the number of cases of meningitis in children by 90%. And an as-yet-unlicensed vaccine against hepatitis A, a severe and sometimes deadly liver infection, was 100% effective in a population of children at risk for the disease.

A study conducted on the Isle of Wight in the U.K. threw new light on the occurrence of disorders such as allergic asthma and eczema in the early years of life. Although a family history of conditions of this sort had long been known to indicate an increased risk, the possible triggering role of certain foods and other substances was uncertain. The study clearly showed that among infants at risk for allergic disorders, exposure to allergens in food and house dust in the first years of life contributes to the development of allergy and eczema, with passive smoking a particularly important factor.

The outcome of another study from the U.K., based at Cambridge, strongly suggested that breast-feeding has a beneficial effect on brain development in preterm infants. When children's IQs were assessed at ages 7½ to 8, they were found to be significantly higher in those who had received maternal milk than in those who had been bottle-fed. This extended a previous report from the same investigators showing high development scores at 18 months in the breast-fed children.

Two large studies during the year indicated that a vasectomy may increase a man's risk of developing prostate cancer. Men who had undergone the surgical procedure more than 20 years earlier had up to an 89% greater risk of such cancer than did men who had not had a vasectomy.

Concern was expressed during the year about the dangers of excessive vitamin D intake, caused by drinking milk overfortified with the vitamin. Although supplementation of milk with vitamin D (first begun in the 1930s) has since greatly reduced the incidence of rickets, U.S. investigators identified several cases of hypervitaminosis D in the U.S. during 1992, in patients ranging in age from 15 months to 81 years. Subsequent analysis of milk and infant-formula preparations showed that they often contained too much—or too little—vitamin D. This finding led to calls for better monitoring of the fortification process.

Dow Corning Corp. reported during the year that studies it had undertaken on laboratory rats revealed that the silicone gel used in breast implants was a strong irritant of the immune system in those animals. More than one million women in the United States had received silicone-gel implants since the early 1960s, and several thousand of them had sued Dow Corning, claiming to have developed autoimmune disorders.

Data collected from throughout the world appeared to show that mammograms do not benefit women under the age of 50. Women in their 40s who had mammograms were found to have the same death rate from breast cancer as those who did not have the screening.

There was a call for greater care in the use of bronchodilator sprays containing beta-agonist drugs for the relief of asthma. This followed the publication of a study from New Zealand, confirmed by findings in Canada, that brought to light a heightened risk of death or near death in patients using these sprays regularly—and particularly in those using more than the prescribed amount. It was unclear whether beta-agonists were themselves responsible for the adverse effects or whether the fatalities and near fatalities indicated the emergence of a more severe form of asthma. Nevertheless, physicians were warned to reevaluate the condition of patients using such sprays heavily.

Mental health. Three important steps toward a deeper understanding of schizophrenia were taken during the past year. The advances resulted from different types of investigation and seemed to confirm that it was unlikely that the condition had any one specific cause.

In the first of these studies, psychiatrists at Harvard Medical School and other centers in Massachusetts investigated 15 male schizophrenics by means of magnetic resonance imaging (MRI). Although comparable to conventional radiography, MRI provides much more detailed information about the inside of the body. It also enables three-dimensional structures to be reconstructed, facilitating accurate measurements of their size. Previous work had suggested that schizophrenics might have abnormalities in one particular part of the brain, the left temporal lobe. The Harvard researchers showed that, compared with 15 normal control subjects, their 15 patients had significant reductions (13–19%) in the volume of gray matter in three specific regions of the left temporal lobe. There were no such differences in any other parts of the brain. The researchers also were able to show that the severity of the patients' thought disorders was paralleled by the reduction in volume of a part of the brain associated with language.

Psychiatrists had known for many years that schizophrenia occurred more frequently in urban than in rural areas. This pattern was thought to reflect the drifting of schizophrenics into cities. This previously unverified hypothesis was tested by scientists at Huddinge (Sweden) University Hospital and the Institute of Psychiatry in London. Data about the childhood locations of a group of some 50,000 young men, drawn from the Swedish Conscript Survey, revealed that schizophrenia was 1.65 times more common among individuals brought up in cities than

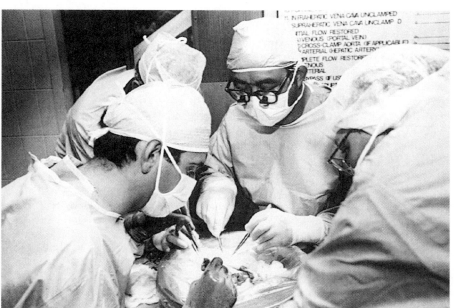

Surgeons at the University of Pittsburgh (Pa.) Medical Center prepare the first baboon liver to be transplanted into a human. The 35-year-old recipient, whose liver had been almost destroyed by hepatitis B, died of a brain aneurysm 71 days after the surgery.

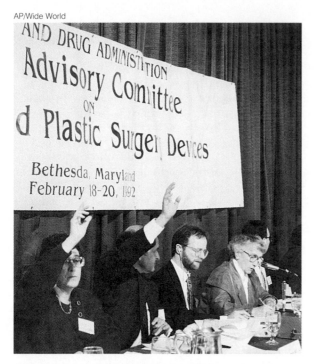

A U.S. Food and Drug Administration (FDA) panel votes on recommendations for the use of silicone-gel breast implants. The FDA followed the panel's suggestions, largely restricting the use of implants to reconstructive surgery.

signed 100 psychiatric emergency patients, aged 16–65, to either conventional hospital outpatient services or multidisciplinary care in the community. There were no restrictions on the treatment given in either setting, and all patients received inpatient treatment when required. Rated by an independent assessor 2, 4, and 12 months later, the individuals referred for community care showed a significantly greater improvement in their symptoms and were more satisfied with their treatment, as compared with the hospital outpatients. Moreover, the latter had spent eight times as many days as hospital inpatients as those treated in the community.

There was a major extension in the understanding of dyslexia, a learning disorder whose victims have great difficulty in learning to read. Previously, dyslexia was thought to be a distinct, all-or-nothing condition, caused by a discrete abnormality in the brain. Careful monitoring of more than 400 Connecticut children from school grades one to six showed this to be untrue. The real pattern of differences in reading ability was much more like that of variations in height or blood pressure—a continuum on which no particular group was sharply demarcated from the rest of the population. The researchers concluded that there were actually different degrees of dyslexia, which formed a continuum with normal reading ability.

—Bernard Dixon; Gail W. McBride

Dentistry

During the past year the American Dental Association (ADA) joined other leading national health organizations in an effort to adopt a preliminary blueprint for health care reform. The plan, which was expected to be set forth in its final form at the 1993 ADA annual meeting, called for Medicaid to be altered so as to provide uniform benefits, including comprehensive dental services, for all persons in the United States below the federal poverty line. The ADA also recommended that all employers provide basic preventive medical and catastrophic hospital surgical benefits after out-of-pocket health care spending reached 10% of gross income. The plan also suggested that federal vouchers be provided for preventive dental services for all children, through age 18, not covered by Medicaid or commercial dental insurance, beginning with the families with the lowest incomes.

In another first, the ADA Council on Dental Therapeutics granted the Association's Seal of Acceptance to Starbrite Bleaching Solution, a tooth whitener manufactured by Stardent Laboratories in Murray, Utah. The whitener would be used only in the dental office. "We realize that esthetic dentistry is a growing part of the profession," said Kenneth

among those who spent their youth in a rural area. Even when the investigators adjusted their figures to compensate for potentially relevant factors such as parental divorce, use of marijuana, and family history of psychiatric disorder, the clear association remained. They concluded that as-yet-unidentified environmental factors found in cities increased the risk of schizophrenia.

A third study supported the notion that malfunctioning of the body's immune defenses was responsible for some cases of schizophrenia. There had been previous suggestions that the disease was initiated in one subgroup of individuals when the immune system began to attack nerve cells in the brain. Researchers in New York City confirmed this theory. They analyzed blood samples from 32 otherwise healthy institutionalized schizophrenics. Fourteen of them (44%) were found to have antibodies against a particular protein that occurs in a human nerve cell malignancy. Although the patients were not suffering from this or any other type of tumor, the discovery indicated that schizophrenia was related to abnormal antibody production in a substantial minority of patients.

The British policy of transferring psychiatric care out of hospitals and into the community was vindicated by the results of a study conducted at St. Mary's Hospital, London. Researchers randomly as-

Burrell, council director. While the council decided that this whitener was safe and effective, the U.S. Food and Drug Administration (FDA) remained undecided as to whether it should be declared a drug or a cosmetic aid.

Food-borne tooth injury. While the U.S. government monitored the impact on public health of infectious and chronic diseases and adverse drug reactions, little attention was paid to injuries usually attributed to heated or sharp food items. A study by the FDA Center for Food Safety and Applied Nutrition found that the largest single category of complaints involved the presence of foreign objects such as glass, blades, bolts, nails, plastic, and stones in food items. Not included in this study were reports of suspected or confirmed tampering with food products.

Of all the reported cases of exposure to foreign objects, 14% resulted in illness or injury. In the 123 documented reports of illness or injury, the oral region was the most common site, with 46 individuals (37%) reporting lacerations or abrasions of soft oral tissues such as the gums and cheeks, including the throat. Another 18 persons (15%) reported damage to teeth, 3 reported damaged dental restorations, and 3 had broken dentures.

Lasers for space-age cavities. Dentists might sometime in the future abandon X-ray machines in favor of tiny lasers that used visible light to find cavities. Speaking at the scientific session of the Radiological Society of North America, Abund Wist, assistant professor of radiology at the Medical College of Virginia, said that the experimental technology might also replace X-rays in other medical applications, such as using mammography to detect breast cancer in women. In many cases his equipment was able to spot cavities that conventional X-rays could miss.

Though dental X-ray machines were safe and effective, Wist said, a laser system could offer advantages by eliminating exposure to radiation and by providing higher resolution of images and greater speed. He noted that lasers shining focused light through dental tissues to tiny sensors could be left in place during dental treatment, thus providing a computer image of the tooth to aid in filling cavities and in performing root canal therapy with greater precision.

Mother-to-baby tooth decay. The next time your dentist finds a cavity in your mouth and gets ready to apply the drill to remove diseased tissue, maybe you should blame it on your mother. A dental researcher at the University of Alabama School of Dentistry in Birmingham proposed that mothers kissing their babies during the 12 months following the eruption of baby teeth might actually infect their children with a cavity-causing bacteria. Page Caufield said that his suggestion was backed by a sophisticated technique

of "DNA fingerprinting" that he used on 45 mother-child pairs during the 12-month period after baby teeth eruption.

The decay-causing bacterium, *Streptococcus mutans,* is spread through saliva, Caufield explained. Although kissing could be the most direct means of transmission, it was not the only way. "Saliva is ubiquitous. It can be spread simply by talking," he said. Although other, earlier studies suggested that mothers play a significant role in spreading the bacteria, Caufield claimed that his research was the first to point to the mother as the prime source. If dental scientists could find ways to bar this infection during the crucial 12-month period, perhaps 95% of all cavities could be prevented, he asserted.

Fortifying ailing teeth quickly. Dental scientists at the National Institute of Standards and Technology, Gaithersburg, Md., found an ingenious way to fortify ailing teeth rapidly. With a unique method that replaced the tooth mineral, they were able to repair early cavities, make teeth less sensitive, and provide a better and stronger way of bonding restorative materials that improved appearance. The method involved a pressurized carbon dioxide system to coat teeth quickly with calcium phosphate, a basic component of the tooth's hard tissues. This coating then converted to tooth mineral in a process called remineralization. M.S. Tung told the annual meeting of the American Association for Dental Research that the carbon dioxide aerosol increased the amount of calcium phosphate that could be applied to teeth and

A laser beam is bounced off a mirror (top) and onto a tooth sitting in a bracket. Dental researchers during the past year found that lasers were able to detect cavities that had been missed by conventional X-rays.

Abund Wist, Medical College of Virginia

deposited it more quickly than could currently available remineralizing solutions. This process helped arrest and repair early cavities by strengthening tooth enamel.

Tung and his research team discovered that, in addition to inducing remineralization, the use of the aerosol increased the strength with which restorative materials bonded to tooth dentin, the hard tissue that surrounds the tooth's softer center and is covered by an outer shell of enamel. Although dentin was often involved in tooth repairs, it was difficult for dentists to bond restorative materials to the dentin surface. Applying the aerosol to dentin during bonding produced strong bonds, thus creating new treatment options.

Special treatment for women. Women present a health profile that influences the ways in which dentists should approach their dental treatment, according to Barbara Steinberg, a professor of medicine at the Medical College of Pennsylvania. Puberty, menstruation, pregnancy, lactation, and menopause are the stages in women's lives when oral health problems are most likely to occur. During those times, fluctuations in hormones can cause problems with the oral health tissues. A "high level of progesterone can alter the blood vessels of the mouth, increasing the chances for getting gingivitis [gum disease]," Steinberg maintained. This change in the blood vessels of the gums makes them more susceptible to the detrimental effects of bacteria in the mouth. "An increase in hormonal levels in itself does not cause these problems. There is usually a co-factor involved," she added. A woman who already has problems with gum disease, for example, finds that they get worse during pregnancy. The ADA estimated that 30–60% of pregnant women develop red, tender, or bleeding gums.

Menopause can cause a dry mouth, changes in taste sensations, or a burning feeling in the mouth. Some women may also have receding gums or a decrease in jawbone substance. Treatment for menopause is usually a team approach by a dentist and patient's gynecologist.

Smokeless tobacco and gum disease. During the past year smokeless tobacco, which had previously been strongly linked to the development of oral cancer, was also implicated in causing gum disease by breaking down the natural antibacterial defenses in the human mouth. J.B. Babu and colleagues at the University of Tennessee at Memphis re-created the oral environment in the laboratory, collecting cells from the mouths of healthy volunteers. They then added tobacco extract, a solution drawn from chewing tobacco, to half of the cells and spinach extract to the remaining cells to serve as controls. Finally, they added bacteria associated with gum diseases to both sets of cells.

The scientists found that from 60 to 80% more of the harmful bacteria became attached to the cells treated with tobacco extract than to the control cells. Not only were more bacteria attached to the tobacco-treated cells, but also the ability of the "defender" cells to guard against injury and infection was impaired by the tobacco extract. Specifically, the immune system's neutrophils—cells that migrate toward bacteria and engulf them in a fighting fashion—suffered an 83% decrease in their ability to migrate when treated with tobacco extract. Tobacco extract also impaired the functions of the fibroblasts—cells that make collagen, a component of connective tissue that is essential for healthy gums. Tobacco extract inhibited the growth of fibroblasts by 80% compared with the controls.

Gum disease bacteria and HIV patients. The prevalence of certain bacteria that cause gum disease differs between homosexual men infected with the human immunodeficiency virus (HIV, which causes AIDS) and HIV-infected males who are intravenous drug users. Speaking at the annual meeting of the International Association for Dental Research in Glasgow, Scotland, Joseph J. Zambon, professor of periodontology at the University of Buffalo, N.Y., reported that his research, using immunofluorescence microscopy, looked for the presence of different bacteria that caused periodontal disease in 136 patients. Results showed that there was a distinct difference in the count of various oral bacteria found in each group. For instance, only 37% of the HIV-positive homosexual men harbored the strain *B. forsythus*, compared with 82% of the HIV-positive drug users. Zambon noted that this supplemented previous research by his team that found that drug users have a higher prevalence of oral lesions than homosexual males, whether or not they are infected with HIV.

—Lou Joseph

Veterinary medicine

Unlike the medical challenges of the physician, who deals with one species of patient, veterinarians are challenged by the medical problems of a vast array of patient species. Veterinary medical challenges are made especially difficult by the lack of drugs approved by the U.S. Food and Drug Administration (FDA) for the treatment of many of these species. For some nonfood animal species such as pet fish, the demand for a particular type of drug may be too small to attract the interest of pharmaceutical manufacturers; for food-animal species, the cost of gathering data demonstrating not only efficacy and safety but also lack of hazardous residues in the animal products may exceed the potential market for the drug. For the treatment of the diseases that affect the 100 species of finfish and shellfish cultured in the U.S., only five approved products were available in 1993.

This situation places veterinarians in the position of using drugs in an "extralabel" manner if appropriate health care is to be provided to many species. Extralabel use refers to use of a drug for a species, in a dosage, or for a disease that is not listed on the drug's label; listings on labels are based on FDA approval. The Federal Food, Drug, and Cosmetic Act prohibits extralabel use. However, interpretations of FDA regulations governing drug use, while not approving extralabel use, indicate that the FDA's major enforcement actions will generally be limited to extralabel drug use causing residues in food animals.

The American Veterinary Medical Association (AVMA) was concerned that the lack of statutory authority for extralabel use placed veterinarians in an untenable position as they attempted to provide the best health care to their patients. This was true even in nonfood animals, for which veterinarians had to use many drugs developed for humans, because a veterinary equivalent was not available. A good example is insulin for treatment of diabetes in a dog. The AVMA undertook a major legislative initiative to amend the Federal Food, Drug, and Cosmetic Act so that it would explicitly permit discretionary use of FDA-approved drugs by veterinarians. The justification for extralabel use by veterinarians was based on their training in animal disease diagnosis, pharmacology, toxicology, drug interactions, and therapeutics.

A complicating factor in concerns for residue problems in food animals was the over-the-counter availability of more than 80% of the drugs used in food animals. Because of this, veterinarians had a relatively small role in supervising drug use in food animals. The new legislation was designed to give veterinarians more responsibility for the manner in which drugs were used on food animals.

Ostrich health care. The ratite industry in the U.S. continued to grow during the past year. The ratite group of flightless birds includes the ostrich, emu, and rhea. These birds, particularly ostriches, were being raised in the U.S. as breeding stock to develop herds for commercial production of meat, feathers (plumes), and hides, which provide a soft, fine-grained leather. A fertile ostrich egg sold for as much as $1,000 and a breeding pair for as much as $50,000. An ostrich lays 50 to 70 eggs each year for about 25 years. Ostrich meat is of interest because it is a red meat that is similar to beef in taste but contains twice the protein of beef and has fewer calories, less fat, and less cholesterol than chicken or beef. Veterinary practitioners were becoming involved in the management and health care of these unusual birds, but medical information on ratites was quite limited.

The ostriches have considerable curiosity and will readily ingest foreign objects, which may require surgical correction. They are also especially susceptible to leg injuries, including fractures, which are difficult to repair. Adult ostriches stand 1.8–2.7 m (6–9 ft) tall and weigh 110–182 kg (240–400 lb). Thus, restraint of these large birds for treatment or examination may require the help of several persons.

Diagnostic methods and treatments. Horses occasionally suffer from paralysis of a muscle in the larynx, causing the muscle to flutter as the horse breathes and resulting in a "roaring" sound. During exercise this condition can cause oxygen deprivation, which is hazardous to the horse's health. A new treatment for this problem, developed at Michigan State University College of Veterinary Medicine, involves surgical implantation of a nerve-muscle graft. Recovery is slow, requiring from three months to a year, but modifications of the procedure were being evaluated and were expected to speed recovery.

Muscle tissue breakdown, or rhabdomyolysis, can cause in horses a serious lameness problem that is termed the "tying up" syndrome. Through the use of a nuclear imaging technique that employs calcium-binding radioisotopes, researchers at the Tufts University School of Veterinary Medicine, Boston, were able to identify muscles affected by this disease and to differentiate the disease from a simple muscle strain or tear.

The growing emphasis in veterinary medicine on the use of advanced diagnostic technology was well illustrated by ultrasound, which had grown in veterinary medicine to the extent that at least five manufacturers of this equipment had established divisions concerned with veterinary applications. It was expected that by the year 2000 ultrasound equipment would be a standard diagnostic resource in most veterinary practices. Major applications include evaluation of heart failure in old animals and of congenital heart problems. Ultrasound has also proved useful in differentiating types of diseases of the prostate gland in dogs and in evaluating the viability of fetuses in pregnant animals. Because it uses no ionizing radiation, ultrasound has a safety advantage over X-ray examinations. Moreover, in contrast to X-rays, ultrasound waves do not penetrate air pockets and bone, which yields certain diagnostic advantages.

Dogs with osteosarcoma were living longer because of a new immunotherapy-based treatment developed at the University of Wisconsin School of Veterinary Medicine. The treatment involves enabling the animal's own scavenger cells to attack and destroy the osteosarcoma cancer cells.

Nineteen veterinary clinical and research centers in the U.S. were involved in the evaluation of the drug enalapril as an adjunct to therapy for dogs with moderate to severe heart failure. A significant

© Ann States—Saba

Ostriches were being raised in the U.S. as breeding stock to develop herds for the commercial production of meat, feathers (plumes), and hides, which provide a soft, fine-grained leather.

clinical improvement in the treated dogs was noted. Enalapril is approved for the treatment of hypertension in humans, and its approval by FDA for use in veterinary medicine was expected in the near future.

New facilities. The Louisiana State University School of Veterinary Medicine was the site during the past year for the relocation of the only leprosy research unit in the U.S. Though leprosy does not affect domestic animals, the causative organism is closely related to organisms causing paratuberculosis in cattle and tuberculosis in cattle and birds. Thus, improved understanding of the prevention and treatment of leprosy may enhance research progress on those animal diseases. This was especially important because the prevalence of tuberculosis in cattle and in captive deer and elk increased in the U.S. during the year, reversing a long downward trend.

The veterinary school at the University of Bristol, England, established the world's first specialized feline immunodeficiency virus (FIV) clinic. FIV, sometimes referred to as feline AIDS, was first diagnosed in 1986 in the U.S., and since then infected cats have been found throughout the world. The clinic planned to monitor the course of the disease and the response to various treatments in as many as 100 cats infected with FIV.

The University of Pennsylvania School of Veterinary Medicine established a Laboratory for Marine Animal Health within the Marine Biological Laboratory at Woods Hole, Mass. Work at the new laboratory was to focus on the health of small marine animals such as sea urchins and shellfish. Research at the laboratory had already made significant contributions to aquatic animal health, including the identification of a parasite responsible for reducing the number of herring offspring. The role of ocean pollution as a cause of shellfish disease was being investigated, as was the use of aquatic organisms as sensitive indicators of environmental pollution.

Diseases. An outbreak of a new equine disease syndrome affecting more than 200 horses at three racetracks in the northeastern U.S. during the summer proved to be baffling to veterinarians examining these horses. The ailment, termed "mystery equine disease," was associated with a moderate fever and swelling of one or more limbs. Affected horses usually recovered within five days. All horses at those tracks were quarantined for a short period. By late summer the occurrence of the disease syndrome was rare, and the quarantine was lifted. A virus that was suspected of causing the disease was being evaluated, but it proved to be difficult to grow in the laboratory.

Also in the Northeast during the same period, more than 12 racing greyhounds died from a rapidly progressive disease, and significant morbidity was noted at several kennels. During the peak of the outbreak, four tracks were quarantined. The affected dogs displayed signs of pneumonia. A bacterium, *Streptococcus zooepidemicus*, which usually causes only lethargy, coughing, and fever, was isolated from several of the affected dogs. Fortunately, antibiotics were effective in limiting the spread of the disease. One theory suggested that environmental factors or other infectious organisms enhanced the pathogenicity of *S. zooepidemicus*. The disease problem in dogs was not related to the problem in horses.

A review of rabies cases reported to the U.S. Centers for Disease Control and Prevention for a recent 10-year period indicated that 89% of the cases involved wildlife, with raccoons being the most common species affected. The destruction of wildlife species as a means of limiting the spread of rabies did not prove successful and was not viewed with favor by many concerned with conservation of wildlife. Vaccination of individual wildlife by injection was impractical because the use of the trap-vaccinate-release method was costly and slow. A vaccine that can be administered via an oral bait attractive to raccoons was being evaluated in field trials. Distribution of the bait by aircraft would be possible and would enable widespread protection of the raccoon population.

In the wake of Hurricane Andrew, a stray dog wanders through the ruins of the Everglades Labor Camp in Homestead, Fla. An estimated 30,000 pets were displaced by the storm.

By early summer more than 1,000 cases of bovine spongiform encephalopathy were being confirmed each week in Britain. The disease was believed to be the result of exposure of British cattle to an infectious agent more than 10 years ago as a result of modification of a method for preparation of certain cattle feed supplements at that time. The disease was first identified in British cattle in 1986. The number of confirmed cases outside Britain was small, with none occurring in the U.S.

A vaccine that will aid in the prevention of canine Lyme disease was granted full licensure by the U.S. Department of Agriculture. Although the vaccine may not prevent the disease, it was expected to reduce markedly the severity of its course.

A new method was successful in achieving "long-distance" administration of vaccines and certain drugs to domestic animals and wildlife. The method involved the use of a rifle powered by compressed air that shoots "biobullets" containing the vaccine. The biobullet penetrates the skin, releases its contents into adjacent tissues, and then dissolves in the tissue fluids. Impact of the biobullet caused little discomfort to the animals.

—John M. Bowen

Optical engineering

As in all technical fields, economics was a major force in optical engineering during the past year. Much of the production and development in electro-optic systems and devices was related to defense needs. Consequently, the anticipated reduction in military spending throughout the world caused companies that traditionally received much of their business through government contracts to try to develop new civilian markets. Economics also caused a reduction of money spent on industrial research and develop-

ment. There were advances in some areas of optical technology, with new ideas in the oldest topic in the field, geometrical optics.

One of the stimulants to optical engineering in past years was the U.S. government's Strategic Defense Initiative, better known as the "Star Wars" research program. This program sponsored significant efforts in the development of space optics, high-power lasers, infrared sensors, and many other technologies. In 1992 the need for such a global defense system became questionable, and the emphasis was changed to a program for warning against tactical missile attacks from limited battlefield areas. The use of high-energy lasers in space was eliminated, and emphasis was placed instead on the development of a distributed set of orbital space sensors dubbed "Brilliant Eyes." This constellation of sensors would provide tracking data on tactical missiles in mid flight to assist in targeting conventional types of antimissile weapons. There was, however, a resurgence of interest in using lasers in a limited protective role on an airplane. A concept similar to the long-terminated Airborne Laser Laboratory was developed and seemed likely to acquire funding in 1993.

Companies in the defense business began to combine with one another in order to strengthen the possibility of obtaining some of the small amount of military contract work that was available. It seemed likely that many of the remaining large firms in the photonics business would change ownership in the next year.

The U.S. government appeared to be willing to support the development of technologies that would be convertible to civilian markets through a series of advanced technology programs jointly sponsored by either the Commerce or the Defense Department and private industry. One of those programs was the Center for Optics Manufacturing, based at the University of Rochester, N.Y. Techniques leading to the

Center for Optics Manufacturing, University of Rochester, N.Y.

Microgrinding glass to directly produce lens surfaces with one wavelength of surface error and about two to three wavelengths of subsurface damage was being achieved at the Center for Optics Manufacturing based at the University of Rochester, N.Y. The subsurface damage was about five times less than that produced by conventional grinding techniques and could be removed rapidly.

economical production of commercial optics were demonstrated at this center. Methods of microgrinding glass were developed that would directly produce lens surfaces with one wavelength of surface error and about two to three wavelengths of subsurface damage as a result of the grinding process. This was about five times less than the subsurface damage produced by conventional grinding techniques. Subsequent polishing of the surface to remove the subsurface damage was then very rapid. This process had the potential for greater speed, and consequent economy, in fabricating a variety of optical components.

Optical computing continued to approach a level of some market interest during the past year, with several companies selling potentially useful components. Practical applications, however, were still years away. Two consortia to develop optical computers, one named ESPRIT in Europe and a second funded by the U.S. Department of Defense, developed new configurations for optical digital correlators and parallel signal processors. Most likely to emerge in the near future were optical switching devices for communications systems, both long distance and within electronic computers.

Lenses. The methods of designing lenses changed rapidly during the past decade, but by 1993 all significant optical design programs were available on personal computers at reasonable costs. This brought the most powerful computing tools for optical design within the reach of all users. New developments in computer techniques for the exact modeling of physical optics (the study of the interaction of light waves by interference and diffraction) as well as geometrical optics (the geometry of paths of light rays and their imagery through optical systems) indicated the coming integration of computer programs that would cover the entire range of needs in designing complex electro-optic systems. Some programs introduced global search techniques that provided a method of assuring that the proposed design of a lens system was indeed the best that could be found for a particular problem.

One example of the newer types of optical components was binary optics, an outgrowth of holography that used semiconductor-production techniques to make specialized diffraction gratings on optical surfaces. (In this case a diffraction grating uses curved, narrowly spaced grooves on a lens surface to correct the aberrations of the lens.) Adding a binary optics grating to a lens surface adds new flexibility to the aberration correction that can be accomplished by each optical surface. Especially important are applications involving microoptics, in which light from lasers is split into parallel channels that may be used in optical communication and computation systems.

Lasers. New developments in lasers that were expected to have an effect on optical devices during the next few years included the production of a one-watt diode laser operating at room temperature in a near-infrared wavelength (985 nanometers) with a single-frequency, diffraction-limited output. A practical diode-pumped solid-state laser with a continuous output of one kilowatt was demonstrated. These lasers were likely to replace gas lasers for high-power applications and, with their ability to carry power through fiber optics, were expected to change significantly the types of industrial cutting and milling machinery.

Practical zinc selenide semiconductor lasers, which generated coherent blue light but required cooling to operate, were demonstrated in Japan. In the U.S. an Advanced Technology Program for the development and application of blue-light lasers to optical data storage systems was funded jointly by industry and the Department of Commerce. Practical realization of such devices could provide increased storage on an optical memory disc.

Medical optics. Medical optics continued to be a growing field. The use of fiber optics in endoscopes and other devices for carrying out surgery with minimum damage to the body increased rapidly. While the use of lasers for the refractive correction of the eye had not become an approved practice, the use of lasers for treating glaucoma and other eye disorders expanded.

Perhaps the most novel use of optical imagery was the processing of images during brain surgery to locate areas of abnormal brain activity. The imaging system was capable of detecting subtle differences in the reflection of red light from various parts of the brain due to changes in blood flow caused by neural activity. The image processing enhanced those differences and presented the results on a display that could be viewed in real time by the surgeon.

Astronomical optics. A milestone in ground-based astronomical optics was reached during the past year. The first 10-m (32.8-ft)-aperture Keck telescope was completed and installed on Mauna Kea in Hawaii. It was the world's largest optical telescope. All 36 segments of the primary mirror were installed and aligned, and some good-quality imagery was obtained. The success of the first telescope resulted in the construction of a second such instrument located 85 m (280 ft) away at the Hawaiian site, and fabrication of the optics for that instrument was under way.

Two of the 8.5-m (28-ft)-diameter primary mirror blanks for the European Southern Observatory telescope array in Chile were cast by Schott Glassworks in Germany. These were expected to proceed soon to the stage of optical polishing. Japan and the National Optical Astronomy Observatory in the U.S.

announced the ordering of 8.5-m-diameter blanks from Corning Glass in the United States.

The University of Arizona cast a 6.5-m (21.3-ft)-diameter borosilicate glass mirror blank for use in an upgrade of the existing Multiple Mirror Telescope. At the end of 1992 the University of Texas announced that it was planning the construction of an 8.5-m-aperture telescope using a segmented primary mirror.

The competitive position of ground-based astronomy relative to space astronomy was enhanced as new methods were used to correct the distorting effects of atmospheric turbulence. The work, carried out at the U.S. Air Force's Phillips Laboratory, Albuquerque, N.M., was intended to improve the accuracy of tracking objects in space from ground-based telescopes and used either bright stars or a laser-produced artificial beacon at high altitude to obtain a measure of the atmospheric deviations. A sensor in the image plane of the telescope evaluated the aberrations and sent signals to a flexible optical component driven by a number of actuators to correct the time-varying atmospheric effects. Demonstrations indicated that full diffraction limit of resolution could be obtained at infrared wavelengths and almost perfect correction at visible wavelengths. Atmospheric turbulence was no longer the limiting factor in telescope resolution. It appeared that space telescopes of the future would concentrate on wavelengths not transmitted by the atmosphere.

Progress continued on making replacement cameras for the Hubble Space Telescope to correct the aberrated image from the flawed primary mirror. Plans were directed toward a launch at the end of 1993 or in early 1994 to install the cameras. Despite

Scientists and engineers at the University of Arizona Steward Observatory load 9,561 kg (21,059 lb) of glass into a 6.5-m (21.3-ft)-diameter mirror mold. Unlike solid-glass mirrors, this and others at the observatory are honeycombed on the inside, created out of borosilicate glass that is formed in a rotating oven. These mirrors can be made larger and much lighter than those of solid glass.

University of Arizona Steward Observatory Mirror Laboratory

A model of the Very Large Telescope (VLT), to be built on a mountain in the Atacama Desert of Chile, reveals that it will be an array of four separate telescopes, each equipped with an 8.2-m (27-ft)-diameter mirror made of a glass ceramic material. The four telescopes will be able to work independently or in combination to achieve maximum light gathering and the highest possible angular resolution. Its light-gathering power will make the VLT the world's largest optical telescope.

the flaw, the productivity of the Hubble Space Telescope had been excellent owing to the development of effective methods for processing computer images. The next great observatory in the National Aeronautics and Space Administration's plans, the Advanced X-ray Astronomical Facility, continued with the fabrication of the complex optical components for the system. Budget restrictions reduced the number of components that would be used in the telescope.

Consumer products. One of the benefits of the conversion of military products to civilian use was the availability of a number of high-quality night-vision and infrared-sensitive viewers. These optical techniques could be used in monitoring scenes under adverse conditions, ranging from examining the heat flow in industrial processes and evaluating the design of electronic components to clandestine observations for law enforcement. New infrared detector arrays could produce imagery of a quality equal to that of television.

New high-resolution sensors reached the market during the past year. Sensors with formats of 1,024 × 1,024 picture elements could be purchased for reasonable cost. They were integrated into electronic camera systems that produced images that were of much higher resolution than those of standard video cameras and were close to photographic quality. Many technical and military applications for these sensors existed. The cost of such high-resolution electronic cameras was significantly greater than that for conventional photographic cameras.

One of the most important innovations in optics that reached consumer market development in 1992 was the Kodak Photo CD. Photographs taken on conventional color film were stored in digital form on a compact disc. The format of this disc permitted the addition of several rolls of negatives as they were developed by the processor. Photo CD players were heavily promoted as a new consumer product in the latter half of 1992. These players permitted the viewing of personal photograph albums on a home television system. The format of the photographs stored on the CD permitted a processor to make additional copies of the picture from the CD, eliminating the need for extensive storage of negatives.

—Robert R. Shannon

Physics

The finding that silicon, the fundamental material in semiconductor technology, can be made to glow upon irradiation with light produced a flurry of excitement in the research community during the past year. Physicists also explored how an atom confined in a small, gold-walled cavity interacts with its own reflection off the cavity walls and studied the collective flow of nuclear matter induced in collisions of atomic nuclei. Particle physicists analyzing high-energy proton-antiproton interactions saw tantalizing hints of the existence of the long-sought top quark.

General developments

Physicists attempting to achieve a unique quantum state representing the lowest possible energy state for matter moved several steps toward their goal during the past year. Other investigators studied the way in which an atom confined in a tiny metal cavity interacts with its own reflection. The validity of the quantum theory of the electromagnetic force received support from experiments making use of uranium atoms stripped of nearly all their electrons, and polymer materials with special optical characteristics were explored as future high-speed switches for digital data transmission.

Search for Bose-Einstein condensation. Atomic physicists in the past year continued their work to achieve Bose-Einstein condensation, a state of matter in which an ensemble of bosons—particles, such as photons or hydrogen atoms, that have an integral spin (0, 1, etc.)—collapses to a single quantum state at very low temperature. According to Carl Wieman of the University of Colorado, Bose-Einstein condensation represents the lowest possible energy state for matter. Wieman was searching for this unique state, named for Albert Einstein and the Indian scientist Satyendra Bose, with the help of a refrigerator that cools down a sample of cesium atoms to a temperature of less than a millionth of a kelvin (*i.e.*, less than a millionth of a degree above absolute zero). The core of the device was arguably the coldest place in the universe.

Daniel Kleppner of the Massachusetts Institute of Technology and colleagues were also trying to achieve Bose-Einstein condensation, in a cloud of atomic hydrogen supercooled by liquid helium. Hydrogen usually exists on Earth as a diatomic molecule (H_2), but atomic hydrogen (H) can be created and maintained at low temperature by spin polarization of the atoms in a magnetic field (orientation of the atoms such that the spin axes of their electrons are aligned in the same direction). The Pauli exclusion principle, which forbids electrons of like spin from overlapping in a H−H molecule, then keeps the atoms from pairing up. The effort is worthwhile because atomic hydrogen is the one substance in nature that remains a gas even at a temperature of absolute zero, making it an interesting test ground for quantum mechanics. Kleppner worked to cool and condense the atoms further through the process of evaporative cooling, whereby the atoms are held in a magnetic field in which the hotter atoms have enough energy to escape. Only the colder atoms remain, clumping together in the trap as a result of their lethargy.

Previous studies of trapped hydrogen atoms, including Kleppner's, had observed the atoms only after they had left the trap. But in the past year atomic hydrogen in a magnetic trap was studied directly by optical spectroscopy for the first time. Jook Walraven and his colleagues at the Van der Waals-Zeeman Laboratory of the University of Amsterdam studied the transmission spectroscopy of hydrogen atoms still in the trap by using pulsed laser light at the so-called Lyman-alpha wavelength (121.6 nanometers [billionths of a meter], corresponding to the transition of the hydrogen atom between the 2P and 1S states). They obtained this short-wavelength (ultraviolet) light by passing comparatively long-wavelength light from a dye laser through a harmonic-conversion process. The spectrum of radiation absorbed by the hydrogen atoms can be used to monitor the temperature and density of the hydrogen sample as a function of time. This diagnostic technique will be useful for later studies of hydrogen at the lower temperatures contemplated by Kleppner and others.

Meanwhile, Wieman was also applying evaporative cooling to his setup of laser-cooled cesium atoms but had yet to achieve a density of atoms sufficiently high to trigger the condensation process. He planned to add a "magnetic lens" that would increase the density to desired levels. Kleppner was adjusting his experiment to better monitor the trapped hydrogen atoms and thereby pinpoint the conditions that would optimize their density and temperature. Both groups and those at other labs were optimistic about achieving Bose-Einstein condensation in the near future.

An atom in a box looks at itself. Many science museums have mirrored compartments in which the viewer can glimpse what looks like an infinite number of reflections of himself or herself. Now consider an atom in a tiny metal cavity. Even though it is neutral, the atom still emanates electromagnetic fields that, in the confines of the cavity, reflect back and forth between the cavity walls. For several years Edward A. Hinds and co-workers at Yale University have been studying how the multiple reflections affect the allowed energy states of the atom. In other words, they have been studying how the atom interacts with its own reflection.

In the Yale research a beam of neutral sodium atoms in their ground states (lowest energy states) is sent into a cavity consisting of two very flat gold mirrors only a micrometer (millionth of a meter) apart. A laser beam then excites the atoms to higher-energy states. The spectrum of light emitted by the atoms as they return to their ground states is monitored as the cavity dimensions are varied. Among their recent discoveries the experimenters found that the shift of the spectrum from its normal free-space shape grew as the cavity shrank; in other words, the more tightly enclosed the atom, the more important the interaction between the atom and its mirror images. This interaction is a manifestation of the van der Waals force, the force between the cavity walls and the dipole moment (the separation of the charge) induced inside the atom. According to Hinds, the Yale experiment provided the first direct quantitative verification of theoretical predictions about the van der Waals interaction between such confined atoms and metal surfaces.

Lithium-like uranium atoms. A uranium atom normally consists of a nucleus containing 92 protons (plus an assortment of neutrons) surrounded by 92 electrons. Under certain circumstances many of these electrons can be stripped off; the remaining electrons are held to the nucleus by enormous electric fields. The study of how the remaining electrons make transitions from one quantum state to another under such severe conditions allows for various tests

A "graphitic onion," shown in an electron micrograph, was produced in experiments prompted by the recent discovery of the 60-carbon molecule buckminsterfullerene. Made of nested shells of carbon atoms in mostly hexagonal arrays, the particle was created during the electron bombardment of carbon soot.

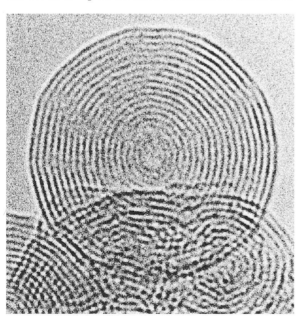

From "Curling and Closure of Graphitic Networks Under Electron–Beam Irradiation," Daniel Ugarte, reprinted by permission of *Nature*, vol. 359, no. 6397, cover, Oct. 22, 1992, © Macmillan Magazines Ltd.

of quantum electrodynamics (QED), the fundamental quantum theory describing the electromagnetic force.

Researchers at the Lawrence Berkeley Laboratory (LBL), Berkeley, Calif., have been able to strip any number of electrons from uranium by passing a beam of uranium atoms produced in the Bevatron heavy-ion accelerator through a piece of aluminum foil. In one experiment the uranium atoms, which normally have 92 electrons, had all but three electrons removed. These "lithium-like" uranium ions, so named because lithium atoms normally possess only three electrons, were chosen for study because the first excited state of the U^{89+} ion survives long enough (an average of 62 picoseconds [trillionths of a second]) for the ion to get free of the foil region before decaying to its ground state, providing a clear picture of the ion's energy state.

The light emitted in this process, an X-ray photon, is recorded in detectors oriented at an angle of 95° relative to the beam direction. Corrected for the amount by which this light is Doppler-shifted owing to the relativistic motion of the uranium ion through the accelerator, the wavelength of the light was measured to be 4.4187 nanometers, or, in terms of energy units, 280.59 electron volts. Theoretical estimates, based on QED, for the energy of this transition only recently were able to match this level of precision and were in agreement with the LBL experimental results, further increasing confidence in the validity of QED.

Polymer materials in nonlinear optics. In coming years the amount of data transmitted in the form of photons along optical fibers, rather than in the form of electrons flowing along metal wires, will greatly increase. Nonlinear materials are an important ingredient in the development of photonic technology. A nonlinear optical material is one in which the intensity of the output light is not proportional to that of the input light. An external electric field applied to such a material can alter the material's index of refraction, which in turn can alter the phase or intensity of the light transmitted. In effect, the material can serve as an optical switch and therefore can be used to modulate laser light into digital bits of information.

One primary class of nonlinear materials consists of polymers containing optically nonlinear molecules called chromophores. To be effective as a nonlinear medium, the chromophores must first be aligned (or "poled") in a single direction by means of a strong electric field. Using a substance prepared in this way, C.C. Teng of Hoechst Celanese Corp., Summit, N.J., switched the light from a diode laser off and on at a rate of 40 billion times a second, a rate 10 times faster than the laser itself can be turned off and on. With this level of switching speed, 40 gigabits (billion bits) of data could be transmitted along optical fiber. Scientists at AlliedSignal, Inc., Morristown, N.J., and Columbia University, New York City, studying the electro-optic response of certain nonlinear polymer systems to laser light, concluded that the transmission rate can eventually reach 460 gigabits.

Although nonlinear polymers have the potential to operate at higher switching rates than do inorganic materials, the polymer materials suffer from the problem of chromophore instability. Over time the chromophore molecules tend to become disoriented, thus losing their nonlinear properties. A collaboration of scientists at Lockheed Corp., Calabasas, Calif., and the University of Pennsylvania were seeking to remedy the problem by curing polymer materials at temperatures above 300° C (570° F). They achieved long-lasting stability in polymer thin films, an important step in making polymer materials useful in fast-switching applications.

—Phillip F. Schewe

High-energy physics

The objective of research in high-energy, elementary particle physics is to understand the nature of all matter and of the interactions between the fundamental constituents of matter. In that context the results of research in recent years have proved very gratifying. Parameters of the so-called standard model of the strong, the electromagnetic, and the weak interactions between quarks and leptons (the constituents of all matter) are becoming known with increasing precision, so much so that, for many aspects of the model, physicists have progressed from questions of "what" to questions of "why." Nevertheless, major unresolved problems remain, and it often seems that two new questions arise for each one answered. Several years ago the reknowned British astrophysicist Steven Hawking predicted the field of elementary particle physics would be "wrapped up" by the end of the 20th century. An assessment of the progress in the field since then, however, makes that prediction seem highly optimistic.

By way of review, it is now known that there are three generations or families of elementary particles (see Table I). Each generation contains a quark with a charge of $-\frac{1}{3}$ ($\frac{1}{3}$ the charge of an ordinary, negatively charged electron), a quark with a charge of $+\frac{2}{3}$, a negatively charged lepton with the charge of an electron, and an electrically neutral, perhaps massless lepton called a neutrino. For each of these particles there is an antiparticle, having the same mass but the opposite sign of electric charge, baryon or lepton number, or other quantum property. The quarks are combined to form the strongly interacting particles (hadrons) and cannot exist as free particles. Thus, baryons (such as neutrons and protons)

are made up of three quarks, and mesons (such as pions and kaons) are made of a quark and an antiquark. The heavier quarks decay radioactively via the weak interaction to lighter quarks and the heavier leptons to lighter leptons. Consequently, virtually all stable matter is composed of quarks and leptons of the lightest generation, with the up (u) and down (d) quarks constituting protons and neutrons, and the lightest charged lepton, the electron, joining in to form ordinary atoms and molecules. Of the six quarks, only the top (t) quark has not yet been clearly identified experimentally.

The strong interaction between quarks is the force that binds them together to form protons and neutrons (nucleons) and other baryons; this force field is propagated by massless quanta, or field particles, called gluons. The electromagnetic interaction acts between all particles possessing electric charge and is propagated by quanta known as photons; this is surely the best-understood and most familiar of all the interaction theories. Photons are the quanta of electromagnetic radiation; *e.g.*, visible light, X-rays, and radio waves. The weak interaction, which operates between all particles (including neutrinos) is propagated by the massive intermediate vector bosons: the charged W^+ and W^- and the neutral Z^0. (*See* Table II.) The electromagnetic and weak interactions are understood to be different manifestations of a single electroweak force, the weakness of the weak interaction being due primarily to the mass of the intermediate bosons.

Results from LEP. Perhaps the most prolific source of new results confirming and refining the standard model since 1989 has been the Large Electron-Positron (LEP) accelerator-collider facility at CERN (European Laboratory for Particle Physics) located in Geneva and neighboring France. At LEP, electrons and positrons (the antimatter counterparts of electrons), each with an energy of about 46 GeV (billion electron volts), collide head-on to produce the Z^0 boson, which has a rest mass of about 91.2 GeV. Details of the decay of the Z make possible many studies, such as the very important determination of the number of kinds of neutrinos and, hence, the number of elementary particle generations, now known to be three to a precision of 1–2% (see *1991 Yearbook of Science and the Future* Year in Review: PHYSICS: *High-energy physics*). A critical parameter in the unified theory of the weak and electromagnetic interactions is the Weinberg angle, Θ_w. This angle relates the ratio of the masses of the charged (W) and neutral (Z) intermediate vector bosons and also enters into the ratio of the coupling strengths of the electromagnetic and the weak interactions. In effect, together with the mass of the W boson, it relates the electric charge of the electron to a corresponding quantity, the weak charge, that characterizes the

Table I. Properties of Quarks and Leptons

Generation	Leptons		Quarks	
	Charge −1	Neutral	Charge +⅔	Charge −⅓
1	electron (0.51)	electron neutrino	up quark, u (~340)	down quark, d (~340)
2	muon (106)	muon neutrino	charmed quark, c (1,550)	strange quark, s (~510)
3	tau (1,784)	tau neutrino	top quark, t (>95,000)	bottom quark, b (4,720)

All charges are in units of the electron's charge (−1). Masses, shown in parentheses, are in millions of electron volts (MeV); the masses of the neutrinos are consistent with zero. The tau neutrino and the top quark have not yet been observed.

weak and electromagnetic interaction. Recent LEP data fixed the value of $\sin^2 \Theta_w$ at 0.2324 ± 0.0011.

For more than 30 years the weak interactions that involve a change of the charge of the particle involved, the so-called charged-current interactions, have been understood to be governed by a mixture of vector and axial vector couplings, in which the values of the relevant coupling constants, g_v and g_a, are equal at the quark level of interaction and are of opposite sign. Again, from recent LEP data (together with earlier experiments on neutrino scattering), the corresponding coupling constants for the weak interactions that are charge-conserving, $i.e.$, the neutral-current interactions, were determined to high precision. Thus, for the neutral currents, $g_v = -0.03531 \pm 0.0022$ and $g_a = -0.49904 \pm 0.0009$.

From the decay of the Z boson to quarks (and hence to jets of mesons), the characteristics of the strong interaction were becoming more precisely determined. As one example, the size of the quark was set below an upper limit of 10^{-17} cm, or about $1/10,000$ the size of a proton. (A centimeter is about 0.4 in.) Quarks are thus very probably fundamental, pointlike objects, as electrons and muons are be-

lieved to be. Further, the magnitude of the strong-interaction coupling constant, α_s, the quantity in the strong interaction that plays a role analogous to the electric charge of the electron in the electromagnetic interaction, was very well determined. At an energy of 91 GeV, corresponding to the mass of the Z, this parameter has a value of 0.124 ± 0.005.

An attractive and plausible theoretical concept is that the strong, electromagnetic, and weak interactions are all as different from each other as they have been found to be only because the energies that have been explored are so very low on some absolute scale. At vastly greater energies per particle, perhaps about 10^{16} GeV, all coupling strengths would prove to be comparable. The LEP data provide the first convincing support for this idea by demonstrating that the strong coupling constant is markedly smaller at 91 GeV than the value determined at lower energies. At 34 GeV, for example, α_s is 0.148 ± 0.018, significantly larger than the 0.124 ± 0.005 value at 91 GeV.

Search for the top quark. The one quark remaining to be definitively identified is the t quark. The other five, less massive quarks—the u, d, s (strange), c (charm), and b (bottom)—have all been clearly identified and studied. Data from LEP strongly suggest that the top quark mass is somewhere in the range of 145 ± 25 GeV. At the Tevatron proton-antiproton collider located at the Fermi National Accelerator Laboratory (Fermilab) near Chicago, two large detector collaborations were engaged in a major search for the t quark. The most promising type of collision event to examine is that in which a t and an anti-t (or $\bar{t}$) are produced together and each decays to a b (or $\bar{b}$) plus a $W^{\pm}$; the b then produces a jet of mesons, and the W decays to a muon or electron and a corresponding neutrino. By the end of 1992 one or two promising t-$\bar{t}$ candidate events had been found, with probable masses in the right range. In view of the large number of background processes that can mimic the t quark signature and the smallness of the expected cross section (the effective target area that one particle presents to another in a collision) for production of t's, it will require observation and study of several candidate events before scientists can be sure that they have indeed found the t-$\bar{t}$

Table II. The Basic Forces or Interactions of Physics

Force	Field particle and rest mass	Strength relative to strong force at 10^{-13} cm distance	Particles that experience force
electromagnetic	γ (photon); 0	10^{-2}	electrically charged particles; all quarks and charged leptons
weak	$W^{\pm}$; 80.6 GeV Z^0; 91.16 GeV	10^{-13}	all quarks and leptons
strong	g (gluon); 0	1	quarks and hadrons (particles composed of quarks)
gravitational	G (graviton)	10^{-38}	all particles with mass

The electromagnetic and weak forces are now understood as special cases of a more general electroweak interaction. The graviton has not yet been experimentally observed.

"Of course Daddy could explain what a superconducting supercollider is, sweetie, but just at the moment Daddy is watching 'America's Most Wanted.' "

"needle" in the "haystack" of expected, ordinary reactions. The Fermilab groups were optimistic and excited, however, as data continued to be collected and analyzed.

New detectors. The 1992 Nobel Prize for Physics was awarded to Georges Charpak (*see* SCIENTISTS OF THE YEAR) of CERN for the development of the multiwire proportional chamber (MWPC) and related particle detection instrumentation. The honor bestowed on Charpak calls attention to the critical role that the sophisticated particle accelerator and detector technologies continue to play in the advance of particle physics. The current major programs in high-energy research involve colliding-beam accelerator systems wherein two oppositely directed beams of particles meet head-on—LEP at CERN for electron-positron collisions and the Tevatron at Fermilab for proton-antiproton collisions—with large detectors surrounding the beam-beam interaction regions. These detectors must record the trajectories and identify as many as a hundred particles or more produced simultaneously. With the aid of a large electromagnet, the curvature of each charged particle's trajectory can be used to determine its momentum.

Charpak's MWPC and its derivatives are used to measure these trajectories in most of the large detectors. The principle of operation of the MWPC detectors is based on the ionization (freeing of electrons from atoms) created by a charged particle in passing through a gas. Electrons from the ionized gas move in an established electric field toward a positive (anode) wire. Close to the wire the electric field is great enough for collisions of the electrons with

gas atoms to produce secondary ionization, causing the detected signal on the anode to be amplified thousands of times. A corresponding positive signal is induced on the other negative (cathode) electrode. By arraying parallel anode wires spaced a few millimeters apart, the trajectory of the high-energy particle can be located with a precision determined by this spacing. (A millimeter is 0.04 in.) Cathode strips at right angles to the parallel anodes, or a plane containing a second set of anode wires perpendicular to the first, permit the location of a track segment for a particle trajectory in two dimensions, and a stack of such MWPC planes can be used to determine particle trajectories in three dimensions. The precision can be improved either by a decrease in the anode wire spacing—down to a millimeter is practical—or by measurement of the time required for the electrons from the primary ionization to drift to the anode wires. Such "drift chambers" can achieve resolutions of better than 0.1 mm.

All this effort would not have been practical were it not for the dramatic evolution of solid-state electronics. Only with highly developed electronics technology has it been possible to instrument the required tens of thousands of MWPC or drift-chamber signal channels required in current colliding-beam detectors within the tight constraints of reliability, space, heat dissipation, costs, and availability. There has been a corresponding, parallel development of the computer components and programs required for converting the signals from the numerous channels to comprehensible particle-track information and thence to physics. The result is that current colliding-beam detectors, such as the two at the Tevatron and the four at LEP, are able to analyze complex events that may occur at rates of millions per second and to intelligently and sensibly search for such rare objects as the t quark.

As Charpak's Nobel Prize correctly ascribes, it is the physicists from within the high-energy physics community itself who have invented and developed these innovative detector technologies. A similar, parallel evolution has occurred in the domain of particle accelerators and storage rings. The 1984 Nobel Prize for Physics was shared by Carlo Rubbia of CERN for the discovery of the W and Z bosons and by Simon van der Meer, also of CERN, for developing a method of accumulating sufficient antiprotons to yield a useful rate of proton-antiproton collisions.

Unsolved problems. In addition to the search for the t quark, high-energy physicists have been seeking evidence of the Higgs particle. The existence of the particle, first proposed by the Scottish physicist Peter Higgs, would provide the theoretical means for endowing the various quarks and leptons with their observed masses. Searches for the Higgs particle thus far have turned up empty, implying that its mass must be at least 60 GeV; its mass could be as great as several hundred GeV.

The neutral kaon system has proved to be a very rich source of insights into the nature of the weak interaction. Neutral kaons are mesons composed of an s (or $\bar{s}$) quark and a $\bar{d}$ (or d) quark. The decays of neutral kaons demonstrate not only parity violation (lack of left-right symmetry) but also, for a small fraction of the decays, asymmetry under the product of parity inversion and charge conjugation (replacing the charge of the particles by the opposite electric charge; in effect, replacing particles with their anti-particles). Since it can be shown that all physical reactions and systems must be invariant under the product P (parity inversion) times C (charge conjugation) times T (time reversal), the discovery of a system like neutral kaon decay that is not symmetrical under PC requires that it also not be symmetrical under T (time reversal).

At both LEP and the Tevatron, as well as at other, lower energy electron-positron colliders, B mesons are produced, and it is now known that the neutral B mesons constitute a system much like that of the neutral kaons. The neutral B mesons are made of a b (or $\bar{b}$) quark and a $\bar{d}$ (or d) quark. As of early 1993, many experiments either under way or planned were focused on the detailed study of the B meson system in order to determine the parameters of decay—in particular the PC nonconserving aspects.

New research facilities. The Higgs particle and the B meson system are but two of the myriad puzzles, enigmas, and searches that challenge high-energy physicists. To help meet these challenges, one new facility recently commenced operation, and two major facilities were begun. In Hamburg, Germany, a specialized colliding-beam system called HERA began collecting data on collisions between 820-GeV protons and 26-GeV electrons. Such collisions make possible the study of the internal structure of the proton to a precision far beyond anything achieved in the past.

In Europe plans were going forward to construct a proton-proton colliding-beam storage-ring accelerator called the Large Hadron Collider, or LHC, in the LEP tunnel at CERN. Experiments were being designed, and accelerator magnets were being designed and tested. The LHC will accelerate and store protons with energies of almost 8 TeV (trillion electron volts), so that head-on collision of two protons will provide nearly 16 TeV in the center of mass, compared with 1.8 TeV available with the Tevatron.

South of Dallas, Texas, tunnel construction was under way for the Superconducting Super Collider, which will bring together two 20-TeV proton beams, making 40 TeV available in the center of mass. Superconducting magnets were successfully tested, and two major experimental collaborations were busy de-

signing two large detectors. Both the SSC and the LHC were expected to be completed near the end of the 1990s.

—Lawrence W. Jones

Nuclear physics

Significant advances were made in the past year in understanding several key questions in nuclear physics. The long-standing problem of the equation of state of nuclear matter was clarified through the analysis of collisions of atomic nuclei; the analysis revealed a pattern of disappearance and reappearance of the collective flow of matter as the energy of the collision increased. The dynamics of nuclear collisions depends on the degree to which nuclear matter is compressible at high densities and on how the change in nuclear density affects the interaction of the nucleons (protons and neutrons) within the nucleus. This density-dependent modification of the nucleon-nucleon force also was probed by the use of intense beams of protons to measure the response of a nuclear target for different orientations of the incident proton's spin. These data, together with related information obtained from experiments with beams of electrons (e^-) and positive K mesons (kaons; K^+), elucidated the nature of the strong interaction between nucleons in a nucleus. In addition to conventional nuclei, composed of neutrons and protons, there also exist hypernuclei in which one or more nucleons are replaced by particles called lambda (Λ) hyperons. In the Λ, a close relative of the neutron and proton, a strange quark (s) replaces one of the up (u) and down (d) quarks that make up the nucleon. Evidence for hypernuclei containing two bound Λ's was obtained recently, permitting a glimpse at the nature of the strong interaction between Λ particles.

Collective flow in heavy-ion collisions. A central issue in nuclear physics is the equation of state of nuclear matter, which expresses the relationship between the energy and the density of the system. A key parameter in the equation of state is the nuclear compressibility (symbolized K), which is proportional to the second derivative (the rate of change) of the energy with respect to the density. Estimates of nuclear compressibility have been obtained from analyses of phenomena as diverse as the production of pi mesons (pions) in collisions of heavy ions (atoms stripped of their electrons), supernova explosions, masses of neutron stars, and the energies of collective "giant resonances" in nuclei.

An alternate approach is to study the development of collective nuclear motion, or "flow," in heavy-ion collisions. Such a pattern of flow, akin to that in ordinary fluids, was predicted on the basis of a hydrodynamic description of nuclear collisions. For a heavy-ion collision, physicists define a reaction plane in

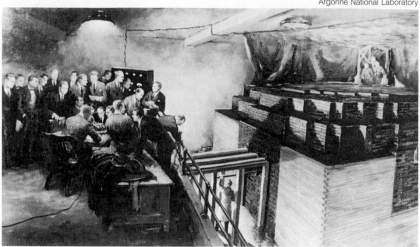

The year 1992 marked the 50th anniversary of the achievement of the first controlled, self-sustaining nuclear chain reaction, which took place Dec. 2, 1942, under the stands of Stagg Field stadium at the University of Chicago. As portrayed in a 1957 painting (right) by Gary Sheahan, a scientist partly withdraws the last neutron-absorbing cadmium control rod from the graphite-uranium pile as most of the research team, led by Enrico Fermi, watch from the balcony.

terms of the direction of motion of the ion beam and a weighted sum of the linear momenta of nuclear fragments produced in the collision. Collective flow occurs when the in-plane components of momentum perpendicular to the beam direction are in opposite directions for particles emitted in the forward and backward hemispheres defined by the center-of-mass system. The phenomenon of flow reflects a competition between the attractive component of the average nuclear potential and a repulsive component characteristic of individual nucleon-nucleon scatterings. In comparatively low-energy collisions, say, 20–50 MeV (million electron volts) per particle, light fragments are emitted preferentially at negative scattering angles, indicating the dominance of the attractive nuclear mean field. At higher energies, of the order of 100–800 MeV per particle, fragments appear mostly at positive angles, corresponding to repulsive scattering. At some intermediate value of energy, called the balance energy, the effects of attractive and repulsive scattering compensate each other, and the pattern of collective flow is observed to disappear.

Experiments to study collective flow have been performed in the past few years at the Streamer Chamber facility at the Bevalac accelerator of the Lawrence Berkeley Laboratory, Berkeley, Calif., the K1200 cyclotron at the National Superconducting Laboratory of Michigan State University, and the GANIL facility in France. The most recent results from the Streamer Chamber demonstrated that collective flow vanishes at 50 MeV per nucleon for collisions involving two lanthanum-139 nuclei and at 60 MeV per nucleon for those involving two niobium-93 nuclei. At higher energies flow reappears.

A theoretical framework that describes the dynamics of nuclear collisions in this energy regime is the Boltzmann-Uehling-Uhlenbeck (BUU) model, in which the transport of nuclear fluid occurs under the influence of a density-dependent average potential field as well as individual nucleon-nucleon collisions. The essential parameters extracted from the data are the compressibility (K) and the in-medium nucleon-nucleon scattering cross section (σ), the effective area associated with a nucleon-nucleon collision. A lower value of K allows the system to be compressed more easily, and hence the balance energy is lowered, while a decrease in σ raises the balance energy. The data, which depend more strongly on σ than on K, are consistent with the BUU transport model if σ is close to its value for two nucleons interacting in free space, in agreement with theoretical expectations.

Spin-isospin excitations in nuclei. The neutron and proton, the familiar constituents of nuclei, form an isospin doublet; *i.e.,* a two-particle family whose members differ principally in the values of their electric charge. The neutron and proton each possess an isospin quantum number (T) of $\frac{1}{2}$ and a component T_z along the axis of quantization, z, of either $\frac{1}{2}$ or $-\frac{1}{2}$. Thus, the neutron and proton are said to be described by the isospin quantum numbers $T = \frac{1}{2}$ and $T_z = \pm \frac{1}{2}$. Both the neutron and the proton possess an intrinsic spin (J) of one-half unit of angular momentum ($J = \frac{1}{2}$), whose component along the z axis can have one of two possible values ($J_z = \pm \frac{1}{2}$). A beam of protons or neutrons can be prepared in a polarized state, one in which the spin axis of each particle in the beam points in a particular direction; say, $J_z = + \frac{1}{2}$. When a polarized beam interacts with a nuclear target, which may also have an intrinsic spin, the spin states of the projectile and target may change during the collision. In addition, an incident proton may emerge from a collision as a neutron, owing to a charge-exchange reaction.

The processes of spin and isospin transfer are of interest in nuclear physics since they reflect the meson-exchange picture underlying nucleon-

nucleon forces. For instance, proton-neutron charge-exchange reactions, in which protons are transformed into neutrons and vice versa, are mediated by the transfer of spinless ($J=0$) pions (π), or by rho mesons (ϱ), which have a spin $J=1$. Such exchanges are called isovector since they involve a change in isospin (symbolized $\triangle T$) of one unit ($\triangle T=1$). Measurements of the dependence of scattering cross sections on the spin orientation for nucleon-nucleus elastic and inelastic collision processes reveal the spin-isospin structure of the effective nucleon-nucleon interaction within the nucleus. A key question is how this in-nucleus interaction compares with that of two nucleons in free space.

Several recent experiments, carried out at the Indiana University Cyclotron Facility (IUCF) and at the Los Alamos (N.M.) Meson Physics Facility (LAMPF), shed new light on the nature of the effective nucleon-nucleon interaction. The IUCF experiment was performed with a 200-MeV polarized proton beam incident on a target of boron-10 (^{10}B). The K600 magnetic spectrometer was used to measure the momentum of the inelastically scattered protons. The spin state of the protons was determined by a polarimeter mounted in the spectrometer, using the known spin dependence of elastic proton-carbon scattering. The measured quantity was the polarization transfer coefficient (D), which reflects a change in the spin orientations of the projectile and target. The inelastic process studied was the transition from the $J=3$, $T=0$ ground state of ^{10}B to the $J=0$, $T=1$ state at 1.74 MeV of excitation energy. In the meson-exchange picture, this $\triangle T=1$ transition is mediated by the exchange of the isovector π and ϱ mesons. The nuclear transition densities were determined independently by inelastic electron-scattering experiments. The measurement of D thus provided a clean test of the spin dependence of the effective nucleon-nucleon interaction, essentially independent of the details of nuclear structure. The results of the IUCF experiment were striking; the data on D were in strong disagreement with predictions based on the nucleon-nucleon interaction in free space. A model in which the ϱ meson has less mass within the nucleus than in free space led to a better description of the data.

In the LAMPF experiment, the nucleon-nucleon interaction was explored under different kinematic conditions; namely, in the regime of quasi-free nucleon-nucleon scattering, in which the energy transfer to the nucleus is large (30–160 MeV). The proton-neutron charge-exchange reaction with polarized protons having an energy of 495 MeV was studied at the new neutron time-of-flight facility at LAMPF, using targets of deuterium, carbon, and calcium. The LAMPF data on polarization transfer are sensitive to the balance between the contributions of π and ϱ exchange, as in the IUCF experiment, but in this case the momentum transfer imparted to the nucleus can be varied, yielding additional constraints on the theoretical description. The LAMPF data did not suggest an enhanced pion field within the nucleus, as proposed in some models, but indicated a strong degree of cancellation between π and ϱ spin-dependent forces. This emerges naturally if the ϱ meson mass is lowered in the nucleus. An active experimental and theoretical program was continuing on medium-energy (a few hundred McV) probes of nuclei, with the goal of further delineating the spin dependence of strong interactions in nuclei.

Multistrange nuclei. A hypernucleus is a bound system of particles consisting of neutrons, protons, and one or more Λ hyperons. There exists a modest body of data on hypernuclei that contain one Λ and, thus, one strange quark, which has a strangeness quantum number (S) of -1 ($S=-1$). This work has yielded some insights into the nature of the Λ-nucleon interaction. On the other hand, the data on doubly strange hypernuclei, those containing two strange quarks ($S=-2$), are very sparse. Recently, a series of experiments to explore the $\Lambda\Lambda$ hypernucleus was initiated at the KEK proton synchrotron in Tsukuba, Japan. A beam of negative kaons (K^-; strangeness $S=-1$) at a momentum of 1.66 GeV/c (1.66 billion electron volts divided by the speed of light) impinges on a proton target, leading to the production of a positive kaon (K^+; $S=+1$) and a negatively charged xi (Ξ^-) hyperon ($S=-2$, carrying two strange quarks) by means of strong interactions, which conserve the strangeness quantum number S. The K^+ is detected in a magnetic spectrometer, and the Ξ^- is slowed down in a nuclear emulsion and captured by an emulsion nucleus after it comes to rest. The emulsion contains carbon-12, nitrogen-14, oxygen-16, and heavier nuclei. After the Ξ^- is captured in an atomic orbit, it can react with a proton in the nucleus and produce two Λ hyperons, which can either be ejected as free particles or remain bound to a nuclear fragment.

The probability that both Λ's are captured in a bound state is very small. Nevertheless, several $\Lambda\Lambda$ hypernuclei were seen in the KEK experiment. One of them is the hypernucleus $^{13}_{\Lambda\Lambda}$B, consisting of a ^{11}B core plus two Λ's bound in the lowest quantum state of zero orbital angular momentum (the $1s$ state). The $^{13}_{\Lambda\Lambda}$B system decays via the weak interaction, leading to the emission of an energetic pion (π^-). The π^- and other charged decay remnants leave telltale tracks in the emulsion. From the observed kinetic energies associated with the tracks, the binding energy of $^{13}_{\Lambda\Lambda}$B can be established, which in turn leads to information on the strength of the $\Lambda\Lambda$ interaction. This important piece of information sheds light on the strong interactions of strange quarks.

Remarkably, the ΛΛ interaction was seen from the KEK experiment to be quite strong and attractive, about one-half to three-fourths the strength of the nucleon-nucleon force. This feature was not predicted by conventional meson-exchange models and points to additional short-range attraction, or at least diminished repulsion, which arises at the underlying level of quark interactions. The strong attraction may also signal the existence of a two-body ΛΛ bound state, somewhat akin to the deuteron (a proton bound to a neutron). In the quark model, a more deeply bound six-quark configuration with $S = -2$ may also exist. Active searches for such an object were under way at KEK and at the Alternating Gradient Synchrotron at Brookhaven National Laboratory, Upton, N.Y. A strongly attractive hyperon-hyperon interaction also implies the existence of a vast array of stable multistrange conglomerates of arbitrarily large baryon number, which decay only by weak strangeness-changing processes. Thus, the observed properties of a light system such as $_{\Lambda\Lambda}^{13}B$ may have implications for a macroscopic system such as a neutron star, the core of which can contain strange matter at high densities.

—Carl B. Dover

Condensed-matter physics

In the past year significant progress was made in first-principles quantum mechanical simulations of crystalline-matter systems consisting of large numbers of atoms. The advance opened the way for theoretical studies of the atomic structure of metal and semiconductor surfaces, atomic diffusion, and solid-liquid phase transitions. In addition, new effects associated with the spatial confinement of electrons were experimentally observed in two different systems: "quantum dots" and "porous" silicon. As a result of these developments, physicists achieved control of electric current on a single-electron basis and produced visible-light emission from silicon.

Computer simulations. Of enduring interest to condensed-matter physicists over the past 40 years has been the desire to determine the structural, electronic, vibrational, and magnetic properties of real material systems from a first-principles quantum mechanical method in which the only experimental inputs are the atomic numbers and masses of the atoms making up the system. Since typical macroscopic systems consist of a vast number of atoms, of the order of 10^{23} atoms per cubic centimeter (0.06 cu in), it is in general impossible to apply first-principles methods to arbitrary systems. A major exception occurs for crystalline solids, for which it is usually possible to determine the physical properties by focusing on the microscopic building blocks, which contain a more manageable number of atoms. For

example, scientists can determine the bulk electronic and structural properties of important semiconductors like silicon and gallium arsenide by using unit cells containing as few as two atoms per cell. Modern theoretical techniques together with the availability of fast computers have made it possible to predict the properties of these and other crystalline systems containing as many as 100 atoms per unit cell with high accuracy. Over the past decade the equilibrium crystal structure, bond length, cohesive energy, elastic stiffness, vibrational modes, electronic band gaps and charge densities, temperature- and pressure-dependent effects, and even the superconducting transition temperature have been determined from such first-principles, or ab initio, calculations.

There are many important phenomena, however, such as diffusion, crystal growth, defect formation and migration, surface structure, and melting, for which a unit cell containing 100 atoms is insufficient and for which a 1,000-atom cell is more appropriate. In the past year theorists made significant gains in extending the range of first-principles calculations from 100 atoms to 1,000 atoms. The noteworthy aspect of the achievement is that the difficulty in carrying out such larger-scale calculations increases not linearly but, with the best currently available computer approaches, at least as the square of the number of atoms involved. The development opened the way for significant broadening of the range of application of ab initio techniques.

The first problem to be attacked with a 1,000-atom unit cell was the atomic structure and energetics of formation of the cleavage surface of crystalline silicon (Si). The cleavage surface is the atomic plane along which a crystal splits when subjected to a sharp impulse. In the case of silicon, the cleavage surface corresponds to a (111) atomic plane; i.e., the vector normal to this plane is parallel to a cubic (111) axis. It has long been known that at least two different stable atomic arrangements are possible on a clean Si(111) surface. A freshly cleaved Si(111) surface has a "2×1" periodicity; i.e., the two-dimensional unit cell for the surface is twice as large along one axis as it is for an identical plane in the bulk of the material. The doubling of the periodicity is caused by atomic displacements at the surface. As a result of the displacements, the minimum cell size necessary to describe the surface region becomes twice as large as in a corresponding plane in the bulk of the material.

The unit cell of the 2×1 structure has only two atoms. Theoretical studies of the surface generally involve the use of a slab geometry. A slab as thin as 10–20 atomic planes is usually sufficient for understanding the surface properties because the perturbation caused by the surface is damped exponentially with distance away from the surface. The correct atomic structure of the 2×1 surface was first proposed from a theoretical study in 1981. The atoms at the surface rearrange themselves to form a zigzag chain that is stabilized by a π-bonding interaction. The small size of the unit cell has made it amenable to extensive theoretical studies over the past decade, and its atomic and vibrational spectra and surface energy have been determined.

The 2×1 surface is well known to be stable at low to moderate temperatures. When the surface is subjected to thermal annealing at temperatures of 500°–700° C (930°–1,290° F), however, it transforms into a second stable arrangement with a much larger, 7×7 periodicity. The new surface has an area 49 times larger than that of a similar plane in the bulk, and it possesses one of the largest surface unit cells known. The main features in the atomic structure of this intriguing surface were first revealed in 1983 by Gerd Binnig and Heinrich Rohrer at the IBM Research Laboratory in Zürich, Switz., soon after their invention of the scanning tunneling microscope. They found that each unit cell contains 12 "extra" atoms (adatoms) as well as large "holes" at the corners and smaller ones along the unit cell boundaries. A complete structural determination made possible by the knowledge obtained from this work was obtained in 1985 by Kunio Takayanagi and co-workers of the Tokyo Institute of Technology as a result of their transmission electron diffraction measurements. The structure was subsequently confirmed by means of surface X-ray diffraction measurements by Ian Robinson and co-workers of AT&T Bell Laboratories, Murray Hill, N.J. The results of the investigations showed an extensive rebonding of atoms at the surface extending three layers below the uppermost atomic layer. The experiments left unanswered, however, the fundamental reason why (and how) the surface undergoes such a massive atomic rearrangement to create a periodic array of 7×7 cells.

Until 1992 the large size of the 7×7 surface unit cell had hindered a full first-principles study of the properties of this surface. A simulation of the surface requires 49 atoms per atomic layer, or about 1,000 atoms for a two-dimensionally periodic slab that is only 20 atomic layers thick in its third dimension. The first ab initio quantum mechanical calculations on this surface were carried out by two groups, one at the Massachusetts Institute of Technology under John Joannopoulos and the other at the University of Cambridge under Michael Payne. Using an approximately 1,000-atom unit cell in their calculations on the structural and energetic aspects of the surface, the two groups clearly demonstrated that the silicon 7×7 surface does indeed have the lowest surface energy of any known structure. The difference in energy between the 7×7 and 2×1 structures was

found to be about 0.06 electron volt (eV) per surface atom, which, even though small compared with a Si-Si bond energy of 2.45 eV, is still sufficiently large to lead to the drastic change in surface structure with thermal annealing. Surfaces with 3×3 and 5×5 periodicities but with the same distinguishing features as the 7×7 surface also were examined to find out what aspects of the latter surface lead to its stability. Important differences were found in the electronic charge distribution over the surface atoms between the various surfaces with differing periodicities. The 3×3 surface was found to be the least stable and the 5×5 to be closest in energy to the 7×7 surface. This finding is consistent with frequent experimental observations of a 5×5 periodicity during the 2×1 to 7×7 transition.

The atomic coordinates of all the surface atoms were determined theoretically through an energy-minimization procedure, and comparison with experimental results from surface X-ray diffraction data showed excellent agreement. Such calculations were extended by Payne and co-workers to "vicinal" surfaces of silicon; i.e., those for which the vector normal to the surface is in the vicinity of one of the three primary cubic axes. The work was helping to clarify the properties of these interesting surfaces, which have a combination of bonding that is characteristic of each of the three primary surfaces.

The advances are important not only because they successfully attacked a long-standing structural problem but also because they opened up the possibility of simulating a variety of experiments that are extremely difficult, time consuming, or otherwise nearly impossible to do. In early 1993 intensive work by various groups was under way on solid-liquid phase transitions in such systems as carbon, silicon, and water and on the diffusion of impurities and defects. New insights into the underlying mechanisms for these phenomena should be forthcoming in the near future.

A "quantum-dot" electron turnstile. The discreteness of electric charge can sometimes lead to dramatic effects in the transport properties of electronic structures that are submicrometer (smaller than a millionth of a meter) in size. Such effects are not ordinarily seen because the addition of a single electron to a system normally causes only an imperceptible change in the energy of the system. The same effects can become quite important, however, at reduced sizes and at low temperatures where thermal excitation can be suppressed. Several experiments during the past year revealed such effects.

The magnitude of the increase in energy of a system upon electrical charging is related to its capacitance. The capacitance is a measure of the amount of charge that can be placed on a body for a given applied voltage. The change in energy of the sys-

Physics

tem with charging is also related to its capacitance. For a given capacitance (symbolized C) the addition of one electron to a charged object increases its electrostatic potential by e/C, in which e is the electron charge. For the capacitors used in common electronic devices, the addition of a single electron changes the potential imperceptibly, typically in the range of 10^{-16} to 10^{-7} volt. Since thermal excitation energies, even at one degree above absolute zero, are about 10^{-4} eV, single-electron charging effects are never observed in such systems.

As might be expected, the capacitance of a system and the total amount of charge it can hold increase with its size. In order to see effects associated with single-electron charging, it is necessary, therefore, to go to very small dimensions. Novel effects should occur when the energy required for adding each electron to the system becomes larger than thermal fluctuation energies. Such effects were recently observed in submicrometer-sized "quantum dots" for which the addition of each electron increases the potential by a few thousandths of a volt. For quantum dots the total electric charge on the dot does not increase continuously as the applied voltage is increased but instead shows a series of spikes at regularly spaced voltages. The spacing between the spikes is equal to e/C. At each spike an electron obtains sufficient energy to overcome the coulombic repulsion (repulsion of like electric charges) of the other electrons already in the quantum dot.

Several versions of structures exhibiting single-electron charging effects were devised by various groups worldwide. The basic geometry is simple. The first step is to create an electron reservoir in the form of a nearly two-dimensional electron gas. A particularly effective method involves the growth of a layer of gallium arsenide (GaAs) over a substrate layer of aluminum gallium arsenide (AlGaAs) doped with electron-donor impurity atoms to make an n-type semiconductor. The donor electrons in the AlGaAs region move to the interface between GaAs and AlGaAs to take advantage of the lower energy of the conduction band and form a nearly two-dimensional electron-gas sheet. The next step is to deposit, via lithographic techniques, very thin metallic strips on top of the GaAs layer about 100 Å (about a millionth of a centimeter) above the GaAs-AlGaAs interface. The geometry of the strips defines a circular or square electron-confinement region—the quantum dot—and at the same time forms a junction to the dot. By applying a negative bias to the metallic strips, one can precisely control the number of electrons in the underlying two-dimensional electron gas inside the dot.

Single-electron charging effects were observed for these structures; i.e., by changing the junction potentials, investigators increased the number of elec-

trons in the dot in a controlled manner one at a time. In effect, they created a quantum-dot electron turnstile. Most interestingly, by modulating the voltage between the junction electrodes at a given frequency (f), they also achieved a tunneling effect in which one electron passes through the dot every $1/f$ seconds. This gives rise to an electric current that is exactly equal to ef. Since the frequency of modulation can be set with high accuracy, quantum-dot devices make possible the regulation of extremely precise current flows. In the future such devices may be used to set a new standard of current.

By early 1993 research into quantum dots had become very active. The effects of electron-electron correlations and the manifestation of subtle quantum mechanical effects on the transport properties of these systems were among the interesting problems under investigation.

Visible-light emission by porous silicon. Ordinary silicon is a semiconductor having a fairly small (1.2-eV) energy gap between its valence and conduction bands. An electron excited from the valence band into the conduction band can return to its original state through a radiative transition in which it loses an amount of energy (E) equal to the band gap. The frequency (ν) of the emitted light is related to this energy difference through the relation $E = h\nu$, in which h is Planck's constant. The 1.2-eV band gap of silicon leads to emission in the (invisible) far-infrared region of the electromagnetic spectrum. Under normal circumstances bulk silicon is a very inefficient emitter of radiation because it is an "indirect band-gap" material. The most efficient light-emitting semiconductor diodes are made of direct band-gap materials, in which the initial and final states of the electrons involved in the radiative transition have equal momenta. In crystalline silicon the two states have different momenta, and the transition cannot occur without the intervention of crystalline-lattice vibrations needed for momentum conservation. The participation of lattice vibrations slows down the emission process, thereby allowing nonradiative transitions, which reduce luminescence efficiency, to take over.

Several methods for overcoming the low radiative efficiency of silicon are possible. An approach that has been tried before is to introduce a large number of impurity atoms in the system. Such heavy doping has the effect of breaking the crystalline periodicity and, as a consequence, the momentum conservation rule for electronic transitions. Forbidden transitions occur much more readily in such heavily doped systems, resulting in higher radiative efficiency. Another approach that has become popular in the past few years is to make structures so small that so-called quantum size effects become important. Confinement of electrons to a small space has two favorable

Rolf E. Hummel and Sung–Sik Chang, University of Florida, Gainesville

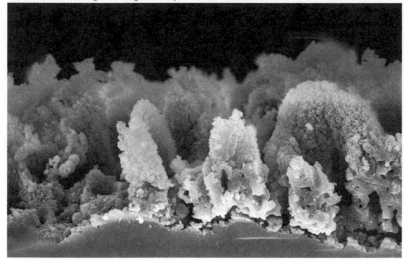

A microscopic column-and-channel structure covers the surface of a silicon wafer made porous by several hours' erosion with high-voltage sparks. After irradiation with a laser beam, samples of porous silicon produced by this "dry" process emitted visible red photoluminescence.

by-products. First, as in the case of heavy doping, it disrupts the crystalline periodicity, thereby allowing forbidden transitions. Second, the localization leads to a quantization of electronic levels, which increases the energy gap between the occupied and empty bands and thus shifts the emission toward the visible part of the spectrum. Theoretically, the energy gap increases as the inverse square power of the size of the microstructure.

Both electrolytic and "dry" processes for creating small-sized structures have recently been developed. In the electrolytic process, a silicon wafer is exposed to hydrofluoric acid (HF), which gradually etches the silicon and creates microcavities. The cavities are in the form of channels that run perpendicular to the surface of the wafer. The mechanism of formation of these micropores and the reason why the material between the pores becomes resistant to further chemical attack are not well understood. The overall effect of the chemical treatment is the creation of so-called porous silicon. When the material is more than 75% porous, the remaining silicon takes the form of thin columns that are isolated from each other. In this regime, where the width of the remaining silicon columns is 50 Å or less, visible red photoluminescence (luminescence stimulated by exposure to light) is observed at room temperature. Another novel technique for the creation of porous silicon is a dry process; *i.e.,* one that does not involve an electrolytic solution. Developed by R.E. Hummel and co-workers of the University of Florida, it is based on spark erosion carried out at high voltage in air at room temperature or in a pure nitrogen atmosphere. The observation that the frequency of the emitted light from porous silicon increases as the inverse square of the column width provides the most important clue for the role of electron localization effects.

The idea that the luminescence property of porous silicon is the result of atomic confinement to small spaces is not universally accepted, and a possible chemical origin has been suggested. The idea is motivated by the observed similarity of the luminescent and vibrational properties of porous silicon to those of siloxene ($Si_6O_3H_6$) crystals. According to Peter Deak and co-workers of the Max-Planck Institute, Stuttgart, Germany, the photoluminescence may be due to silicon-oxygen bonds at the surfaces of the silicon columns. The luminescence is suggested to come only from atoms in the vicinity of the surface region, and the influence of the breakdown in lattice periodicity on the efficiency of radiative transitions is argued to be weak without the chemical bonding effect. Although the hypothesis provides an interesting alternative to the usual confinement model for oxidized samples, it has been challenged by the observation of luminescence from freshly prepared porous silicon samples not yet exposed to oxygen. The most recent studies, by L.T. Canham of the Defense Research Agency, Malvern, England, support the confinement picture and provide evidence that lattice vibrations in porous silicon play an important role in light emission.

Visible light emission from porous silicon is an interesting phenomenon both from a fundamental point of view and for its promise of applications in totally silicon-based integrated optoelectronic systems. Many papers dealing with the properties of this system were appearing in the scientific and technical literature. (For further information on porous silicon, *see* Year in Review: CHEMISTRY: *Applied chemistry.*)

—James D. Chadi

See also Feature Articles: LITTLE SCIENCE, BIG SCIENCE, MULTINATIONAL SCIENCE; A MATTER OF ANTIMATTER; THE REVOLUTION IN COSMOLOGY; THROUGH A PROBE BRIGHTLY: THE NEW MICROSCOPY.

Psychology

Among major areas of concern for psychology during the past year were early measures of intelligence, the role of the two cerebral hemispheres in human gesticulation, the right to admit and discharge hospital patients, and the resurgence of psychoanalytic training and research. An interesting and unusually direct application of experimental research was the use of an implicit-memory test as a means of detecting malingering by persons claiming to be amnesiac.

Science instruction. The American Psychological Association (APA) played a leading role in a recent attempt to improve the teaching of science and mathematics in the United States. Spearheading this movement was the University of South Florida's Charles Spielberger, a past president of the APA, who cochaired the steering committee for a 1992 conference sponsored by the Council of Scientific Society Presidents. The conference brought together teachers and teacher educators along with mathematicians, physicists, chemists, biologists, and psychologists. The consensus of the conference was that what was known about the best learning procedures needed to be more clearly described by the research community and more adequate resources needed to be given teachers if they were to put these principles into practice.

Although these conclusions were not surprising, the novel element in the conference was provided by the detailed manner in which both the problems and their potential solutions were spelled out by the several working groups. On the negative side, major obstacles to the implementation of any changes were emphasized. For example, few teachers were aware of the latest developments in research on science instruction, and fewer still, perhaps, had the training and the resources needed to take advantage of them. Many classroom teachers lacked access to the amenities that academicians took for granted—even basic conveniences like offices and telephones, not to mention computers and electronic mail. Probably more important were certain traditional attitudes held by a large proportion of teachers and school administrators, such as the belief that the basic instructional objective was to "cover content" rather than attempt to adopt any of the new proposals that they thought often seemed to offer essentially a succession of untried fads. This attitude was hostile to what was regarded as perhaps the single most important change discussed at the conference, the encouragement of students to be active learners rather than simply passive recipients of information. Hands-on approaches to scientific principles and problem-solving efforts in classrooms and laboratories were generally regarded as essential parts of improved scientific curricula.

It would be difficult to exaggerate the magnitude of the problems confronting the science teachers and the national organizations that were just beginning to coordinate their efforts to improve instruction in mathematics and science. A telling illustration of such difficulties was provided by a common complaint of the teachers at the conference; they had to struggle to attend it because in order to do so they had to overcome supervisory resistance and, in some cases, needed to pay for substitute teachers themselves. Nevertheless, there were encouraging signs that the newly coordinated efforts to achieve this kind of educational reform had now gained some long-awaited momentum and that at least guarded optimism about the future prospects of scientific instruction in the U.S. might be justified.

Undergraduate psychology curriculum. A national conference on undergraduate education in psychology was sponsored during the past year by the APA. The meeting highlighted a number of profound changes that had occurred since the last similar conference, which was held in 1960. At that time there were slightly more than 8,000 students receiving bachelor's degrees in psychology each year. In 1992 more than 40,000 such degrees were awarded. In 1960 the great majority of psychology majors were male Caucasians; if they did anything with their psychology degree, it was to move directly into graduate study. By 1993 approximately 70% of psychology majors were women, and about 14% were minority students. Moreover, only about 25% proceeded into graduate study in any field.

Three problems were emphasized in the recent conference. There was considerable concern with ways in which the undergraduate psychology curriculum could be (1) more meaningfully related to minority interests and needs; (2) more meaningfully related to basic psychological principles, for the greater benefit of all students; and (3) more vocationally oriented, since that had become the primary concern of most of the majors.

The conference considered a number of alternative steps in the direction of these changes in the curriculum, such as the initiation of faculty-development programs and closer interrelationships among different types of undergraduate departments within a geographic area. These considerations suggested that there was a general recognition of the need to adjust the traditional curriculum so as to better reflect societal changes.

New looks at the gifted. Gifted children posed some difficult questions for educators. The results of three recent studies funded by the U.S. Department of Education indicated that intellectually gifted children generally received the same curriculum as regular students and as a consequence were not challenged in their schoolwork. The current trend toward "equity" and against "elitism" in education was regarded as a critical factor in this situation.

Soon after the release of these reports, the University of Kansas hosted the second of three conferences on education of gifted children that were funded by a special bequest to the American Psychological Foundation. Especially noteworthy contributions to the conference were made by Bruce Shore of the department of educational psychology at McGill University, Montreal. He reported the results of more than a decade of study of the thinking habits of gifted children, teenagers, and young adults. These gifted subjects were found to work much in the same way that experts work, taking more time than normal subjects did to plan strategies and less time to carry out actual procedures. They also seemed to prefer complex problems and were able to identify crucial factors and coordinate them, while paying relatively little attention to the unimportant details on which normal subjects often spent unduly large amounts of time and effort.

Shore expressed the encouraging belief that these strategies could be taught to less gifted children. He also suggested that the best way to advocate increased attention to the gifted was to base it on the proposition that the education of all children would benefit from the adoption of the more effective learning programs initially designed for the gifted.

Measuring early intelligence. Another speaker at the Kansas conference was developmental psychologist John Colombo of the University of Kansas. He reviewed a large number of studies of the intelligence of infants that had been carried out during the past dozen years. The major thrust of Colombo's review was to question the long-held belief that there was no correlation between measures of intelligence taken in infancy and those taken later in development. He pointed out that, if reliable, predictive measures of early intellectual status could be developed, they would be useful in identifying the children most in need of early intervention.

Several lines of research were summarized. For example, in studies of three- to nine-month-old infants, the duration of their responses to visual cues was compared with intelligence scores later obtained on those subjects at ages two to eight; the infants who persisted in looking at the cues were found to be "at risk" for later cognitive deficits. In another set of studies, infants who more often looked at new pictures, thus showing "novelty preference," were later found to have higher IQs. In still another large study, babies who more quickly anticipated the pattern in which lights were flicked on and off on the two sides of a screen later also made higher scores on an intelligence test.

Gesticulation and hemispheric functions. Some new and important results in linguistic research were reported at the 1992 meetings of the American Association for the Advancement of Science by psychologist David McNeil of the University of Chicago. McNeil studied gestures in relation to more orthodox linguistic functions. In his latest report he described, for the first time, results from subjects with damaged right cerebral hemispheres. The main significance of these results was that they suggested an intimate interaction between the two hemispheres in linguistic functions, in contrast to the usual assignment of such functions exclusively to one or the other of the hemispheres. McNeil's right-hemisphere-damaged subjects were able to make gestures, though at a

A baby is tested for "recognition memory visual discrimination." In this "paired comparison novelty preference test," the baby has seen the N's before but looks at the Z's this time. Researchers determined that infants who looked more often at new pictures were later found to have higher IQ scores.

John Colombo, University of Kansas, Lawrence

Saddam (center, in lunging position), an adult male pigtail macaque monkey at the Yerkes Primate Research Center, challenges a young female of higher rank (left), who responds by jumping and calling to her mother and other allies that a monkey of lower rank is threatening her. Researchers have studied the calls among these monkeys and found consistent dialect differences between families.

reduced rate, but did not coordinate them properly. For example, they made discrete rather than continuous gestures and tended to end them prematurely by putting their hands in their laps.

McNeil concluded that the right hemisphere provides the imagery, such as wiggling the fingers to represent walking, in speech production. Support for this idea was provided by his analysis of the linguistic behavior of people with split hemispheres (an operation used to control extremely severe epileptic conditions). Such subjects had difficulty in producing the usual gestures. They apparently depended on what is called "cross-cuing," in which the two hemispheres seem to take turns in responding to each other, in contrast to the fully coordinated manner in which various gestures are integrated into normal speech.

These results and interpretations in no way questioned the dependence of the basic linguistic functions, such as syntax, on the left hemisphere. They did suggest, however, that the right hemisphere also has an important, interactive role in linguistic behavior.

Monkey communication. Experimental psychologists have worked intensively on the linguistic abilities of the higher primates, especially chimpanzees, in an effort to learn more about basic linguistic functions. Only recently did they turn to more readily available and less expensive monkeys as subjects in such research.

New research results on monkey communication were reported during the past year by a husband-wife team at the Yerkes Primate Research Center near Atlanta, Ga. Sarah and Harold Gouzoules spent the last two decades studying various facets of communication between monkeys. Although they first used

rhesus monkeys, they recently turned to the more sociable pigtail macaque monkeys. The nuances in their calls communicated surprisingly detailed information, such as the type of danger disturbing the caller. Moreover, using highly sophisticated technology, these investigators transformed the sounds into graphic portrayals that revealed subtle but consistent dialect differences among families. They said that they could even identify families with 90% accuracy just from listening to the calls. As Sarah Gouzoules stated, "The more we study calls, the more amazed we are at how complex primate communication is. We're only beginning to scratch the surface."

Clinical psychology. A landmark legislative achievement for clinical psychology—the right to admit and discharge patients in hospitals—took place during the past year. This legislation was drafted and passed in less than one calendar year in the state of Wisconsin. The process was unexpectedly smooth, considering the adversarial potential from hospitals and psychiatrists. By working closely with consumers, psychiatrists, family practitioners, and hospital administrators, a relatively small group of psychologists was able to produce this rather remarkable result.

A major factor in the speedy approval of the new legislation was the prospect of improved access to mental health treatment, especially for rural patients. The need for improvement was graphically demonstrated by charts showing the relatively sparse distribution of psychiatrists in hospitals in some areas; some patients needed to travel as far as 320 km (200 mi) to receive treatment.

Some of the hospitals in underserved areas, including the inner city of Milwaukee as well as rural locations, were actively preparing the bylaws neces-

412

sary for activation of the legislation. Coupled with the recently gained limited privilege to prescribe medication, the achievement of the hospital-admission privilege represented a significant step forward in clinical psychology's efforts to gain more nearly equal legal status with psychiatrists.

Resurgence of psychoanalysis. The resurgence of psychoanalysis in a "liberated" form was a significant recent development in the field of mental health. To a large extent the changes in psychoanalysis could be attributed to the opening up of the field to nonmedical trainees, a move that was made possible by an out-of-court settlement of a 1989 suit brought by four psychologists against the American Psychoanalytic Institute and the International Psychoanalytic Institute.

There seemed to be no question that U.S. psychologists had taken advantage of the newly available opportunities. The APA's Division 39 (Psychoanalysis), with more than 3,600 members and 27 local chapters, was during the past year the fastest growing of the association's 47 divisions. According to psychiatrist George Allison, president of the American Psychoanalytic Association, "We have many more applications than we used to, and the trainees in our institutes are increasingly psychologists. That's part of what's making us more enriched."

Concurrent with this upsurge of psychoanalytic training and study, there occurred both a weakening of the orthodox Freudian constraints on theory and practice and a flourishing of new perspectives and problems. As succinctly put by psychologist Stephen Mitchell, a training analyst at the White Institute, New York City, "The idealization of Freud that dominated psychoanalysis is fading, opening up the possibility for people to take a fresh look at ideas he struggled with." Prominent among the many new developments was the increased number of women in psychoanalytic training and practice. Long restricted by Freud's negativism toward them as psychoanalysts, women were taking an increasingly active role in the new institutes and training groups. In fact, by 1993 women were in the majority (51%) in the APA's Division 39.

Although the many ways in which psychoanalysis was changing could not be described here in any detail, a good summarizing comment was made by psychologist Karen Rosica, cofounder of the Colorado Center for Psychoanalytic Studies, Denver. She pointed out that "treatment is being fit to the patient more than the patient being fit to the treatment."

Amnesiac malingering. An interesting application of experimental principles to a practical problem, the detection of malingering, was reported during the year by a team of researchers headed by Keith Horton at Wilfrid Laurier University, Waterloo, Ont. College students first studied a list of words and then were given an implicit-memory test, such as the completion of words from word fragments. Subjects who were instructed to simulate amnesia for the studied words completed fewer of the test items than control subjects (no special memory instruction). This result, if replicated, should make it possible to detect amnesiac malingering on the basis of such reduced word-completion rates because true amnesiacs do not generally differ from normal subjects on implicit-memory tests even while they are unable to perform effectively on the more usual explicit-memory tests, typically recall or recognition.

—Melvin H. Marx

International developments. The APA celebrated its hundredth anniversary in 1992. In recognition of the importance of international psychology and in honor of its centennial, the association introduced a major new award for "Distinguished Contributions to the International Advancement of Psychology." The first award was made posthumously to Otto Kleinberg, who died in March 1992 at the age of 92. The citation made reference to his "sustained contributions to the development of international cooperation in psychology over many years; for exemplary leadership in cross-cultural research on intelligence, inter-group relations, and mental health; and for his tenacious pioneering efforts on behalf of racial equality culminating in the 1954 Supreme Court decision to end school segregation." Kleinberg made distinguished and significant contributions to four areas of social psychology: cross-cultural study, race differences, international affairs, and the social psychology of mental health and mental illness, all of which he saw as interrelated.

Recent studies in the social psychology of mental health and mental illness revealed evidence that, unless managed with care, economic development might be injurious to mental health in Buddhist Southeast Asian countries when urbanization and industrialization cut off villages from family and community systems that provided support in times of stress. Refugees and immigrants to the West suffered similar problems, as there was little understanding of or sympathy with the culturally different basic belief structures that governed their feelings in relation to mental health. People from Buddhist cultures see the world quite differently from those brought up in the West. Buddhism stresses balance and harmony through collectivism and maintaining order, rather than emphasizing the self-fulfillment of the individual, as in the West. Self-control rather than spontaneity is regarded as an important attribute of a mentally healthy person. Effective therapeutic approaches would have to take cultural background into account and not assume that interventions based on Western models of mental health would be appropriate.

In July 1992 the Belgian Psychological Society was host to the 25th International Congress of Psychology, the quadrennial meeting of the International Union of Psychological Science (IUPsyS). It drew nearly 5,000 psychologists from around the world. The program of the congress consisted of 12 keynote addresses, 22 state-of-the-art lectures, more than 130 invited symposia, and hundreds of workshops and interactive poster sessions. Invited lecturers and conveners of symposia were encouraged to focus their presentations on recent advances in their specialty area so that colleagues from other areas could learn about cutting-edge developments.

Like the APA, the IUPsyS was also entering the second century of its existence. Under the aegis of the IUPsyS, the fifth edition of the *International Directory of Psychology* was published, providing an account of how psychology was organized in each country. Two other important publications were *International Psychological Science: Progress, Problems, and Prospects,* edited by Mark Rosenzweig, which includes results of an international survey of the human and financial resources for psychological research, and the *Concise Encyclopedia of Psychology,* edited by A. C. Jing, which was published in China as a major effort to acquaint Chinese-speaking psychologists with standard psychological terms and the concepts and theories of psychology throughout the world.

Special projects sponsored by the IUPsyS focused on such activities as the International Network of Human Development and Child Research Centres, which participated in a UNESCO initiative program in the field of human development. This concentrated on community school projects for the development of the young child and the family in Third World countries. Other international networks were concerned with psychology-based, man-computer interaction; research centers in cognitive science; artificial intelligence in neuroscience; and psychological issues of communication. The Committee for the Psychological Study of Peace succeeded in publishing a directory of active researchers in that field. Topics of study by these researchers ranged from education programs for a peaceful world to making cross-cultural comparisons of coping strategies in times of conflict.

—Colin V. Newman

Space exploration

The United States had a highly successful year in space, with the space shuttle flying several intense, productive science missions and the Mars Observer probe embarking on the first exploration of that planet since the 1970s. Worldwide economic prob-

lems caused Russian, U.S., and European space programs to retrench even as changing political structures made joint international efforts more attractive and feasible.

Manned flight

Space shuttle. The U.S. National Aeronautics and Space Administration (NASA) enjoyed a successful year in orbit with the space shuttle even as budget problems challenged it on Earth. From March 24 to April 2, 1992, the shuttle orbiter *Atlantis* carried ATLAS-1 and a seven-person crew (commander Charles Bolden; pilot Brian Duffy; mission specialists Michael Foale of the U.K., Kathryn Sullivan, and David Leestma; and payload specialists Dirk Frimout of the European Space Agency (ESA) and Byron Lichtenberg). ATLAS comprised atmospheric instruments that NASA intended to refly once a year in an effort to characterize the chemistry and dynamics of the middle and upper regions of Earth's atmosphere; some had been first flown on Spacelab 1 in 1983. The ATLAS instruments, which were to be recalibrated after each flight to ensure accuracy, analyzed not only the atmosphere but also the solar radiation that drives the atmosphere. During the ATLAS-1 mission ESA scientists were able to control their instruments from the European Space Science and Technology Center in Noordwijk, Neth.

The shuttle orbiter *Endeavour* made its debut in a mission on May 7–16. With a seven-person crew (commander Daniel Brandenstein; pilot Kevin Chilton; and mission specialists Thomas Akers, Richard Hieb, Bruce Melnick, Kathryn Thornton, and Pierre Thuot), it rescued an Intelsat 6 satellite left in a low orbit by a Titan III launch vehicle in 1990. Added risks for the mission were a large solid-fuel rocket motor inside Intelsat as well as a larger motor that was to be attached to it for its launch by *Endeavour* into geostationary orbit (an orbit over the equator in which a satellite travels at the same speed as the Earth rotates).

Initial attempts by Thuot and Hieb to snag the satellite were thwarted when a capture bar on *Endeavour*'s robot arm did not find and grab the satellite's rim as planned. Akers then joined Thuot and Hieb for the first-ever three-man space walk. Each gingerly grasped the satellite by the edge of its solar panel drum and attached the capture bar so that the robot arm could place the satellite on a new rocket motor. After Intelsat was sent into its new orbit, Thornton and Akers walked in space to demonstrate techniques that would be used in building space station *Freedom.* They assembled a number of 7-m (14.8-ft) struts into tetrahedrons that had the same size and fittings as those that would be used on *Freedom.* Because of the extra time spent rescuing

Astronauts Richard Hieb, Thomas Akers, and Pierre Thuot (left to right) work in space to attach a specially designed capture bar underneath an Intelsat 6 so that the satellite can be moved to the shuttle orbiter Endeavour and fitted with a new rocket engine for a launch into geostationary orbit. A cloud-covered part of the Earth provides the background for this mission.

Intelsat, a second space walk to expand on those techniques was canceled.

Columbia returned to service with a mission from June 25 to July 9. It carried U.S. Microgravity Laboratory 1 (USML) and a seven-person crew (commander Richard Richards; pilot Kenneth Bowersox; mission specialists Bonnie Dunbar, Ellen Baker, and Carl Mcadc; and payload specialists Lawrence De-Lucas and Eugene Trinh). Its two-week duration made it the longest U.S. mission in space since the last Skylab crew stayed aloft 84 days in 1974. *Columbia* had been refitted with a special cargo of liquid hydrogen and oxygen tanks to power its fuel cells for missions that might last as long as 16 days. Scientists reported that protein crystals were growing faster than expected in the weightlessness of space; however, some specimens would have needed a full month to crystallize. Adaptation of the crew to space was measured with a device that reduced air pressure around the legs in an attempt to shift body fluids toward the feet, the reverse of what happens in space. A new glove box for handling hazardous or sensitive specimens was successfully used in a number of experiments.

Atlantis flew again, from July 31 to August 8, with the Tethered Satellite System and the European Retrievable Carrier and a seven-person crew (commander Loren Shriver; pilot Andrew Allen; mission specialists Franklin Chang-Diaz, Claude Nicollier of Switzerland, Jeffrey Hoffman, and Marsha Ivins;

and payload specialist Franco Malerba of Italy). The tether was designed to be trolled above the shuttle. However, no more than 260 m (853 ft) of the 20-km (12.4-mi) Kevlar-and-copper line would unreel because, as postflight inspections showed, a small tension-relief nut jammed the line. The tether did generate a small electrical current as it cut through the Earth's magnetic field, but important experiments on the wave motions of a long tether could not be performed. The crew also deployed the European Retrievable Carrier (Eureca), an automated experiment platform that was to be retrieved by a shuttle orbiter in 1993. At 4,491 kg (9,898 lb), Eureca was ESA's largest satellite.

Endeavour's second flight of 1992, (September 12–20, carried Spacelab J and a seven-person crew (commander Robert Gibson; pilot Curtis Brown; mission specialists Mark Lee, Jan Davis, Mae Jemison, and Jerome Apt; and payload specialist Mamoru Mohri of Japan). Japan provided most of the experiment payload, primarily in materials and life sciences. An intravenous fluid demonstration was accomplished on a mannequin's arm. While weightlessness is ideal for many materials experiments, it can also let air bubbles get into an intravenous line. The flight also marked the first flights of an African-American woman (Jemison) and a married couple (Lee and Davis).

Columbia (October 22–November 1) carried a six-person crew (commander James Wetherbee; pilot

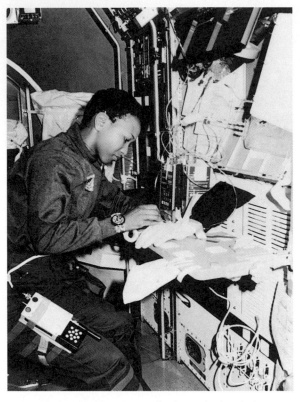

Astronaut Mae Jemison injects a fluid into the hand of a mannequin in the Spacelab J of the shuttle orbiter Endeavour *in order to evaluate the effects of weightlessness on the behavior of injected fluids.*

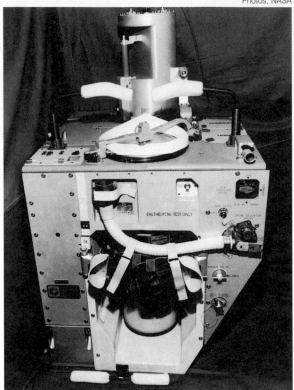

An improved waste-collection system for the shuttle orbiter Endeavour *was larger than previous models, had more powerful fans, and did not have to be removed from the spacecraft to be readied for the next flight. It cost $23 million.*

Michael Baker; mission specialists Charles Veach, William Shepherd, and Tamara Jernigan; and payload specialist Steven MacLean). The principal payload was the second Laser Geodynamics Satellite (LAGEOS II), an Italian spacecraft studded with laser reflectors (LAGEOS I was launched in 1976). It was boosted to 4,900 km (3,038 mi), where it was to be targeted by laser range finders in studies to measure precisely the distance between specific points on the continents. *Columbia* also carried the automated U.S. Microgravity Payload and an array of technology experiments.

Discovery (December 2–9) made the last classified mission of the space shuttle program. The U.S. Department of Defense decided that in the future unmanned launchers would be used to boost its satellites into orbit. *Discovery*'s five-man crew (commander David Walker, pilot Robert Cabana, and mission specialists Guion Bluford, Michael Crawford, and James Voss) were believed to have deployed a radar mapping spy satellite.

A number of unclassified payloads were also flown on the mission. These included an experiment simulating the handling of rocket propellants in weightlessness, a special camera that used signals from the

NavStar navigation satellites to tag its pictures with latitude and longitude, and a number of medical and technology experiments. Because of an electrical problem, small radar-reflecting spheres were not deployed as had been planned.

NASA started 1993 with the deployment by *Endeavour* (January 13–19) of the last Tracking and Data Relay Satellite (four already were operating, and one was lost on *Challenger*). The crew (commander John Casper; pilot Don McMonagle; and mission specialists Mario Runco, Greg Harbaugh, and Susan Helms) also operated a pair of diffuse X-ray spectrometers that surveyed the skies, and they conducted life and physical sciences experiments. On the fifth day Runco and Harbaugh took a space walk to refine space-walk procedures (including carrying each other and handling large tools) for later missions. The crew also played with toys as they talked with students at their old elementary schools as part of a program to demonstrate basic science for children.

The rest of 1993 was expected to be less intense than 1992, although the repair of the Hubble Space Telescope was scheduled for late in the year. A Russian was to ride aboard the shuttle in 1993, and a

416

U.S. shuttle orbiter was to dock to the Russian space station *Mir* in 1995.

Results from the Space Life Sciences mission flown aboard the shuttle *Columbia* in June 1991 showed unexpected space travel effects. One astronaut flew with a blood pressure catheter inserted through his left arm into his heart. Data indicate that, contrary to expectation, his blood pressure rose 50% and remained high throughout the flight. Astronauts also lost up to 25% of the muscle mass in their thighs and calves during the nine-day flight and regained only half the loss in the same period after landing. Rats carried on the flight as test subjects were found to have 57% more nerve synapses in their balance organs than do rats on the ground. In a related project, Russia launched the Biocosmos 10 satellite (December 29) on a two-week mission carrying two rhesus monkeys plus rats, insects, frogs, fish, and seeds.

In November the U.S. National Space Council's Space Policy Advisory Board recommended that the space shuttle be phased out as soon as possible in favor of an air force-developed Spacelifter system operated by an air force-run national space launch authority. The proposal ran into stiff opposition from NASA and industry officials.

Russia's *Buran* space shuttle, which had flown only once (1988), was expected to make a second flight, to *Mir,* in November 1993. Sergey Krikalev and Vladimir Titov were slated to be *Buran*'s first crew. The shuttle had been grounded by lack of funding and difficulties in developing software for its flight computers.

Hermes, ESA's proposed three-person shuttlecraft, was reduced in scope to a technology-development project because of ESA's budget woes. (Similar problems stalled a comparable Japanese project.) ESA signed contracts worth more than $5 million to explore Russian space technology and possibly make Hermes a joint Euro-Russian project.

Space stations. Operations aboard Russia's *Mir* space station continued, although they generated fewer headlines. On March 25 Sergey Krikalev (dubbed the "Time Traveler" by the Russian media), launched in May 1991, came back to Earth. He was to have returned in October 1991, but the breakup of the Soviet Union delayed the trip. First, Russia and the new state of Kazakhstan argued over the launch fees from Kazakhstan's Baikonur Cosmodrome, and then the Russians decided to scrub one mission in the fall and leave Krikalev in orbit a few more months.

In September *Mir*'s crew made a series of space walks to install new thrusters and make other upgrades to the station. Krikalev and Aleksandr Volkov, launched in October 1991, were replaced by Aleksandr Kalery and Aleksandr Viktorenko, who were launched aboard Soyuz TM-14 on March 17. German scientist Klaus Dietrich-Flade rode with the replacement crew and returned with the old crew. They, in turn, were replaced by Anatoly Solovyev and Sergey Avdeyev, aboard Soyuz TM-15, in the fall. On Jan. 24, 1993, Gennaidy Manakov and Aleksandr Polishchuk were launched aboard Soyuz TM-16 to replace Solovyev and Avdeyev for six months. On February 4 they released a 20-m (65-ft)-wide solar sail to demonstrate the technology for illuminating various parts of the Earth by night.

Freedom, the U.S. space station project, moved into its critical design phase as NASA and industry

Russian cosmonauts Aleksandr Kalery (left) and Aleksandr Viktorenko (center) and French research specialist Michel Tognini (right) rest on their return to Earth in August 1992 after several months aboard the Russian space station Mir.

teams reviewed details of plans for the orbital international laboratory. The critical design review, to be completed in June 1993, was the final step before the release of drawings for building hardware. NASA also announced management changes intended to streamline the operation of the program. Earlier, in July, NASA and its congressional supporters defeated an attempt to cancel *Freedom*'s funding. In the wake of the breakup of the Soviet Union, NASA and the Russian company NPO Energiya, on Dec. 11, 1992, signed an agreement certifying Russia's Soyuz TM spacecraft as fit to be a lifeboat for *Freedom*. This would allow astronauts to live permanently aboard the station by 1997, three years earlier than if a U.S. lifeboat were built.

Freedom's design comprised a main truss with pressurized modules attached at the center and solar arrays deployed from the ends (viewed head-on, it resembled a capital I on its side). The U.S. was to provide the truss, solar arrays, a habitation module, and a laboratory module plus four nodes to connect the modules and allow the space shuttle to dock. ESA and Japan's National Space Development Agency each would supply a laboratory module, and the Canadian Space Agency planned to furnish a mobile robotic system to help assemble and repair the station.

Europe, Japan, and Canada also would share in experiment and crew assignments aboard *Freedom*. The first element of the station was to be launched in 1996. In December NASA started static test firings of thrusters that were designed to help the station maintain its orbit. Full-scale models of the main truss were built and assembled on the ground and in underwater simulations. Elsewhere, NASA was also testing life-support, electrical-power, docking, and other systems. New foot restraints designed for *Freedom* were tested by a shuttle crew.

ESA, its member nations facing economic troubles, struggled at the year's end to redesign its portion of *Freedom* in the face of a 10% budget cut. The agency, however, took a major step toward supporting *Freedom* with an experiment in which four people participated in a two-month mission simulation in a high-altitude chamber; it also started a program of underwater tests to simulate working on space-station elements in space.

Lunar missions. NASA released preliminary plans to send humans back to the Moon by the year 2000. The program would require a booster larger than the Saturn V used by Project Apollo in the 1960s and would put four people on the Moon for a 45-day mission. At least two launches would be required, one for a large habitat and the other to carry the crew in a return craft. Plans for two unmanned orbiters to map the Moon were, however, canceled by budget cuts.

Personnel. Veteran astronauts Kathryn Sullivan, Vance Brand, Bruce Melnick, John Creighton, David Hilmers, James Adamson, James Buchli, and Daniel Brandenstein left NASA. In their place NASA selected 19 new astronaut candidates. ESA selected six astronaut candidates to help fill Europe's slots on space stations.

Space probes

The launch of a new probe to Mars and the rerouting of Galileo and Ulysses capped a busy year in deep space exploration. The exploration of Venus drew to an end, at least temporarily, and plans were advanced for the detailed exploration of Saturn.

Venus. A golden era of exploration of Venus neared a close as the Pioneer Venus orbiter entered the atmosphere and incinerated on October 8 and NASA shut down the Magellan Venus radar mapper. The Pioneer Venus orbiter, circling the planet since 1978, had studied its atmosphere and made extensive radar surveys of its surface. In the fall of 1978 it ran out of maneuvering fuel to maintain its altitude and attitude and started a slow descent into the Venusian atmosphere.

Magellan, a more recent arrival, was in good shape after completing its third mapping cycle despite some transmitter problems. But NASA was running low on money and planned to shut it down after it completed a gravity survey of the planet. Magellan's radar, more powerful and sensitive than anything else orbited around Venus, already had mapped 99% of the planet's surface at a level of detail greater than any other spacecraft. Among its recent finds was evidence of landslides on two volcanoes. Because Venus is permanently shrouded in thick clouds of acid droplets, only radar can see its surface.

Mars. On September 25, NASA launched Mars Observer, its first mission to the "red planet" since the Viking landers in the 1970s. With a detailed survey of the planet's surface and chemical composition, the mission was expected to set the stage for future exploration. The spacecraft was scheduled to arrive in an elliptical orbit around Mars on Aug. 19, 1993, the middle of summer in Mars's northern hemisphere. During the next four months thrusters were to nudge the spacecraft into a lower, 400-km (248-mi) polar orbit that would allow it to cover the entire surface.

Instruments aboard Mars Observer were to map the planet in a manner similar to the way in which remote-sensing satellites surveyed the Earth. Scientists expected to build a detailed "global portrait" that would help them understand how the Martian atmosphere worked and which areas of the surface were most attractive for detailed investigation by landers and, eventually, manned missions. Major

The Mars Observer space probe is launched toward the planet Mars by a Titan III rocket in September 1992. The probe was scheduled to begin orbiting and mapping Mars in August 1993.

objectives were to identify and map surface elements and minerals; measure the surface topography and features; define the gravitational field (which would allow deductions about subsurface structures); determine the distribution, abundance, sources, and destinations of water, carbon dioxide, and dust in the atmosphere; and explore the circulation of the atmosphere.

To achieve those objectives Mars Observer carried instruments that would "see" Mars in a spectral range from infrared light to gamma rays. The greatest public interest was expected to be generated by cameras that would transmit wide-angle and telephoto images of the surface. The first of two wide-angle cameras was designed to send daily "weather maps" with a resolution of 7,500 m (24,600 ft). Medium-resolution images 480 m (1,575 ft) would be sent by

a second wide-angle camera. The cameras were to be used primarily to monitor the weather and major changes on the surface. Areas of great interest were to be imaged by the high-resolution camera, which would see details as small as 1.4 m (4.6 ft) across (it could not be used continuously because it would flood the craft's data system).

Water, the most tantalizing question about Mars, was to be sought by a gamma-ray spectrometer. Gamma rays are produced when cosmic rays (streams of atomic nuclei) strike the atmosphere or surface of Mars. The spectral signatures of such gamma rays are unique to each chemical and can indicate the presence of water (as permafrost at the Martian poles), carbon dioxide, and surface minerals.

A thermal emission spectrometer was designed to measure heat radiated from the surface. A pressure modulator infrared radiometer would analyze the tenuous atmosphere, measuring pressure and determining water vapor and dust content. A laser altimeter was to measure topography precisely, and a magnetometer/electron reflectometer would monitor the near-space environment. Data from several instruments would be combined. The thermal emission spectrometer, for example, would be used with the gamma-ray spectrometer, to deduce which chemicals are on the surface, and with the pressure-modulated infrared radiometer, to understand the structure and dynamics of the atmosphere.

Mars Observer also carried a French Mars Balloon Relay to collect instruments that were to be landed by Russia's Mars 94 mission and also a balloon from the Mars 96 mission. The balloon would be heated by sunlight during the day and pushed by the wind to a new site. At night it would cool and descend, allowing measurements to be taken on the surface.

Russian plans to launch Mars 94 with three landers were changed by that nation's budget woes; only two landers were to be sent. The canceled lander was to have carried two NASA experiments, which might be accommodated on the remaining two. Russia also said that it was still planning to launch Mars 96 on schedule.

Jupiter and beyond. Galileo continued to frustrate ground controllers trying to release its stuck main antenna. Several attempts at soaking it in heat or cold yielded no results, and in January, with little left to lose, ground controllers "hammered" the antenna by rapidly switching its motors off and on. If the antenna remained stuck, data would have to be transmitted through a lower-power antenna, greatly reducing the mission's scientific production, especially in imagery. Galileo made a second flyby of the Earth on December 8 at an altitude of 304 km (188 mi) for a final kick onto the outbound leg to Jupiter. (An earlier flyby of Venus and then of Earth each increased Galileo's speed and reshaped its orbit.) As it passed the Earth, Galileo recorded with its cameras the first infrared and visible light images of the Moon's north pole. Chemical assays taken via those images indicated that the Moon was volcanically active earlier in its life than once thought. Galileo was scheduled to arrive at Jupiter on Dec. 7, 1995, and release a probe into the planet's atmosphere before going into orbit around it.

Ulysses, the international solar polar mission, made a hairpin turn around Jupiter on Feb. 8, 1992, and headed for a high pass over the Sun's south pole in 1994. Flying past Jupiter required about a third as much energy as that needed to fly directly over the Sun's poles, and so the longer, indirect route was chosen for the mission. During the encounter phase of the mission, February 2–14, instruments aboard Ulysses found that Jupiter's magnetosphere was larger than when the Voyagers flew by the planet in 1979 and that it apparently was expanding and contracting rapidly in response to changes in the solar wind. Other findings indicated that ions from the solar wind penetrate deep into the Jovian magnetosphere and that ions from Io (Jupiter's volcanically active moon) spread throughout the environment. Strong streams of ions and electrons, flowing against each other, were found at high latitudes, apparently making up large currents that feed the planet's auroras.

Ulysses also found that volcanoes on Io had weakened, leaving a "chewed doughnut" rather than a complete torus of oxygen and sulfur plasma. The probe also detected interstellar hydrogen and oxygen ions and neutral helium, as well as six dust streams in highly inclined orbits some 750 million km (465 million mi) from the Sun.

The Cassini orbiter/probe mission, to be launched to Saturn and its moon Titan in October 1997, was scaled down, and increased authority was vested in technical managers to reduce costs. Cassini was scheduled to carry a European probe, Huygens, which would be dropped into the methane atmosphere of Titan. The spacecraft were to arrive at Saturn in November 2004. Pioneer 10, launched in 1972, was by 1993 more than eight billion kilometers (five billion miles) away from Earth, but it continued to send data from seven instruments that could still detect the solar wind.

Small bodies. Because of Galileo's antenna problem, data from its October 1991 encounter with asteroid 951 Gaspra did not became available until 1992. Gaspra appeared to have a weak magnetic field and thus might be made of nickel and iron. The 11 × 12 × 19-km (6.8 × 7.4 × 11.8-mi)-diameter rock resembles Phobos, the largest of Mars's moons. Gaspra is peppered with more than 600 craters up to one kilometer (0.6 mi) wide and has marks possibly caused when it broke off from a larger body.

Giotto, the European probe that flew past Halley's Comet in 1986, flew past Comet Grigg-Skjellerup on July 10 after being reawakened from a long electronic sleep. Water-group ions were detected up to 440,000 km (270,000 mi) away from the comet, and its magnetic field was stronger than Halley's. The comet's bow shock (where its magnetic field runs into that of the Sun) was stronger than expected for an old, weak comet. About 20,000 km (12,400 mi) from the comet, the probe started detecting dust, and a collision with a large dust particle slowed the spacecraft slightly (about 0.4 mm per second) and slightly changed its spin rate as it passed within 200 km (124 mi) of the nucleus. Giotto was scheduled to pass 219,000 km (135,000 mi) from Earth on July 1, 1999, but there were no plans to reuse it at that time.

NASA asked scientists to propose ideas for the Clementine Deep Space Program Science Experiment. In January 1994 the Strategic Defense Initiative Organization planned to launch Clementine, a small probe with advanced miniature sensors, to orbit the Moon for two months and then rendezvous with asteroid 1620 Geographos in August 1994. Clementine would carry an array of cameras and charged-particle detectors to survey the asteroid.

Future missions. At the year's end NASA and researchers from Carnegie Mellon University, Pittsburgh, Pa., tried to send Dante, an eight-legged

Dante, an eight-legged robot, undergoes tests to prepare for entering the mouth of Mt. Erebus, an active volcano in Antarctica, in a simulation of robotic rover explorations planned for the Moon and Mars.

robot, into the mouth of Mt. Erebus, an active volcano in Antarctica. Dante was linked by a fiber-optic line to a transmitter that sent images and accepted commands from a space center outside Washington, D.C. This simulated the way in which planetary rovers might be operated on the surface of Mars and other planets. Dante also carried instruments to measure hot gases inside the mouth of Erebus, where it is too hazardous for humans to go. Unfortunately, the fiber-optic line snapped after Dante had moved only a few meters, and the weather precluded sending in a replacement. Scientists, however considered the mission a successful trial run for similar missions on Mars. In Death Valley, California, Russia and McDonnell Douglas, a U.S. firm, jointly tested a Russian design for a Mars rover.

—Dave Dooling

Transportation

Despite the slow recovery from the recession in the United States and other major industrialized nations during 1992, the continued growth of high-tech innovations in transportation was clearly illustrated in a detailed analysis by Ohio State University logistics scholars who surveyed U.S. shippers to determine changing practices in their handling of both inbound and outbound freight. Because such executives' responsibilities have during recent years expanded greatly in regard to such logistics concerns as transport, warehousing, inventory control, packaging, order processing, and procurement, these many interrelated functions have stimulated adoption of a variety of high-tech aids to ease the burden.

The survey stressed three key areas of logistics: just-in-time transportation (JIT), bar-code applications (BA), and electronic data interchange (EDI). JIT requires the other two for reliable and fast routing and tracking of shipments. The survey covered actual operations in 1990 and 1992 and estimated operations from 1995 to 2000. The use of both JIT and BA rose steadily from 15–20% of total shipments in 1990 to 30% in 1992—with an estimated growth to 60 and 40%, respectively, by the year 2000. For EDI the growth was not as dramatic because the great number of different EDI systems makes interlinking with the shippers more difficult. Nevertheless, growth was expected to increase from the estimated 23% of total shipments in 1992 to about 55% in the year 2000—assuming current efforts to standardize EDI systems prove successful.

The worldwide growth in EDI use between 1988 and 1992, despite standardization roadblocks, was estimated as more than sixfold—with the number of "paperless" companies increasing from 5,000 to 31,000. U.S. transportation carriers are heavy users of the new communications technology. AMR Corp., owner of American Airlines, and CSX Corp., which operates in the rail, truck, and water transport fields, formally announced a joint venture, under the name Encompass, to utilize EDI to electronically link carriers in all modes of transportation for complete automated facilitation of shipping. It was designed to overcome the limitations of present EDI systems, which are single modal.

Extensive tests of Encompass were completed, and it became operational in early 1992. Designed for use with IBM-compatible personal computers, Encompass was expected to fill a demand by shippers in the intermodal transport cargo field for data such as location, schedule compliance, and condition of shipments. The new system was scheduled to be in full operation in early 1993. Comparable EDI systems also were being set up by European, Asian, and other air carriers, including Air Canada, Air France, British Airways, Japan Airlines, and Lufthansa.

Air transport. Harris Corp. was awarded a $1.6 billion contract by the U.S. Federal Aviation Administration (FAA) to install at the FAA's 22 en-route air traffic control centers the new voice switching and control system (VSCS), which is designed to provide virtually error-free voice linkage between aircraft and traffic controllers. VSCS, which will be a major feature of the FAA's National Airspace System Plan, will employ touch-screen display monitors, microprocessor-based digital switches, advanced computer controls, and an automatic fault isolation to provide such communications. While the existing system, which uses toggle switches, vacuum tubes, and handwritten instructions, was very reliable, by 1993 it was operating virtually at capacity and had become difficult to maintain because of the scarcity of replacement parts.

VSCS was also required to be out of service for no more than three seconds a year. Following tests and final evaluation, the first operational system was scheduled for installation in Seattle, Wash., in 1994 and later that same year in Atlanta, Ga.; Chicago; and Fort Worth, Texas. In 1995 it was expected to be installed at centers in another dozen U.S. cities.

Lack of unanimity among air carriers planning to purchase the new Boeing 777 twinjet transport forced the manufacturer to revise significantly its plans for offering a paperless cockpit through use of a unique electronic library system (ELS) that automatically displays on the cockpit's instruments such data as flight operations, maintenance manuals, and navigation charts. Since airlines differed greatly on what data they wanted, Boeing would have to work with each one and tailor the ELS to cover what each needed—thus sharply increasing ELS costs.

A revolutionary X-shaped midfield terminal was opened at the Greater Pittsburgh (Pa.) International

Airport. Designed to facilitate both aircraft and passenger movements, the unique configuration permitted rapid access to aircraft by means of the 75 gates now open; the number could increase to 100 if needed. Passengers moving between gates were assisted by moving sidewalks, which were designed to cover the greatest distance between any two gates in about 11 minutes. Passengers also were able to use an underground people-mover rail system that provided about one-minute trips between the midfield and the original edge-of-field terminals.

Federal Express reported that it was developing a Global Operations Control Center (GOCC) that would link 38 of its information systems now isolated from one another for more efficient operations and also provide managers with analyses of the impacts of their decisions on future operations of the airline's 2,500 pickup-and-delivery trucks, 252 jet transports, and 200 feeder aircraft. Three major components of the GOCC included: an integrated computerized data system covering total operations and weather conditions throughout its network; use of the FAA's Aircraft Situation Display, which provides real-time flight status; and use of the Total Airspace and Airport Modeller (TAAM) for analyzing upcoming aircraft and airport operations. The first stage of the GOCC project was to link such data, by the end of 1993, to as many as 200 Federal Express personnel who supervise each of the airline's five major work divisions. An early goal would be to provide more efficient maintenance of aircraft and, if successful, improved aircraft flight schedules.

Federal Express was not the only user of TAAM, which was developed by the Preston Group, an Australian computer software automation systems specialist. Originally designed and applied for use by the Australian Civil Aviation Authority, TAAM also developed specialized models for the Port Authority of New York-New Jersey; in addition, the British Civil Aviation Authority approved its use for an analysis of air traffic in the London area. During the past year TAAM's potential use for improved airport control was being examined at the Düsseldorf Airport in Germany. The possible benefits included more efficient runway and taxiway utilization, improved allocation of gates, and more effective use of aircraft deicing.

The financially depressed aviation industry was forced during the past year to cut back sharply on its acquisition of new, high-tech air transports; and aircraft manufacturers had to do the same in regard to developing innovations for the air transports of the future. The European consortium Airbus Industrie reported that it was undertaking exploratory research for the development of a 600-seat ultrahigh-capacity aircraft (UHCA), even though actual construction of such an aircraft was not expected until 1997. While all major large-engine manufacturers (General Electric, Pratt & Whitney, and Rolls-Royce) had engines capable of powering such aircraft, other problems first had to be resolved; they included constraints on airport facilities, safety problems such as the requirement to evacuate hundreds of passengers in 90 seconds, and possible environmental concerns. Advantages of such an aircraft include relieving of airway and airport traffic congestion and reducing direct aircraft operating costs by 15–20%. Proponents believed that the major market for such aircraft would be airlines serving the Asia-Pacific region. They also claimed that 100 of the 800 long-range airline routes around the world had traffic of sufficiently high density to be suitable for UHCA aircraft.

McDonnell Douglas Helicopter Co. evaluated wind tunnel tests of an innovative bearingless rotor, and it claimed that the results indicated that the rotor would be a key component of the company's next-generation civil/military helicopter. McDonnell said that another innovation would be a fiberglass epoxy flexbeam, which would replace hinges and bearings in the rotor system to attach the all-composite rotor blades to the engine hub. These changes, the company said, should result in a lubrication-free system with improved reliability and less required maintenance. It also claimed that the new rotor system would have no set number of hours of operation before retirement—with an estimated minimum of 10,000 hours of service—and would also be 25% quieter than current helicopters.

The FAA approved the testing in 1993 at Newark (N.J.) International Airport of a new, high-tech scanning system believed capable of detecting any type of plastic explosive concealed in aircraft luggage. The new scanner was developed, under a $3 million FAA contract, by an affiliate of Rutgers University, New Brunswick, New Jersey., and Scan-Tech Security of Northvale, N.J.

Highway transport. Spurred by California's law to require progressively more new automobiles operating in that state to emit no exhaust (from 2% in 1998 to 10% in 2003), U.S., Japanese, and European automakers increased their efforts to develop an economical and efficient electric car—the most likely candidate to meet this challenge. The Hughes Aircraft Co. subsidiary of the General Motors Corp. demonstrated a high-performance charging system to help remove one obstacle to the widespread use of electric cars. The Hughes system bypasses the plug-and-socket recharge system by using a round plastic paddle-type device that transfers electricity through a magnetic field. Hughes claimed that with this device it could fully recharge a car's battery in two to three hours or provide a quick recharge in less than one hour.

The MD Explorer *begins its first flight on December 18 at the McDonnell Douglas Helicopter Co. facility in Mesa, Ariz. An eight-seat, twin-engine design, the helicopter featured a bearingless rotor and a fiberglass epoxy flexbeam that replaced hinges and bearings in the rotor system to attach the rotor blades to the engine hub.*

Since a lighter and more powerful battery than those now in use remains a necessity for the development of a practical electric automobile, the big three U.S. automakers (General Motors, Ford Motor Co., and Chrysler Corp.) teamed up with the U.S. Department of Energy to finance a $260 million program via contracts with various innovators to develop and manufacture batteries able to power electric autos and operate economically under existing traffic conditions—and at a reasonable cost. Late in the year, however, General Motors announced that it was cutting back sharply its research-and-development program for electric automobiles because of high costs and questionable customer interest.

J.B. Hunt Transport Co. announced a $20 million commitment to install an onboard computer providing a two-way communications system on its large trucking fleet. During the past year it began field-testing such a system on 85 of its trucks in the southeastern U.S. The Arkansas-based carrier also announced that it planned to test the IBM RoadRider system for mating it to two-way mobile communications devices. The RoadRider is a laptop-sized portable computer designed for mounting in a truck cab. It uses a touch screen instead of a keyboard and also contains a large microprocessor chip, giving it the ability to connect to two-way vehicle communications systems. The linkage of the

A high-tech scanning system designed to detect any kind of plastic explosive concealed in airplane luggage is tested at the Newark (N.J.) International Airport.

two innovations would allow Hunt to send and receive messages such as order information, routing, delivery instructions, fuel-stop locations, and other reports throughout its system, eliminating the need for many telephone reports.

Schneider National Carriers Inc., the largest U.S. truckload carrier, cited its use of a satellite communications system for rapid truck tracking and routing as a major reason for its phenomenal success (rise in revenues from $215 million to $961 million between 1980 and 1991). It spent $40 million to equip its truck fleet with high-tech equipment for direct linkage to the system and thus provide shippers with the just-in-time, low-inventory service they were demanding. The company said that some retailers wanted to turn over their inventory as many as 90 times a year.·

Both Schneider National and J.B. Hunt Transport were heavy users of rail freight service in trailer-on-flatcar and container-on-flatcar intermodal operations. The latter asked three major truck trailer manufacturers (Stoughton Trailers, Inc.; Great Dane Trailers; and Monon Corp.) to develop standards for the next generation of intermodal containers. Spurred by plans by Hunt to purchase 14,000 new container and chassis intermodal units in 1993, at a cost of about $50 million, the manufacturers began testing six prototypes of 16-m (53-ft)-long containers that could be handled two at a time in double stacks on a rail flatcar. The long containers would also have greater capacity throughout, which requires lighter construction materials.

Perceptronics Inc. of Woodland Hills, Calif., reported that North American Van Lines and the U.S. Army were two major advocates of its Professional Truckdriving Simulator, with the Army planning to buy 10 of the units at a unit cost of about $220,-000. A major reason for their interest was a possible shortage of drivers because of tougher licensing and mandatory alcohol and drug testing that could result in suspension or revocation of licenses. North American claimed that it would use the devices primarily to improve its drivers' skills rather than spending from $4,000 to $8,000 to recruit and train a new driver. The device provides a 180° view of the road and simulates virtually any real-life driving situation, including different types of road conditions such as hills, curves, ice, and fog. An average 40–50 hours of training per driver was estimated to be needed with the simulator, along with actual road training.

Intelligent Vehicle-Highway Society of America, a nonprofit educational and scientific association that formally advises the U.S. Department of Transportation on its implementation of a $660 million, six-year IVHS program approved by Congress in 1991, submitted a strategic plan covering the next 20 years. The plan called for initial emphasis on many related high-tech projects already under way or in an active research and development phase. For additional information, *see* Feature Article: INTELLIGENT VEHICLE-HIGHWAY SYSTEMS.

Pipelines. Construction and further development of coal-slurry pipelines in the U.S. remained at a standstill during the past year, not because of any technological obstacles but because of continued strong opposition by railroads, the nation's major transporters of coal. Another major reason was that both oil and natural gas prices remained too low for such slurry lines to compete with them. On the other hand, Snamprogetti, an Italian petrochemical engineering company, claimed it had developed an advanced coal-slurry technology that featured a 50–50 mixture of coal and water that could be used as a fuel without dewatering. The only coal-slurry line in the U.S., the Southern Pacific Railroad's Black Mesa line in Arizona and Nevada, moved a 70–30 coal-water mix, but it had to return the coal into a solid form before it could be used as fuel. Snamprogetti announced that it was starting up a 255-km (160-mi) 50–50 mix line from Belovo to Novosibirsk in Russia and that William Technologies Inc. of Oklahoma had joined it in negotiations with other former Soviet republics and China for construction of other coal-slurry projects.

The utilization of novel technology to achieve more efficient and economical deep-water pipe-laying was reported in the installation of oil and gas pipelines for the Exxon-Santa Ynez project off the coast of Santa Barbara, Calif. The installation contractor, Allseas Marine Services of Essen, Belgium, said that separate 50-cm (20-in)-diameter oil emulsion pipeline sections were connected, without use of divers, at water depths up to 475 m (1,155 ft) by a unique method. As described by Allseas, the new technique consisted of first laying on the seabed a section of pipe that contained a preinstalled sled at one end, which could be pulled into a special preinstalled receiver at the bottom of the platform structure. This was done with cables that extended from the platform to the sled and were connected to it by a remotely operated and controlled vehicle. Once the sled and its attached pipe were pulled into the platform's special receiver, a hydraulic system made a pressure-tight connection between the pipeline and the platform piping.

Railroad transport. An Association of American Railroads task force developed, for approval by the association's board in early 1993, a computer system that by early 1995 would allow shippers to interchange data between their own and the railroads' computers in order to obtain estimated times of arrival for all freight cars in interline service. The AAR task force said that railroads, as leaders in EDI development, had to be able to compete more effec-

A high-speed Swedish-built passenger train on loan to Amtrak features a tilting system that allows it to operate at much higher speeds than nontilting trains can on existing U.S. tracks.

tively with long-haul truckers, and it pointed out that its carrier-shipper computer linkage at present was largely limited to single-line car tracking and tracing. With interline and rail intermodal service expanding so rapidly, the task force concluded that such a system was necessary and would stimulate this trend.

Amtrak reported on several high-tech innovations that were being tested on its passenger routes. It took delivery of a Swedish-built high-speed passenger train featuring a built-in tilting system that allowed it to operate at much higher speeds than nontilting trains on existing U.S. tracks. The train, on loan from Swedish State Railways, following road tests, was scheduled for early 1993 passenger service in the Northeast Corridor between Washington, D.C., and New York City—to be extended later to New Haven, Conn. Test runs would then be made between New Haven and Boston, a section of the route having many sharp curves that currently forced trains to slow down. The train was to be returned to Sweden in August 1993.

The many advances in high-speed rail passenger-train technology created growing concern by U.S. and Canadian freight railroads—whose tracks handled the passenger trains—about safety because of the great difference in train speeds. One possible solution was to use a new satellite communications system being tested by Amtrak on its route between Chicago and Seattle/Portland on Burlington Northern and Soo Line rail freight lines. The satellite system permitted continuous monitoring of the passenger train and of communication between its conductor and the dispatcher—thus allowing mixed freight- and passenger-train operations despite the wide variation of speeds.

Similar benefits could be expected if road tests of the Advanced Electronics System (ARES) on Amtrak passenger trains proved as successful as did Burlington Northern Railroad's tests of this innovation on its Northern Iron Range routes in Minnesota. The Burlington Northern was forced by budget constraints to delay expansion of this system to other freight routes, but the Amtrak tests were expected to be made with U.S. government financial assistance under recently approved legislation. If approved by Congress, the project would provide ARES implementation over a 4,400-km (2,700-mi) route and include three control centers, the installation of 491 wayside interface units, and the equipping of 540 locomotives for ARES operation. One objective of such sophisticated automatic train control was to permit safe mixed freight- and passenger-train operations by providing more efficient train spacing.

A possible roadblock to the introduction of very high-speed passenger train operations in the U.S. was removed when a Texas court ruled that the Texas High Speed Rail Authority could proceed with awarding a multibillion-dollar franchise to the Texas TGV Corp., a French-U.S. consortium of 27 firms, to build a 950-km (590-mi) double-track system connecting that state's five largest cities: Austin, Dallas, Fort Worth, Houston, and San Antonio. Employing the latest technology used in the famous French TGV (*trains à grande vitesse*) high-speed passenger trains, which had operated at test speeds of up to 515 km/h (320 mph), the Texas project expected to have its version in operation by 1999, with trains operating at 320 km/h (200 mph). Morrison Knudsen, a large engineering/construction firm that headed the consortium, estimated total system costs at $5.8 billion in 1990 dollars, and it predicted that the trains would move 9.5 million persons by the year 2000.

The completion of the Channel Tunnel connecting England and France in late 1993 was expected to open up sizable marketing opportunities for both passenger and freight services of the two nations' national railroads—since the Tunnel would handle only rail operations. This opened the door to the huge European truck market. For example, the European railways' container-marketing consortium Intercontainer ordered a fleet of flatcars able to handle containers up to 277 cm (109 in) high. Because existing British-European surface-transport freight service currently had to be broken up for slow and cumbersome ferries, the savings in time provided by the tunnel could be at least 24 hours on average. Initially, 27 freight trains a day would move in each direction through the tunnel, which should increase to 35 each way by 1995.

Ten U.S. and Canadian railroads agreed to cooperate in sponsoring a project, at a cost of more than $40 million, to determine whether their future locomotives should utilize alternating current (AC) traction rather than the direct current (DC) traction now used. The former was widely used in Europe but not in North America because of its more rugged operating and environmental conditions. The Association of American Railroads asked four manufacturers to supply up to 26 locomotives with AC traction and 5,000 minimum horsepower, about 25% more than current DC units. Expected advantages of AC traction included reduced maintenance, greater adhesion to rails, and less wheel slip. A major goal of the project was to satisfy the railroads that the AC units were reliable.

Water transport. Controversy continued to block moves to amend the Oil Pollution Act of 1990, which required that by the year 2015 all oil tankers operating in U.S. waters be shielded against spills by a double hull. Because of the high costs of doing this, Asian and European naval architects developed alternate designs. These included tankers equipped with systems on a mid deck that maintained the oil being transported at lower pressure than that of the ocean water, thus preventing major spills in accidents. Double hulls, because of the cushion of air between them, were claimed to be less vulnerable to spillage from minor groundings and collisions. Environmental groups, stressing the need to prevent the far more frequent minor spills, thus favored double hulls. The alternative received endorsement of the London-based International Maritime Organization and the U.S. National Academy of Sciences as being less costly and more effective. Regardless, at the end of 1992 the U.S. Coast Guard, which had to enforce the law, reported, after extensive study, that the double-hull requirement should remain since "no other designs are available that would provide equal or greater protection to the environment."

The U.S. Federal Maritime Commission announced new start-up times during 1993 for the filing of ocean shipping tariffs for use in its Automated Tariff Filing and Information System. Software companies claimed that they were ready for the rapid implementation of the long-delayed and controversial high-tech system. Further obstacles were possible, however, because of strong opposition to the 46-cents-per-minute fee for its use.

The U.S. Federal Communications Commission (FCC) ruled that by 1999 all large U.S. ships (those that carried more than 12 persons or more than 300 gross tons of cargo) had to install equipment that would include unified satellite technology, automated reception of maritime safety data, and rapid distress communications with rescue-coordination centers. By such action the U.S. joined most other major seafaring nations that were implementing the new Global Maritime Distress and Safety System developed by the UN International Maritime Organization. The FCC also ruled that until the U.S. Congress amended existing statutes, all such ships had to continue to carry a radio officer and radiotelegraphy units.

The U.S. St. Lawrence Seaway Development Corp. announced that in order to keep pace with highly competitive railroad and shipping lines, it would strongly urge the introduction and utilization of high-tech innovations that offered more efficient and safer maritime support services. Such actions were to include a new, in-operation weather display system that provided vessel-traffic controllers with up-to-the-minute data for any area of the Great Lakes Seaway system. It was linked with three new weather stations along the St. Lawrence River and two weather data bases covering the Great Lakes region. Plans called for the incorporation by 1994 of a satellite-based navigation system that would include vessel-tracking, buoy-positioning, and ship-navigation aids. The Canadian Seaway Authority was expected to join, within a few years, in the vessel-tracking aspect of the satellite system.

The financially hard-pressed U.S. shipbuilding industry got a boost with the completion of the only large commercial vessel to have been built in the U.S. since 1987—Matson Navigation Co.'s new flagship, the *R.J. Pfeiffer*. It was built to handle the shipping line's future ocean services on its high-density Hawaiian-U.S. route. Matson said that the ship offered a number of technological features, including new diesel engines that were designed to reduce fuel costs by 30–40% and sophisticated automation and navigation systems that would permit the ship to operate with a crew of 12 rather than the standard 35. Matson also announced that the configuration of the vessel would enable it to handle a wide variety of container sizes for transporting the

Built by a Japanese research consortium, the 185-ton Yamato 1 *is propelled by an almost silent power system without moving parts, called magnetohydrodynamic propulsion. It utilizes the principle that a flow of electricity into a magnetic field causes strong forces perpendicular to the magnetic field to be generated.*

full range of commodities that moved in this large and growing trade.

On June 16, 1992, a revolutionary vessel built by a Japanese research consortium (as part of a six-year, $40 million research and development project) was launched in Kobe Harbor. Named the *Yamato 1,* the 30-m (100-ft)-long, 185-ton test vessel was propelled slowly by a virtually silent power system, without moving parts, called magnetohydrodynamic propulsion (MHD). It utilized a long-known principle of electricity and magnetism: when a flow of electricity enters a magnetic field, strong forces perpendicular to the magnetic field are generated. The current success was made possible by the use of so-called superconductors (still in the development stage), which when spun into a coil can generate an extremely powerful magnetic field. When seawater entering the bow of the vessel is first passed through an electric current and then through the coil's magnetic field perpendicular to it, the force of the water increases sharply and propels the ship as the water is released from the ship. Larger and faster MHD-powered vessels were being planned.

—Frank A. Smith

U.S. science policy

Scientists and scientific research once occupied an enviable place in American society. Money for research was plentiful, as was respect for researchers. If scientists had a hard time explaining to the general public exactly what they were doing with the billions of federal dollars being lavished on them, most people did not seem to mind. The accepted explanation was that most research was too complicated for the nonspecialist to understand. Few questioned that it was money well spent.

If there was any doubt that those days are long gone, the events of the past year erased it. In addition to their awareness of continuing investigations of misconduct by famous scientists and of improper spending of federal dollars by research institutions, people began to look at scientific projects not only for what they would add to knowledge but also for how they could improve prosperity. The hallowed principle that scientists themselves were the best to judge which projects deserved support came under intense scrutiny as the U.S. Congress and other influential bodies began to insist that users of scientific discoveries as well as scientists themselves play a role in the process of setting priorities.

Many scientists saw this change in emphasis as a threat to their very existence. They worried that society had a fundamental misunderstanding of the scientific process and that they would be expected to churn out new, important, potentially lucrative discoveries targeted to specific problems—or else. Others were more philosophical about the future role of scientists. They took hope in the calls for renewed emphasis on scientific education, and they tirelessly pointed out that if scientific discoveries were crucial for future economic prosperity, as nearly everyone agreed was the case, money would have to be found for training a new generation of scientists.

National Science Foundation. Nowhere was the debate over the future of science being played out more clearly than at the National Science Foundation (NSF). The NSF was created after World War II to be the most important civilian agency for supporting basic research. For decades its primary support came in the form of small ($50,000) grants awarded to individual researchers for projects that they themselves had proposed. But beginning in the mid-1980s, under the directorship of Erich Bloch, the NSF began to experiment with alternative mechanisms for supporting research. Engineering Research Centers came first, followed by Science and Technology Centers. The centers' budgets could be as high as $1 million per year. The idea was to bring together scientists from a variety of disciplines to work on a task that was bigger than any individual could accomplish—searching for dark matter in the universe or designing high-speed automated machinery for sequencing DNA. These centers were also asked to establish links with private industry so that there could be the flow of ideas and technology from the lab to the marketplace.

The NSF's new director, Walter Massey, proposed taking that idea even further. He suggested that part of the NSF's mandate should be to facilitate technology transfer and that, while the agency would continue to support individual researchers, it would place increasing emphasis on providing for the needs of industry. That might include offering training grants in areas of interest to specific industries in order to ensure an adequate supply of trained employees and also encouraging private industry to apply directly for NSF support.

Massey's ideas had congressional backing. A Senate appropriations subcommittee with responsibility for the NSF's budget wrote a report urging Massey to take his agency in essentially that direction. Massey's plans were met with an avalanche of criticism from the scientific community, however. At the urging of the National Science Board, the NSF's independent governing body, Massey held off implementing his notions, and the board convened a special panel to consider the future of the NSF. The panel, chaired by Washington University (St. Louis, Mo.) Chancellor William Danforth and Robert Galvin, chairman of Motorola, Inc., presented its conclusions in November. It suggested that the NSF concentrate on its core activities of supporting basic research and science education. Nevertheless, the panel supported "a reallocation of expenditures to strengthen certain priority areas: process research and development; engineering research; emerging and precompetitive technologies; and fundamental research with ties to future industrial interests."

Of course, the NSF's future course was expected to be heavily influenced by the new man in the White House. Although Bill Clinton gave no specific indication during his election campaign about the direction of science agencies in his administration, he did make it clear by his choice of vice president that science and technology would be a priority. As a senator, Al Gore had paid particular attention to science policy, especially with regard to global change and

high-performance computing—both areas in which the NSF played an important role.

The other factor that was bound to have a major impact on the NSF's future was the prospect that Massey would leave the agency for an academic position shortly after the new president took office. Rumors to that effect abounded toward the end of 1992, and in late January 1993 Massey announced that he was going to leave the NSF to become vice-chancellor of the University of California.

National Institutes of Health. A similar debate was being played out at the National Institutes of Health (NIH). Soon after she took over as director of the agency in April 1991, Bernadine Healy began a strategic planning exercise to set a clear course for her agency. By the end of 1991 the Strategic Plan had taken shape, but once again an outcry from the scientific community as well as negative signals from the NIH's political masters in the Department of Health and Human Services forced a reevaluation. Under initial drafts of the plan, the NIH would have reemphasized its role in improving health in the U.S. and also would have paid closer attention to how the development of new drugs and products for a burgeoning biotechnology industry could foster economic growth. While many agreed with those plans in principle, they worried about where the money to finance them would come from. The NIH's budget had grown steadily throughout the 1980s but not at a rate that would accommodate all of Healy's initiatives. Scientists feared that basic research would be shortchanged, that young scientists would be discouraged from pursuing research careers, and that long-term stability of the scientific enterprise would be sacrificed for short-term payoffs.

Throughout 1992 Healy sought to reassure basic research scientists that they would not be left out of her plans. She held several meetings during the

Bernadine Healy

year at which scientists were encouraged to express their concerns. The heart of her plans remained the same, however, and scientists remained nervous. It was left to the Clinton administration to determine whether to accept the direction Healy had proposed.

Whatever other legacy Healy left from her tenure at the NIH, she would certainly be remembered as a director who brought the agency into the political limelight. She won praise for launching the Women's Health Initiative, a 14-year program of clinical trials, epidemiological studies, and educational campaigns intended to redress years of neglect of the special health problems of woman. (Her critics, however, noted that the basic outline of the program was in place before she arrived.) She also launched the minority health initiative, a similar attempt to bring the fruits of medical knowledge to historically underserved segments of U.S. society. During 1992 the NIH also gained three new institutes—the National Institute of Mental Health, the National Institute on Drug Abuse, and the National Institute on Alcohol Abuse and Alcoholism. The growth came as a result of a breakup of the Alcohol, Drug Abuse, and Mental Health Administration (ADAMHA). Those three research-intensive institutes were shifted to the NIH, and ADAMHA's human services functions were placed in a new agency named the Substance Abuse Mental Health Services Administration.

The dismantling of ADAMHA may have solved some organizational problems, but it did not deflect criticism of an initiative that was linked to the agency. During 1992 ADAMHA and other agencies of the Public Health Service, an operating division of the Department of Health and Human Services, began drafting a so-called violence initiative—a project intended to treat violence as a public health problem. The initiative would have included behavioral research into the causes of violence, demonstration programs testing violence-reduction strategies, and better measurement of death and injury related to preventable violent acts. The violence initiative never made it past the planning stages, however. It was attacked by critics as racist—as a government-sponsored attempt to stigmatize African-Americans. Critics were particularly outraged by a conference, not strictly part of the initiative, that was supposed to investigate whether criminal behavior had a genetic basis. An outcry prompted the NIH to cancel funds for the conference, despite protests from its organizers that their motives were anything but racist and that canceling the project was a form of censorship.

Healy's biggest political foray, one that left her with several enemies on Capitol Hill, involved the use of fetal tissue in transplantation research. In 1988 the Public Health Service imposed a moratorium on federal funding for transplantation research using tissue from induced abortions. A special panel

was convened that year to consider the ethics of such research, and it concluded that, as long as abortion was legal, fetal tissue could be treated like any other material of human origin used in research and, with appropriate safeguards, could be used. Healy, then the director of research at the Cleveland (Ohio) Clinic, agreed with the majority that the moratorium should be lifted, but the administration of Pres. George Bush rejected the panel's advice and extended the moratorium indefinitely.

In Congress this raised hackles. A law that would have ended the ban passed both houses of Congress, but it was vetoed by President Bush. Healy, now a member of the administration, lobbied vigorously on behalf of the president. Ultimately, Congress failed to override the veto, but many legislators were upset that Healy worked so hard against legislation they knew she had once supported. After his election as president, Clinton said that one of his first orders of business would be to end the moratorium by executive order, and he did so his first week in office.

Office of Scientific Integrity. One important office that left the NIH during the year was the Office of Scientific Integrity (OSI). The OSI was responsible for investigating allegations of scientific misconduct for all agencies of the Public Health Service, and from the start critics contended that it was impossible to expect a scientific agency to police itself. Rep. John Dingell (Dem., Mich.) was the OSI's most persistent critic, particularly for the way it conducted the investigations of Nobel Prize-winning biologist David Baltimore and AIDS researcher Robert Gallo. In the Baltimore case, one of his colleagues was found to have fabricated research data (a federal district attorney, however, declined to bring criminal charges in the case). In the Gallo affair, a 2½-year investigation concluded that Gallo was not guilty of misconduct in connection with certain misstatements that appeared in a 1984 scientific paper describing the first successful attempt to grow the AIDS (acquired immune deficiency syndrome) virus in tissue culture. The investigation essentially dismissed allegations that Gallo had stolen a virus given him by French collaborators and then had pretended that it was his discovery. Gallo's collaborator on the 1984 paper, Mikulas Popovic, was found guilty of several minor offenses.

The OSI's functions were taken over by a new office, the Office of Research Integrity (ORI), which operated out of the Office of the Assistant Secretary for Health. On the last day of 1992, the ORI issued a report that found both Gallo and Popovic guilty of misconduct and recommended as punishment that both scientists be supervised in their future research. But Dingell's staff indicated that he was not satisfied with the ORI's investigation, and the case threatened to continue for years to come. Gallo was

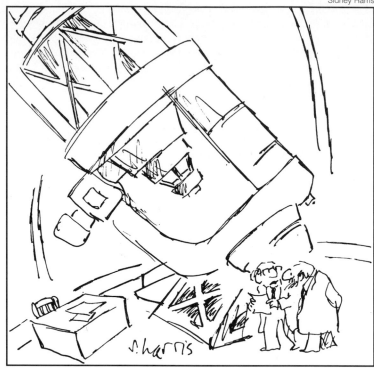

"The only part of the universe which isn't expanding is the budget for this place."

also dissatisfied, stating that he intended to appeal the ORI finding.

AIDS. The Gallo case could have international implications. In 1987 the governments of France and the U.S. signed an agreement sharing patent royalties for an AIDS blood test that was developed by Gallo, based on the virus that a French scientist, Luc Montagnier, was the first to identify. When news of Gallo's alleged misconduct became public, the French government asked for the agreement to be redrawn.

Lawyers began to play an increasingly important role in the development of an AIDS vaccine. Although several pharmaceutical companies had vaccine-development programs, several others declined to get involved for fear of potential legal liability. A trial of a vaccine in pregnant women was delayed by Abbott Laboratories because of liability questions.

An AIDS case involving a Florida dentist who apparently gave the disease to several of his patients also made it into the courtroom during the past year. A judge in Florida would have had to decide whether molecular epidemiology of the AIDS virus was sophisticated enough to prove that transmission had occurred from dentist to patient. The AIDS virus mutates constantly, and it was only now becoming possible to determine when different strains of the virus first arose. In the end, the case was settled out of court, but this might ultimately be added to DNA fingerprinting as a tool of the modern forensic biologist.

Biotechnology. One of Healy's decisions during the year could have enormous economic impact on the biotechnology industry. In 1991 the NIH announced that it would seek patents for literally hundreds of gene fragments that had been isolated from DNA taken from human brain cells. Although the fragments were clearly part of a gene, in most cases the researchers who isolated them had no idea what their function was. By holding a patent on the fragments, the NIH could argue that if the gene to which the fragment belonged had commercial value—such as a compound that promoted nerve growth—then the NIH would be entitled to a share of the royalties from sales of such a compound. Biotechnology companies in the U.S. and around the world howled with dismay. How, they asked, would anyone take a risk of spending years to search for a gene if at the end of that time they would find that the fragment and, therefore, the gene belonged to the government.

Although as of early 1993 the U.S. Patent and Trademark Office had not decided whether to award the patent, just the fact that the NIH asked for it led to a public and acrimonious debate between Healy and James Watson, head of the NIH's Human Genome Project. The genome project, run jointly by the NIH and the U.S. Department of Energy, was an attempt to construct a genetic road map of the 23 chromosomes found in all human cells and then to generate the sequence of base pairs of the DNA in those chromosomes. Watson, who shared the 1962 Nobel Prize for Physiology or Medicine for the dis-

430

covery of the structure of DNA, was widely credited with getting the genome project off the ground. The dispute over the gene-patenting issue prompted Watson to resign from the project, saying that he was dismayed by what he saw as Healy's unwillingness to listen to his advice.

Big Science. Despite Watson's departure, the genome project was on the soundest footing of the three Big Science projects launched by federal agencies during the past decade. The NIH scored a coup by luring Francis Collins from the University of Michigan to the NIH to replace Watson. By contrast, the Superconducting Super Collider (SSC), a giant particle accelerator being constructed near Dallas, Texas, was facing a major budgetary struggle. Physicists agreed that, to reach a better understanding of the fundamental particles of nature, they needed an atom smasher with the power of the SSC. In a time of soaring budget deficits, however, many in Congress and even segments of the scientific community not involved in high-energy physics questioned whether the U.S. could afford such a major undertaking; the estimated cost of the SSC was $8,250,000,000. The Department of Energy was forced to admit during the year that it had not been able to find any foreign partners willing to make significant financial contributions to the project.

Although it survived a congressional attempt to kill it in 1992, many wondered whether the third Big Science project, the space station, would suffer a similar fate. The National Aeronautics and Space Administration (NASA) had proposed space station *Freedom* as the logical next step in the nation's space program. It would be a permanently occupied orbiting laboratory that would carry out scientific studies and be a staging point for missions to neighboring planets. But cost overruns and design flaws prompted Congress to require NASA to conceive a less ambitious project. As with the SSC, the space station's high price tag gave it an uncertain future. Unlike the case of the SSC, however, the U.S. had successfully extracted financial commitments from Japan, Canada, and the European Space Agency to support space station activities; thus, canceling the project might do long-term damage to international scientific cooperation.

NASA Administrator Daniel Goldin also upset scientists when he dismantled the Office of Space Science and Applications, spreading responsibility for scientific projects into several different offices and creating a special Office for Mission to Planet Earth—an effort centered on the $8 billion Earth Observing System. NASA's science missions had been plagued by problems in recent years. The Hubble Space Telescope was hobbled by an incorrectly shaped primary mirror, and the main antenna failed to unfurl on the Galileo spacecraft heading for Jupiter.

Not all was gloom and doom in space. The Magellan Venus radar mapper created an outstanding contour map of the planet's surface; Hubble had provided some intriguing results on black holes and planetary formation; the Gamma Ray Observatory was performing well; and the Mars Observer was heading for a rendezvous with Mars in August 1993.

Government and universities. In the mid-1980s several universities began hiring lobbyists to try to persuade legislators to include new science facilities in appropriations bills. The success that a few universities enjoyed brought more into the game, so by 1992 hundreds of millions of dollars were being doled out to universities.

This put university administrators in an awkward position. For years they had argued that scientific awards should be based on merit, with a panel of experts ranking requests according to their excellence. Yet by using lobbyists they were seeking to bypass that system and appeal directly to the congressmen from their state or district for money. The universities argued that there was no other way to get the money. But George Brown, (Dem., Calif.) rallied his colleagues to combat the process. In a surprising success on the floor of the House of Representatives, he was able to strip $94.8 million from an energy and water appropriations bill, a favored place for including such facilities as science buildings.

This dilemma was part of a difficult policy problem: how to rebuild the country's scientific infrastructure, specifically buildings and facilities at universities. The budgets of science agencies rarely contained specific appropriations for infrastructure—universities were supposed to build their own buildings. The money that could be provided came in the form of indirect costs; a percentage of each academic grant to institutions was earmarked to pay the costs associated with supporting research, costs such as electric bills, library services, and administrative support.

Indirect cost payments recently began undergoing careful scrutiny, however. Ever since it was revealed in 1990 that Stanford University had used its indirect costs to pay for expensive furniture and floral arrangements, there had been pressure on the government to cut payments. For universities this pressure came at a particularly bad time. The troubled economy provided few means for universities to increase revenues; state governments could not help, tuitions were already high, and the return on endowments was low. A report from the Presidential Council of Advisers on Science and Technology warned of a dark time for universities unless the partnership between the government and universities was restored to its former status.

—Joseph Palca

See also Feature Article: LITTLE SCIENCE, BIG SCIENCE, MULTINATIONAL SCIENCE.

Scientists of the Year

Honors and awards

The following article discusses recent awards and prizes in science and technology. In the first section the Nobel Prizes for 1992 are described in detail. The second section is a selective list of other honors.

Nobel Prize for Chemistry

The winner of the 1992 Nobel Prize for Chemistry, Rudolph A. Marcus of the California Institute of Technology (Caltech), was cited for his contributions to the theory of electron-transfer reactions in chemical systems. The processes that Marcus studied, the transfer of electrons between molecules in solution, underlie a number of important chemical phenomena in the living and nonliving worlds, and the practical consequences of his theory extend to all areas of chemistry. The Marcus theory, which by the 1990s was standard fare in modern undergraduate science textbooks, helped scientists better understand such widely differing phenomena as photosynthesis, chemiluminescence ("cold light") in fireflies, metabolism in living cells, the conductivity of electrically conducting polymers, the emission of light by diodes, and simple corrosion.

Intrigued by a graduate student's question, Marcus began formulating his theory in 1952. He published his first paper on the subject in 1956 and continued to develop and refine his ideas in a series of papers for the next nine years while at the Polytechnic Institute of Brooklyn, N.Y. (later the Polytechnic Institute of New York and Polytechnic University), and then at the University of Illinois. Marcus described what is perhaps the simplest of all chemical reactions—the transfer of an electron between two molecules. Although no chemical bonds are broken in such a reaction, changes do take place in the molecular structure of the reacting molecules and their nearest neighbors in solution. These molecular changes influence the ability of electrons to jump between the molecules.

Marcus was among the first researchers to grasp this fact. Although many researchers suspected that structural changes played a role in electron-transfer reactions, it was thought that other factors, such as the electronic interaction between reactants, were also important. Marcus suggested that electronic interaction was negligible in most cases, and he developed a simple mathematical expression that described the rate of the electron-transfer reaction in terms of the structural changes involved. With this equation he was able to calculate and explain the great differences in the rates that are observed for various electron-transfer reactions.

As Marcus extended his theory during the next few years, he came to describe the electron-transfer process in terms of two intersecting parabolas, one parabola for the energy of the reactants and the other for the energy of the products. This simple representation has been hailed by his colleagues as an invaluable means of communicating the implications of his theory. Today most chemists use the representation of intersecting parabolas in their discussions of electron-transfer reactions.

Because certain of Marcus' predictions were counterintuitive, his theory initially caused considerable controversy. Most notably, his theory predicts an "inverted effect." Specifically, it predicts that, as the driving force initially increases, so does the rate of the chemical reaction, as would be expected. However, as the driving force continues to increase, he stated that the rate of the reaction reaches a maximum and then actually decreases. Chemists long found this prediction difficult to accept and confirm, and it was not until 1985 that they succeeded in verifying it experimentally.

The Marcus theory has since proved useful in interpreting many chemical processes and has been applied in widely different arenas. According to the Nobel citation, "In the mathematical connection the Marcus theory makes between theoretical and experimental quantities, experimental chemists gained a valuable tool."

One of the areas in which the Marcus theory has been applied is in the study of photosynthesis and other forms of energy storage, whereby a series of electron transfers converts solar energy to chemical energy. Scientists now believe that the inverted effect may play a part in these processes and may be a means by which solar-energy systems might be constructed.

Marcus was born in Montreal on July 21, 1923. He received a Ph.D. in physical chemistry from McGill University, Montreal, in 1946. After his graduation, he worked at the National Research Council of Canada as a postdoctoral research associate un-

Rudolph A. Marcus
Caltech; photo, Bob Paz

432

til 1949. Because Canada was not then conducting theoretical research in his area of interest, Marcus moved to the U.S. to investigate theories of electron-transfer reactions in chemical systems. He continued his postdoctoral work at the University of North Carolina until 1951. Marcus then joined the faculty of the Polytechnic Institute of Brooklyn, where he became a full professor in 1958. That same year he became a U.S. citizen. (When he later investigated the idea of obtaining dual citizenship, he found that it was not possible under the Canadian law of the time.) In 1964 Marcus became professor of physical chemistry at the University of Illinois at Urbana-Champaign, and in 1978 he accepted the Arthur Amos Noyes chair of chemistry at Caltech.

Marcus received many scientific distinctions, including the Alexander von Humboldt Foundation's senior U.S. scientist award (1976), the Langmuir and Pauling awards of the American Chemical Society (1978 and 1991, respectively), the Robinson and Centenary medals of the Royal Society of Chemistry (1982 and 1988, respectively), the prestigious Wolf Prize for Chemistry (1985), and the National Medal of Science (1989). He also received honorary doctor of science degrees from the University of Chicago (1983), Polytechnic University (1986), the University of Göteborg, Sweden (1987), and McGill University (1988). In 1986 the *Journal of Physical Chemistry* devoted a special issue to the 30th anniversary of the Marcus theory.

Nobel Prize for Physics

The 1992 Nobel Prize for Physics was awarded to Georges Charpak of CERN (European Laboratory for Particle Physics), Geneva, for his invention and development of a particle detector known as the multiwire proportional chamber. Largely as a result of his pioneering work, which was carried out in 1968, particle physicists have been able to study very rare particle interactions—as rare as one interaction in a billion.

Particle physics has long relied on recording the trail of ionizations (the creation of electrically charged atoms or molecules) left by a high-energy particle as it passes through matter. The photographic methods that traditionally had been used, although adequate to track comparatively common particles, were not precise or fast enough to allow detection of more exotic varieties. Such methods could not discern the few relevant interactions from the multitude of irrelevant ones that occurred in particle-beam collision experiments, and their recording speeds were not high enough to match increasingly intense accelerator beams. Charpak's chamber used electronics to increase the speed of data collection by a factor of a thousand and to improve the spatial resolution. Ac-

cording to the Nobel committee, "His fundamental idea has since been developed and for more than two decades Charpak has been at the forefront of this development."

A single interaction, or collision, between two high-energy particles can create as many as several hundred particles that spray out in all directions. To interpret such an event, scientists often must record the trajectory of every emerging particle. In the years before Charpak's contribution, the event was usually recorded photographically in a bubble chamber, a tank of superheated liquid hydrogen that revealed the passage of particles as trails of gas bubbles. The photographs were then analyzed with the help of special measuring devices, a slow and laborious process.

Charpak's invention used an earlier development, the proportional counter, in an unconventional way. The classic proportional counter consists of a thin wire running down the long axis of a gas-filled tube about a centimeter (0.4 in) in diameter. When a high voltage is applied between the wire and the tube wall and an electric field is established between them, a charged particle passing through the tube will ionize the gas. In this process, negatively charged electrons are liberated from the neutral gas atoms, which then become positively charged ions. In the electric field, the electrons move toward the central wire, the anode, which is positively charged, while the ions move toward the glass wall, the cathode, which is negatively charged. As the electrons approach the wire, they are accelerated by the increasingly strong electric field. They gain enough energy to ionize gas atoms with which they collide; this liberates more electrons and ions, and the process continues. The cumulative result is an avalanche of electrons and positive ions moving in opposite directions in the tube. It is this movement that gives rise to a detectable electric signal in the circuit connecting the elements of the counter.

By the use of a classic proportional counter, the position of the charged particle that started the ionization in the gas can be determined with a precision of only about a centimeter—the diameter of the tube. To cover larger surfaces with layers of proportional tubes is impractical and does not allow for the spatial precision necessary in particle-collision experiments. Charpak's invention of the multiwire proportional chamber provided the breakthrough. It consists of a large number of thin parallel wires, about a tenth of a millimeter (0.004 in) in diameter, arranged at intervals of a few millimeters in a plane passing between two cathode plates that are a few centimeters apart. Charpak realized, contrary to the general belief of the time, that each wire in the chamber would behave as a proportional counter and result in a spatial precision of about a millimeter

433

Georges Charpak
CERN

or less. In addition, each wire could handle several hundred thousand particle encounters per second, at that time an exceptionally high rate. Each wire is equipped with an electronic amplifier, and the signals are analyzed with computers, speeding the process enormously.

Charpak also suggested possible refinements of the multiwire proportional chamber. Most significantly, he pointed out that it was possible to make use of the time between the initial ionization of the gas and the arrival of the electron pulse at the anode wire, an interval called the drift time. A measurement of the drift time results in an improved spatial precision—better than a tenth of a millimeter in some cases.

Charpak's invention launched a massive development of different types of wire chambers. By the early 1990s almost every experiment in particle physics used some type of detector derived from Charpak's original concept. Charpak was at the center of this development, from which thousands of scientists, both at CERN and elsewhere, subsequently profited. When the J/psi particle (and support for the existence of charmed quarks) was found in 1974, resulting in the award of the 1976 Nobel Prize for Physics to Burton Richter and Samuel C.C. Ting, several multiwire proportional chambers were used. The wire chamber was also used in the discoveries of the W and Z intermediate vector bosons at CERN in 1983; for that achievement the 1984 Nobel physics prize was awarded to Carlo Rubbia and Simon van der Meer. In the 1990s detectors developed by Charpak were being used increasingly in applications outside physics—for example, in medicine to detect X-rays and in the autoradiography of biological samples.

Charpak, a French citizen, was born on Aug. 1, 1924, in Poland. He moved to Paris with his Polish parents in 1932 at the age of seven. During World War II he served in the resistance and was jailed by the Nazis for a year at the infamous Dachau concentration camp. In 1959 Charpak received a Ph.D. from the Collège de France in Paris. He began working at CERN in 1959 and also became Joliot-Curie professor at the School of Advanced Studies in Physics and Chemistry, Paris, in 1984. He held

an honorary doctorate from the University of Geneva and in 1985 was made a member of the French Academy of Sciences. In 1989 he received the High Energy and Particle Physics Prize from the European Physical Society.

Nobel Prize for Physiology or Medicine

The 1992 Nobel Prize for Physiology or Medicine was awarded jointly to University of Washington emeritus professors Edmond H. Fischer and Edwin G. Krebs for their discoveries concerning a biochemical mechanism that governs the activity of cell proteins—a process called reversible phosphorylation.

A large number of proteins in a living cell participate in regulating the cell's reactions and activities. Their functions in turn are governed by complex, delicately balanced interactions with other proteins. For example, various proteins maintain the cell's metabolic flux, dictate growth and cellular division, release hormones, and mediate muscular work. One of the important means of controlling those proteins is reversible phosphorylation—the attachment or detachment of phosphate groups to a protein—a mechanism regulated by enzymes. (Enzymes are themselves proteins with the specific role of catalyzing biochemical reactions.) Fischer and Krebs were the first scientists to purify and characterize one of the enzymes involved in these processes. According to the Nobel citation, "Their fundamental finding initiated a research area that today is one of the most active and wide-ranging."

The three-dimensional structure of a protein molecule, which is made up of a folded chain of amino acid building blocks, determines its function. Phosphorylation, the attachment of phosphate groups to the protein, and dephosphorylation, the reverse process, change the structure and charge of the protein and thereby its function. In this manner the biological function of a protein is regulated.

Fischer and Krebs made their basic discoveries in the mid-1950s while studying muscle systems. Muscles are composed of a large number of cells capable of contraction and relaxation. For a resting muscle to contract, it must get energy in the form of the simple sugar glucose. The glucose is released from glycogen, the form in which the body stores sugar in the liver and in muscle cells. When muscles begin to contract, they quickly mobilize their glycogen deposits, converting them to glucose. To accomplish the conversion the body uses a specific protein, an enzyme called phosphorylase. (The discovery of that enzyme won biochemists Carl and Gerti Cori the 1947 Nobel Prize for Physiology or Medicine.)

Fischer and Krebs wanted to find out exactly how phosphorylase works and how the activity of the enzyme can switch on and off on demand. They

434

discovered that phosphorylase is converted from an inactive to an active form by the attachment of a phosphate group and that the removal of the phosphate group inactivates the phosphorylase again. The scientists demonstrated that it is the phosphorylation-dephosphorylation mechanism that turns muscle contraction on and off. Their discovery was first reported in a scientific journal in 1956, though the scientific community did not begin to understand the significance of their work until the mid-1970s.

The enzymes that catalyze the attachment of phosphate groups to proteins are called protein kinases. The enzymes that catalyze phosphate detachment are known as phosphatases. Guided by the initial work of Fischer and Krebs, scientists have discovered more than 80 additional kinases and several phosphatases that regulate specific processes in cells. The innumerable cellular processes governed by reversible protein phosphorylation affect almost all processes necessary for life. Imbalance between kinases and phosphatases can cause disease. According to the Nobel committee, "We therefore expect the development of drugs that make it possible to influence imbalances by supplying inhibitors and activators directed against the phosphorylation/dephosphorylation components."

The laureates' work led to a greater understanding of the immune response, in which certain kinases add phosphates to other kinases in a biochemical cascade that amplifies the initial immune reaction. Cyclosporine, a drug used to suppress graft rejection, was shown to work by inhibiting a phosphorylation reaction and inactivating a phosphatase. Protein phosphorylation also plays a role in the development of cancer. In several cases—chronic myelogenous leukemia, for example—poorly regulated kinase activity is responsible for the abnormal cellular growth characteristic of cancer. Protein phosphorylation also plays a part in blood pressure, inflammatory reactions, and brain signals and may have a role in diabetes.

Fischer was born of Swiss parents in Shanghai on April 6, 1920. He received a Ph.D. in chemistry from the University of Geneva in 1947 and con-

Edmond H. Fischer
© The Nobel Foundation

Edwin G. Krebs
© The Nobel Foundation

ducted research there until 1953, when he went to the U.S. to work as a research associate in biology at Caltech. That same year he joined the faculty of the University of Washington as an assistant professor of biochemistry. He became a full professor at the university in 1961. In 1992 he was engaged in research on the cell transformation involved in the development of cancer.

Fischer served as an adviser for the U.S. National Institutes of Health. Among his professional honors were the Warner Medal of the Swiss Chemical Society (1952), the Guggenheim Foundation Award (1963–64), the Jaubert Prize of the University of Geneva (1968), and the Laureate Passano Foundation Award (1988). He held honorary degrees from the University of Montpellier, France (1985), and the University of Basel (1988). He was a dual citizen of the U.S. and Switzerland.

Krebs was born on June 6, 1918, in Lansing, Iowa. He earned a bachelor's degree in chemistry from the University of Illinois in 1940 and then received an M.D. from Washington University, St. Louis, Mo., in 1943. After active duty as a medical officer in the U.S. Navy, Krebs took up research at the University of Washington in 1948 as one of the first professors in the newly established medical school. He became a full professor of biochemistry in 1957. He left that university in 1968 to work for several years at the University of California at Davis but returned in 1977. In recent months as a professor of pharmacology and biochemistry at the University of Washington and a senior investigator emeritus for the Howard Hughes Medical Institute, he was focusing on the processes of hormonal regulation and their role in such diseases as diabetes.

Krebs served as an adviser for the National Institutes of Health. His numerous professional honors included Canada's Gairdner Foundation Award (1978), the George W. Thorn Award for scientific excellence (1983), the Research Achievement Award of the American Heart Association (1987), the Albert Lasker Basic Medical Research Award (1989), and the CIBA-Geigy-Drew Award in chemistry (1991).

—Carolyn D. Newton

Scientists of the Year

AWARD	WINNER	AFFILIATION
ARCHITECTURE AND CIVIL ENGINEERING		
Carlsberg Architectural Prize	Tadao Ando	Osaka, Japan
Gold Medal of the American Institute of Architects	Kevin Roche	Kevin Roche John Dinkeloo & Associates, Hamden, Conn.
Praemium Imperiale	Frank O. Gehry	Frank O. Gehry and Associates Inc., Venice, Calif.
Pritzker Architecture Prize	Alvaro Siza	Oporto, Portugal
World Habitat Award	Lawrie Baker	
ASTRONOMY		
Charles A. Whitten Medal	Irwin I. Shapiro	Harvard-Smithsonian Center for Astrophysics
Brouwer Award	Martin Schwarzschild	Princeton University, Princeton, N.J.
Dannie Heineman Prize for Astrophysics	Bohdan Paczynski	Princeton University, Princeton, N.J.
Distinguished Public Service Medal	John Bahcall	Institute for Advanced Study, Princeton, N.J.
Exceptional Scientific Achievement Award	William Jefferys	University of Texas, Austin
George Ellery Hale Prize	Horace W. Babcock (Retired)	Observatories of the Carnegie Institution of Washington (D.C.), Pasadena, Calif.
George Van Biesbroeck Award	Robert Krucz	Harvard-Smithsonian Astrophysical Observatory, Cambridge, Mass.
Gerard P. Kuiper Prize	Peter Goldreich	California Institute of Technology, Pasadena
Harold C. Urey Prize	Jack J. Lissauer	State University of New York, Stony Brook
Masursky Award for Meritorious Service	Harlan J. Smith (Deceased)	University of Texas, Austin
CHEMISTRY		
Albert Einstein Award of Science	Raymond Lemieux (Retired)	University of Alberta, Edmonton
Arthur C. Cope Award	Peter B. Dervan	California Institute of Technology, Pasadena
Arthur C. Cope Scholar Award	Peter Beak	University of Illinois, Urbana-Champaign
Arthur C. Cope Scholar Award	Peter Chen	Harvard University, Cambridge, Mass.
Arthur C. Cope Scholar Award	Alexander M. Klibanov	Massachusetts Institute of Technology, Cambridge
Arthur C. Cope Scholar Award	Robert L. Letsinger (Emeritus)	Northwestern University, Evanston, Ill.
Arthur C. Cope Scholar Award	Josef Michl	University of Colorado, Boulder
Arthur C. Cope Scholar Award	Joanne Stubbe	Massachusetts Institute of Technology, Cambridge
Arthur C. Cope Scholar Award	Fred Wudl	University of California, Santa Barbara
Arthur W. Adamson Award	David M. Hercules	University of Pittsburgh, Pa.

AWARD	WINNER	AFFILIATION
Award for Creative Work in Fluorine Chemistry	Ronald E. Banks	University of Manchester, England
Award for Creative Work in Synthetic Organic Chemistry	Kyriacos C. Nicolaou	University of California, San Diego
Award for Distinguished Service in the Advancement of Inorganic Chemistry	Theodore L. Brown	University of Illinois, Urbana-Champaign
Award for Initiatives in Research	Alice P. Gast	Stanford University, Calif.
	Sangtae Kim	University of Wisconsin, Madison
Award for Nuclear Chemistry	Richard M. Diamond (Retired)	Lawrence Berkeley Laboratory, Calif.
Award in Analytical Chemistry	Jeanette G. Grasselli	Ohio University, Athens
Award in Chemical Sciences	Donald J. Cram	University of California, Los Angeles
Award in Inorganic Chemistry	Gregory J. Kubas	Los Alamos National Laboratory, N.M.
Award in Organometallic Chemistry	Robert H. Crabtree	Yale University, New Haven, Conn.
Award in Polymer Chemistry	Takeo Saegusa	Kansai Research Institute and Kyoto University (Emeritus), Japan
Award in Pure Chemistry	Jeremy M. Berg	Johns Hopkins University, Baltimore, Md.
Award in Separations Science and Technology	James R. Fair	University of Texas, Austin
Award in Theoretical Chemistry	Martin Karplus	Harvard University, Cambridge, Mass.
Benedetti-Pilcher Memorial Award	Robert G. Michel	University of Connecticut, Storrs
Charles H. Stone Award	Craig L. Hill	Emory University, Atlanta, Ga.
Charles Holmes Herty Award	Isiah Warner	Emory University, Atlanta, Ga.
Claude S. Hudson Award	Irwin J. Goldstein	University of Michigan, Ann Arbor
Dexter Award	John T. Stock (Emeritus)	University of Connecticut, Storrs
Dr. Paul Janssen Prize	Philip D. Magnus	University of Texas, Austin
Earle B. Barnes Award	William D. Emmons	Rohm & Haas
Elsevier Chemometrics Award	Lutgarde Buydens	Catholic University of Nijmegen, The Netherlands
E.O. Lawrence Memorial Award	Richard Smalley	Rice University, Houston, Texas
Ernest Guenther Award	Amos B. Smith III	University of Pennsylvania and Monell Chemical Senses Center, Philadelphia
E.V. Murphree Award	James J. Carberry	University of Notre Dame, Ind.
Founders Award	Donald F. Othmer (Emeritus)	Polytechnic University, Brooklyn, N.Y.
Francis P. Garvan-John M. Olin Medal	Edith M. Flanigen	UOP, Terrytown, N.Y.
George C. Pimentel Award	George B. Kauffman	California State University, Fresno
Glenn T. Seaborg Actinide Separations Award	E. Philip Horwitz	Argonne National Laboratory, Ill.
Henry H. Storch Award	Martin L. Gorbaty	Exxon Research & Engineering Co.
Hirschfelder Prize	Benjamin Widom	Cornell University, Ithaca, N.Y.
Izatt-Christensen Award	Eiichi Kimura	Hiroshima University, Japan
James Flack Norris Award	Keith U. Ingold	National Research Council and Carleton University, Ottawa, Ont.
Kilby Young Innovator Award	Richard Smalley	Rice University, Houston, Texas

Scientists of the Year

AWARD	WINNER	AFFILIATION
Linus Pauling Award	Kenneth Wiberg	Yale University, New Haven, Conn.
National Medal of Science	Howard Simmons (Retired)	E.I. du Pont de Nemours
National Medal of Technology	Delbert Meyer (Retired)	Amoco Chemical Co.
National Medal of Technology	Paul Weisz	University of Pennsylvania, Philadelphia
Pfizer Award	Michael H. Gelb	University of Washington, Seattle
Priestley Medal	Robert W. Parry	University of Utah, Salt Lake City
Richard C. Tolman Medal	George A. Olah	University of Southern California, Los Angeles
Robert A. Welch Award	Richard E. Smalley	Rice University, Houston, Texas
Roger Adams Award	E. J. Corey	Harvard University, Cambridge, Mass.
Solid-State Chemistry Fellowship Award	William S. Hammack	Carnegie Mellon University, Pittsburgh, Pa.
U.S. Senior Scientist Award	Lester R. Morss	Argonne National Laboratory, Ill.
Wolf Prize	John A. Pople	Carnegie Mellon University, Pittsburgh, Pa.

EARTH SCIENCES

Alexander Agassiz Medal	Joseph L. Reid	Scripps Institution of Oceanography, La Jolla, Calif.
Allen Prize	Chris A. Hostetler	University of Illinois, Urbana-Champaign
Arthur L. Day Medal	Susan W. Kieffer	U.S. Geological Survey
Ben H. Parker Memorial Medal	Wayne A. Pettyjohn	Oklahoma State University, Stillwater
Charles A. Whitten Medal	Irwin Shapiro	Harvard-Smithsonian Center for Astrophysics, Cambridge, Mass.
Charles Doolittle Walcott Medal	Stefan Bengtson	Uppsala University, Sweden
Common Wealth Award	Susan Solomon	National Oceanic and Atmospheric Administration
Donath Medal	John P. Grotzinger	Massachusetts Institute of Technology, Cambridge
Golden Door Award	Farouk el-Baz	Boston University, Mass.
Harry H. Hess Medal	George W. Wetherill	Carnegie Institution of Washington (D.C.)
Henry Bryant Bigelow Award in Oceanography	Alice L. Alldredge	University of California, Santa Barbara
	Mary Wilcox Silver	University of California, Santa Cruz
James B. Macelwane Medal	David G. Sibeck	Johns Hopkins University, Baltimore, Md.
James B. Macelwane Medal	Thorne Lay	University of California, Santa Cruz
John D. and Catherine T. MacArthur Foundation Award	Stephen Schneider	Stanford University, Calif.
	Geerat Vermeij	University of California, Davis
Leadership Award	Walter W. Hays	U.S. Geological Survey
Martin Van Covering Memorial Award	Susan M. Landon	Denver, Colo.
Maurice Ewing Medal	Charles D. Keeling	Scripps Institution of Oceanography, La Jolla, Calif.
National Medal of Science	Eugene Shoemaker	U.S. Geological Survey

438

AWARD	WINNER	AFFILIATION
Penrose Medal	John F. Dewey	University of Oxford, England
Public Service Award	Meredith E. Ostrom (Emeritus)	University of Wisconsin, Madison
Robert Dexter Conrad Award	Robert D. Ballard	Woods Hole Oceanographic Institution, Mass.
Rosenstiel Award	Sallie Chisholm	Massachusetts Institute of Technology, Cambridge
Walter Bucher Medal	Seiya Uyeda	Texas A & M University, College Station, and Tokai University, Tokyo

ELECTRONICS AND INFORMATION SCIENCES

AWARD	WINNER	AFFILIATION
Adolph Lomb Medal	Mohammed N. Islam	AT&T Bell Laboratories
Charles Hard Townes Award	Nick Holonyak, Jr.	University of Illinois Center for Advanced Studies
Engineering Excellence Award	Bertrand H. Johnson	AT&T Bell Laboratories
Engineering Excellence Award	Louis Koszi	AT&T Bell Laboratories
Grace Murray Hopper Award	Feng-hsiung Hsu	IBM Corp.
Industrial Application of Science Award	Nick Holonyak, Jr.	University of Illinois Center for Advanced Studies
John D. and Catherine T. MacArthur Foundation Award	John Holland	University of Michigan, Ann Arbor
John Tyndall Award	Donald B. Keck	Corning Inc.
Marconi International Fellowship Award	James L. Flanagan	Rutgers University, New Brunswick, N.J.
National Medal of Science	W. Lincoln Hawkins (Deceased)	AT&T Bell Laboratories
National Medal of Science	Allen Newell (Deceased)	Carnegie Mellon University, Pittsburgh, Pa.
National Medal of Science	John Whinnery (Retired)	University of California, Berkeley
National Medal of Science	N. Joseph Woodland	IBM Corp.

ENERGY

AWARD	WINNER	AFFILIATION
Award in Petroleum Chemistry	Bruce C. Gates	University of California, Davis
Gold Medal for Distinguished Achievement	Clifton C. Garvin, Jr. (Retired)	Exxon Corp.

ENVIRONMENT

AWARD	WINNER	AFFILIATION
Arthur Dehon Little Award	John R. McWhirter	Pennsylvania State University, University Park
Global 500 Award	Colleen McCrory	New Denver, British Columbia
Goldman Award	Colleen McCrory	New Denver, British Columbia
International Saint Francis Prize for the Environment	Thomas F. Malone	North Carolina State University, Raleigh
John D. and Catherine T. MacArthur Foundation Award	John Terborgh	Duke University, Durham, N.C.
Robert E. Wilson Award	Finis S. Patton, Jr.	Martin Marietta Energy Systems Inc., Oak Ridge, Tenn.
Science and Technology Meritorious Service Medal	Mohamed Noordin Hassan	Former Minister of Science, Technology, and the Environment, Malaysia
T.J. Hamilton Memorial Award	Richard D. Siegel	ENSR Consulting & Engineering, Acton, Mass.

AWARD	WINNER	AFFILIATION
Sasakawa Environment Prize	Yuri Izrael	Russia
	Geping Qu	Environmental Protection Agency, Beijing, China
Tyler Prize for Environmental Achievement	Perry L. McCarty	Stanford University, Calif.
	Robert M. White	National Academy of Engineering

FOOD AND AGRICULTURE

Frank N. Meyer Medal	Carlos Ochoa	International Potato Center, Lima, Peru
John D. and Catherine T. MacArthur Foundation Award	Wes Jackson	Land Institute, Salina, Kan.
John D. and Catherine T. MacArthur Foundation Award	Sharon Long	Stanford University, Calif.
Outstanding Senior Scientist	Orville A. Levander	U.S. Department of Agriculture
Outstanding Senior Scientist	Timothy L. Mounts	U.S. Department of Agriculture
Superior Performance Award	Paul F. O'Connell	U.S. Department of Agriculture
World Food Prize	Raymond Bushland (Retired)	U.S. Department of Agriculture
	Edward Knipling (Retired)	U.S. Department of Agriculture

LIFE SCIENCES

Alfred Bader Award	W. Wallace Cleveland	University of Wisconsin, Madison
Arthur C. Cope Scholar Award	Tohru Fukuyama	Rice University, Houston, Texas
Arthur C. Cope Scholar Award	Andrew G. Myers	California Institute of Technology, Pasadena
Arthur C. Cope Scholar Award	Chi-huey Wong	University of California, San Diego
Award in Molecular Biology	Bruce Baker	Stanford University, Calif.
	Thomas W. Cline	University of California, Berkeley
Charles A. Dana Award	Masakazu Konishi	California Institute of Technology
	Fernando Nottebohm	Rockefeller University, New York, N.Y.
Crafoord Prize	Adolf Seilacher	Germany
Daniel Giraud Elliot Medal	George C. Williams (Emeritus)	State University of New York, Stony Brook
Gairdner Foundation International Award	Leland H. Hartwell	University of Washington, Seattle
Gairdner Foundation International Award	Yoshio Masui	University of Toronto, Ont.
Gairdner Foundation International Award	Paul M. Nurse	University of Oxford, England
Golden Brain Award	William Newsome	Stanford University, Calif.
Gold Medal of the Acoustical Society of America	Ira J. Hirsh	Washington University, St. Louis, Mo.
Henry Shaw Medal	José Sarukán Kermez	National Autonomous University of Mexico, Coyoacán
Inventor of the Year Award	Ray Schwarz	Lyndon B. Johnson Space Center, Texas
	Tinh Trinh	Lyndon B. Johnson Space Center
	David Wolf	Lyndon B. Johnson Space Center
John D. and Catherine T. MacArthur Foundation Award	Gunter Wagner	Yale University, New Haven, Conn.

AWARD	WINNER	AFFILIATION
King Faisal International Prize for Science	Sydney Brenner	Medical Research Council, Cambridge, England
Leeuwenhoek Medal	Carl Woese	University of Illinois, Urbana-Champaign
Marvin J. Johnson Award	Alexander M. Klibanov	Massachusetts Institute of Technology, Cambridge
National Medal of Science	Howard Temin	University of Wisconsin, Madison
Nichols Medal	Koji Nakanishi	Columbia University, New York, N.Y.
Pfizer Award	Carl Pabo	Massachusetts Institute of Technology, Cambridge
Professional Progress Award	Michael L. Shuler	Cornell University, Ithaca, N.Y.
Repligen Award	Jeremy R. Knowles	Harvard University, Cambridge, Mass.
Rumford Premium	Joseph J. Katz	Argonne National Laboratory, Ill.
Rumford Premium	James R. Norris	Argonne National Laboratory, Ill.
Walter J. Johnson Prize	Donald E. Gullberg	Uppsala, Sweden
	James M. Pash	National Institutes of Health
	Mark Thiry	University of Liège, Belgium

MATERIALS SCIENCES

AWARD	WINNER	AFFILIATION
Charles M.A. Stine Award	Robert Langer	Massachusetts Institute of Technology, Cambridge
International Ceramics Prize	Robert E. Newnham	Pennsylvania State University, University Park
Prize for Industrial Applications of Physics	François M. d'Heurle	IBM Corp.

MATHEMATICS

AWARD	WINNER	AFFILIATION
Award in Applied Mathematics and Numerical Analysis	Andrew J. Majda	Princeton University, N.J.
Award in Mathematics	Robert MacPherson	Massachusetts Institute of Technology, Cambridge
Citation for Public Service	Andre Z. Manitius	George Mason University, Fairfax, Va.
Distinguished Public Service Award	I.M. Singer	Massachusetts Institute of Technology, Cambridge
John D. and Catherine T. MacArthur Foundation Award	Ingrid Daubechies	Rutgers University, New Brunswick, N.J.
John D. and Catherine T. MacArthur Foundation Award	Philip U. Treisman	University of Texas, Austin
Leroy P. Steele Prize	Jacques Dixmier	University of Paris
Leroy P. Steele Prize	Peter D. Lax	Courant Institute of Mathematical Sciences
Oswald Veblen Prize	Andrew J. Casson	University of California, Berkeley
Oswald Veblen Prize	Clifford H. Taubes	Harvard University, Cambridge, Mass.
Rumford Medal	H.N.V. Temperley (Emeritus)	University of Wales, Cardiff
Ruth Lyttle Satter Prize	Dusa McDuff	State University of New York, Stony Brook
Steele Career Prize	Armand Borel	Institute for Advanced Study, Princeton, N.J.

AWARD	WINNER	AFFILIATION
Steele Prize for a Fundamental Paper	Eugenio Calabi	University of Pennsylvania, Philadelphia

MEDICAL SCIENCES

AWARD	WINNER	AFFILIATION
Award for Creative Invention	Albert A. Carr	Marion Merrell Dow Research Institute, Cincinnati, Ohio
Bower Award and Prize	Denis P. Burkitt (Retired)	Medical Research Council, England
Canadian Doctoral Prize	Kerry Reimer	Carlsberg Research Centre, Denmark
Charles A. Dana Award	Stanley B. Prusiner	University of California, San Francisco
Ciba-Geigy Animal Health Prize	Albert Osterhaus	National Institute for Public Health and Environmental Protection, Bilthoven, The Netherlands
Distinguished Achievement Award	Bernadine P. Healy	National Institutes of Health
Distinguished Scientist of the Year	John R. Gorham	U.S. Department of Agriculture
Distinguished Service Award	John W. Eckstein (Emeritus)	University of Iowa, Iowa City
Distinguished Service Citation	Alfred S. Ercolano (Retired)	College of American Pathologists, Washington, D.C.
Distinguished Service Citation	Lew R. Wasserman	MCA Corp.
Eli Lilly Award	Stuart L. Schreiber	Harvard University, Cambridge, Mass.
Elliott Cresson Medal	Lap-Chee Tsui	Hospital for Sick Children, Toronto, Ont.
Farrington Daniels Award	Robert J. Schulz (Emeritus)	Yale University, New Haven, Conn.
	M. Saiful Huq	Thomas Jefferson University, Philadelphia, Pa.
	Natarajan Venkataramanan	Winthrop Hospital, Mineola, N.Y.
	Kazi Motakabbir	Yale University, New Haven, Conn.
Gairdner Foundation Wightman Award	John R. Evans	Allelix Biopharmaceuticals Inc., Mississauga, Ont.
Gairdner Foundation International Award	Richard Peto	University of Oxford, England
Gairdner Foundation International Award	Bert Vogelstein	Johns Hopkins University, Baltimore, Md.
Gairdner Foundation International Award	Robert A. Weinberg	Massachusetts Institute of Technology, Cambridge
Joseph B. Goldberger Award	Charles H. Halsted	University of California, Davis
Karl Landsteiner Memorial Award	Paul I. Terasaki	University of California, Los Angeles
King Faisal International Prize for Medicine	Attilio Maseri	Catholic University of Rome and Policlinico Agostino Gemelli
Manning Award	Kelvin Ogilvie	Acadia University, Wolfville, Nova Scotia
Marie Curie Award	Linda K. Olson	University of California, San Diego
National Esselen Award	Bruce N. Ames	University of California, Berkeley
National Medal of Technology	Charles Kelman	New York Medical College
National Medal of Technology	Merck & Co.	Rahway, N.J.
Sylvia Sorkin Greenfield Award	D. Louis Collins	McGill University, Montreal, Quebec
	Christopher J. Henri	McGill University, Montreal, Quebec
	Terence M. Peters	McGill University and McConnell Brain Imaging Centre, Montreal
Tetalman Memorial Award	Mark A. Green	Purdue University, W. Lafayette, Ind.

AWARD	WINNER	AFFILIATION
William D. Coolidge Award	Nagalingam Suntharalingam	Thomas Jefferson University, Philadelphia, Pa.

OPTICAL ENGINEERING

Albert A. Michelson Medal	John W. Hardy (Retired)	Litton Itek Optical Systems, Lexington, Mass.
David Richardson Medal	Ichiro Kitano	Nippon Sheet Glass Co.
Engineering Excellence Award	LeRoy D. Dickson	IBM Corp.
Engineering Excellence Award	Jitendra S. Goela	Morton International
Engineering Excellence Award	Anthony Phillips	GCA Tropel, Fairport, N.Y.
Engineering Excellence Award	Michael A. Pickering	Morton International
Engineering Excellence Award	Raymond L. Taylor	Morton International
Frederic Ives Medal	Robert W. Terhune	Jet Propulsion Laboratory, California Institute of Technology, Pasadena
Joseph Fraunhofer Award	James C. Wyant	University of Arizona and WYKO Corp., Tuscon
Max Born Award	Rodney Loudon	University of Essex, England
R.W. Wood Prize	Yuri N. Denisyuk	A.F. Ioffe Physical-Technical Institute, St. Petersburg, Russia

PHYSICS

Award in Magnetism	Arthur Freeman	Northwestern University, Evanston, Ill.
Boltzmann Medal	Joel L. Lebowitz	Rutgers University, New Brunswick, N.J.
Boltzmann Medal	Giorgio Parisi	University of Rome
Charles Vernon Boys Prize	Nicolas Ellis	CERN (European Laboratory for Particle Physics)
Dannie Heineman Prize for Mathematical Physics	Stanley Mandelstam	University of California, Berkeley
Davisson-Germer Prize	Larry Spruch	New York University
Delmer S. Fahrney Medal	Harold P. Furth	Princeton University, Princeton, N.J.
Dirac Medal	N.N. Bogolubov (Deceased)	Joint Institute of Nuclear Research, Dubna, Russia
Dirac Medal	Yakov Sinai	Landau Institute, Moscow
Duddell Award	Peter F. Smith	Rutherford Appelton Laboratory, Oxfordshire, England
E.O. Lawrence Memorial Award	Zachary Fisk	Los Alamos National Laboratory, N.M.
E.O. Lawrence Memorial Award	Richard Fortner	Lawrence Livermore National Laboratory, Calif.
E.O. Lawrence Memorial Award	Rulon Linford	Los Alamos National Laboratory
E.O. Lawrence Memorial Award	Pace Van Devender	Sandia National Laboratories
Excellence in Plasma Physics Research Award	Nathaniel J. Fisch	Princeton University, Princeton, N.J.
Farrington Daniels Award	Bruce A. Faddegon	National Research Council of Canada, Ottawa, Ont.
	David W.O. Rogers	National Research Council of Canada, Ottawa, Ont.
	Carl K. Ross	National Research Council of Canada, Ottawa, Ont.

Scientists of the Year

AWARD	WINNER	AFFILIATION
Forum Award	Luis Masperi	Atomic Center, Bariloche, and Instituto Balseiro, Argentina
	Luis Pinguelli Rosa	Federal University of Rio de Janeiro, Brazil
	Alberto Ridner	Argentine National Atomic Energy Commission, Buenos Aires
	Fernando de Souza Barros	Federal University of Rio de Janeiro, Brazil
Franklin Medal	Frederick Reines	University of California, Irvine
Herzberg Medal	Robert Kiefl	University of British Columbia, Vancouver
Hughes Medal	M.J. Seaton (Emeritus)	University College, London
John Price Wetherill Medal	Gerald Brown	State University of New York, Stony Brook
Karl Taylor Compton Medal	Victor Weisskopf (Emeritus)	Massachusetts Institute of Technology, Cambridge
Lilienfeld Prize	Claude N. Cohen-Tannoudji	Collège de France, Paris
Lilienfeld Prize	Alan H. Guth	Massachusetts Institute of Technology, Cambridge
Max Born Prize	Joachim Heintze	Heidelberg, Germany
Maxwell Medal and Prize	Neil Turok	Imperial College, London
National Medal of Science	Calvin Quate	Stanford University, Calif.
Oersted Medal	Eugen Merzbacher	University of North Carolina, Chapel Hill
R. Bruce Lindsay Award	Anthony A. Atchley	Naval Postgraduate School, Monterey, Calif.
Rutherford Award	Erwin Gabathuler	CERN (European Laboratory for Particle Physics)
	Terry Sloan	CERN
Shock Compression Science Award	Lev Vladimirovich Al'tshuler	Russian Academy of Sciences, Moscow
Simon Ramo Award	Wim Pieter Leemans	Lawrence Berkeley Laboratory, Calif.
Stuart Ballantine Medal	Rolf Landauer	IBM Corp.
Szilard Award	Kurt Gottfried	Cornell University, Ithaca, N.Y.
Tom W. Bonner Prize	Henry G. Blosser	Michigan State University, East Lansing
	Robert E. Pollock	Indiana University, Bloomington
Wigner Medal	Julius Wess	University of Munich and Max Planck Institute, Germany
	Bruno Zumino	University of California, Berkeley
Will Allis Prize	James E. Lawler	University of Wisconsin, Madison
William F. Meggers Award	Joseph Reader	National Institute of Standards and Technology
Wilson Prize	Rolf Wideroe (Retired)	Brown Boveri & Cie., Baden, Switzerland
W.K.H. Panofsky Prize	Robert Palmer	Brookhaven National Laboratory, Upton, N.Y.
	Nicholas Samios	Brookhaven National Laboratory
	Ralph Shutt	Brookhaven National Laboratory
Wolf Prize	Joseph H. Taylor, Jr.	Princeton University, Princeton, N.J.

AWARD	WINNER	AFFILIATION
PSYCHOLOGY		
Award for Distinguished Scientific Achievement in Psychology	Richard Haier	University of California, Irvine
National Medal of Science	Eleanor Gibson (Emerita)	Cornell University, Ithaca, N.Y.
Troland Research Award	Martha Farah	Carnegie Mellon University, Pittsburgh, Pa.
SCIENCE WRITING		
American Institute of Physics Science Writing Award	Harold W. Lewis (Emeritus)	University of California, Santa Barbara
Childrens Science Writing Award	Gloria Skurzynski	Salt Lake City, Utah
James T. Grady-James H. Stack Award	Tom Siegfried	*Dallas Morning News*
Steele Prize for Expository Writing	Jean-François Treves	Rutgers University, New Brunswick, N.J.
Walter Sullivan Award	Cory Dean	*New York Times*
OTHER AWARDS		
Award for Scientific Reviewing	Robert T. Watson	NASA
Distinguished Service Award	Ruth Hubbard (Emerita)	Harvard University, Cambridge, Mass.
Einstein Peace Prize	Hans A. Bethe (Emeritus)	Cornell University, Ithaca, N.Y.
	Joseph Rotblat (Emeritus)	University of London
John D. and Catherine T. MacArthur Foundation Award	Evelyn Fox Keller	University of California, Berkeley
Medal for Outstanding Career Achievements	Jane H. Wallace	U.S. Geological Survey
National Medal of Science	Maxine Singer	Carnegie Institution of Washington (D.C.)
National Medal of Technology	Joseph Juran (Emeritus)	Juran Institute, Wilton, Conn.
Theodore van Karman Award	B.J. Habibie	Minister of Research and Technology, Indonesia
Westinghouse Science Talent Search	1. Elizabeth M. Pine	Illinois Mathematics and Science Academy, Aurora
	2. Xanthi M. Merlo	Washington Park High School, Racine, Wis.
	3. Lenhard Lee Ng	Chapel Hill High School, Chapel Hill, N.C.
	4. Constance Lee Chen	La Jolla High School, San Diego, Calif.
	5. Ryan D. Egeland	Wayzata Senior High School, Plymouth, Minn.
	6. Wei-Hwa Huang	Montgomery Blair High School, Silver Spring, Md.
	7. Mahesh K. Mahanthappa	Fairview High School, Boulder, Colo.
	8. Steve S.T. Chien	Montgomery Blair High School, Silver Spring, Md.
	9. Elizabeth D. Mann	Montgomery Blair High School, Silver Spring, Md.
	10. Zachary Z. Freyberg	Midwood High School, Brooklyn, N.Y.

Obituaries

Asimov, Isaac (Jan. 2, 1920—April 6, 1992), U.S. science-fiction writer, explored extraterrestrial horizons and the role of robotics in a futuristic society as the enormously popular and prolific author of more than 400 books. Among the most notable were *Foundation* (1951), *Foundation and Empire* (1952), and *Second Foundation* (1953), a panoramic trilogy detailing the impending collapse of a far-flung galactic empire and the work of an organization of psychologists and social scientists to sow the conditions for a better empire to follow. Asimov, a self-described compulsive writer, was renowned for the clarity of his writing and for his superb storytelling. He was credited both with popularizing science-fiction writing and with elevating the genre from pulp-adventure stories to a higher intellectual plane, encompassing sociology, history, mathematics, and science. He also published nonfiction books on such wide-ranging subjects as the Bible, Shakespeare, Gilbert and Sullivan, humor, limericks, history, and a variety of scientific topics. A precocious child who immigrated to the U.S. with his family when he was three, Asimov sold his first story, "Marooned off Vesta," to the magazine *Amazing Stories* in 1938. Three years later *Astounding Science Fiction* magazine published "Nightfall," which describes the shattering events that take place on the planet Lagash, a world with six suns, when, during an eclipse, the stars make their once-in-2,000-year appearance. The story was hailed as a masterpiece and 30 years later was voted by the Science Fiction Writers of America as the best science-fiction short story ever written. A year after earning (1948) a Ph.D. in chemistry from Columbia University, New York City, Asimov joined the faculty of Boston University; after 1958 he did not teach or receive a salary, but he remained professionally associated with the university. Asimov published his first book, *Pebble in the Sky,* in 1950 and followed

Isaac Asimov
AP/Wide World

it with the short-story collection *I, Robot,* which included his famous "Three Laws of Robotics" that helped establish the popular conception of robots, both fictional and real, as benign creations rather than monsters bent on destroying humanity. Asimov was awarded numerous prizes and awards for his works, including five Hugos (given by fans) and three Nebula Awards (given by fellow science-fiction writers). Among his remarkable output are *The Stars, like Dust* (1951), *The Chemicals of Life* (1954), *The Caves of Steel* (1954), *Inside the Atom* (1956), *The Naked Sun* (1957), *The Human Brain* (1964), *ABC's of Ecology* (1972), *Asimov's Guide to Science* (1972), *The Gods Themselves* (1972), *Our World in Space* (1974), *Views of the Universe* (1981), *The Robots of Dawn* (1983), *Foundation's Edge* (1982), *Foundation and Earth* (1986), *Prelude to Foundation* (1988), *Nemesis* (1989), *Asimov Laughs Again* (1992), and *Forward the Foundation,* scheduled to be published posthumously. He also produced two volumes of autobiography, *In Memory Yet Green: The Autobiography of Isaac Asimov, 1920–1954* (1979) and *In Joy Still Felt: The Autobiography of Isaac Asimov, 1954–1978* (1980), and regularly contributed to several magazines, including *Fantasy and Science Fiction, Isaac Asimov's Science Fiction,* and *American Humanist.*

Bacon, Francis Thomas (Dec. 21, 1904—May 24, 1992), British engineer, developed the first practical hydrogen-oxygen fuel cells, which convert air and fuel directly into electricity through electrochemical processes. This high-efficiency, pollution-free technology gained its first practical application in the U.S. space program, which used Bacon's alkaline fuel cells to provide in-flight power, heat, and clean drinking water (a by-product of the electrochemical reaction) in Apollo space vehicles. A graduate of Eton College and Trinity College, Cambridge (B.A., 1925; M.A., 1946), Bacon became intrigued with fuel cells while working (1925–40) for the electrical company C.A. Parsons Co. Ltd. in Newcastle-on-Tyne. Although Sir William Grove had discovered the principle of fuel cells in 1842, they were considered a scientific curiosity until the early 1940s, when Bacon, then working at King's College, London, proposed their use in submarines. He continued his research with the Anti-Submarine Experimental Establishment, then returned (1946) to Cambridge, where he demonstrated a successful six-kilowatt fuel cell in 1959. As principal consultant to National Research Development Corp. (1956–62), Energy Conservation Ltd. (1962–71), and the U.K. Atomic Energy Authority (1971–73), Bacon sought new applications for fuel cells. By the 1990s there were fuel-cell power plants in operation in Japan, and the technology was being developed in many other countries. Bacon was made an Officer of the

Order of the British Empire (1967), elected a fellow of the Royal Society (1973), and awarded the first Grove Medal (1991).

Bovet, Daniel (March 23, 1907—April 8, 1992), Swiss-born Italian physiologist, won the 1957 Nobel Prize for Physiology or Medicine for his discoveries of certain synthetic chemotherapeutic substances, notably curare-like muscle relaxants, which are used in conjunction with anesthetics to facilitate surgery, and the first antihistamines, which are effective in the treatment of allergic reactions. Bovet was educated at the University of Geneva (D.Sc., 1929) and took a research position at the Pasteur Institute in Paris. There he found that the dye Prontosil, which had been shown to cure bacterial infections, actually contained a simpler active compound, sulfanilamide. This discovery led to the development of hundreds of antibacterial sulfa "wonder drugs." Bovet was named director of the Pasteur Institute in 1936, and in 1944 he discovered pyrilamine (mepyramine), the first antihistamine. In 1947 he was invited to establish a laboratory of chemotherapeutics at the government-sponsored Superior Institute of Health in Rome. Although he synthesized some 400 compounds that produced curare's paralyzing effects in differing degrees, Bovet filed no patents and received no income from any of his discoveries. Later he moved away from pure research, becoming professor of pharmacology at the University of Sassari (1964–71), director of the psychobiology and psychopharmacology laboratory at the Italian National Research Council (1969–75), and professor of psychobiology at the University of Rome (1971–82).

Eagle, Harry (July 13, 1905—June 12, 1992), U.S. medical scientist, spent more than 60 years delving into such fields as immunology, microbiology, and bacteriology and made numerous discoveries, notably his 1959 formulation, called "Eagle's growth medium," of the essential compounds needed to sustain the reproduction of human and other mammalian cells in the laboratory. This finding was crucial in paving the way for research on viruses, genetic defects, and cancer. Eagle earned his M.D. in 1927 from Johns Hopkins University, Baltimore, Md. For the following 20 years he taught and conducted research there. As director of its Venereal Disease Research Laboratory and Laboratory of Experimental Therapeutics, he devised (during the early 1940s) a diagnostic test for syphilis and helped discover that penicillin was effective in treating the disease. He also found that penicillin could be used to prevent gonorrhea when taken shortly after exposure to infection. Eagle then worked at the National Institutes of Health (1947–61), serving in laboratories devoted to research on cancer, cell biology, and allergy and infectious diseases. During this period he discovered that blood clotting is an enzyme process, devised a

treatment for arsenic poisoning, found a cure for trypanosomiasis (African sleeping sickness), described the metabolic differences between normal and cancerous cells, advanced cancer chemotherapy, and helped develop a freeze-drying technique for long-term storage of perishable lifesaving serums. In 1961 he joined the Cancer Research Center at the Albert Einstein College of Medicine, New York City, where he remained until his retirement in 1988. A year earlier Pres. Ronald Reagan had awarded him the National Medal of Science, the highest science honor in the U.S.

Feinberg, Gerald (May 27, 1933—April 21, 1992), U.S. physicist, contributed significantly to the theoretical basis of particle and atomic physics and endeavored through books and public lectures to make a wide range of science accessible to readers without formal scientific training. In 1958, working with data collected from experiments with muons, heavy relatives of electrons, he wrote perhaps his best-known theoretical paper, arguing that there exist two distinct kinds of particles known as neutrinos (rather than the single neutrino then postulated), one associated with the electron and the other with the muon. Four years later the U.S. physicists Leon Lederman, Melvin Schwartz, and Jack Steinberger confirmed this prediction with their discovery of the muon neutrino in an experiment for which they won the 1988 Nobel Prize for Physics. After earning a Ph.D. in physics (1957) from Columbia University,

Gerald Feinberg
Columbia University;
photo, Eileen Barroso

New York City, Feinberg went on to postdoctoral work at the Institute for Advanced Study, Princeton, N.J., and Brookhaven National Laboratory, Upton, N.Y. He joined the physics department (1959) at Columbia, where he remained the rest of his professional life, becoming full professor (1965) and serving as department chairman (1980–82). A true polymath, Feinberg manifested his diverse interests in several books written for a popular audience, including *The Prometheus Project: Mankind's Search for Long-Range Goals* (1968), *Consequences of Growth* (1977), *What Is the World Made of? Atoms, Leptons, Quarks, and Other Tantalizing Particles* (1977), and *Life Beyond Earth: The Intelligent Earthling's Guide to Life in the Universe* (1980, with Robert Shapiro). For more than two decades his talents for explaining science benefited readers of the *Yearbook of Science and the Future,* for which he contributed the "High-energy physics" section every other year beginning in 1970.

Haury, Emil Walter (May 2, 1904—Dec. 5, 1992), U.S. anthropologist and archaeologist, was for more than 50 years considered one of the preeminent scholars of Southwestern U.S. prehistory. Haury credited a chance introduction to archaeology at a National Geographic Society project site with inspiring him to explore the cultures of the ancient Americas. He received both a B.A. (1927) and an M.A. (1928) from the University of Arizona and a Ph.D. (1934) from Harvard University. Returning to the University of Arizona, he served as head of the department of anthropology (1937–64) and was a full professor (1938–80). During his tenure his department was widely recognized for the excellence of its research and education programs. Haury's own scholarship was exceptionally wide ranging, covering the three major prehistoric cultures—the Hohokam, Mogollon, and Anasazi Indians. His fieldwork and analyses were considered of the highest order. Haury also served as director (1938–64) of the university's Arizona State Museum. He was a member of many boards and committees, was chairman of anthropology at the National Academy of Sciences, and served as an adviser to the National Park Service. His last book, published in 1976, was *The Hohokam, Desert Farmers and Craftsmen: Excavations at Snaketown, 1964–1965.*

Emil Walter Haury

Courtesy of the Arizona State Museum

Hawkins, W(alter) Lincoln (March 21, 1911—Aug. 20, 1992), U.S. chemist and inventor, as a member from 1942 of the technical staff and as assistant director from 1974 to 1976 of the chemical research laboratory at AT&T's Bell Laboratories, Murray Hill, N.J., conducted fundamental research on plastics and on the degradation and stabilization of high polymers. Hawkins, who earned a Ph.D. (1939) in cellulose chemistry from McGill University, Montreal, taught there and did research at Columbia University, New York City, before becoming the first black to join the technical staff at Bell Labs. During World War II he worked on synthetic substitutes for rubber because its supply was under enemy control. Later, with Vincent Lanza, Hawkins discovered antioxidizing agents that gave plastic, which heretofore had rapidly deteriorated, a 70-year useful life span. As a result, heavy, expensive, and unwieldy lead-coated telecommunications wires could be shielded with plastic coatings. This application saved billions of dollars and helped launch worldwide telephone service. After retiring from Bell Labs in 1976, Hawkins served (1976–84) as research director of the Plastics Institute of America, Fairfield, N.J. Both during his career and after his retirement, he helped promote chemistry among minority students and expand science courses at predominately black colleges. He held 18 U.S. and 129 foreign patents. In June 1992 he was awarded the National Medal of Technology by Pres. George Bush in recognition of his scientific achievements and of his efforts on behalf of minority students.

Loutit, John Freeman (Feb. 19, 1910—June 11, 1992), Australian-born hematologist and radiobiologist, was a pioneer in the study of the biological effects of radiation. As the founding director (1947–69) of the Radiobiology Unit of the British Medical Research Council (MRC), he assembled and led interdisciplinary teams that explored the possibility of biological hazards from the peaceful use of atomic energy and indicated that radiation could be effective in the treatment of leukemia and certain other forms of cancer. He also developed a storage medium of acidified citrate and dextrose that extended the shelf life of red blood cells. Loutit accepted (1930) a Rhodes scholarship to the University of Oxford, where he eventually completed his medical education (M.S., 1938; D.M., 1946). He held several clinical appointments (1935–39) and served as director of the South London Blood Transfusion Service (1940–47) before heading the MRC Radiobiology Unit. Loutit resigned as director in 1969, but he continued to work in the unit laboratory until 1988. His best-known book, *Irradiation of Mice and Men,* was published in 1962. Loutit was made Commander of the Order of the British Empire in 1957 and elected a fellow of the Royal Society in 1963.

Barbara McClintock
AP/Wide World

McClintock, Barbara (June 16, 1902—Sept. 2, 1992), U.S. geneticist, during the 1940s and '50s uncovered complex and profound discoveries about the nature of mobile genetic elements; the findings were so revolutionary at the time she presented them (1951) that scientists were unable to verify or comprehend their importance. However, their significance was eventually appreciated, and this work won her the Nobel Prize for Physiology or Medicine in 1983. McClintock, the daughter of a physician, earned a Ph.D. in botany (1927) from Cornell University, Ithaca, N.Y. She taught there and helped show through her laboratory experiments that trait-determining (genetic) information is transferred between chromosomes—a process called crossing over—during cell division. McClintock joined the Carnegie Institution of Washington, D.C., and conducted research on the Indian corn plant (maize) for Carnegie's Cold Spring Harbor (N.Y.) Laboratory, which later became a self-governing organization. There, from 1941 until her death, the maverick researcher worked alone by choice; she preferred receiving letters to telephone calls and only reluctantly installed a telephone in 1986. She possessed an uncanny ability to decipher the nature of genes and was a scrupulous investigator. Using pigmentation changes in the kernels of corn as her model and microscopically examining their chromosomes, she traced how mobile genetic elements (nicknamed "jumping genes" by a later generation of geneticists) cause mutations and control growth and development in cells. Her work was not validated until James D. Watson and Francis Crick discovered the molecular structure of DNA, which led to a rediscovery of mobile elements in the chromosomes of many plants and animals. McClintock won belated acclaim for her work and was revered as a giant in the field of genetics. Besides the Nobel Prize, she was the recipient of the National Medal of Science (1970) and the first MacArthur Laureate Award (1981), a lifetime annual prize of $60,000. A biography that detailed her pioneering work, *A Feeling for the Organism,* appeared in 1983.

Mitchell, Peter Dennis (Sept. 29, 1920—April 10, 1992), British biochemist, received the 1978 Nobel Prize for Chemistry in recognition of his chemiosmotic theory explaining the mechanisms by which energy is converted for use within the cells of living creatures. In 1961 Mitchell and his longtime research associate, Jennifer Moyle, published his theory that the enzyme-studded interior membranes of mitochondria (in animal cells) and chloroplasts (in plant cells) are actively involved in the transfer of energy in food, sunlight, and oxygen to adenosine triphosphate (ATP), the molecule that serves as the "currency" of exchange in cell processes. This breakthrough theory, for which Mitchell had no experimental proof, contradicted all conventional wisdom at that time and was vehemently opposed by most of the scientific community. He persisted in the development of this hypothesis, however, and experimental evidence eventually proved him correct. In 1974 he was made a fellow of the Royal Society, which awarded him its highest honor, the Copley Medal, in 1981. Mitchell studied biochemistry at Jesus College, Cambridge (Ph.D., 1950), and taught there until 1955, when he was named director of the chemical biology unit at the University of Edinburgh. In 1963 he moved to Cornwall, where he founded the Glynn Research Laboratories (from 1987, Glynn Research Institute).

Newell, Allen (March 19, 1927—July 19, 1992), U.S. scientist, studied the nature of the human mind and its thought processes, developed computer models of human cognition, and was credited with pioneering the field of artificial intelligence together with Herbert A. Simon, Marvin Minsky, and John McCarthy. Newell earned a B.S. (1949) from Stanford University and joined (1950) the RAND Corp. in Santa Monica, Calif., as a research scientist before completing work on a Ph.D. (1957) in industrial administration at the Carnegie Institute of Technology (later Carnegie Mellon University), Pittsburgh, Pa. At RAND he became fascinated with the human thought process after working on an air force project to simulate an early-warning radar station. In trying to predict how station crew members would react, he set out to study and simulate human thinking by means of computer programs. By 1955 Newell had teamed up with Simon and Cliff Shaw, and the three designed a computer program, called the General Problem Solver, that could discover proofs for theorems in logic by heuristic search, or "means-ends analysis." They then created list-processing languages, notably IPL-V, the earliest and most important processing language of the 1950s, so that they could program their findings. These discoveries were the foundation for the discipline of artificial intelligence, revolutionized the field of cognitive psychology, and had wide applications in computer science. In the 1980s Newell devised Soar, a sophisticated software system that learned and solved problems in a way similar to human mental processes. After leaving RAND in 1961, he joined the faculty of Carnegie Mellon University, where he helped create the School of Computer Science and served as professor of computer science from 1976 until his death. For his ground-breaking work Newell was the recipient of the Turing Award (1975) and the National Medal of Science, which he received the month before he died. Newell was also the author of numerous scientific papers and 10 books.

Gerard Kitchen O'Neill
UPI/Bettmann

O'Neill, Gerard Kitchen (Feb. 6, 1927—April 27, 1992), U.S. physicist, formulated in 1956 the storage-ring principle for colliding particle beams—that the collision of beams of subatomic particles traveling in opposite directions in storage rings would increase the energy output from particle accelerators—and was an early proponent of establishing permanent, self-sustaining colonies in space as a solution to such terrestrial problems as pollution, overpopulation, and energy shortages. After earning a Ph.D. in physics from Cornell University, Ithaca, N.Y., in 1954, O'Neill joined the faculty at Princeton University, where he taught until his retirement in 1985. Besides his storage-ring principle, which provided the basis for much of the research in particle physics in recent decades, O'Neill designed and publicized during the late 1960s a blueprint for establishing self-supporting habitats in space that would be positioned equidistant from the Earth and the Moon and powered by solar energy. In his book *The High Frontier* (1976), O'Neill maintained that a "breakout" of human beings from Earth was unavoidable.

He was also the author of the graduate-level textbook *Elementary Particle Physics: An Introduction* (1979; with David Cheng), *2081: A Hopeful View of the Human Future* (1981), and *The Technology Edge: Opportunities for America in World Competition* (1983). He formed various private nonprofit organizations devoted to technological development, including the Space Studies Institute and the Geostar Corp., the latter of which supplied the first private satellite navigational system used to guide travel on Earth. At the time of his death, O'Neill was working on a high-speed ground-based form of transportation called a magnetic flight system. It comprised a small-diameter car that would "float" on a magnetic field in a vacuum tube on land or underground, enabling it to traverse the distance from Boston to Los Angeles in about an hour.

Oort, Jan Hendrik (April 28, 1900—Nov. 12, 1992), Dutch astronomer, dominated the quest to understand the nature of the Milky Way Galaxy and was respected as one of the world's preeminent astronomers; he was considered by many to be the father of Dutch astronomy. Oort first studied at the University of Groningen under Jacobus Kapteyn, a pioneer devoted to mapping the Galaxy from photographic plates. With this work as his foundation, Oort focused his attention on stars of high velocity after joining the Leiden (Neth.) Observatory in 1924. By calculating the speeds of various stars, he confirmed in a series of papers published in 1927 that the Galaxy rotates in its own plane around its distant center, a hypothesis first put forth by Bertil Lindblad and now generally accepted. Soon after having been named a professor at Leiden (1935), Oort used the newly emergent science of radio astronomy to determine that the Sun is 30,000 light-years from the center of the Galaxy and takes 225 million years to complete an orbit around it. In 1950 he proposed

Jan Hendrik Oort
The New York Times

that a vast cloud containing billions of Sun-orbiting comets exists beyond the solar system and that when other stars approach it some comets' orbits are altered and can then pass close to the Sun; the existence of the "Oort cloud" became generally accepted by astronomers. Oort lobbied for the construction of what was then the world's largest steerable radio telescope at Dwingeloo; upon its dedication he noted that "the heavens are now wide open." Oort also served as general secretary (1935–48) and president (1958–61) of the International Astronomical Union.

Page, Robert Morris (June 2, 1903—May 15, 1992), U.S. physicist, during the 1930s invented the technology for pulse radar, a system that detects and locates distant objects by sending out short bursts of electromagnetic radiation and then using the intervals between bursts to receive and display the echoes that return from the objects. His invention was vital to the Allies during World War II for detecting enemy planes and other targets. Page initially studied theology while attending Hamline University, St. Paul, Minn., but he changed his major to physics in his senior year. After graduating in 1927, he joined the U.S. Naval Research Laboratory (NRL) in Washington, D.C., and he earned an M.A. (1932) from George Washington University, Washington, D.C. Page conducted pioneering experiments in radar with A. Hoyt Taylor, Lawrence A. Hyland, and Leo C. Young at the same time that a British scientist, Sir Alexander Watson Watt, was doing similar studies. In the 1940s the U.S. and British scientists pooled their work at the Radiation Laboratory of the Massachusetts Institute of Technology. Page, who held 75 patents on inventions in precision electronics, developed the first radar duplexer capable of using a single antenna for transmitting and receiving; the planned position indicator, the first radar technology to identify the direction and range of a target simultaneously; and Project Madre, a radar system that could bend its beam to the curve of the Earth and thus "see" over the horizon. Page successively served at the NRL as a physicist and head of the Radar Research Section (1938–45), superintendent of Radio Division III (1945–52), associate director of research in electronics (1952–57), and director of research (1957–66). He was the recipient of the Distinguished Civilian Service Award (1945), the Presidential Certificate of Merit (1946), and the President's Award for Distinguished Federal Civilian Service (1960). Page was the author of *The Origin of Radar* (1962).

Paine, Thomas Otten (Nov. 9, 1921—May 4, 1992), U.S. government official, presided over the U.S. National Aeronautics and Space Administration (NASA) from March 1969 to September 1970, when the space program reached a zenith in exploration. Paine, who succeeded James Webb (*q.v.*)

as head of NASA, was at the helm when the first men landed on the Moon in 1969. During Paine's tenure at NASA, he helped restructure the agency, which was still reeling from the 1967 deaths of three astronauts in a fire on the launching pad. He was appointed deputy administrator of NASA by Pres. Lyndon Johnson in 1968. Though seven Apollo missions were launched during Paine's relatively short time as NASA's administrator, public and political support for the expensive space program waned, partly because of the high costs associated with the Vietnam war. When NASA's budget was drastically reduced, Paine stepped down and returned to General Electric (GE), where he had worked for 25 years before joining NASA. Paine was a Ph.D. graduate (1949) in physical metallurgy from Stanford University. During World War II he served in the navy as a submarine officer. While at GE he was a research associate in the company's laboratory in Schenectady, N.Y., manager of engineering applications, and manager of Tempo, the company's think tank in Santa Barbara, Calif. He left GE in 1976 to join the Northrop Corp., from which he retired in 1982.

Rainey, Froelich Gladstone (June 18, 1907—Oct. 11, 1992), U.S. archaeologist and anthropologist, as the director (1947–76) of the Museum of Archaeology and Anthropology at the University of Pennsylvania, spearheaded some 230 expeditions, many of which focused on research in the Arctic and West Indies. Rainey earned a B.A. from the University of Chicago and a Ph.D. in English from the American School in France and another in anthropology from Yale University. From 1935 to 1942 he served as professor of anthropology at the University of Alaska. As a young researcher there, he was among one of the first to discover major artifacts supporting the theory that humans migrated across the Bering Strait to North America. He found bones that hunters had fashioned as spears when they killed game for food. During World War II, Rainey served on the Board of Economic Warfare and orchestrated a mission in Ecuador to hijack bark that had been gathered for shipment to Germany for use as quinine. As museum director at the University of Pennsylvania, he was responsible for helping to revive and expand the museum's budget and collections. He organized expeditions on six continents, notably ones to the ancient Greek community of Sybaris; Ban Chiang, Thailand, renowned for its Bronze Age artifacts; and Tikal, Guatemala, prized for its Mayan treasures. In 1951 Rainey launched and served as the host of the unexpectedly successful network television program "What in the World," a game show that was broadcast from Philadelphia. The show, which ran until 1955, invited a panel of experts to identify the origin and purpose of archaeological artifacts. Rainey, a longtime contributor to the *Yearbook of Science*

451

and the Future, was also the founder of *Expedition* magazine and the author of such books as *Eskimo Prehistory* (1941) and the autobiographical *Reflections of a Digger* (1992).

Rocard, Yves-André (May 22, 1903—March 16, 1992), French mathematician and physicist, contributed to the development of the French atomic bomb and to the understanding of such diverse fields of research as semiconductors, seismology, and radio astronomy. Rocard received doctorates in mathematics (1927) and physical science (1928) from the École Normale Supérieure (ENS) in Paris and went to work in the electronics industry. During World War II he joined the Resistance and supplied British scientific intelligence with vital information, including details on a new radio navigational beam station. For this assistance he was made Commander of the Order of the British Empire (1946). He was later awarded the French Legion of Honour and the Order of Merit. After the war Rocard returned to the ENS as head of the physics department, and in 1951 he was named to the French Atomic Energy Commission. His professional reputation suffered somewhat in later years when he concentrated on the scientific study of biomagnetism and dowsing. Rocard's son, Michel, served as French prime minister from 1988 to 1991.

Salk, Lee (Dec. 27, 1926—May 2, 1992), U.S. child psychologist, as an expert on family relationships, stressed the crucial role played by the family in fostering the development of children; he popularized his views about the emergence of changing American values regarding the upbringing of children as the author of eight books, as a columnist for *McCall's* magazine, and as a frequent guest on such television shows as "Today," "Good Morning America," and "Nightline." Salk earned his A.B., M.A., and Ph.D. from the University of Michigan and first gained public acclaim when he published (1960) a study demonstrating that newborn babies exposed to the sound of a mother's heartbeat were more tranquil than those who were placed in a quiet environment. He advised parents to pick up their crying babies without worrying about spoiling them and stirred controversy when in his 1973 book, *What Every Child Would Like His Parents to Know,* he cautioned against abandoning full-time motherhood. His popularity was attributed to his reliance on common sense, and he urged parents to tell their children the truth and to discipline them in a consistent manner. He pioneered research in sudden infant death syndrome and on the effects of early experiences on later behavior and at the time of his death was studying the relationship between adolescent suicide and conditions at the time of a child's birth. Some of his books include *How to Raise a Human Being* (1969), *Preparing for Parenthood: Understanding Your Feel-*

ings About Pregnancy, Childbirth, and Your Baby (1975), *My Father, My Son: Intimate Relationships* (1982), and *Familyhood, Nurturing the Values That Matter,* which was published posthumously. At the time of his death, Salk was a professor of psychology in pediatrics and psychiatry at Cornell University Medical Center, Ithaca, N.Y., attending psychologist at two New York City medical centers, and adjunct professor at Brown University, Providence, R.I. His older brother, Jonas, developed a vaccine for poliomyelitis, and his other brother, Herman, was a renowned veterinarian.

Sheehan, John Clark (Sept. 23, 1915—March 21, 1992), U.S. chemist, synthesized the penicillin molecule in 1957 after spending nine years developing a successful method. This task was so formidable that many scientists had deemed it impossible. Though natural penicillin had been discovered in 1928 by Sir Alexander Fleming, it took months to generate the antibiotic from mold cultures. Sheehan's process, though quicker, was more complex and was not commercially successful until the 1960s, when scientists used his basic research to turn out hundreds of kinds of bacteria-specific penicillin drugs. Sheehan was also credited with discovering ampicillin, a semisynthetic penicillin that could be taken orally rather than by injection. After earning (1941) a Ph.D. in organic chemistry from the University of Michigan, he worked as a senior research chemist at Merck & Co., Rahway, N.J., before joining (1946) the faculty of the Massachusetts Institute of Technology. It was there, where he remained for more than 30 years, that he conducted his pioneering work on the synthesis of penicillin; his research was partly funded by Bristol Laboratories of Syracuse, N.Y. Earlier, Sheehan and W.E. Bachmann of the University of Michigan had discovered a new explosive (HMX) that was important to the military during World War II. They also devised a new and practical process of manufacturing the military high explosive RDX (cyclonite, cyclotrimethylenetrinitramine). Sheehan was the author of more than 100 scientific papers and one book, *The Enchanted Ring: The Untold Story of Penicillin* (1982).

Smith, Cyril Stanley (Oct. 4, 1903—Aug. 25, 1992), British-born U.S. metallurgist, made important contributions to several different scientific disciplines during his long career. He was first noted for determining (1943–44) the properties and technology of plutonium and uranium—needed for the construction of the atomic bombs that were first exploded in 1945—and he later advanced the use of metallography in the examination of archaeological artifacts. After graduating (1924) from the University of Birmingham, Smith pursued his studies in the U.S. at the Massachusetts Institute of Technology (MIT), where he earned a Ph.D. in 1926. He then spent

15 years with the American Brass Co. at Waterbury, Conn., conducting research on copper alloys. From 1936 to 1942 he helped Martha Teach Gnudi translate Vannoccio Biringuccio's *Pirotechnia,* which had appeared in 1540 in Italian and was the first printed work on metallurgy. Smith, who was recognized as an expert on metals through his various writings, was recruited to join the Manhattan Project at Los Alamos, N.M., where he directed (1943–46) the preparation of the active metals for the first three atomic bombs and did research on tungsten carbide and boron. He then served as founding director (1946–56) of the Institute for the Study of Metals at the University of Chicago before moving to MIT in 1960 to hold dual posts in the departments of metallurgy and humanities. There he established the laboratory for research in archaeological materials and examined the structure of inorganic matter by analyzing the shape of metal grains. Some of his writings include *A Search for Structure* (1981), *From Art to Science* (1980), and *A History of Metallography: The Development of Ideas on the Structure of Metals to 1890* (1988). Smith was awarded the Presidential Medal for Merit (1946), the Platinum Medal of the Institute of Metals, London (1970), and the Dexter Award of the American Chemical Society (1981).

Stirling, Sir James Frazer (April 22, 1926—June 25, 1992), British architect, designed public buildings and multiunit housing that, while often criticized or misunderstood by the general public, were regarded as classics of Postmodernism. Stirling trained at the University of Liverpool's School of Architecture (1945–50) and worked for the firm of Lyons, Israel and Ellis in London until 1956, when he formed a partnership with James Gowan. Stirling and Gowan's projects were commonly identified as New Brutalist (an English reaction against the International Style), which emphasized functional principles and materials, including exposed concrete and brick ma-

Sir James Frazer Stirling
Camera Press/Globe Photos

sonry. Their commissions included low-rise housing units in London's Ham Common (built in 1957) and the award-winning engineering building at the University of Leicester (1959–63). After Stirling's breakup with Gowan in 1963, his style evolved into a more avant-garde high-tech Postmodernism. One building, the University of Cambridge history faculty library (1964–67), proved to be so unpopular that British anti-Modernists used it as a rallying point, while a concrete housing project at Runcorn New Town (1967–76) was later demolished. The Neue Staatsgalerie (1977–84) in Stuttgart, Germany, a combination of classicism and colorful geometric abstraction designed by Stirling and his partner (from 1971) Michael Wilford, was heralded as an icon of Postmodernism. Stirling won the Royal Institute of British Architects' Gold Medal in 1980 and the Pritzker Prize in 1981. In 1991, after a long and bitter fight, planning permission was granted for his controversial No. 1 Poultry, to be built in the heart of London's conservation area. He was knighted only 12 days before his death.

Volwiler, Ernest Henry (Aug. 22, 1893—Oct. 3, 1992), U.S. chemist, as the developer with Donalee Tabern of two important drugs, made pioneering contributions to pharmacology while working at Abbott Laboratories near Chicago. In 1930 the two developed Nembutal, a barbiturate that could induce sleep within 20 minutes without causing a hangover or side effects, and in 1936 they produced sodium pentothal ("truth serum"), a highly effective anesthetic that was also used to treat mental disorders. Volwiler received a B.A. (1914) from Miami University, Oxford, Ohio, and an M.A. (1916) and Ph.D. (1918) from the University of Illinois. He joined Abbott Laboratories as plant chemist in 1918, successively serving as chief chemist (1920–30), director of research (1930–33), vice president in charge of research and development (1933–46), executive vice president (1946–50), president (1950–58), and chairman (1958–59). Volwiler was the recipient of the Modern Pioneers Award (1940), the Priestley Medal (1958), and the Gold Medal of the American Institute of Chemists (1960). He was inducted into the National Inventors Hall of Fame in 1986.

Voorhees, Arthur B., Jr. (1922—May 12, 1992), U.S. physician, constructed and implanted the first successful artificial artery in a human patient. In 1947, when Voorhees was conducting a postmortem examination of a laboratory animal, he discovered that a silk suture had inadvertently been left in a ventricular cavity several weeks earlier. He observed that the thread had become coated with natural endocardial tissue cells. That discovery launched his pioneering work in fashioning arterial prosthetic materials. His first artery was made from a silk handkerchief, and the next one was improved by the use of vinyon-N cloth, a Union Carbide Co. remnant left from the manufacture of World War II parachutes. One of his first designs was implanted in a dog, which lived several years after the surgery. In 1952, during an emergency operation at Columbia-Presbyterian Hospital in New York City, he was forced (there were no animal or human graft donors available) to use his synthetic artery on a human patient who had a ruptured aortic aneurysm. Voorhees successfully completed that surgery and 18 others similar to it. His basic procedure was refined and modified by other surgeons, who used a variety of new materials, as they became available, to replace blocked, ruptured, or defective vascular tissue. After Voorhees graduated from the University of Virginia in 1943, he attended the Columbia College of Physicians and Surgeons, where he completed his medical residency. He set up a private practice in 1953 and was attending physician at Columbia-Presbyterian Hospital until his retirement in 1983.

Webb, James Edwin (Oct. 7, 1906—March 27, 1992), U.S. government official, guided the U.S. National Aeronautics and Space Administration (NASA) from its infancy in 1961 into one of its most ambitious periods, culminating with the Apollo manned landing on the Moon in 1969. Webb, a skilled administrator and even-tempered manager, conceived plans and implemented them to help in America's bid to gain dominance in space over the Soviet Union, which in 1957 had forged the space-race lead by launching Sputnik 1, the first artificial satellite. During Webb's tenure NASA scored numerous successes, including America's first manned space flight, by Alan B. Shepard, Jr.; the first orbital flight, by John Glenn; the first two-man flights; and the first walk in space, by Edward H. White II. Other accomplishments included unmanned flights to observe Venus and Mars, the development of militarily and commercially important weather and communi-

James Edwin Webb
NASA

cations satellites, and technical innovations in aviation. Though no astronauts were lost in space while Webb was in office, three died in a capsule fire during a routine ground test on Jan. 27, 1967, and the Apollo program had to be restructured. Though he left NASA a few months before the lunar landing, Webb was still credited with reaching the goal given him by Pres. John F. Kennedy in 1961—landing men on the Moon within a decade. Earlier he had served in the federal government as director of the Bureau of the Budget (1946–49) and under secretary of state (1949–52). He was a lawyer by profession and also had been a successful businessman, holding high executive positions in Sperry Gyroscope Corp. and Kerr-McGee Oil Industries.

Zygmund, Antoni (Dec. 26, 1900—May 30, 1992), Polish-born mathematician, as a university professor in Europe and after 1947 at the University of Chicago, exerted a major influence on 20th-century mathematics through his research, his teaching, and the work of his students. Zygmund's interest lay in the broad division of mathematics known as analysis, and he was particularly well known for his contributions to harmonic analysis, a field relied on in science and technology for the formulation of descriptions of periodic phenomena such as waves, vibrations, and regularly repeating structures. In 1986 he received the U.S. National Medal of Science for creating the so-called Chicago School of Analysis, the "strongest school of analytical research [particularly Fourier analysis and its applications to partial differential equations] in the contemporary mathematical world." Zygmund's legacy from nearly six decades of teaching included more than 80 Ph.D. students and hundreds of second-generation mathematical descendants. His book *Trigonometric Series* (1935 and later editions) remained the definitive treatment of the subject. Zygmund obtained his Ph.D. from the University of Warsaw in 1923. Between 1922 and 1929 he taught at the Polytechnical School in Warsaw, and between 1926 and 1929 he was also at the University of Warsaw. After a year in England on a Rockefeller fellowship, he became professor of mathematics at the University of Wilno (later Vilnius, Lithuania). In 1940, following a period of service in the Polish army, Zygmund escaped with his wife and son from his German-overrun homeland to the U.S. Successive posts at Mount Holyoke College, South Hadley, Mass., and the University of Pennsylvania led to an invitation in 1947 to join the faculty of the University of Chicago, where Zygmund remained until his retirement in 1980. His other books include *Analytic Functions* (1938, with Stanislaw Saks) and *Measure and Integral* (1977, with R.L. Wheeden). Zygmund held membership in the national academies of science of four countries: the U.S., Poland, Argentina, and Spain.

Contributors to the Science Year in Review

D. James Baker *Earth sciences: Oceanography.* President, Joint Oceanographic Institutions Inc., Washington, D.C.

Harold Borko *Electronics and information sciences: Information systems and services.* Professor, Graduate School of Library and Information Science, University of California, Los Angeles.

John M. Bowen *Medical sciences: Veterinary medicine.* Associate Dean for Research and Graduate Affairs and Professor of Pharmacology and Toxicology, College of Veterinary Medicine, University of Georgia, Athens.

Keith J. Bowman *Materials sciences: Metallurgy.* Associate Professor of Materials Engineering, Purdue University, West Lafayette, Ind.

George G. Brown *Life sciences: Zoology.* Professor of Zoology and Genetics, Iowa State University, Ames.

George R. Brubaker *Chemistry: Inorganic chemistry.* Director, U.S. Food and Drug Administration, Chicago District Laboratory, Chicago.

Paul J. Campbell *Mathematics.* Professor of Mathematics and Computer Science, Beloit College, Beloit, Wis.

James D. Chadi *Physics: Condensed-matter physics.* Senior Member, Research Staff, NEC Research Institute, Princeton, N.J.

Douglas E. Comer *Electronics and information sciences: Computers and computer science.* Professor of Computer Science, Purdue University, West Lafayette, Ind.

Alan T. Crane *Energy.* Senior Associate, Office of Technology Assessment, Congress of the United States, Washington, D.C.

Bernard Dixon *Medical sciences: General Medicine* (in part). Science Writer; Consultant. European Editor, *Bio/Technology*; Editor, *Medical Science Research*. Author of *Health and the Human Body* and others.

Dave Dooling *Space exploration.* D² Associates, Freelance Science Writing and Aerospace Consulting, Huntsville, Ala.

Carl B. Dover *Physics: Nuclear physics.* Senior Scientist, Brookhaven National Laboratory, Upton, N.Y.

F.C. Durant III *Electronics and information sciences: Satellite systems* (in part). Aerospace Historian and Consultant, Chevy Chase, Md.

David Guise *Architecture and civil engineering.* Professor Emeritus of Architecture, City College of New York, and private practice of architecture, New York, N.Y.

R. Cargill Hall *Electronics and information sciences: Satellite systems* (in part). Aerospace Historian, Center for Air Force History, Bolling Air Force Base, Washington, D.C.

Robert Haselkorn *Life sciences: Molecular biology.* F.L. Pritzker Distinguished Service Professor, Department of Molecular Genetics and Cell Biology, University of Chicago, Ill.

Lawrence W. Jones *Physics: High-energy physics.* Professor of Physics, University of Michigan, Ann Arbor.

John Patrick Jordan *Food and agriculture* (in part). Administrator, Cooperative State Research Service, U.S. Department of Agriculture, Washington, D.C.

Lou Joseph *Medical sciences: Dentistry.* Science writer, Chicago.

Allan P. Katz *Materials sciences: Ceramics.* Technical Manager for Structural Ceramics, Wright Laboratory, Materials Directorate, Wright-Patterson Air Force Base, Ohio.

George B. Kauffman *Chemistry: Applied chemistry.* Professor of Chemistry, California State University, Fresno.

David B. Kitts *Earth sciences: Geology and geochemistry.* Professor Emeritus of the History of Science, University of Oklahoma, Norman.

Patricia Brazeel Lewis *Food and agriculture* (in part). Public Relations Consultant, New Jersey Agricultural Experiment Station, Rutgers University, New Brunswick, N.J.

Melvin H. Marx *Psychology* (in part). Professor of Psychology, Western Carolina University, Cullowhee, N.C., and Professor Emeritus of Psychology, University of Missouri, Columbia.

Gail W. McBride *Medical sciences: General medicine* (in part). Free-lance Medical Writer and Editor; formerly Medical News Editor, *Journal of the American Medical Association*.

John E. McMurry *Chemistry: Organic chemistry*. Professor of Chemistry, Cornell University, Ithaca, N.Y.

Franz J. Monssen *Electronics and information sciences: Electronics*. Instructor, Department of Electronic and Computer Engineering Technology, Queensborough Community College, New York, N.Y.

Charles S. Mueller *Earth sciences: Geophysics*. Geophysicist, U.S. Geological Survey, Menlo Park, Calif.

Larry L. Naylor *Anthropology*. Chair, Anthropology, Institute of Anthropology, University of North Texas, Denton.

Colin V. Newman *Psychology* (in part). Executive Secretary, British Psychological Society, Leicester, England.

Carolyn D. Newton *Scientists of the Year: Nobel prizes*. Free-lance Writer and Editor, Seattle, Wash.

Joseph Palca *U.S. science policy*. Science Correspondent, National Public Radio, Washington, D.C.

Roger A. Pielke *Earth sciences: Atmospheric sciences*. Professor of Atmospheric Science, Colorado State University, Fort Collins.

W.M. Protheroe *Astronomy*. Professor Emeritus of Astronomy, Ohio State University, Columbus.

John Rhea *Defense research*. Free-lance Science Writer, Woodstock, Va.

Phillip F. Schewe *Physics: General developments*. Chief Science Writer, American Institute of Physics, New York, N.Y.

Robert R. Shannon *Optical engineering*. Professor Emeritus and Past Director, Optical Sciences Center, University of Arizona, Tucson.

Lawrence J. Shimkets *Life sciences: Microbiology*. Associate Professor of Microbiology, University of Georgia, Athens.

Albert J. Smith *Life sciences: Botany*. Professor of Biology, Wheaton College, Wheaton, Ill.

Frank A. Smith *Transportation*. Executive Consultant, Eno Transportation Foundation, Leesburg, Va.

Leslie Smith *Earth sciences: Hydrology*. Professor of Geological Sciences, University of British Columbia, Vancouver.

Robert E. Stoffels *Electronics and information sciences: Communications systems*. Editor, *Telephone Engineer & Management* magazine, Chicago.

Philip R. Watson *Chemistry: Physical chemistry*. Professor of Chemistry, Oregon State University, Corvallis.

Kenneth E.F. Watt *Environment*. Professor of Zoology, University of California, Davis.

James D. Wilde *Archaeology*. Director, Office of Public Archaeology, Brigham Young University, Provo, Utah.

Contributors to the Encyclopædia Britannica Science Update

Graeme Pierce Berlyn *Trees* (in part). Professor of Forestry and Environmental Studies, Yale University, New Haven, Conn. Editor, *Journal of Sustainable Forestry;* coauthor, *Botanical Microtechnique and Cytochemistry*.

Thomas H. Everett *Trees* (in part). Author, *Living Trees of the World*.

Glenn F. Knoll *Analysis and Measurement, Physical and Chemical*. Professor of Nuclear Engineering, University of Michigan, Ann Arbor.

Steven W. Squyres *Solar System, The*. Associate Professor of Astronomy, Cornell University, Ithaca, N.Y.

Lillian M. Weber *Trees* (in part). Chief Horticulture Assistant to the Senior Horticulture Specialist, New York Botanical Garden, Bronx. Collaborating Editor, *New Illustrated Encyclopedia of Gardening*.

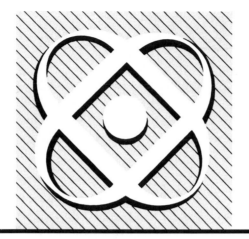

A
Science
Classic

The *Yearbook of Science and the Future* commemorates its 25th
anniversary by reprinting, from its first edition, one of its own classics,
"The Language of Life," by Nobel Prize winner Francis H.C. Crick.

A Nobel Prize winner tells the dramatic story of the genetic code and how it determines the very essence of man.

The Language of Life

by Francis H.C. Crick

*In 1967, science achieved what Pres. Lyndon B. Johnson later hailed as an "awesome accomplishment" by producing in the laboratory a "lifelike" environment in which the essential part of a virus could be copied. This dramatic achievement added still another link to a long chain of impressive advances in the field of molecular biology, involving hundreds of scientists around the world. Together, their partial unveiling of the mystery of life indicates that many known hereditary diseases may one day be eliminated. The step-by-step accumulation of theory and factual evidence behind this revolution in biology is a story in itself. The editors of the **Britannica Yearbook of Science and the Future** have asked Francis H.C. Crick, the British molecular biologist who shared the 1962 Nobel Prize for Physiology or Medicine with Maurice H.F. Wilkins and James D. Watson for their discovery of the DNA structure, to explain the chemistry of genetics.*

Genetics—The New Language

The field of genetics, as the scientific study of heredity is called, has known two periods of rapid, unexpected growth during the 20th century. The first took place shortly after 1900, when the ideas and experiments of Gregor Mendel were rediscovered. In 1865 Mendel, an Austrian monk, reported the results of many years of breeding experiments with pea plants. The experiments demonstrated that several characteristics of the plants, such as coloring and size, were transmitted to their offspring without change. From these results, Mendel concluded that the transmitted characteristics were determined by certain inborn factors that were handed down from one generation to the next with their nature essentially unaltered.

For 35 years Mendel's work was almost completely ignored, but about 1900 a number of scientists again took up the study of Mendel's inborn factors, which were soon given the name of genes. Before long it was discovered that the genes were arranged on threadlike bodies, called chromosomes, that are located in the nucleus of each cell. In addition, the genes on a chromosome were found to be arranged in a line, and they could be mapped by special genetic techniques.

The second period of rapid growth in genetics began after World War II and continues to this day. In this period, geneticists have sought to understand the mechanisms of genetics on a finer scale than had earlier been possible. They have looked for the answers to such questions as: Of what is a gene made? How does it affect the rest of the cell? What turns it on or off? Most of these questions have now been answered, at least in part, and the answers have turned out to entail as much chemical as biological information.

DNA—The Genetic Molecule

In 1950, when the more recent period of rapid growth in genetics began, it appeared likely that all of the detailed instructions needed to produce an organism, even one as complicated as a human being, must be contained in the two sets of genes that the organism inherits from its parents. One set of genes comes from the unfertilized egg of the mother, the other from the sperm of the father. The head of the sperm, where the male chromosomes are all tightly packed together, is far too small to be visible to the naked eye; yet, within this small space must be contained a complete set of genetic instructions for the eventual creation of every cell, tissue, and organ of the entire human body. To fit into such a small space, the instructions obviously must be written in a language with exceedingly minute letters. Modern research has discovered the chemical formulas of the small groups of atoms used to construct these letters of the genetic language.

The chief class of chemicals involved in the genetic language is that of the nucleic acids, of which there are two large families—DNA (deoxyribonucleic acid) and RNA (ribonucleic acid). For the moment, let us consider just DNA, which is found chiefly in the chromosomes. Each molecule of DNA looks enormously long under high magnification, and yet it is built on a very simple plan. It features a backbone, in which the same pattern of atoms occurs over and over again, in some cases as often as several million times. Two alternating groups, a type of sugar (D-deoxyribose) and a phosphate, are joined together to give the sequence: phosphate-sugar-phosphate-sugar-phosphate-sugar, and so on.

Thus the backbone is very regular and always has the same pattern. To each sugar is attached a side group that is made of carbon, oxygen, nitrogen, and hydrogen atoms. Only four types of side groups occur in DNA: adenine, guanine, thymine, and cytosine. (Their names can scarcely be avoided, since they are as important to biology as the elements are to chemistry.) Collectively, these side groups are referred to as "bases." Even though all DNA molecules are built on the same general plan, each one is different from every other because of the varying sequence in which the bases are attached to the backbone. It is this sequence that spells out the genetic instructions that determine each inherited characteristic. And yet, for all the thousands of variations in sequence that are possible, the genetic message is written in a language having only four symbols, consisting of the four bases: adenine, guanine, thymine, and cytosine.

The Two Strands of DNA

The actual structure of DNA, as we normally find it, is somewhat more complicated than the simple picture we have just described. DNA normally consists of two long strands standing side by side, their bases joined together in pairs—a base on one strand being linked by weak bonds, known as hydrogen bonds, to a base on the opposite strand. But not all pairs will fit into the structure, because two of the bases are large and two are small. To match, a pair must consist of one large and one small base; moreover, their hydrogen bonds must fit snugly together.

The only possible pairs, we have found, are adenine with thymine and guanine with cytosine. If one strand, or chain, contains adenine at a certain point, the other one must contain thymine at the corre-

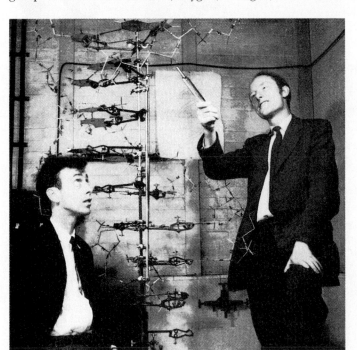

James Watson (left) and Francis Crick (right) display a model of the DNA molecule. For determining the molecular structure of DNA, which codes genetic information for the transmission of inherited traits, the two scientists, along with Maurice Wilkins, shared the 1962 Nobel Prize for Physiology or Medicine.

From *The Double Helix* by James D. Watson, Atheneum Press, New York City, 1968; photo, Cold Spring Harbor Laboratory Archives

sponding point, and vice versa. The same is true of guanine and cytosine. The sequence of bases in the two chains thus becomes complementary, not identical. If the sequence of bases on one chain of the pair is known, it is possible to identify the base sequence on the other chain, using this same complementary, base-pairing rule. The fact that the genetic information occurs twice, once on each strand, provides a most useful form of insurance. If one strand is damaged, the cell can repair it by using the undamaged companion as a guide.

Two further points about the structure of DNA: the sequence of bases in one strand travels in an opposite direction from the sequence of bases in the other. If the sequence in one chain runs up, the other runs down. Second, the two chains do not lie side by side in straight lines, but are twisted around one another to form a double helix—a kind of three-dimensional spiral built around a stationary axis, somewhat like a curved staircase. The arrangement of the backbones, however, is of high symmetry, with the sugars and the phosphates in the same relationship to one another wherever they occur. Only the sequence of the bases differs from point to point.

The Replication (Self-Duplication) of DNA

When a cell divides, its genetic material must be copied exactly in the daughter cells. The structure of DNA immediately suggests how this might happen. Imagine that the two chains of the double helix are separated. Each chain can then act as a template, or mold, to guide the synthesis of a new companion chain. Provided the rules for base pairing are always observed, the new companion will be identical with

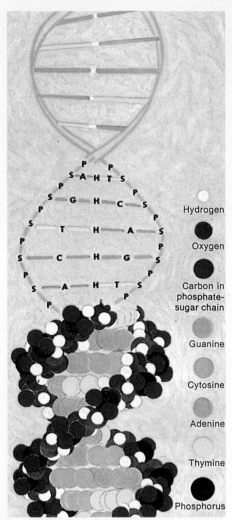

Above, the double-helical structure of DNA is depicted in three ways. At the top the DNA helix is shown as a ladder with flexible uprights that are twisted lengthwise. The mid portion of the diagram shows the sequence of molecules in the helices: the hydrogen bonds between complementary base pairs and the sugar-phosphate backbone. The lower portion reveals the three-dimensional relationship of the various components in the structure. The diagram at the left illustrates the pairing of bases by hydrogen bonds: adenine to thymine and guanine to cytosine.

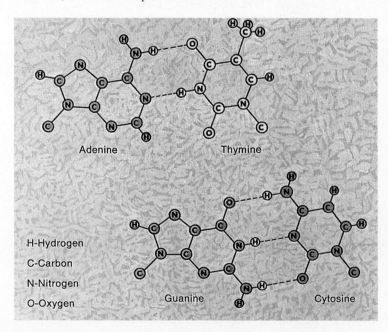

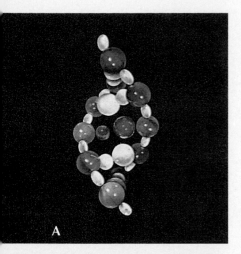

A

A model illustrates the principle of DNA duplication during cell division. Following the resting state (A), the chains separate when the complementary bases break their hydrogen bonds (B). Each base of the original chains then acquires a new complementary base, to which phosphate and sugar molecules are attached (C and D). The two new DNA molecules that are produced each contain one-half of the original molecule (E). (Key: sugar, large dark-blue ball; phosphate, blue ovoid; cytosine, small light-blue ball; guanine, large light-blue ball; adenine, large green ball; thymine, small green ball).

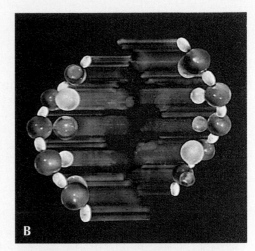

B

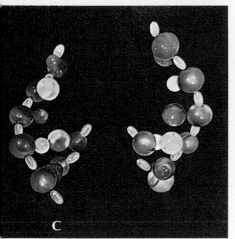

C

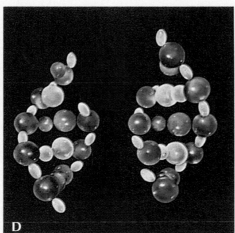

D

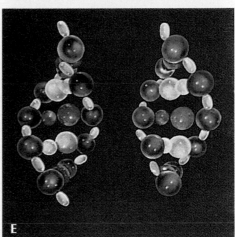

E

the old companion chain. If both original chains act in this way, we will end up with two double helices, each one an exact copy of the complicated base sequence in the original helix. We are almost certain now that this process is what actually occurs when DNA duplicates itself.

To supply the material that must be available for the new companion strand, four kinds of small molecular building blocks are used. Each block consists of one of the four DNA bases, one sugar unit, and three phosphate groups. Only one of the phosphates ends up in the new DNA. The other two are split off, and in the process they provide the energy to drive the synthesis forward. A large protein molecule acts as a catalyst to accelerate the reaction. Although the catalyst itself does not determine which of the four bases will be added to the growing chain at any point—this is handled by the base already present on the template chain—it does greatly increase the precision of selection simply by holding the reacting molecules steady. This special catalyst, an enzyme, was discovered in 1956 by the brilliant experiments of Arthur Kornberg and his co-workers,

then at Washington University in St. Louis, Mo. (For this work Kornberg received part of the 1959 Nobel Prize for Physiology or Medicine.)

The whole process is so flexible that it will copy *any* sequence of the four bases, always using the same catalyst. On rare occasions one of the bases in DNA is altered by an accident or by an incorrect choice of bases made during the copying process. In such cases a mutation, or change, in the base sequence results. Because the copying mechanism does not recognize the mutation as an error, the mutation is preserved in the DNA each time it is copied. Such a change in the base sequence may, of course, be reflected in a physical alteration of some kind in the organism carrying the changed DNA. Most such mutations are disadvantageous to an organism, but a few turn out to be improvements, creating organisms that are better able to survive and to leave more descendants in succeeding generations. In this way, favorable mutations will be preserved and will spread through a population. In fact, under appropriate environmental conditions the accumulation of such changes can lead to the formation of an entirely new species. This process is believed to be one of the principal mechanisms of evolution, which, over many millions of years, produced a complicated creature like man from the first primitive organisms.

Even though the mechanism of DNA replication (self-duplication) is now understood in principle, much remains to be discovered. We know by direct experiment that during replication the two original chains come apart, and that each new double helix contains one old chain and one new chain. We also know that the chains do not separate completely before replication starts. Rather, the process begins at one part of the chain, with the unwinding and synthesis of new chains proceeding simultaneously. We still do not know exactly what causes the two chains to untwist, nor do we know precisely how the enzyme acts in the synthesis of the new chain.

Copying Genes in the Test Tube

How accurate is the copying process? In the living cell the mechanism appears to make very few mistakes. Even in the test tube, where the scientist seeks to duplicate the process, errors are rare. The DNA molecules produced in the test tube seem very similar to those created by natural replication. The most stringent test is to add some biologically active DNA to a test tube solution. If the catalyzing enzyme is able to synthesize new DNA molecules that also are active, then the experiment is a success. Disappointingly, this process has proved difficult to carry out because the new synthetic DNA branches off occasionally in some unexpected way, so that it is not an exact copy of the original. Why? Possibly because the enzyme discovered by Kornberg is not the actual copying enzyme used by the cell, but is rather a "repair" enzyme—one that performs best when it can use a single strand of DNA as a template, rather than the usual double helix.

In 1967, Kornberg and Mehran Goulian, a colleague at Stanford University, along with Robert Sinsheimer of the California Institute of Technology, made use of the repair enzyme, and various biochemical innovations, to copy the single-stranded DNA from a virus. The new DNA produced in this way was able to infect bacteria, evidence that very exact copying must have taken place. Sol Spiegelman and his colleagues at the University of Illinois achieved a similar result in 1965 with another kind of virus. It is, therefore, possible to take the crucial part of a biological object—in this case, the DNA of a virus—and replicate it in the test tube; although at the moment a special substance from a living cell, an enzyme, must be used to catalyze the process. In time, it may be possible to accomplish the same result through chemistry alone.

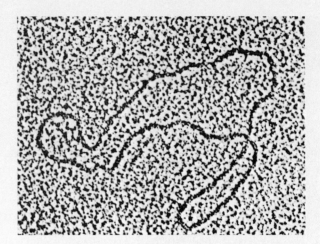

An electron photomicrograph shows the viral ring of DNA synthesized by Arthur Kornberg at Stanford University. This fully infectious viral DNA directed the production of exact replicas of itself.

The Importance of Proteins

We have said that genes are made of nucleic acid, and that the genetic information is transmitted by the exact sequence of the four kinds of bases in the DNA molecule. But how do genes influence the cell? To understand this, we must first consider another great family of biological molecules, the proteins. Protein molecules exist in many different forms, but all are built on the same general plan as the nucleic acid molecule—a long chain (in this case, called a polypeptide), with a uniform backbone, and with side chains attached at regular intervals. The backbone of the protein chain differs from that of nucleic acids, however, and instead of having four kinds of side chains, as does the nucleic acid molecule, a protein has as many as 20 different kinds.

Protein molecules are synthesized by joining together, head to tail, smaller molecules called amino acids. Each amino acid unit in the protein molecule, then, consists of one side chain and its associated piece of backbone. Different proteins have molecular chains of different lengths, averaging a few hundred amino acid units each. The 20 different amino acids used to make proteins are only a sampling of the many kinds of amino acids found in nature, but the same set of 20, with minor variations, is found in the proteins of all living things, from microorganisms to man.

Proteins are highly versatile substances. Not only are they the materials used to make biological structures, such as hair, muscle, and connective tissue, but all enzymes also are made of protein. The chemical conditions inside a living cell are normally mild—a low temperature, and neither strongly acidic nor alkaline—so that most of the requirements for chemical reactions are not present within cells. As we have already seen, if chemical reactions are to occur under such conditions, enzymes must be present to act as catalysts; moreover, each such chemical reaction that is to occur within a cell must have its own special enzyme catalyst. Even a small bacterial cell probably contains over a thousand different kinds of enzymes and, of course, each one is a protein.

How can molecules built on such a simple ground plan as the proteins act in so many different ways? The polypeptide chain of a protein folds up into an intricate three-dimensional form, usually rather like a ball, tucking inside the side groups that repel water and leaving outside those that attract water. This process produces specially shaped crevices in the surface of the molecule, each of which is lined with active chemical groups. These special surface forms, in turn, bind other molecules and react with them chemically.

The possible number of different protein molecules is inconceivably vast. Even a chain only 70 amino acid units long, having 20 alternatives at each position, can in theory have more sequences than there are atoms in the entire visible universe. Whereas only a minute fraction of these molecules is likely to be active as chemical catalysts, natural selection—the process in nature that determines which creatures shall survive and which shall not—has evolved those sequences that can act most rapidly and precisely.

The Synthesis of Proteins

To make a particular protein, one must combine its amino acids in the correct sequence. Once this is done the protein will fold itself up and carry out its biological role, which could be either that of serving in a structural capacity or acting as a catalyst. How does the cell produce the amino acid sequence? The process is controlled by nucleic acids and, ultimately, by the sequence of bases along a particular stretch of a DNA molecule.

This control, however, is not exerted directly. The cell keeps the DNA in its chromosomes as the master copy and produces working copies of the sequences required at any one time. The production of the working copies involves the second of the two large nucleic acid families, RNA (ribonucleic acid), which is built in a fashion very similar to DNA. Although the sugar in the RNA backbone is slightly different, D-ribose instead of D-deoxyribose; three of the bases are identical to those in the DNA molecule. Instead of thymine, however, which is chemically defined as 5-methyluracil, RNA has the closely related base uracil.

RNA has several natural functions. For some small viruses, such as the polio virus, it constitutes the actual genetic material instead of DNA. RNA is also used for parts of the machinery of protein synthesis. But most important of all, it is used as the working copy of the genetic material and is thus a kind of messenger between the DNA in the nucleus of the cell and the rest of the cell. This particular RNA is known, therefore, as messenger-RNA (written m-RNA). It is produced by a special enzyme that makes a complementary copy of a limited part of one strand of the DNA double helix, utilizing a base-pairing mechanism similar to that used in replicating DNA. Along this single-stranded RNA move extremely complicated biological particles called ribosomes, that "read" off the genetic message carried in the messenger-RNA, translating the base sequence of the RNA into an amino acid sequence. At any one time several ribosomes may be traveling along a single piece of messenger-RNA, one behind the other, each reading off the sequence next to it. The details of this translating mechanism of protein synthesis are quite complicated and are only partly understood at the present time.

The Genetic Code

The ribosome reads the four-letter, base language of the m-RNA and translates it, with the help of a number of subsidiary molecules, into the 20-letter, amino acid language of protein. To do this, the cell clearly requires the equivalent of a "dictionary," or set of rules. In this case the rules for translating from one language to another are called the genetic code, which is either the same, or very similar, in all organisms so far studied.

The set of rules that makes up the genetic code is remarkably simple. The RNA is read by the ribosomes in groups of three bases at a time. Each such triplet of bases, called for convenience a codon, stands for one of the 20 amino acids, or for the signal "end chain." (In bacteria, special signals also indicate "begin chain," but it is not known whether similar signals exist in higher organisms.) Since there are 64 different triplets, but only 20 amino acids, most amino acids are coded by more than one codon. The amino acid leucine, for example, has six codons, proline has four, and tyrosine has two. Only methionine and tryptophan have one each.

Although the genetic code is relatively simple, it has not been an easy matter to discover it experimentally. Whereas we can determine the amino acid sequence of a protein—provided that it is not too long and that a high-purity sample is available in reasonable amounts—it is much more difficult, for various technical reasons, to find the base sequence of a piece of nucleic acid. Consequently, it has not yet been possible to determine directly the base sequence of a gene and compare it with the amino acid sequence of the protein for which it codes. More indirect methods, too complex to describe here, have to be used. But thanks to the excellent work of Marshall Nirenberg, H. Gobind Khorana, Severo Ochoa, and their respective colleagues during the period 1961 to 1965, such methods have been remarkably successful.

Gene Action

What activates genes and turns them on and off? Our knowledge of this phenomenon is still rather fragmentary. In bacteria, genes with similar functions often occur next to each other on the DNA and are turned on and off together. This action is apparently controlled by a special protein that is weakly bonded to the nucleic acid near the first gene of the set, and prevents the whole group of genes from acting—possibly by stopping the synthesis of the relevant messenger-RNA. Certain small molecules can combine with this protein, causing it to leave the nucleic acid and thereby allowing the genes to act. In this way one small, specific molecule can control the working of a whole set of genes. Whether this same process is used in organisms higher than simple bacteria, and whether they have other, more elaborate control mechanisms, is not yet known.

In summary, the gene—a stretch of DNA molecule with a characteristic base sequence—is replicated by a rather simple process using the specific pairing of the bases. It functions by producing a one-stranded working copy made of RNA, which then directs the synthesis of the polypeptide chain of a particular protein. The protein is used by the cell for a constructional purpose, *e.g.,* for building muscle or connective tissue, for control, or as an enzyme, Because most enzymes contain only one polypeptide chain, the phrase, "one gene-one enzyme," which was first coined by George Beadle, former president of the University of Chicago and co-winner of the 1958 Nobel Prize in Physiology or Medicine, lies at the heart of genetics.

The flow of information can be illustrated by this rather compact diagram:

$$\circlearrowleft$$
$$DNA \rightarrow m\text{-}RNA \rightarrow protein$$

The arrows do not represent the flow of material, but of a sequence of information carried by the m-RNA. As far as we know, the information cannot flow in the opposite direction. That is, the cell cannot translate backward from the detailed amino acid sequence of a protein to the base sequence of the relevant piece of DNA.

The Case of Sickle-Cell Anemia

For a specific example of the way in which genetic information contained in a particular gene is expressed in an organism, let us consider the case of the human disease sickle-cell anemia. To understand how this disease comes about, one must first look at the function of hemoglobin, which is the protein in red blood cells that picks up oxygen in the lungs and carries it to the body tissues. Each hemoglobin molecule actually consists of four polypeptide chains, two of one kind and two of another. The oxygen molecule is weakly bonded to an iron atom in the middle of the heme, a small molecule that fits into a cavity formed by the intricate folding of each polypeptide chain. It is the heme group that absorbs visible light and makes blood red—or blue, whenever it is not combined with oxygen.

There are two separate hemoglobin genes, one for each kind of polypeptide chain. Sickle-cell anemia is caused by a mutation in one of these two genes, which codes a polypeptide chain 146 amino acid units in length. The mutation alters only one amino acid in the entire chain, changing a glutamic acid present in normal hemoglobin into another amino acid, valine. This change was probably due to the chance alteration of a single base of the DNA in some ancestor of the afflicted person.

We all have two copies of each hemoglobin gene, one from each of our parents. If one copy has this particular abnormality, while the other is normal, an individual then suffers from a mild condition known as sickle-cell trait, because half his hemoglobin molecules are abnormal. However, if both genes are changed in this way, all the hemoglobin has the same small alteration. The unfortunate result: the abnormal hemoglobin, in its deoxygenated, or blue, form, distorts the blood cells into the shape of a sickle and frequently may damage them. Persons with this condition, because of its severity, almost always die in their teens. Thus, the astonishing effect that a variation in a few atoms in the genetic material—provided it has happened to both copies of the gene—becomes a deadly affliction.

Finally, one might ask, why is this mutation not eliminated by natural selection? In Africa, where the disease is common, the mutation has been preserved, most likely because individuals with sickle-cell trait, that is, having only one copy of the mutant gene, have an increased resistance to malaria. We still do not know exactly why. Inasmuch as malaria is very prevalent in those districts where the sickle-cell mutant is commonly found, it appears that the mutant offers a selective advantage to those bearing it.

Biological Magnification

How can minute genetic changes like those in sickle-cell anemia have such serious consequences? The answer lies in the tremendous magnification that can occur in a biological system. During the devel-

GLOSSARY

amino acids
A group of organic compounds which are the basic components of protein molecules.

base
In genetics, any one of four side groups composed of carbon, oxygen, hydrogen, and nitrogen atoms attached to the backbone of the DNA molecule.

catalyst
A substance that speeds up or slows down a chemical reaction but does not itself undergo a permanent chemical change; may also initiate a chemical reaction and enable it to proceed under milder conditions than otherwise possible.

chromosome
A microscopic threadlike structure in which the genes are located; develops in the nucleus of a cell prior to cell division; number, size, and form are constant for each species.

codon
A triplet of bases that represents one of the 20 amino acids used in the synthesis of protein molecules in humans.

deoxyribonucleic acid (DNA)
A substance carried by the proteins of genes in the nucleus of living cells; plays an important part in the transmission of hereditary characteristics.

enzyme
An organic catalyst, usually a protein produced by living cells; initiates or accelerates chemical reactions at body temperatures but is not changed in the process.

gene
The unit in chromosomes that governs the transmission of a specific hereditary trait; believed to be a molecule of deoxyribonucleic acid.

genetic code
During protein synthesis, the set of rules followed by ribosomes when translating the base sequence of messenger-RNA into an amino acid sequence.

genetics
The branch of biology that deals with the heredity and variation of organisms and with the mechanics by which these are effected.

messenger RNA (m-RNA)
The ribonucleic acid in a living cell that becomes a working copy of a segment of a strand of deoxyribonucleic acid; serves as a mechanism for transmitting genetic instructions from the DNA in the nucleus of a cell to the rest of the cell.

mutant
An organism differing from its parents in one or more inheritable characteristics.

mutation
A sudden change in one or more characteristics of an organism that can be transmitted to subsequent offspring.

nucleic acid
A complex, weakly acidic, chemical compound found especially in the nucleus of all living cells; may be either ribonucleic acid (RNA) or deoxyribonucleic acid (DNA) and usually occurs in combination with proteins, with which it is thought to control the cell's growth.

nucleus
In living cells, a dense, rounded body containing complex chemical substances that are essential in the process of heredity; also controls such vital cellular activities as metabolism and division.

polypeptide
A compound formed by the union of two or more amino acids.

protein
Any one of a large group of complex organic compounds that are essential constituents of all living cells; composed principally of amino acid molecules joined in varying combinations to make one large molecule.

ribonucleic acid (RNA)
A complex chemical substance found in all living cells and thought to serve as a pattern for the synthesis of proteins and enzymes in the cell.

ribosome
A complex biological particle that moves along a segment of messenger-RNA during protein synthesis, "reading" the genetic message and translating the base sequence of the m-RNA into an amino acid sequence.

opment of the human embryo the DNA is replicated many times, so that an initial mistake of one base in the egg and another in the sperm can be repeated in the DNA of every cell of the organism, or more than a million million times. Of course, not all of these cells manufacture hemoglobin—it is produced by developing red cells, mainly in the bone marrow.

Nonetheless, this multiplication of cells and their mutant DNA occurs throughout life, and nearly 4 million new red cells pour into the bloodstream every second.

Each hemoglobin gene in the developing cells is copied many times onto the messenger-RNA, and each molecule of messenger-RNA acts many times to guide the production of the polypeptide chains of hemoglobin, until every red cell contains about 300 million molecules of hemoglobin. What was originally an alteration of a few atoms in a pair of DNA molecules, therefore, is multiplied by these successive processes until it affects literally hundreds of grams of the final product. Small wonder that such a change can have a lethal effect!

What Remains to be Discovered?

While we now understand the chemistry of heredity in outline, almost every aspect of it requires further study. We still do not know what signals are present on the DNA that show where a gene begins and where it ends, though they are likely to be discovered in the next few years. We do know that in certain bacterial cells all the DNA is in one long piece, in the form of a large circle, containing several million base pairs. But we do not understand the internal organization of the chromosomes of higher organisms, which not only have more DNA, but which contain many kinds of associated proteins, and can also fold up into very compact shapes when the cell goes through cell division.

The total amount of DNA in any one of our cells is very large, amounting to about 8 billion (8×10^9) base pairs, and having a total length of some 80 in. (203 cm) if laid end to end. All this must function in the nucleus of each cell, a body of only a few thousandths of an inch in diameter. We do not know if all of this DNA is generally functional in the way described above. If it is, then by a rough estimate we can inherit perhaps several million different genes from each parent. So far, the correct figure is unknown. The total length of DNA in our bodies is so great that if all the DNA molecules from all the cells of one individual were laid end to end, they would extend most of the way across the solar system.

Much also remains to be discovered about the chemical details of the processes involved, from comparatively simple ones, like the copying of DNA, to the very intricate chemical translation from one molecular language to another that occurs in protein synthesis. Just because we have discovered the genetic code, we cannot simply "read off" the genetic message. Our ignorance of human genetics is profound. We still do not know the detailed organization of a small bacterial cell, let alone complicated multicellular structures like ourselves. Generations of thought and research are needed before we can understand, at the molecular level, how the fertilized egg develops into the mature adult.

Applications of the New Knowledge

What use can be made of our new but limited knowledge of genetics? Are we likely to be able to perform astonishing feats of genetic engineering, altering genes at will and correcting hereditary defects by ingenious chemical and biochemical methods? This may well be possible in the distant future, but so far no likely way of accomplishing such feats is in sight.

The difficulties are great. We can make alterations to the base sequence of a piece of DNA by chemicals or by radiation, but we can only do so in a hit-or-miss way. We cannot yet change a particular base at a particular point in the sequence, nor can we easily add a piece of DNA to our chromosomes. We can, by various means, make hybrid cells containing chromosomes from two different species, but it is most unlikely that such mixed cells could produce a viable organism, even though they can sometimes be grown in the test tube. One day, perhaps, it may be possible to produce a human being having one pair of chromosomes from a chimpanzee—but is it very likely that this would be considered an improvement? I think not.

The Importance of Biological Knowledge

The importance of the profound knowledge we have acquired about the fundamental molecular basis of all living things is not in immediate spectacular applications, but in the solid foundations it gives to our understanding of a whole variety of biological and medical problems. Just as our knowledge of organic chemistry has enabled us to develop new materials and new drugs to make life more convenient and more secure, so this new biological knowledge will undoubtedly assist man in controlling such problems as virus infection, certain auto-immune diseases, such as rheumatoid arthritis, and, it is to be hoped, even cancer and old age.

But beyond these eventual applications is the value of the new knowledge for the light it throws on our place in the universe. The fact that all living things on the earth use the same genetic mechanisms emphasizes how closely we are linked to the rest of nature. Many biological processes that were once considered utterly mysterious can now be understood in terms of modern chemistry and physics. We can now think more effectively about the origin of life, because it must have been intimately connected with the origin of the genetic code. We can also begin to speculate about life on other worlds.

Some will regret the loss of mystery they associate with living things. But for others, the contemplation of the vast complexity of nature at the molecular level, and of the rather simple chemical ground plan on which it is based, will provide immense aesthetic satisfaction. We shall forever marvel at the astonishing truth that beings as intricate as ourselves can be produced by the long operation of natural selection.

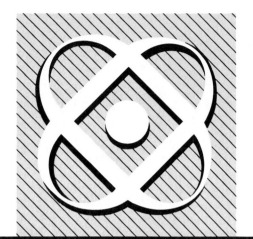

Institutions

of

Science

The Savannah River Ecology Laboratory

by Anne R. Gibbons

More than 40 years ago a small team of biologists began studying the effects of a new U.S. government plutonium plant on the local environment. No one realized at the time that they were founding what would become a world-recognized laboratory for ecological research.

The scene: The year is 1951. By direction of the U.S. government, six thousand residents and their belongings have been moved from a tract of land in South Carolina hundreds of square kilometers in extent. Abandoned domestic animals roam the area; nature reasserts itself. Near the center of the property, which has become a federal reservation, the U.S. Atomic Energy Commission (AEC) prepares to build nuclear reactors to produce the raw materials needed for America's post-World War II nuclear weapons.

The director: a university

The producer: a federal agency

The players: research scientists

The action: basic studies to gain knowledge about the Earth and the plants and animals that inhabit it

The stage is set for an outdoor ecology laboratory that will achieve national and international recognition in the coming four decades. Enter a young biologist from the University of Georgia.

Historical background

Early in 1951 the AEC made it known that it was interested in funding ecological studies on the land surrounding its recently established Savannah River Plant (SRP), where the commission would soon begin producing plutonium for nuclear weapons. The AEC recognized the need to inventory the local plants and animals before the reactors were built and put into operation in order to assess the environmental effects of their presence, and local universities were an obvious source for the proposed research.

Eugene Odum, then an associate professor of biology at the University of Georgia, eagerly put together an ambitious proposal for studying the

Photos, SREL

In 1951 Eugene Odum (above) founded what would become the Savannah River Ecology Laboratory (SREL). The Savannah River Plant site offered Odum special opportunities to study plants and animals in the process of recolonizing abandoned farm fields. Robert Norris (above right, holding bird), the laboratory's first full-time resident ecologist, examines a netted Savannah sparrow with colleagues in an early 1950s field study.

ANNE R. GIBBONS *is a free-lance writer and editor.*

(Overleaf) Bottomland cypress-tupelo swamp along the Savannah River floodplain is one of several types of habitat on the Savannah River Site (SRS). Photograph by David E. Scott; courtesy of the Savannah River Ecology Laboratory

biological life at the SRP site. His plan included a request for $150,000 for the first year, which the AEC promptly rejected. Odum downgraded his next proposal to a modest $11,934: $2,200 each for three graduate students, $1,750 for a pickup truck, $1,700 for field expenses, $1,000 worth of field equipment and supplies, and $884 for overhead. The university would provide the support for two senior researchers, secretarial assistance, and a reference collection and library.

Odum's revised proposal was submitted to the AEC on June 14, 1951, and was approved six days later. Three days after that, University of Georgia researchers were in the field. For the first several years Odum and his group of scientists, many of whom simply donated their time and expertise, focused on two areas of research. One was an inventory of conspicuous features of the environment of the site and a census of populations of "indicator" species, those plants and animals that might be expected to respond in some predictable way to major environmental change. This mission, in fact, was the primary one envisioned by the AEC. The other focus was basic, long-term ecological research. The site offered special opportunities for Odum—who would later be called the "father of modern ecology"—and his colleagues to study such phenomena as old-field succession (the gradual takeover by nature of abandoned crop fields), the role of competition among populations of different organisms in their natural settings, and the organization of food chains.

The Georgia researchers' first on-site headquarters occupied the top level of a two-story barn. Later they moved into a cottage that had belonged to the barn's owner. From 1953 to 1955 the scientists rented makeshift laboratory space in a duplex apartment in Jackson, South Carolina, a short ride from the boundary of the SRP reservation. In 1955 the AEC increased the annual budget for the University of Georgia's on-site ecological research to a level high enough for the school to hire the site's first full-time resident ecologist, Robert A. Norris. At the same time, the university requested and received laboratory space on site. The Bush House, one of the few original homes that had not been torn down or moved off SRP property, served as headquarters.

470

From 1955 to 1961 University of Georgia researchers at the Savannah River site began intensively to explore radioecology—*i.e.,* the study of the fate and effects of radioactive contaminants in the environment and the use of radioactive tracers to follow ecological processes—publishing about 30 scientific papers and establishing the international reputation in radiation research they enjoy today. By 1961 research efforts and results clearly demonstrated the need for a permanent on-site laboratory. The AEC made available two buildings and again boosted the budget to about $60,000 annually. A year later Frank B. Golley became the first director of the Laboratory of Radiation Ecology. During his five-year tenure the laboratory budget increased to $170,000, and the staff grew from two Ph.D.'s, two technicians, a secretary, and a graduate student to a laboratory of 15–20 scientists and support staff. Over the same period laboratory researchers published 100 technical papers.

The laboratory took on its present name of Savannah River Ecology Laboratory (SREL) in 1964, reflecting the broad spectrum of ecological studies being conducted at the site. In 1967 Golley was succeeded by Robert J. Beyers, an SREL faculty member since 1964. During Beyers' six-year term as director, the laboratory's operating budget nearly doubled, and its research staff continued to publish extensively.

In 1972 the AEC designated the Savannah River Plant reservation America's first National Environmental Research Park, an outdoor laboratory for investigating the effects of energy technology and production on the environment. Because the site was—and remains—off-limits to the general public, field research could be conducted without concern for human interference. It became one of the few outdoor laboratories in the world where researchers could set up experimental equipment, leave it overnight, and be assured that it would be undisturbed the

SREL

In a field project of the late 1960s Michael Smith (right), the current director of SREL, and researcher Ron Blessing collect an on-site soil sample.

A raccoon in search of an easy meal invades a research project's pitfall trap intended for live capture of small reptiles and amphibians (above). Such disruptions notwithstanding, field studies at the SRS can be carried out and equipment set up without concern for human interference because the site is off-limits to the general public (below).

next day—undisturbed by humans, that is, raccoons and alligators being another matter.

In 1973 Michael H. Smith, who had joined the lab as a postdoctoral fellow in 1966, took over as the third and latest director of SREL. That same year the AEC awarded the laboratory a prime contract, assuring it the funding to expand its research, both basic and applied.

The site

The Savannah River Site (SRS), the name by which the federal reservation has been known since 1989, is located in southwestern South Carolina about 30 kilometers (20 miles) southeast of Augusta, Georgia. Roughly circular in shape, with a 16-kilometer (10-mile) radius and an area of almost 780 square kilometers (300 square miles), the tract is bordered on the southwest by the Savannah River, which separates it from Georgia. The SRS represents 1% of the total land area of South Carolina. Administered by the U.S. Department of Energy (DOE), the successor to the AEC, it is the largest controlled-access area in the eastern United States. The protection of its research areas from public disturbance, coupled with its large size and high natural diversity of species, creates an ideal environment for basic ecological research and experimentation.

Terrestrial and aquatic communities typical of the region exist naturally on the site. They include bottomland hardwood forests, cypress-tupelo swamps, turkey-oak–longleaf-pine sandhill associations, upland-oak–hickory forests, and blackwater streams. The site also protects 200 shallow, roughly elliptical wetlands called Carolina bays. Once abundant throughout the southeastern coastal plain from Georgia to Virginia, Carolina bays are disappearing from the natural environment—the victims of agricultural and industrial development. Their protected status on the Savannah River Site provides unparalleled opportunities for SREL researchers to study wetland habitats.

Also abundant are human-influenced habitats, including old farm fields, abandoned farm ponds, thermally altered (temperature-changed)

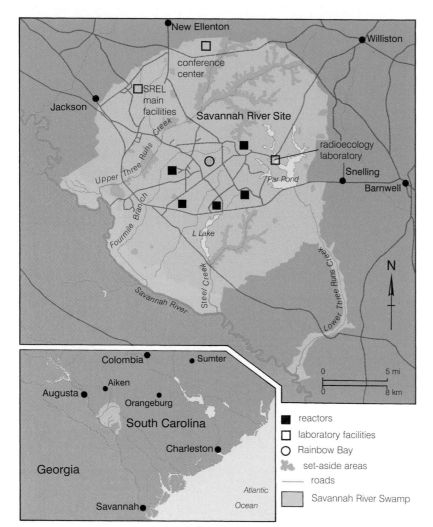

The SRS (left), located in southwestern South Carolina, is roughly circular in shape with an area of almost 780 square kilometers (300 square miles). Administered by the U.S. Department of Energy, the federal reservation is the largest controlled-access area in the eastern U.S. It is bordered on the southwest by the Savannah River (below), whose floodplain forms the Savannah River Swamp.

SREL; photo, David E. Scott

lakes and streams, and extensive pine plantations, which are planted, monitored, and harvested by the U.S. Forest Service. An extensive human-made reservoir system on the SRS includes Par Pond (originally 1,000 hectares [2,500 acres]) and L-Lake (400 hectares [1,000 acres]). Both were used as reactor cooling ponds and have provided unique opportunities to address questions about the environmental effects of the thermal alteration of aquatic habitats.

In 1967 the AEC began establishing protected areas on the SRS through what is known as the set-aside program. As of 1993 more than 4,860 hectares (12,000 acres) have been designated as set-aside areas, to be kept in their natural state, *i.e.,* unaltered by human activity, and protected for the purpose of conducting ecological research. These natural environments include several kilometers of the upper reaches of Upper Three Runs Creek and its tributaries, major portions of bottomland hardwood areas, numerous Carolina bays, and a significant part of Savannah River Swamp. The set-aside program enhances SREL's research programs, particularly for environmental comparison with other

473

SREL; photos, David E. Scott

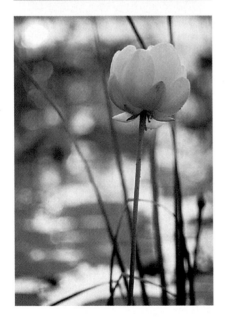

The large size and high species diversity of the SRS make the area ideal for ecological research. The cottonmouth (top left) is among 36 species of snakes found on the site. Several rare plants and animals native to the general region, like the pine barrens tree frog (center left), have not yet been reported from the SRS but are actively being sought. Plant species at Par Pond reservoir include the American lotus (bottom left). The cubs at play (bottom right) are red foxes, which SREL scientists began censusing in the early 1950s. A cypress forest thrives in a Carolina bay (top right), one of about 200 such shallow wetlands protected within the SRS boundary.

on-site areas affected by site operations. Set-aside areas are also used for projects conducted by visiting researchers from institutions other than the University of Georgia.

The facilities

The Savannah River Ecology Laboratory moved to its present 2,790-square meter (30,000-square foot) main building in 1977. An additional 4,650 square meters (50,000 square feet) of specialty research facili-

474

ties allow the laboratory to conduct studies anywhere on the protected habitats of the SRS and in virtually any area of ecology. Numerous outdoor enclosures, including avian flight cages, greenhouses, experimental ponds, a rhizotron/lysimeter facility for conducting experiments on roots and soil, and fenced areas for research on land animal populations, surround the main building. By means of these outdoor facilities, hypotheses based on field observations can be tested under replicated semicontrolled conditions.

SREL has two laboratories dedicated to genetic studies on plants and animals. One focuses on identifying patterns of protein variation by means of a technique known as electrophoresis; the other examines variability of DNA. SREL also has a clean room for detecting environmental contaminants like heavy metals that may be present at trace levels. Completion of a large animal-care facility, to be used for educational displays as well as for research, is scheduled for 1994. According to Robert I. Nestor, SREL's assistant director for administration, the laboratory is also expanding its main building in 1993 to provide additional office space and to double the library's capacity.

Organization

Research at SREL is carried out within three divisions: biogeochemical ecology, wetlands ecology, and wildlife ecology and toxicology. Formal partitioning aside, however, one of the laboratory's most striking characteristics is that collaboration and the free exchange of ideas among

Upper Three Runs Creek set-aside area is part of a program begun in 1967 to keep large tracts of the SRS in their natural state. By the early 1990s more than 4,860 hectares (12,000 acres) had been incorporated into the program.

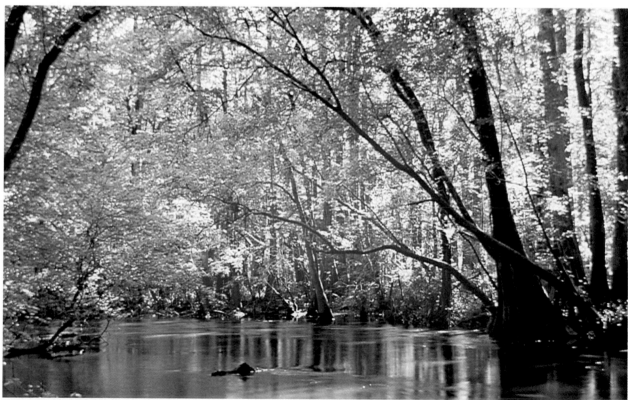

SREL; photo, David E. Scott

all of the faculty, technicians, and students are not just permitted but encouraged. Recognized by scientists worldwide as one of the leading laboratories in ecological research, SREL embodies a rich tradition of multidisciplinary endeavors.

Despite the research divisions' close cooperation, each one has a clearly stated objective. In the early 1970s SREL researchers expanded their studies of mineral cycling and the movement, fate, and effects of contaminants, including radioactive elements (radionuclides), organic contaminants like oil, and trace metals like aluminum and mercury. Reflecting this expansion, the Division of Biogeochemical Ecology is dedicated to understanding biogeochemical principles in terrestrial and aquatic ecosystems.

In view of the public attention currently being given to the issue of wetlands—how to define them, how to protect them, how to decide whether disrupted wetlands can be reclaimed—research in SREL's Division of Wetlands Ecology is particularly relevant. The division emphasizes the study of biological community development and the factors that affect this development in natural and disturbed wetland habitats of the Savannah River Site. The reservation offers a wealth of wetland habitats for study ranging from bottomland forests along stream and river floodplains to beaver ponds and oxbow lakes to isolated temporary ponds and Carolina bays. As with many of the projects undertaken at the laboratory, the ongoing success of wetlands ecology studies depends to a great extent

(Below) Aerial view of the principal SREL facilities shows part of the main laboratory (far right), greenhouses and experimental ponds (top center), artificial ponds (far left), rhizotron/lysimeter facility (center), and aviaries in the wooded area (bottom). Sweet gum seedlings grow in one of the greenhouses (above).

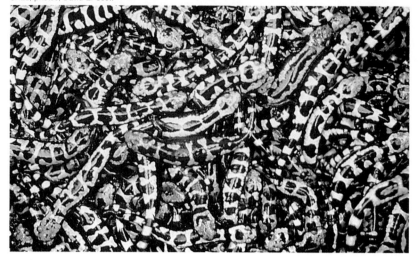

on the protected status of the site and DOE's long-term commitment to environmental research.

The Division of Wildlife Ecology and Toxicology focuses on the study of natural populations and communities of animals and plants, with an emphasis on determining the influence of human-caused disturbances to and stresses on ecosystem stability. Research efforts include investigating the effects of reactor effluents on aquatic organisms, determining the effectiveness of offering alternative habitats to populations whose primary habitats have been destroyed, mitigating contaminated habitats, and studying the ecology of endangered species.

SREL's personnel roster has grown significantly from its modest beginnings. As of early 1993 the resident faculty consists of 35 Ph.D.'s who encompass a broad range of research interests. Most are faculty members at the University of Georgia; they also serve as adjunct faculty at more than a dozen other academic institutions. Faculty supervise doctoral and master's graduate students as well as summer undergraduates; they are assisted by technicians and support staff, who bring the total number of personnel to more than 180.

Through a prime contract with DOE, the laboratory has an annual budget that exceeds $10 million. Over the years SREL has received additional funding from other national sources, including E.I. Du Pont de Nemours and Co., the National Science Foundation, the National Turkey Federation, Sigma Xi Research Awards, the University of Georgia Research Foundation, the Department of the Interior, the Environmental Protection Agency, the U.S. Forest Service, and the Westinghouse Savannah River Co.

Projects and accomplishments

The focus and direction of research at the Savannah River Ecology Laboratory have evolved over the years in response to the AEC's and DOE's changing needs as well as to the results of the laboratory's own studies. For the 1990s three major areas of research are being empha-

Research at SREL is carried out within one of three divisions. Many projects in the Division of Wildlife Ecology and Toxicology have centered on salamanders (top left, marbled salamanders shown), which are important components of natural habitats although seldom seen by casual observers. A student takes a water sample (top right) for a study in the Biogeochemical Ecology Division, whose researchers assess the fate and effects of toxic chemicals and other pollutants in aquatic and terrestrial ecosystems. Native aquatic plants like the white water lily (above) have been a major research focus in the Division of Wetlands Ecology.

477

sized: radioecology, genotoxicology, and biodiversity. Research efforts in all three areas will rely on the expertise of the current staff and the foundation of ecological information from previous research at SREL.

Lowering the water level of Par Pond reservoir in 1991 exposed radioactively contaminated sediment. It also created a paradox—a contaminated site with ecological value, the ideal situation for conducting experiments on remediation and reclamation techniques. The soil at Par Pond has detectable levels of several radionuclides, which to Domy Adriano is a radioecologist's dream come true. Adriano, who is head of SREL's Division of Biogeochemical Ecology, began studying radionuclides in 1975 when he joined the laboratory. He and other members of his division are working to develop techniques that will help make soil with low-level radioactive contamination suitable for growing food crops. The problem, of course, is to keep the plants from absorbing the contaminants.

One approach being investigated is to add substantial quantities of potassium to the soil. The chemical behavior of potassium is similar in many ways to that of cesium, whose radioactive isotope cesium-137 is present in Par Pond sediment. Researchers are conducting experiments to determine if plant roots growing in the sediment will preferentially pick up harmless potassium instead of the radioactive cesium. Another experiment involves a commercial product called Biobarrier. Essentially a nonwoven fabric permeated with a slow-release herbicide, Biobarrier separates the plant's roots from contaminated soil. The herbicide prevents the roots, which are in clean soil, from penetrating into the contaminated soil, thus inhibiting absorption of contaminants. Still another technique involves putting layers of clean soil on top of contaminated sediment to minimize the plants' uptake of contaminants.

SREL's new radioecology laboratory is located at Par Pond, which was used as a reactor cooling pond and whose sediments contain cesium-137 and other radionuclides. Studies at the laboratory will help scientists better understand the health and environmental problems posed by radioactively contaminated aquatic sites.

SREL; photo, David E. Scott

Ward Whicker, a leading researcher in radioecology and a senior ecologist at SREL, points out that at any contaminated aquatic site 99% of radioactive contamination is in the sediments. It is critical, he stresses, to determine and clearly understand what levels of radioactive contamination pose health or environmental problems. According to Whicker, although a massive cleanup program for contaminated sites may be popular because it means big money to some people, "the only way to make decisions about cleaning up contaminated sites is with facts." A new state-of-the-art radioecology lab built at Par Pond in early 1993 will help SREL researchers find some of those facts.

Studying genotoxicity, the harmful chemical and radiological effects of contaminants on the genetic integrity of organisms, in laboratory settings is nothing new. But SREL is a pioneer in genotoxicity research on natural populations living in habitats that have low-level radioactive or heavy-metals contamination. Largemouth bass, abundant at the Savannah River Site in aquatic habitats both pristine and contaminated, are a major focus of research. Mosquito fish, turtles, and a variety of plants are also being studied on site.

Genotoxicological research focuses on the response of DNA to environmental contaminants. Various environmental factors, including contaminants, can cause breakage in strands of DNA. Although normal cellular processes usually repair or replace damaged DNA, environmental contaminants sometimes overwhelm or inhibit that ability. According to Ronald K. Chesser, who heads SREL's Division of Wildlife Ecology and Toxicology, research at the laboratory runs the gamut from looking at causative agents of DNA breaks and mutations to identifying factors that inhibit natural repair.

Research involving DNA has been greatly enhanced by a recently introduced technique called the polymerase chain reaction, which allows investigators to amplify large quantities of DNA rapidly and efficiently for

Reactor seepage basins (above left) that received radioactive contaminants, including strontium-90, were discovered to be a source of radioactive turtles found on the SRS (above). Because the basic ecology of freshwater turtles on the site was already well known, SREL researchers were able quickly to determine the points of origin of the turtles, the extent of their dispersal, and their potential as a radiation hazard.

479

SREL; photo, David E. Scott

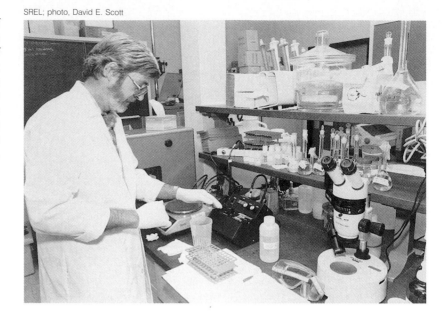

analysis. According to Charles Lydeard, SREL assistant ecologist, the use of this approach will enable investigators to address questions previously intractable and to study the ecological genetics of rare or endangered species in a nondestructive manner.

Many scientists believe that the presence of a great biodiversity, or diversity of species, in a given environment is one indicator of the ecosystem's ability to resist disturbance. Knowledge of an environment's natural biodiversity is important in environmental remediation and reclamation. Researchers at SREL emphasize that the first step in environmental restoration is knowing what an environment is like in its natural state. As a leader in national environmental research programs, SREL is examining the impact of land-use management on native animal and plant communities.

Biodiversity is not limited to the plants and animals visible to the human eye. Microorganisms also play a vital role in any ecosystem, and research at SREL on thermally altered aquatic systems has revealed effects on what Odum dubbed "hidden biodiversity." Some species of microscopic and near-microscopic aquatic organisms (phytoplankton and zooplankton) are very rare at natural temperatures. When the water is warmed, however, heat-tolerant species quickly become dominant—an illustration of how this hidden biodiversity can be dramatically altered by human modification of the environment.

One of the newest areas of research at SREL is conservation biology, the effort to address global declines in biological diversity by applying ecological models. "Sustainable development" is a key phrase in this discipline, the idea being to meld ecological principles and economic necessities into a balanced solution for managing natural resources. As expressed by Gary Meffe, an associate ecologist at SREL and a founding editor of *Conservation Biology*, an important principle of conservation biology is the realization that human welfare depends on the welfare of

480

the natural world. To conservation biologists remediation and restoration are acceptable ways to correct humanity's past errors—but not an excuse to neglect appropriate conservation practices. They believe that ultimately the most effective way to retain diversity of genes, species, and habitats is to protect the structure and processes of natural systems. Many of SREL's research programs are directed toward understanding the principles underlying ecological organization and function.

Naturally, high technology plays an important role at SREL. Using remote sensing techniques and geographic information systems (GIS), researchers have acquired a substantial data base on biodiversity and community composition at the Savannah River Site. Remote sensing, usually carried out from aircraft or satellites, uses measurements of the reflectance of different wavelengths of light from the Earth's surface to produce maplike imagery, from which scientists can evaluate patterns of vegetation, land use, and development. Remote sensing can also reveal water quality because water gives different reflectance patterns depending on the amounts of suspended solids in it. Powerful microcomputers store spatial data gathered by remote sensing and display maps and images in color; the data can be combined and analyzed to aid research and land-use management. Through GIS, which essentially are computerized ways to relate and display collected data in terms of geographic location, SREL research staff and students are developing a relational data base that will help researchers understand historical environmental processes and predict future changes.

Researchers, for example, can use remote sensing to determine locations of edge habitat; that is, areas where two habitats, such as open fields and woods, converge. GIS can tell the researcher how much and what kinds of edge habitat are available. Animals like deer and quail thrive in edge habitat. If it is scarce, wildlife-management officials can expect deer and quail to be scarce also.

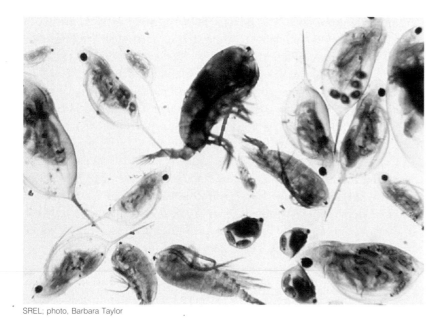

SREL; photo, Barbara Taylor

Biodiversity, or diversity of species, is not limited to the organisms visible to the naked eye. Numerous species of zooplankton (left), i.e., microscopic or near-microscopic aquatic animals, inhabit the wetlands of the SRS. Such "hidden biodiversity" is especially high in Carolina bays.

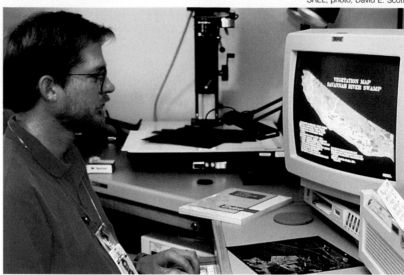

Working in SREL's Remote Sensing/GIS Laboratory, researcher Allen Cook studies a display of vegetation patterns in the Savannah River Swamp. Geographic information systems (GIS) use computers to relate collected images and data by geographic location. These systems help SREL scientists understand environmental processes that have occurred in the past and anticipate future changes.

Rebecca R. Sharitz, head of the Division of Wetlands Ecology, believes that a laboratory like SREL must ensure that its research has application to current environmental issues. For many years SREL scientists have studied the effects on wetlands of environmental changes, both natural and human-made. Some of their findings are surprising. Changes in hydrology, especially the timing of human-generated floods off site, may be having as significant an effect on the Savannah River floodplain as the on-site reactor operations. Certainly the discharge of near-boiling water into the streams and estuaries has visibly dramatic effects on the environment, such as the death of mature trees, but human-caused changes in river levels could affect the future of the forest even more—by preventing the recruitment and growth of new seedlings.

Value of long-term studies

One of the features that sets SREL's field research apart from that of other laboratories is the ability to conduct uninterrupted, long-term research. For more than nine years Barbara Taylor, an associate ecologist, has studied the population ecology of zooplankton at Rainbow Bay, one of the site's small, ephemeral Carolina bays. One aspect of her research offers an insight into the controversy over the definition of wetlands. During her study, water has been in Rainbow Bay for as long as nine months and as short as five days in any one year.

Taylor emphasizes that in studying a place "you don't figure out what is going on in just a year or two. You don't even figure out what species are there." SREL researchers recognize that variances in the population can be understood only through observation over a long period. Some variations occur naturally, and long-term data help determine which variances are natural and which stem from human-induced environmental changes.

In an article in the Aug. 23, 1991, issue of *Science,* SREL researchers stressed the importance of long-term studies in understanding the causes

SREL associate ecologist Ken McLeod checks on a wetlands restoration project under way in the delta of Fourmile Branch at its junction with the Savannah River. McLeod and other researchers have planted young trees in the delta to replace older ones killed by hot-water discharge from SRS reactors.

(Left) Associate ecologist Barbara Taylor (at right in photo) and co-workers use a sieve to collect zooplankton from Rainbow Bay (bottom), one of the SRS's small, ephemeral Carolina bays. The protected status of the SRS has allowed Taylor the opportunity to study undisturbed the population ecology of Rainbow Bay for more than nine years.

of a recently observed decline worldwide in populations of amphibians. Their data from a 12-year study of amphibian populations at Rainbow Bay support previous admonitions that distinguishing natural population fluctuations from human-caused declines may be difficult. Long-term surveys at numerous sites are important in accurately determining the causes of population fluctuations and declines.

The longest uninterrupted study of freshwater turtles in the world, spanning 26 years and involving more than 20,000 turtles, has been directed by J. Whitfield Gibbons, a senior ecologist at SREL. Because of the long-term nature of the research and the use of nondestructive sampling techniques, a variety of findings have emerged. For example, the study has documented that the maximum longevity of turtles living

SREL; photo, David E. Scott

under natural conditions is measured in decades and that even the oldest turtles in the study show none of the signs of senescence typical of other vertebrates.

For more than 20 years SREL director Smith has conducted a study on the genetics of white-tailed deer. Using deer killed in automobile accidents or in the on-site controlled-hunting program, Smith and his co-workers have employed electrophoresis to examine proteins, the products of genes, in fluids extracted from the animals' tissues. The researchers determined that the genetic characteristics of the herd were changing, and the changes did not stem from SRS operations. "Evolution was thought to be a process that occurred over geologically relevant time periods," Smith says. "But the deer were evolving as we were studying them. That a relatively long-lived animal like deer would change detectably over short periods of time was a new insight."

A two-decade study of white-tailed deer on the SRS (above) revealed that the genetic characteristics of the herd changed detectably during the study and that the changes were not caused by SRS operations. That the evolution of a relatively long-lived animal could be observed over so short a time was unexpected. Populations of amphibian species like the ornate chorus frog (below) have been surveyed at Rainbow Bay since 1979. Hatchling snapping turtles (below right) represent one of many turtle species studied on the SRS for more than a quarter century—the longest uninterrupted study of freshwater turtles in the world.

SREL; photos, David E. Scott

Genetic variability turned out to be an important factor in the physical characteristics of deer. Deer having greater genetic variability—that is, those whose parents are comparatively dissimilar genetically—are stronger, bigger, and more vigorous than those having less variability. And genetically varied females produce more and larger young. The size and spread of the males' antlers (*i.e.*, the trophy value) also increase with higher genetic variability.

During Smith's early years as director, SREL formally began a thermal ecology program to investigate the effects of warm effluents from the SRS reactors on animals and plants associated with local streams, ponds, and swamps. A leader in developing the field of thermal ecology, SREL held its first symposium on the topic in 1973 and launched a continuing symposium series. The meetings have brought scientific focus to pertinent environmental issues, and nine books have been published based on the proceedings.

Endangered and threatened species

Not surprisingly, SREL research includes studies on endangered and threatened species. Two SREL projects involving endangered birds are prime examples of success stories in the mitigation of dwindling populations.

Wood storks are the largest wading birds that breed in North America. They are tactile feeders, wandering around in water with their mouths open to catch whatever they touch with their long beaks. In the early 1980s a small population of wood storks foraged on the SRS in Steel Creek. The creek had once received effluents from a reactor, but the reactor had been shut down, and the water level had dropped to an acceptable level for the feeding wood storks.

Then DOE decided to restart the reactor. Water used to cool the reactor would again be discharged into Steel Creek, and the higher

Sequence of photos of part of the Savannah River Swamp before (below), during (bottom left), and after (bottom right) hot-water discharges from SRS reactors illustrate the dramatic effects of thermal effluents on aquatic habitats. SREL has been a leader in developing the field of thermal ecology and maintains a continuing symposium series on this topic and other environmental subjects.

SREL; photos, David E. Scott

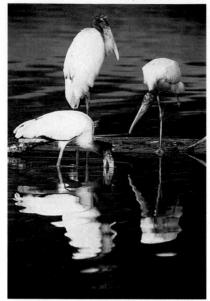

Juvenile wood storks, an endangered species, forage at one of four artificial ponds created at South Carolina's Kathwood Lake with the advice and guidance of SREL. The planned return to operation of an SRS reactor had jeopardized the birds' natural foraging habitat in Steel Creek, making it necessary to develop an alternative habitat before the reactor was restarted.

A researcher takes measurements of a red-cockaded woodpecker, an endangered species having a recently established population on the SRS. By comparing the on-site birds with more than two dozen other woodpecker populations, SREL scientists are gathering information that may help save the birds from extinction.

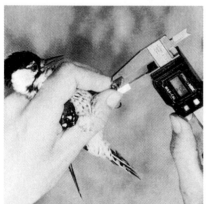

water levels would eliminate the wood storks' on-site foraging habitat. Meanwhile, the birds had been listed as an endangered species by the U.S. Fish and Wildlife Service. The agency decreed that an alternative habitat would have to be found for the wood storks or the reactor could not be restarted. For assistance DOE turned to SREL, whose scientists found the problem appealing.

In 1985, with the advice and guidance of SREL, DOE created a 14-hectare (35-acre) artificial foraging habitat at Kathwood Lake on the National Audubon Society's Silver Bluff Plantation Sanctuary in Jackson, South Carolina. Four ponds were built in which the water level could be artificially raised and lowered. Under a contract with DOE, the National Audubon Society oversees the maintenance of the ponds. SREL researchers carefully monitor the population demography and behavior of the birds. In the first year of the experiment, just under 100 storks foraged at the Kathwood Ponds; by 1993 the count approached 300.

Another endangered species has also been the beneficiary of a collaborative venture. In 1985 the red-cockaded woodpecker was virtually extinct on the Savannah River Site. Through the combined research efforts and forest management approaches of SREL, DOE, the Savannah River Forest Station, the Southeastern Forest Experiment Station, and Clemson (South Carolina) University, by 1993 more than 30 of the birds were once again living on site.

Red-cockaded woodpeckers require live pine trees more than 80 years old in which to roost and build nests. Because much of this habitat throughout the United States was lost to logging activities in the 1950s and '60s, the species exists in the form of highly fragmented populations. And the smaller a population, the less genetic variability it is likely to have.

SREL researchers have conducted genetic surveys of the SRS birds; measured the birds' legs, wings, and beaks; taken feather and blood samples; and compared the on-site birds with 26 other woodpecker populations. Researchers emphasize that population size must increase if genetic problems are to be avoided. Importing birds from other populations is one way to increase genetic variability. Natural population growth is another. The plight of the red-cockaded woodpecker offered SREL scientists an excellent opportunity to study genetic variability and the population ecology of an endangered species. And the cooperative venture of research scientists, government agencies, and private organizations has given new hope to at least one population of the birds.

Environmental outreach and education

SREL's stated mission is to acquire and communicate knowledge of ecological principles and processes. It is no surprise then that researchers, technicians, and students at the laboratory are all busily engaged in gathering ecological information. It is perhaps surprising, however, that they are also integrally involved in imparting that information through media other than the 35 technical books and 1,700 scientific articles that the SREL staff has published over the years.

486

Gibbons heads SREL's Division of Environmental Outreach and Education. With the assistance of Tony Mills, Jane Sanders, and others, Gibbons gives talks to students, teachers, and the general public both on site and off. But disseminating information is not limited to the members of his division. The lab boasts experts in topics that range from aging phenomena in turtles to endangered plants, from microorganisms to alligators, from aquatic ecology to mercury toxicology, from wetlands restoration to coal fly ash contaminants. And those experts communicate their knowledge to audiences ranging from first graders to schoolteachers, from residents of retirement communities to forestry service workers.

SREL emphasizes communication to the general public as well as to the scientific community. As science becomes ever more technical, the ability to effectively communicate the results of research becomes increasingly important. To make an informed decision, the decision maker—whether voter or elected official, industrialist or environmentalist—must have access to and understand the facts. SREL's mission of acquiring and communicating ecological information is a critical one.

The student and teacher research participation program at SREL is one way in which the lab fulfills its mission. Each year about 80 participants, who over the years have represented all 50 states and Puerto Rico, take part in ecological research. The undergraduate program, initiated in 1968, has been supported in most years by the National Science Foundation as well as DOE. College juniors and seniors who are considering careers in ecological disciplines work closely with SREL faculty advisers on independent research projects. Most of the 400-plus students who have participated in the program have gone on for advanced degrees and careers in environmental science.

The graduate research participation program provides support for qualified graduate students who conduct full-time thesis or dissertation research on site. Graduate students from more than 50 U.S. universities have participated in the program, and more than 150 doctoral disser-

SREL; photo, Rick O'Quinn

SREL's Environmental Outreach Program has set up numerous exhibits each year, including one for Earth Day 1992 at the University of Georgia (left). The exhibits can attract thousands of visitors.

SREL; photo, David E. Scott

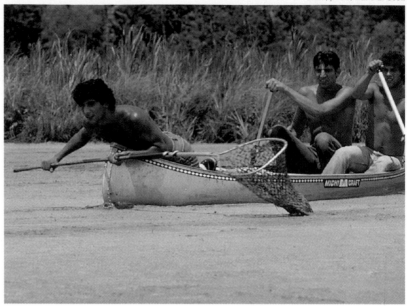

Students engaged in an SREL research project collect specimens with a dip net. Dozens of high school, undergraduate, and graduate students from throughout the U.S. participate annually in the laboratory's education program.

tations and master's theses have been completed by students who have worked at SREL. Graduate students play an important role at SREL as authors of more than two dozen scientific publications each year. In 1992, for example, two new species of caddisflies, aquatic insects, were discovered on the SRS by a doctoral student in the program.

The faculty research participation program supports visiting college and university faculty members who are conducting research in collaboration with an SREL colleague. The program also acts as host to faculty on sabbatical and sponsors at least two visiting scientists each year. DOE's Historically Black Colleges and Universities Program funds faculty participants in summer research programs.

A new 460-square meter (5,000-square foot) facility will enhance SREL's educational capabilities. Ten minutes by car from the main building, near one of the set-aside areas, the SREL Conference Center will accommodate small workshops and groups. Seminars will be held on a regular basis, and displays will be set up for educational materials. The center will be built on land provided to the University of Georgia Research Foundation through an arrangement with DOE.

The future

Operating on the principle that a foundation of ecological knowledge through research is vital in addressing today's environmental issues, SREL's faculty and staff will pursue their mission of acquiring and communicating that knowledge. The critical need for environmental understanding by a broad spectrum of society promises that they will have an increasingly large and interested audience.

Index

red-cockaded woodpecker
Savannah River Ecology
Laboratory 94–486
"Red Data Book"
New Zealand's fauna 93–63
red helium-neon laser 92–386
red-leg disease
amphibian decline 94–355
red meat 92–379
Red Sea 94–330
red shift
cosmology 94–48, ils. 50, 58
red shift survey
cosmology 94–57
red-sided garter snake il. 93–148
red tide algae
increase of toxicity 93–323
microbiology 94–363
red wolf 92–200, il. 201
Redoubt, Mount (U.S.) 92–317, il.
redshift: see red shift
Reduced Instruction Set Computer, or RISC
93–331
Reed, Robert H. 93–310
reef: see coral reef
reflecting telescope 93–258
reflection
energy state of atom 94–398
reflective null corrector 92–38
refracting telescope, or refractor 93–256
refractive index
microscopy 94–106
refrigerator
Bose-Einstein condensation 94–398
energy technology 94–350
regenerative repeater
fiber optics 94–332
regulation (govt.)
energy 93–346
Reidemeister, Kurt 93–80
Reightler, Kenneth 93–413
reinforcement (psychol.) 92–401
reintroduction
species restoration 92–197
relativistic heavy ion collider, or RHIC
93–401
relativistic mass 93–232
relativity theory: see general relativity
remineralization
dentistry 94–390
remote control 93–205
remote sensing technique
information systems 93–337
Savannah River Ecology Laboratory
94–481
wind profilers 93–313
renewable energy 94–349
renin 92–128
reptile 92–202
repulsion
nuclear physics 94–404
research and development, or R and D
Big Science 94–13
Congressional funding 94–427; 93–425
electronics 92–329
food and agriculture 94–358
"Intelligent Vehicle-Highway Systems"
94–189
magnetohydrodynamic propulsion
94–427
materials sciences 94–375
Research Libraries, Association of, or ARL
93–337
Research Libraries Group, Inc., or RLG
(U.S.) 94–341; 92–334
reservoir
drought 94–353
resolution
microscopy 94–104
see also optical resolution
resonant sound
ultrasound 94–143
RESORS
information systems 93–337
restriction endonuclease, or EcoRI
chloroplast DNA 93–359
restriction fragment length polymorphism,
or RFLP 92–128, 349
"Rethinking High-Level Radioactive Waste
Disposal" (report) 92–318
retinoic acid receptor, or RAR
hormone regulation 94–368
retinoid
hormone regulation 94–368
retinoid X receptor, or RXR
hormone regulation 94–368
retrosynthetic analysis 92–423
retroviral vectors 93–128
reverse transcriptase
antiviral bacteria 93–363
genetic information flow 93–364
"Revelle, Roger Randall Dougan 93–325, 449
"Revolution in Cosmology, The" (feature
article) 94–48
REX (U.S.): see Northwest Atlantic Regional
Energetics Experiment
RFLP: see restriction fragment length
polymorphism

rhabdomyolysis
horses 94–392
Rhea, John
"The Many Worlds of Virtual Reality"
93–188
Rheobatrachus silus: see gastric brooding
frog
rhesus monkey
sexual physiology 93–154
RHIC: see relativistic heavy ion collider
rhinencephalon
sense of smell 93–142
rhinitis 94–386
rhinoceros
flehmen il. 93–153
Rhinolophus ferrumequinum: see greater
horseshoe bat
rhinovirus type 14 92–123
rhodium 92–134
catalytic systems 94–154
rhyolite dome
topography of Venus 93–119
ribonucleic acid: see RNA
ribozyme 92–119
RNA replication 93–175
ribulose bisphosphate carboxylase/
oxygenase, or RuBisCO
molecular chaperones 93–368
rice 92–92
Richards, Richard 92–406
rifting
Lake Baikal 94–208
plate tectonics 94–320
Riger, Stephanie 93–409
Right Livelihood Award 92–277
Rindos, David
archaeology 94–286
RISC: see Reduced Instruction Set
Computer
RISC System/6000, or RS/6000 92–326, il.
Rivest, Ronald 93–383
RLG: see Research Library Group
RNA, or ribonucleic acid
directed evolution 92–363
enzymatic abilities 92–119
molecular biology 93–364
wet system replication 93–175
see also guide RNA; leucine transfer
RNA; messenger RNA; pre-mRNA;
transfer RNA
RNA editing 93–364
RoadRider system
computerized vehicle communications
system 94–423
roads and highways 94–422; 93–419;
92–413
"Intelligent Vehicle-Highway Systems"
94–178, ils. 180–188
Roadway Package System, or RPS
transportation 93–421, il. 420
Roberts, Walter Orr 92–444
Roberts, Victoria A.
"Computer-Aided Molecular Design"
94–88
Robertson, Paul B.
"Bats: Fragile Masters of the Night"
92–174
Robinson, Larry il. 93–275
robot, or robotics
artificial life 93–179 ils. 180
teleoperation 93–200
Robson, E. Ian 93–291
Rocard, Yves-André 94–452
Roche, Kevin
architecture 94–291
rock
bacterial weathering 94–364
"Minerals and Rocks" (MACROPAEDIA
revision) 93–242
rock rose, or Cistus salvifolius 92–86, il.
Rockwell, Norman 92–17
Rocky III explorer 93–179
Roger Williams Park Museum of Natural
History (Providence, R.I., U.S.)
92–332
Rohrer, Heinrich 92–389
condensed-matter physics 94–407
Romania
libraries 93–335
psychology 93–411
Romein, A. J. T. 93–92
Röntgensatellit, or ROSAT (spacecraft)
92–44, il.
Rookery, the (bldg., Chicago, Ill., U.S.)
94–291, 290
room-temperature fusion: see cold fusion
Roosevelt, Theodore 92–13
root (plant)
gravitational effect 92–72
Root, Michael
"Nature's Detectives: Biological Pollution
Monitors" 92–210
root canal, or endodontics 92–382
Rosado-May, Francisco J. 92–356
ROSAT (spacecraft): see Röntgensatellit
Rosen, Harold A. 92–355
Rosenberg, Michael
agriculture origins 94–286

Rosenberg, Steven A. 93–134; 92–419
Rossi, Aldo 92–286
Rossiter, Margaret 93–235
Rossman, Michael 92–123
6.4-rotane 94–300
Rothschild, Nathanial Mayer Victor
Rothschild, Baron 92–444
rotor
ceramics 94–375
Round Island (Maur.) 93–74
Rousettus aegyptiacus: see Egyptian
fruit bat
Rousseau, Denis L.
cold fusion 94–309
Rovee-Collier, Carolyn 92–403
Rovelli, Carlo 93–76
RPS: see Roadway Package System
RS/6000: see RISC System 6000
RSA: see Russian Space Agency
RSA
Digital Signature Standard 93–383
RuBisCO: see ribulose bisphosphate
carboxylase/oxygenase
Rudaux, Lucien 92–13, il. 14
Rudolph, David 93–322
ruff (bird) il. 94–213
Rugar, Dan 92–400
Runco, Mario
space shuttles 94–416
runoff
hydrology 92–317
Russia
electronics industry 93–333
Lake Baikal 94–208, ils. 211–224
oceanography 94–328
satellite technology 94–342; 93–338
space exploration 94–416; 93–411
space probes 94–419
taiga logging 94–363
see also Union of Soviet Socialist
Republics
Russian Space Agency, or RSA 94–342
Rütimeyer, Karl
cats in ancient Europe 94–163
RXR: see retinoid X receptor

S

sac-winged bat 92–183
Saccharomyces cerevisiae, or baker's yeast
92–299
Sacramento River (Calif., U.S.) 93–348
Safdie, Moshe
architecture 94–291, il. 290
safety: see accident and safety
SAGE: see Soviet-American Gallium
Experiment
saguaro cactus il. 92–190
St. Lawrence Seaway Development Corp.
shipping 94–426
Sakmann, Bert 93–431
salamander
decline 94–355
Salicornia bigelovii
salt-tolerant plants 93–359
saliva
tooth decay 94–390
Salk, Lee 94–452
Salk Institute for Biological Studies (Calif.,
U.S.) 93–234, il.
salmon
aquaculture 93–392
Saloman, Michael H. 92–302
salt
crop-plant tolerance 93–359
environmental destruction 93–46
salt marsh
Persian Gulf war 93–48
"Salvation Islands, The" (feature article)
93–60
Salyut 7
reentry problem 93–415
Soviet space program 92–408
San Andreas Fault
earthquakes 94–322
San Diego (Calif., U.S.) 94–23
San Francisco Bay (Calif., U.S.) 92–342
Sandell, Goran 93–291
Saphikon Inc. 92–370
sapphire filament 92–370
SAR: see synthetic aperture radar
Sardar Dam (India)
architecture 94–292
Sardinia (It.)
Roman shipwreck salvage 93–282
Sargasso Sea
spawning site for eels 94–371
Sargent, Anniela 92–290
Sarkar, A. 93–314
Sarracenia (bot.) 92–88, il. 89
Sarsat/Cospas: see Search and Rescue
Satellite-Aided Tracking system
Sarton, George 93–228
SAS (U.K.): see Small Area Statistics
Satellite pour Observation de la Terre: see
SPOT

satellite systems 94–342; 93–337; 92–334
defense research 93–308
oceanography 94–328
ozone depletion 93–312
transportation 94–424
wireless communications 94–332
see also space probe; and individual
satellites by name
Saturn 92–13, ils. 22, 23
Hubble Space Telescope 92–288, il. 39
space probes
Cassini mission 94–420
Voyager missions 93–475, il. 476
Saudi Arabia 93–48, 341, il.
Savannah River Ecology Laboratory, or
SREL, or Laboratory of Radiation
Ecology
"The Savannah River Ecology
Laboratory" 94–468
Savannah River Plant, or SRP 94–468
Savannah River Site, or SRS 94–472
Scan To Automate Receipt, or STAR
93–421
scanned force microscope: see atomic
force microscope
scanned probe microscope 94–114
scanning ion conductance microscope
94–119
scanning probe microscopies 94–307
scanning system
aircraft safety 94–422, il. 423
scanning transmission electron microscope,
or STEM 94–115
scanning tunneling microscope, or STM
condensed-matter physics 93–406;
92–399
microscopy 94–116
physics research 92–389
scientific terminology 94–238
SCC: see stress-corrosion cracking
scent
human response 93–140
scent-receptor cell 93–142
schizophrenia 94–388
Schmidt, Maarten 93–293
Schmidt telescope 93–259
Schneider, Donald 93–293
Schneider National Carriers Inc. 94–424
Schnitman, Paul 92–382
Schott Glassworks
astronomical optics 94–396
Schottky barrier
metal-semiconductor interfaces 93–406
Schreiber's bent-winged bat, or Miniopterus
schreibersii il. 92–183
Schwitters, Roy 93–427
SCID: see severe combined
immunodeficiency disease
"Science" (Am. period.)
linguistic accessibility 94–229
Molecule of the Year 92–304
"Science and Social Welfare in the Age of
Newton" 93–227
Science and Technology Centers (U.S.)
94–428
science fiction
"Imagining Aliens" 94–68
science instruction 94–410
U.S. science policy 94–427
Science overview 94–278; 93–274; 92–272
science policy, U.S.: see U.S. science
policy
Science Service
Westinghouse Science Fair 93–160
"Science Studies" (mag.) 93–233
"Science, Technology and Society in
Seventeenth-Century England"
93–230
science writing, or science journalism
science honors 94–445; 93–440; 92–436
Sciences, Academy of (Russ. org.) 94–211
"Science's 'Intellectual Hotel': The Institute
for Advanced Study" (feature article)
92–472
"Scientific American" (journ.) 94–229
scientific attitude 94–282
scientific journal
accessibility 94–229
scientific misconduct 94–429
scientific paradigm 93–231
Scientific Society Presidents, Council of
science and mathematics instruction
94–410
scientific workstation 93–314, 328
Scientists of the year 94–432; 93–429;
92–423
scopolamine (drug) 94–305
scorched-earth tactic 93–15, il.
Scots pine, or Pinus sylvestris 93–360
Scott Paper Co. (U.S.)
harmful projects 92–277
Scotti, James V. 93–288
scraper tool il. 93–23
screwworm il. 93, 388
Scrimshaw, Nevin 93–357
scroll
gasifier assembly mechanism 94–375
Scud missile 93–308, 339

Acknowledgments

6   (Top to bottom) NASA; copyright © by Universal Studios Inc.
     Courtesy of MCA Publishing Rights, a Division of MCA Inc./
     Photofest; Computer graphics and photography: G.P. Gippert,
     The Scripps Research Institute; Paul Hanny—Gamma/Liaison

7   (Top to bottom) British Library/ET Archive; © Doug Allan—
     Oxford Scientific Films; illustration by Ron Villani; SREL, photo
     by David E. Scott

31–44   Illustrations by Kathryn Diffley

69   (Top left) Photo by courtesy of the Museum of Modern Art/Film
      Stills Archive, New York City; (top right) Photofest

83   (Bottom) By courtesy of Space Art International

85   (Top) By courtesy of Space Art International

89   Illustration by Steven N. Kapusta

107–120   Illustrations by Stephanie Motz

142–144   Illustrations by Steven N. Kapusta

166   For more information see The Archaeology of Animals by Simon
       David, Yale University Press, pp. 133–134, 1987

195, 203   Illustrations by Steven N. Kapusta

307   From "Dynamics of Cluster-Surface Collisions," Charles L.
       Cleveland and Uzi Landman, Science, vol. 257, no. 5068,
       pp. 355–361, July 17, 1992, © 1992 AAAS

308   Adapted from "A Polymer Gel with Electrically Driven Motility,"
       Yoshihito Osada, Hidenori Okuzaki, and Hirofumi Hori,
       reprinted by permission of Nature, vol. 355, no. 6357,
       pp. 242–243, Jan. 16, 1992, © Macmillan Magazines Ltd.

364   From "New 'Phantom' Dinoflagellate is the Causative Agent
       of Major Estuarine Fish Kills," JoAnn M. Burkholder, Edward J.
       Noga, Cecil H. Hobbs, and Howard B. Glasgow, Jr., reprinted
       by permission of Nature, vol. 358, no. 6385, pp. 407–410,
       July 30, 1992, © Macmillan Magazines Ltd.

460   Illustrations by Richard A. Thompson

462   UPI/Bettmann

473   Illustration by John L. Draves